[

Readings in
ANIMAL BEHAVIOR

Readings in

ANIMAL BEHAVIOR

EDITED BY

Thomas E. McGill

WILLIAMS COLLEGE

HOLT, RINEHART AND WINSTON

New York   Chicago   San Francisco   Toronto   London

PREFACE

The science of animal behavior is rapidly becoming a distinct academic discipline. This is evidenced by the following: the growing number of colleges and universities that offer undergraduate courses in animal behavior; the formation of several graduate departments of animal behavior; the existence of research laboratories and institutes devoted exclusively to the study of the behavior of animals; recent "summer institutes" designed to train college teachers in the subject; and several scientific journals and "associations" that specialize in animal behavior.

Historically, new sciences developed by disengagement from larger disciplines. The science of animal behavior, however, is being formed in a slightly different way: by the recombination of parts of several sciences into one discipline.

The rather eclectic nature of the new science creates special problems for those engaged in teaching the subject. It is axiomatic that advanced undergraduates and graduate students should have experience in reading journal articles and other primary sources. However, it is very difficult to arrange for the availability of such source material in an area where major contributions have come from a great diversity of academic specialties. Endocrinologists, ethologists, geneticists, physiologists, psychologists, zoologists, among others, have contributed to the field. Consequently, the reports have appeared in a bewildering variety of journals and books, and the instructor finds it difficult to arrange an adequate and representative "reserve shelf." *Readings in Animal Behavior* was designed to meet this need—to serve as an aid, either as core text or as collateral reading, in the teaching of advanced-undergraduate and graduate courses in animal behavior. It is hoped that the book may in this way contribute to the development of the science.

Four criteria were used in selecting the readings that are included in this volume. First, an effort was made both to secure a representation from a wide variety of disciplines and to obtain a broad sample of animal subjects. Second, whenever possible, contributions were selected that illustrate a *program* of research—the long-range work of one scientist or one laboratory. A third criterion was recency of publication; only three of the articles appeared before 1956, and the median publication date is 1961. Finally, an attempt was made to include representative samples of both theoretical reviews and reports of specific experiments.

The stylistic idiosyncracies of the various sources have been maintained in the reproductions that make up this volume. For example, if the summary or abstract preceded the article proper in the original journal, it does so in the reprinted version; if titles were omitted in the original reference list, they are omitted in the reproduction. This procedure should serve to familiarize the student with a variety of journal styles.

A difficult problem encountered in the preparation of a book of readings is organization, determining the categories for major sections and the ordering of studies within each section. It is obvious that many papers could logically be placed in any of several sections. Thus any particular arrangement must be arbitrary. Further, although a given arrangement may suit one instructor, others may find the sequence completely unworkable. For this reason, a simple alphabetical or chronological order was considered. But because this seemed a bit faint-hearted, if not downright cowardly, the decision was made to provide a scheme of classification for the material. It is the editor's sincere hope that at least some of his colleagues in the teaching of animal behavior will find the present organization useful.

Each major section and individual reading is preceded by an editor's introduction. The introductions to sections contain outlines of major problems in the areas covered, general introductions to the studies included, and suggestions for further reading. The introductions to the individual papers contain, in various combinations, necessary information on the background of the problem or author, cross-references to related studies in the book, definitions of abbreviations or terms used in the paper, aspects of the paper the student should note particularly or questions he should keep in mind as he reads the article, and suggestions for further reading.

In preparing this book the editor has repeatedly imposed on many of his busy colleagues with requests for suggestions, reprints, permissions, photographs, and moral support. To these most gracious and patient gentlemen, most of whose names appear in the Table of Contents—thank you. The editor is also grateful to his Williams colleagues, Professors William C. Grant, Jr. and Richard O. Rouse, Jr., for careful criticism of the introductions.

T. E. MCG.

Williamstown, Mass.
July 1965

CONTENTS

VII Social Behavior, Ethology, and Evolution 495

Readings in
ANIMAL BEHAVIOR

section
one

INTRODUCTORY READINGS If asked to name
the most basic and recurring problem in their discipline, most
students of behavior would probably claim that the determination
of behavior, its causality, was of prime concern. Why does an organism behave as it does? What determines its behavior? Historically,
the answers to these questions have taken two main forms. On the
one hand were the hereditarians who claimed that behavior is
largely the result of genotype. "Like begets like." "He's a chip off
the old block." On the other hand, opposed to the hereditarians
were the environmentalists who maintained that most behavior is
the product of experience. ". . . as the twig is bent, so is the
tree inclined." In reviewing the history of this controversy, one finds
that through the years the pendulum of scientific opinion has swung,
ponderously but predictably from one school of thought to the other.
The extreme positions occasionally taken by some of the men involved have actually proven dangerous when misused by those with
political and economic, rather than scholarly, motivations. The concepts of the "master-race" and "white supremacy" are prime examples of the dangerous misuse of scientific speculation.

It is hardly surprising that such a broad problem should have concerned those interested in animal behavior. Some of the most extreme (and untenable) theoretical positions were held by scientists
whose empirical work in animal behavior was of the highest quality.
Happily, as time passed, experimentation tended to replace mere
speculation, and most scientists realized that the nature-nurture
controversy, as it came to be called, was largely a response to a
pseudo-problem. The wrong question had been asked. To ask
whether a given bit of behavior is learned or innate is misleading
and restrictive. It states an either-or dichotomy which does not
allow either for *interaction* between the variables or for the operation of variables that could be described as *neither* innate *nor*
learned. As Fuller and Thompson (*Behavior Genetics*, Wiley, 1960,
page 2) have pointed out, "The dichotomy, carried to its logical
conclusion, would define innate behavior as that which appeared
in the absence of environment, and learned behavior as that which
required no organism."

But controversies die hard. As criticism of a controversy increases,
participants tend simply to change the labels and continue business

1

as usual. Even when abandoned, an extreme position may continue to affect research for some time. An example is that of behaviorial research in the United States during the last forty years. Under the combined influences of Watsonian behaviorism and the common interpretation of Freud's theory of personality, this research has been largely "environmental" in its approach. Most studies have been concerned with conditioning and learning (emphasized by the behaviorists) or with the effects of early experience on later behavior (emphasized by the Freudians).

In Europe, on the other hand, under the influence of Darwinism, a school of animal behavior known as "Ethology" has developed. The primary emphasis of the ethologists has been on "innate" patterns of behavior, with the long-range goal of contributing to the study of evolution. The following table compares, in a rather crude and general fashion, these two major branches of the science of animal behavior.

	Comparative Psychologist	Ethologist
Geographical location	North America	Europe
Training	Psychology	Zoology
Typical subjects	Mammals, especially the laboratory rat	Birds, fish, insects
Emphasis	"Learning," the development of theories of behavior	"Instinct," the study of the evolution of behavior
Method	Laboratory work, control of variables, statistical analysis	Careful observation, field experimentation

It is obvious that the two approaches are complementary and that both are necessary (but probably not sufficient) for a complete understanding of behavior. After a period of sometimes vitriolic disagreement, the two schools have reached a happy truce in which each recognizes the importance of the work of the other. Some of the readings included in this section have contributed greatly to the development of this mutual understanding on the part of psychologists and ethologists. In these readings the student will encounter discussions of the instinctive-learned dichotomy and comparisons of ethology and psychology. Particular attention should be paid to definitions and to the positions which the various authors have taken on the issues.

Suggestions for Further Reading:

ANASTASI, ANNE, *Differential Psychology.* New York: Macmillan, 1958. Chapter 3.

BIRNEY, R. C., and R. C. TEEVAN, eds., *Instinct*. Princeton, N. J.: Van
Nostrand, 1961.

DOBZHANSKY, T., *Mankind Evolving*. New Haven: Yale University Press,
1962.

FULLER, J. L., *Nature and Nurture: A Modern Synthesis*. New York:
Doubleday, 1954.

Physiological Mechanisms in Animal Behaviour. London: Cambridge University Press, 1950. Part III.

SCHILLER, C. H., ed., *Instinctive Behavior*. New York: International Universities Press, 1957.

TINBERGEN, N., *The Study of Instinct*. London: Oxford University Press,
1951.

FRANK A. BEACH

1   The Snark Was a Boojum*

Frank A. Beach is a leading American researcher in the area of animal behavior. But the importance of his contributions extends beyond this discipline to all of modern psychology. Beach has been called the "comparative conscience" of American psychology because he has repeatedly sounded the warning that psychological theorizing is based on phylogenetic and empirical foundations that are narrow in the extreme. For those who agree with Beach, the definition of psychology as "the study of learning in the white rat and the college sophomore" is without humor.

"The Snark was a Boojum," although published only fifteen years ago, is recognized as a classic in the field of comparative psychology. Here Beach documents the sins of psychology and pleads for a diversion of psychologists efforts to the study of a broader range of problems in a greater variety of species.

Most students will want to review animal taxonomy by consulting an introductory biology or zoology text in conjunction with their study of this paper.

This article originally appeared in *The American Psychologist*, 1950, 5, 115–124. It is reprinted with the permission of the author and the American Psychological Association.

Those of you who are familiar with the writings of Lewis Carroll will have recognized the title of this address as a quotation from his poem "The Hunting of the Snark." Anyone who has never read that masterpiece of whimsy must now be informed that the hunting party includes a Bellman, a Banker, a Beaver, a Baker and several other equally improbable characters. While

* Presidential address delivered before the Division of Experimental Psychology of the American Psychological Association, September 7, 1949.

they are sailing toward the habitat of their prey the Bellman tells his companions how they can recognize the quarry. The outstanding characters of the genus *Snark* are said to be its taste which is described as "meager but hollow," its habit of getting up late, its very poor sense of humor and its overweening ambition. There are several species of Snarks. Some relatively harmless varieties have feathers and bite, and others have whiskers and scratch. But, the Bellman adds, there are a few Snarks that are Boojums.

When the Baker hears the word, Boojum, he faints dead away, and after his companions have revived him he explains his weakness by recalling for their benefit the parting words of his Uncle.

If your Snark be a Snark, that is right:
Fetch it home by all means—you may serve it
    with greens
And it's handy for striking a light.

But oh, beamish nephew, beware of the day,
If your Snark be a Boojum! For then,
You will softly and suddenly vanish away,
And never be met with again!

Much later in the story they finally discover a Snark, and it is the Baker who first sights the beast. But by great misfortune that particular Snark turns out to be a Boojum and so of course the Baker softly and suddenly vanishes away.

Thirty years ago in this country a small group of scientists went Snark hunting. It is convenient to personify them collectively in one imaginary individual who shall be called the Comparative Psychologist. The Comparative Psychologist was hunting a Snark known as Animal Behavior. His techniques were different from those used by the Baker, but he came to the same unhappy end, for his Snark also proved to be a Boojum. Instead of animals in the generic sense he found one animal, the albino rat, and thereupon the Comparative Psychologist suddenly and softly vanished away. I must admit that this description is somewhat overgeneralized. A few American psychologists have done or are doing behavioral research that is broadly comparative. All honor to that tiny band of hardy souls who are herewith excepted from the general indictment that follows.

It is my aim, first, to trace the initial development and subsequent decline of Comparative Psychology in the United States. Secondly, I intend to propose certain explanations for the attitude of American psychologists toward this branch of the discipline. And finally I will outline some of the potential benefits that may be expected to follow a more vigorous and widespread study of animal behavior.

Instead of beginning with the uncritical assumption of a mutual understanding, let me define the basic terms that will be used. Comparative psychology is based upon comparisons of behavior shown by different species of animals including human beings. Comparisons between *Homo sapiens* and other animals are legitimate contributions to comparative psychology, but comparisons between two or more non-human species are equally admissible. Like any other responsible scientist the Comparative Psychologist is concerned with the understanding of his own species and with its welfare; but his primary aim is the exposition of general laws of behavior regardless of their immediate applicability to the problems of human existence. Now this means that he will not be content with discovering the similarities and differences between two or three species. Comparisons between rats and men, for example, do not in and of themselves constitute a comparative psychology although they may well represent an important contribution toward the establishment of such a field. A much broader sort of approach is necessary and it is the failure to recognize this fact that has prevented development of a genuine comparative psychology in this country.

Past and Current Trends

The history of comparative behavior studies in America is reflected in the contents of our journals that are expressly devoted to articles in this field. They have been the *Journal of Animal Behavior* and its successor, the *Journal of Comparative and Physiological Psychology*. Animal studies have, of course, been reported in other publications but the ones mentioned here adequately and accurately represent the general interests and attitudes of Americans toward the behavior of non-human animals. I have analyzed a large sample of the volumes of these journals, starting with Volume I and including all odd-numbered volumes through 1948. I have classified the contents of these volumes in two ways—

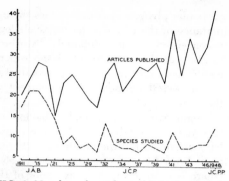

FIG. 1. Number of articles published and variety of species used as subjects.

first in terms of the species of animal used, and second in terms of the type of behavior studied. Only research reports have been classified; summaries of the literature and theoretical articles have been excluded from this analysis.

TYPES OF ANIMALS STUDIED

Figure 1 shows the number of articles published and the total number of species dealt with in these articles. The number of articles has tended to increase, particularly in the last decade; but the variety of animals studied began to decrease about 30 years ago and has remained low ever since. In other words, contributors to these journals have been inclined to do more and more experiments on fewer and fewer species.

Data represented in Figure 2 further emphasize the progressive reduction in the number of species studied. Here we see that the *Journal of Animal Behavior* contained nearly as many articles dealing with invertebrates as with vertebrates; but interest in invertebrate behavior fell off sharply after World War I and, as far as this type of analysis is capable of indicating, it never rose appreciably thereafter. The attention paid to behavior of invertebrates during the second decade of this century is also reflected in the policy of publishing annual surveys of recent research. Each volume of the *Journal of Animal Behavior* contains one systematic review devoted to lower invertebrates, another dealing with spiders and insects with

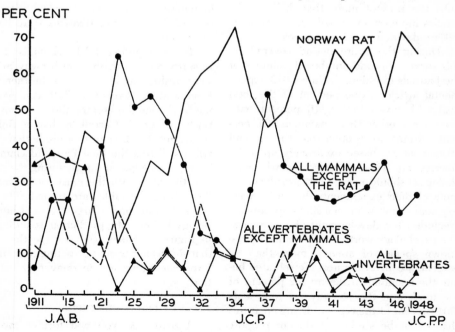

FIG. 2. Percent of all articles devoted to various phyla, classes or species.

the exception of ants, a third summarizing work on ants and a single section covering all studies of vertebrates.

Figure 2 shows that in the early years of animal experimentation sub-mammalian vertebrates, which include all fishes, amphibians, reptiles, and birds, were used as experimental subjects more often than mammals. But a few mammalian species rapidly gained popularity and by approximately 1920, more work was being done on mammals than on all other classes combined. Now there are approximately 3,500 extant species of mammals, but taken together they make up less than one-half of one percent of all animal species now living. A psychology based primarily upon studies of mammals can, therefore, be regarded as comparative only in a very restricted sense. Moreover the focus of interest has actually been even more narrow than this description implies because only a few kinds of mammals have been used in psychological investigations. The Norway rat has been the prime favorite of psychologists working with animals, and from 1930 until the present more than half of the articles in nearly every volume of the journal are devoted to this one species.

During the entire period covered by this survey the odd-numbered volumes of the journals examined includes 613 experimental articles. Nine percent of the total deal with invertebrates; 10 percent with vertebrates other than mammals; 31 percent with mammals other than the rat; and 50 percent are based exclusively upon the Norway rat. There is no reason why psychologists should not use rats as subjects in some of their experiments, but this excessive concentration upon a single species has precluded the development of a comparative psychology worthy of the name. Of the known species of animals more than 96 percent are invertebrates. Vertebrates below the mammals make up 3.2 percent of the total; and the Norway rat represents .001 percent of the types of living creatures that might be studied. I do not propose that the number of species found in a

particular phyletic class determines the importance of the group as far as psychology is concerned; but it is definitely disturbing to discover that 50 percent of the experiments analyzed here have been conducted on one one-thousandth of one percent of the known species.

Some studies of animal behavior are reported in journals other than the ones I have examined but the number of different animals used in experiments published elsewhere is even fewer. The six issues of the *Journal of Experimental Psychology* published in 1948 contain 67 reports of original research. Fifty of these articles deal with human subjects and this is in accord with the stated editorial policy of favoring studies of human behavior above investigations of other species. However, 15 of the 17 reports describing work on non-human organisms are devoted to the Norway rat.

During the current meetings of the APA, 47 experimental reports are being given under the auspices of the Division of Experimental Psychology. The published abstracts show that in half of these studies human subjects were employed while nearly one-third of the investigations were based on the rat.

Is the Experimental Psychologist going to softly and suddenly vanish away in the same fashion as his one-time brother, the Comparative Psychologist? If you permit me to change the literary allusion from the poetry of Lewis Carroll to that of Robert Browning, I will venture a prediction. You will recall that the Pied Piper rid Hamelin Town of a plague of rats by luring the pests into the river with the music of his magic flute. Now the tables are turned. The rat plays the tune and a large group of human beings follow. My prediction is indicated in Figure 3. Unless they escape the spell that *Rattus norvegicus* is casting over them, Experimentalists are in danger of extinction.

TYPES OF BEHAVIOR STUDIED

I trust that you will forgive me for having demonstrated what to many of you

FIG. 3. Current position of many experimental psychologists.

must have been obvious from the beginning—namely, that we have been extremely narrow in our selection of types of animals to be studied. Now let us turn our attention to the types of behavior with which psychologists have concerned themselves.

Articles appearing in our sample of volumes of the journals can be classified under seven general headings: (1) conditioning and learning; (2) sensory capacities, including psychophysical measurements, effects of drugs on thresholds, etc.; (3) general habits and life histories; (4) reproductive behavior, including courtship, mating, migration, and parental responses; (5) feeding behavior, including diet selection and reactions to living prey; (6) emotional behavior, as reflected in savageness and wildness, timidity and aggressive reactions; and (7) social behavior, which involves studies of dominance and submission,

social hierarchies, and interspecies symbiotic relations.

In classifying articles according to type of behavior studied I have disregarded the techniques employed by the investigator. It is often necessary for an animal to learn to respond differentially to two stimuli before its sensory capacities can be measured; but in such a case the article was listed as dealing with sensory capacity rather than learning. The aim has been to indicate as accurately as possible the kind of behavior in which the experimenter was interested rather than his methods of studying it.

It proved possible to categorize 587 of the 613 articles. Of this total, 8.6 percent dealt with reproductive behavior, 3.7 percent with emotional reactions, 3.2 percent with social behavior, 3.0 percent with feeding, and 2.8 percent with general habits. The three most commonly-treated types of behavior were (1) reflexes and simple re-action patterns, (2) sensory capacities, and (3) learning and conditioning. Figure 4 shows the proportion of all articles devoted to each of these three major categories.

The figure makes it clear that condition-ing and learning have always been of con-siderable interest to authors whose work appears in the journals I have examined. As a matter of fact slightly more than 50 percent of all articles categorized in this analysis deal with this type of behavior. The popularity of the subject has increased ap-preciably during the last 15 years, and only once since 1927 has any other kind of be-havior been accorded as many articles per volume. This occurred in 1942 when the number of studies dealing with reflexes and simple reaction patterns was unusually large. The temporary shift in relative em-phasis was due almost entirely to a burst of interest in so-called "neurotic behavior" or "audiogenic seizures."

Combining the findings incorporated in Figures 2 and 4, one cannot escape the con-clusion that psychologists publishing in these journals have tended to concentrate upon one animal species and one type of be-havior in that species. Perhaps it would be appropriate to change the title of our jour-nal to read "The Journal of Rat Learning," but there are many who would object to this procedure because they appear to be-lieve that in studying the rat they are study-ing all or nearly all that is important in behavior. At least I suspect that this is the case. How else can one explain the fact that Professor Tolman's book *Purposive Be-havior in Animals and Men* deals primarily with learning and is dedicated to the white rat, "where, perhaps, most of all, the final credit or discredit belongs." And how else are we to interpret Professor Skinner's 457-page opus which is based exclusively upon the performance of rats in bar-pressing situ-ations but is entitled simply *The Behavior of Organisms?*

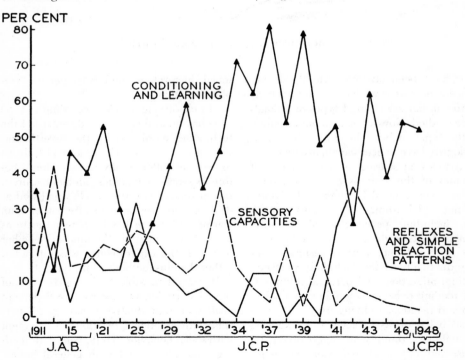

FIG. 4. Percent of all articles concerned with various psychological functions.

Interpretation of Trends

In seeking an interpretation of the demonstrated tendency on the part of so many experimentalists to restrict their attention to a small number of species and a small number of behavior patterns, one comes to the conclusion that the current state of affairs is in large measure a product of tradition. From its inception, American psychology has been strongly anthropocentric. Human behavior has been accepted as the primary object of study and the reactions of other animals have been of interest only insofar as they seemed to throw light upon the psychology of our own species. There has been no concerted effort to establish a genuine comparative psychology in this country for the simple reason that with few exceptions American psychologists have no interest in animal behavior *per se*.

Someone, I believe it was W. S. Small at Clark University in 1899, happened to use white rats in a semi-experimental study. The species "caught on," so to speak, as a laboratory subject, and gradually displaced other organisms that were then being examined. Psychologists soon discovered that rats are hardy, cheap, easy to rear, and well adapted to a laboratory existence. Because of certain resemblances between the associative learning of rats and human beings, *Rattus norvegicus* soon came to be accepted as a substitute for *Homo sapiens* in many psychological investigations. Lack of acquaintance with the behavioral potentialities of other animal species and rapid increase in the body of data derived from rat studies combined to progressively reduce the amount of attention paid to other mammals, to sub-mammalian vertebrates and to invertebrate organisms. Today the trend has reached a point where the average graduate student who intends to do a thesis problem with animals turns automatically to the white rat as his experimental subject; and all too often his professor is unable to suggest any alternative.

To sum up, I suggest that the current popularity of rats as experimental subjects is in large measure the consequence of historical accident. Certainly it is not the result of systematic examination of the available species with subsequent selection of this particular animal as the one best suited to the problems under study.

Concentration of experimental work upon learning seems to stem almost exclusively from the anthropocentric orientation of American psychology. Learning was very early accepted as embodying the most important problems of human behavior; and accordingly the majority of animal investigations have been concerned with this type of activity.

Advantages and Disadvantages of Concentration

I have no wish to discount the desirable aspects of the course which experimental psychology has been pursuing. There are many important advantages to be gained when many independent research workers attack similar problems using the same kinds of organisms. We see this to be true in connection with various biological sciences. Hundreds of geneticists have worked with the fruitfly, *Drosophila*. And by comparing, combining, and correlating the results of their investigations, it has been possible to check the accuracy of the findings, to accelerate the acquisition of new data, and to formulate more valid and general conclusions than could have been derived if each worker dealt with a different species. Something of the same kind is happening in psychology as a result of the fact that many investigators are studying learning in the rat, and I repeat that this is a highly desirable objective.

Another valuable result achieved by the methods currently employed in experimental psychology is the massing of information and techniques pertaining to rat behavior to a point which permits use of this animal as a pedagogical tool. A recent article in the *American Psychologist* reveals that each student in the first course in psychology at Columbia University is given one or two white rats which he will study throughout the semester. This, it seems to me, is an excellent procedure. The beginning student in physiology carries out his first laboratory exercises with the common frog. The first course in anatomy often uses the dogfish or the cat as a sample organism. And college undergraduates learn about genetics by breeding fruitflies. But the usefulness of the rat as a standardized animal for undergraduate instruction, and the preoccupation of mature research workers with the same, single species are two quite different things.

Advanced research in physiology is not restricted to studies of the frog and although many geneticists may confine their personal investigations to *Drosophila*, an even larger number deals with other animal species or with plants. As a matter of fact, the benefits that students can derive from studying one kind of animal as a sample species must always stand in direct proportion to the amount of information research workers have gathered in connection with other species. The rat's value as a teaching aid in psychology depends in part upon the certainty with which the student can generalize from the behavior he observes in this one animal; and this in turn is a function of available knowledge concerning other species.

There is another obvious argument in favor of concentrating our efforts on the study of a single animal species. It is well expressed in Professor Skinner's book, *The Behavior of Organisms.*

In the broadest sense a science of behavior should be concerned with all kinds of organisms, but it is reasonable to limit oneself, at least in the beginning, to a single representative species.

I cannot imagine that anyone would quarrel with Skinner on this point and I am convinced that many of the psychologists currently using rats in their investigational programs would agree with him in his implicit assumption that the Norway rat *is* a "representative species." But in what ways is it "representative," and how has this "representativeness" been demonstrated? These questions lead at once to a consideration of the disadvantages of overspecialization in terms of animals used and types of behavior studied.

To put the question bluntly: Are we building a general science of behavior or merely a science of rat learning? The answer is not obvious to me. Admittedly there are many similarities between the associative learning of lower animals and what is often referred to as rôte learning in man. But the variety of organisms which have been studied, and the number of techniques which have been employed are so limited, it is difficult to believe that we can be approaching a comprehensive understanding of the basic phenomena of learning. It may be that much remains to be discovered by watching rats in mazes and problem boxes, but it is time to ask an important question. How close are we getting to that well-known point of diminishing returns? Would we not be wise to turn our attention to other organisms and to devise new methods of testing behavior before we proceed to formulate elaborate theories of learning which may or may not apply to other species and other situations.

Another very important disadvantage of the present method in animal studies is that because of their preoccupation with a few species and a few types of behavior, psychologists are led to neglect many complex patterns of response that stand in urgent need of systematic analysis. The best example of this tendency is seen in the current attitude toward so-called "instinctive" behavior.

The growing emphasis upon learning has produced a complementary reduction in the amount of study devoted to what is generally referred to as "unlearned behavior." Any pattern of response that does not fit into the category of learned behavior as currently defined is usually classified as "unlearned" even though it has not been analyzed directly. Please note that the classification is made in strictly negative terms *in spite of the fact that the positive side of the implied dichotomy is very poorly defined.* Specialists in learning are not in accord as to the nature of the processes involved, nor can they agree concerning the number and kinds of learning that may occur. But in spite of this uncertainty most "learning psychologists" confidently identify a number of complex behavior patterns as "unlearned." Now the obvious question arises: Unless we know what learning is—unless we can recognize it in all of its manifestations—how in the name of common sense can we identify any reaction as "unlearned"?

The fact of the matter is that none of the responses generally classified as "instinctive" have been studied as extensively or intensively as maze learning or problem-solving behavior. Data relevant to all but a few "unlearned" reactions are too scanty to permit any definite conclusion concerning the role of experience in the shaping of the response. And those few cases in which an exhaustive analysis has been attempted show that the development of the behavior under scrutiny is usually more complicated than a superficial examination could possibly indicate.

For example, there is a moth which always lays its eggs on hackberry leaves. Females of each new generation select hackberry as an oviposition site and ignore other potential host plants. However, the eggs can be transferred to apple leaves, and when this is done the larvae develop normally. Then when adult females that have spent their larval stages on apple leaves are given a choice of materials upon which to deposit their eggs, a high proportion of them select apple leaves in preference to hackberry. This control of adult behavior by the larval environment does not fit into the conventional pigeon-hole labeled "instinct," and neither can it be placed in the category of "learning." Perhaps we need more categories. Certainly

we need more data on more species and more kinds of behavior.

Primiparous female rats that have been reared in isolation usually display biologically effective maternal behavior when their first litter is born. The young ones are cleaned of fetal membranes, retrieved to the nest, and suckled regularly. However, females that have been reared under conditions in which it was impossible for them to groom their own bodies often fail to clean and care for their newborn offspring. Observations of this nature cannot be disposed of by saying that the maternal reactions are "learned" rather than "instinctive." The situation is not so simple as that. In some way the early experience of the animal prepares her for effective maternal performance even though none of the specifically maternal responses are practiced before parturition.

It seems highly probable that when sufficient attention is paid to the so-called "instinctive" patterns, we will find that their development involves processes of which current theories take no account. What these processes may be we shall not discover by continuing to concentrate on learning as we are now studying it. And yet it is difficult to see how a valid theory of learning can be formulated without a better understanding of the behavior that learning theorists are presently categorizing as "unlearned."

Potential Returns from the Comparative Approach

If more experimental psychologists would adopt a broadly comparative approach, several important goals might be achieved. Some of the returns are fairly specific and can be described in concrete terms. Others are more general though no less important.

SPECIFIC ADVANTAGES

I have time to list only a few of the specific advantages which can legitimately be expected to result from the application of comparative methods in experimental psychology. In general, it can safely be predicted that some of the most pressing questions that we are now attempting to answer by studying a few species and by employing only a few experimental methods would be answered more rapidly and adequately if the approach were broadened.

Let us consider learning as one example. Comparative psychology offers many opportunities for examination of the question as to whether there are one or many kinds of learning and for understanding the rôle of learning in the natural lives of different species. Tinbergen (1942) has reported evidence indicating the occurrence of one-trial learning in the behavior of hunting wasps. He surrounded the opening of the insect's burrow with small objects arranged in a particular pattern. When she emerged, the wasp circled above the nest opening for a few seconds in the usual fashion and then departed on a hunting foray. Returning after more than an hour, the insect oriented directly to the pattern stimulus to which she had been exposed only once. If the pattern was moved during the female's absence she was able to recognize it immediately in its new location.

Lorenz's concept of "imprinting" offers the learning psychologist material for new and rewarding study. Lorenz (1935) has observed that young birds of species that are both precocial and social quickly become attached to adults of their own kind and tend to follow them constantly. Newly-hatched birds that are reared by parents of a foreign species often form associations with others of the foster species and never seek the company of their own kind. A series of experiments with incubator-reared birds convinced Lorenz that the processes underlying this sort of behavior must occur very early in life, perhaps during the first day or two after hatching, and that they are irreversible, or, to phase it in other terms, that they are not extinguished by removal of reinforcement.

J. P. Scott's studies (1945) of domestic sheep reveal the importance of early learning in the formation of gregarious habits. Conventional learning theories appear adequate to account for the phenomena, but it is instructive to observe the manner in which the typical species pattern of social behavior is built up as a result of reinforcement afforded by maternal attentions during the nursing period.

The general importance of drives in any sort of learning is widely emphasized. Therefore it would seem worth while to study the kinds of drives that appear to motivate different kinds of animals. In unpublished observations upon the ferret, Walter Miles found that hunger was not sufficient to produce maze learning. Despite prolonged periods of food deprivation, animals of this species continue to explore every blind alley on the way to the goal box.

Additional evidence in the same direction is found in the studies of Gordon (1943) who reports that non-hungry chipmunks will solve mazes and problem boxes when rewarded with peanuts which the animals store in their burrows but do not eat immediately. Does this represent a "primary" drive to hoard food or an "acquired" one based upon learning?

Many experimentalists are concerned with problems of sensation and perception; and here too there is much to be gained from the comparative approach. Fring's studies (1948) of chemical sensitivity in caterpillars, rabbits and men promise to increase our understanding of the physiological basis for gustatory sensations. In all three species there appears to be a constant relationship between the ionic characteristics of the stimulus material and its effectiveness in evoking a sensory discharge. The investigations of Miles and Beck (1949) on reception of chemical stimuli by honey bees and cockroaches provides a test for the theory of these workers concerning the human sense of smell.

The physical basis for vision and the role of experience in visual perception have been studied in a few species but eventually it must be investigated on a broader comparative basis if we are to arrive at any general understanding of the basic principles involved. Lashley and Russell (1934) found that rats reared in darkness give evidence of distance perception without practice; and Hebb (1937) added the fact that figure-ground relationships are perceived by visually-naive animals of this species. Riesen's (1947) report of functional blindness in apes reared in darkness with gradual acquisition of visually-directed habits argues for a marked difference between rodents and anthropoids; and Senden's (1932) descriptions of the limited visual capacities of human patients after removal of congenital cataract appear to support the findings on apes. But the difference, if it proves to be a real one, is not purely a function of evolutionary status of the species involved. Breder and Rasquin (1947) noted that fish with normal eyes but without any visual experience are unable to respond to food particles on the basis of vision.

I have already mentioned the necessity for more extensive examination of those patterns of behavior that are currently classified as "instinctive." There is only one way to approach this particular problem and that is through comparative psychology. The work that has been done thus far on sexual and parental behavior testifies, I believe, to the potential returns that can be expected if a more vigorous attack is launched on a broader front.

We are just beginning to appreciate the usefulness of a comparative study of social behavior. The findings of Scott which I mentioned earlier point to the potential advantages of using a variety of animal species in our investigation of interaction between members of a social group. Carpenter's (1942) admirable descriptions of group behavior in free-living monkeys point the way to a better understanding of dominance, submission, and leadership.

One more fairly specific advantage of exploring the comparative method in psychology lies in the possibility that by this means the experimentalist can often discover a particular animal species that is specially suited to the problem with which he is concerned. For example, in recent years a considerable amount of work has been done on hoarding behavior in the laboratory rat. The results are interesting, but they indicate that some rats must learn to hoard and some never do so. Now this is not surprising since Norway rats rarely hoard food under natural conditions. Would it not seem reasonable to begin the work with an animal that is a natural hoarder? Chipmunks, squirrels, mice of the genus *Peromyscus*, or any one of several other experimental subjects would seem to be much more appropriate.

And now, as a final word, I want to mention briefly a few of the more general facts that indicate the importance of developing comparative psychology.

GENERAL ADVANTAGES

For some time it has been obvious that psychology in this country is a rapidly expanding discipline. Examination of the membership roles of the several Divisions of this Association shows two things. First, that the number of psychologists is increasing at a prodigious rate; and second that the growth is asymmetrical in the sense that the vast majority of new workers are turning to various applied areas such as industrial and clinical psychology.

It is generally recognized that the applied workers in any science are bound to rely heavily upon "pure" or "fundamental" research for basic theories, for general methodology and for new points of view. I do not suggest that we, as experimentalists, should concern ourselves with a comparative approach to practical problems of applied psychology. But I do mean to imply that if we intend to maintain our status as indispensable contributors to the science of behavior, we will have to broaden our attack upon the basic problems of the discipline. This will sometimes mean sacrificing some of the niceties of laboratory research in order to deal with human beings under less artificial conditions. It may also mean expanding the number of non-human species studied and the variety of behavior patterns investigated.

Only by encouraging and supporting a larger number of comparative investigations can psychology justify its claim to being a true science of behavior. European students in this field have justly condemned Americans for the failure to study behavior in a sufficiently large number of representative species. And non-psychologists in this country are so well aware of our failure to develop the field that they think of animal behavior as a province of general zoology rather than psychology. Top-rank professional positions that might have been filled by psychologically trained investigators are today occupied by biologists. Several large research foundations are presently supporting extensive programs of investigation into the behavior of sub-human animals, and only in one instance is the program directed by a psychologist.

Conclusion

If we as experimental psychologists are missing an opportunity to make significant contributions to natural science—if we are failing to assume leadership in an area of behavior investigation where we might be useful and effective—if these things are true, and I believe that they are, then we have no one but ourselves to blame. We insist that our students become well versed in experimental design. We drill them in objective and quantitative methods. We do everything we can to make them into first rate experimentalists. And then we give them so narrow a view of the field of behavior that they are satisfied to work on the same kinds of problems and to employ the same methods that have been used for the past quarter of a century. It would be much better if some of our well-trained experimentalists were encouraged to do a little pioneering. We have a great deal to offer in the way of professional preparation that the average biologist lacks. And the field of animal behavior offers rich returns to the psychologist who will devote himself to its exploration.

I do not anticipate that the advanced research worker whose main experimental program is already mapped out will be tempted by any argument to shift to an entirely new field. But those of us who have regular contact with graduate students can do them a service by pointing out the possibilities of making a real contribution to the science of psychology through the medium of comparative studies. And even in the absence of professorial guidance the alert beginner who is looking for unexplored areas in which he can find new problems and develop new methods of attacking unsettled issues would be wise to give serious consideration to comparative psychology as a field of professional specialization.

REFERENCES

1. BREDER, C. M. and P. RASQUIN: Comparative studies in the light sensitivity of blind characins from a series of Mexican caves. *Bulletin Amer. Mus. Natl. Hist.*, 1947, **89**, Article 5, 325–351.
2. CARPENTER, C. R.: Characteristics of social behavior in non-human primates. *Trans. N. Y. Acad. Sci.*, 1942, Ser. 2, **4**, No. 8, 248.
3. FRINGS, H.: A contribution to the comparative physiology of contact chemoreception. *J. comp. physiol. Psychol.*, 1948, **41**, No. 1, 25–35.
4. GORDON, K.: The natural history and behavior of the western chipmunk and the mantled ground squirrel. *Oregon St. Monogr. Studies in Zool.*, 1943, No. 5, 7–104.
5. HEBB, D. O.: The innate organization of visual activity. I. Perception of figures by rats reared in total darkness. *J. gen. Psychol.*, 1937, **51**, 101–126.
6. LASHLEY, K. S. and J. T. RUSSELL: The mechanism of vision. XI. A preliminary test of innate organization. *J. genet. Psychol.*, 1934, **45**, No. 1, 136–144.
7. LORENZ, K.: Der Kumpan in der Umwelt des Vogels. *J. f. Ornith.*, 1935, **83**, 137–213.

8. MILES, W. R. and L. H. BECK: Infrared absorption in field studies of olfaction in honeybees. *Proceed. Natl. Acad. Sci.*, 1949, **35**, No. 6, 292–310.

9. RIESEN, A. H.: The development of visual perception in man and chimpanzee. *Science*, 1947, **106**, 107–108.

10. SCOTT, J. P.: Social behavior, organization and leadership in a small flock of domes-

tic sheep. *Comp. Psychol. Monogr.*, 1945, **18**, No. 4, 1–29.

11. SENDEN, M. v.: *Raum- und Gestaltauffassung bei operierten Blindgeborenen vor und nach der Operation.* Leipzig: Barth, 1932.

12. TINBERGEN, N.: An objectivistic study of the innate behaviour of animals. *Biblio. Biotheoret.*, 1942, **1**, Pt. 2, 39–98.

E. H. HESS

2   Excerpt from: Ethology: An Approach toward the Complete Analysis of Behavior

The following selection, although the work of a psychologist, presents a well-written and accurate introduction to the concepts of ethology. E. H. Hess has made important contributions to ethologically oriented research through his studies of imprinting and early perception in birds (see reading 24). He was one of the first to demonstrate that ethological findings could be further verified and quantified in a laboratory setting.

The student who is unfamiliar with ethology will find his vocabulary greatly increased through a careful study of this paper. It is important that the terms and concepts of this reading be mastered, because they will occur again without introduction or definition in many of the later readings in this volume.

This reading was excerpted from R. Brown, E. Galanter, E. H. Hess, and G. Mandler, *New Directions in Psychology,* Copyright © 1962, Holt, Rinehart and Winston, Inc. Reprinted by permission.

Suggestion for further reading: Eibl-Eiblesfeldt, I., and S. Kramer, "Ethology, the Comparative Study of Animal Behavior," *Quarterly Review of Biology,* 1958, **33**, 181–211.

DEVELOPMENT OF MODERN ETHOLOGY

In 1898 C. O. Whitman, an American zoologist at the University of Chicago, wrote the sentence that initiated the birth of modern ethology: "Instincts and organs are to be studied from the common viewpoint of phyletic descent" (p. 328). Thus it was he, through the study of orthogenic evolution as opposed to random mutation while cataloguing morphological characteristics of many species of pigeons, who recognized and discovered endogenous movements—movements whose origin came from within—as being a very distinct phe-

nomenon of behavior and therefore able to be systematically studied and evaluated just like any morphological taxonomic characters. It was his contention that "as the genesis of organs takes its departure from the elementary structure of protoplasm, so does the genesis of instinct proceed from the fundamental properties of protoplasm. Primordial organs and instincts are alike few in number and generally persistent" (p. 329). He also criticized the notion that instinctive actions have clock-like regularity and inflexibility, calling it greatly exaggerated; actually, he contended, instinctive movements have only a low degree of variability under normal conditions, the most machinelike instincts always revealing some degree of adaptability to new conditions; thus he echoed Darwin's views.

At very nearly the same time, 1910, Oskar Heinroth, a German zoologist studying ducks and geese, independently came to very similar conclusions. While Whitman's observations on the taxonomic value of innate behavior had been more or less incidental, Heinroth was the first to demonstrate with empirical evidence that the concept of homology applied just as much to movement patterns as to morphological characters, so that these could be used to reconstruct phylogenetic relationships.

Heinroth did not set up any hypotheses about the newly discovered homologies of movement patterns. He described them, studied them, and pointed out the similarities and dissimilarities between various species, genera, and families.

Wallace Craig (1918), Whitman's student, took the first step from the purely descriptive to the analytic stage when he formulated a certain lawfulness in these behavior patterns. He observed that an animal does not only react to a stimulus, but searches, by appetitive behavior, for a certain stimulus situation which allows a consummatory act to run off. Craig defined appetitive behavior as follows: "appetite (or appetence) is a state of agitation which continues as long as a certain stimulus which may be called the appeted stimulus is absent" (p. 91). Craig went on to explain that when a consummatory reaction is released "the appetitive behavior ceases and is succeeded by a state of relative rest" (p. 91). Aversive behavior was similarly defined, but the period of rest comes when the aversive stimulus has been removed.

These consummatory acts were the same as the stereotyped species-specific movement coordinations described by Whitman and Heinroth. In most cases this consummatory act is at the end of a long chain of behavior patterns involved in the appetitive behavior. In some cases, however, the consummatory act occurs so quickly that the appetitive stage is not apparent, but by withholding from the animal the opportunity to perform the consummatory act, appetitive behavior is clearly seen. The fixity of these consummatory acts was shown by the fact that sometimes a species-specific consummatory act that is of selective value in nature is made by the animal in an inappropriate situation, as pointed out by Darwin in the case of dogs trying to cover their excrement in a bare concrete floor. Thus the confusion between desired ends (goals) and the species-preserving function of behavior was eliminated through this analysis, since Craig's standpoint was that the discharge of the consummatory act, not survival value, is the goal of appetitive behavior.

Craig pointed out that the appetitive and aversive factors in instinctive behaviors showed that mere chain reflexes were not the only constituents of such instinctive behaviors. An appetite, furthermore, is accompanied by a certain *readiness to act,* and many of the behavior patterns performed during the appetitive behavior are not innate or completely innate, but must be learned by trial. Thus a cat out looking for food may go to a certain place because he once caught a mouse there, or he may find that he must surmount some unexpected obstacles. But the end action—the consummatory act—of the series of behaviors in the appetitive chain is always innate, as shown by the occurrence of incipient consummatory acts during the appetitive behavior, when the adequate stimulus for the consummatory action has not yet been received.

Craig's scheme was only a beginning that Konrad Lorenz, Heinroth's student, took up and further developed, thus initiating the present period of ethology as a science. In 1935 he described the behavior of birds, drawing from his observations on tame or partly tame birds and paying special attention to the formation of social relationships. In 1937 and 1950 Lorenz elaborated on Craig's behavior analysis by proposing his scheme of *action-specific energy*. He found that the ease with which a given stimulus elicits or releases the corresponding behavior through the innate releasing mechanism (IRM) is dependent on how long it has been since the animal has last given that response. Thus action-specific energy, that is, energy for a particular action, is being produced continuously in an animal's central nervous system, but is held in check by some inhibitory mechanism until the appropriate stimulus releases this energy to certain muscular systems and the reaction takes place. The longer the animal has gone without performing the action in question, the more easily this behavior can be triggered off or released. In fact, in the case of a very prolonged absence of relevant stimulation, this behavior can go off without there being any observable stimulus present. This special case he called the *Leerlaufreaktion* or *vacuum activity*. Similarly, if the relevant stimulation is repeatedly given, the animal's response can decrease to the point where he gives none at all. Lorenz's conceptualization of the way in which a readiness to react is built up and then dissipated through reaction was an extension of Craig's scheme of appetitive behavior seeking the discharge of the consummatory act. One and the same physiological event are probably responsible for the occurrence of appetitive behavior as well as for the raising and lowering of the threshold for response to the stimuli.

Lorenz was careful to point out that this action-specific energy concept did not have anything to do with the exhaustion of or recuperation of muscular systems.

Niko Tinbergen, through his studies on the releasers for innate behavior patterns, further enlarged on the Craig-Lorenz scheme of behavior. Like Lorenz, he postulated (1950) the removal of a central inhibition when an innate behavior pattern is released. He demonstrated, furthermore, that behavior patterns in themselves can function as releasers, as Lorenz had suggested (1935), this finding being based on his studies on the behavior of the three-spined stickleback (1942). Tinbergen (1950) proposed that there was a hierarchical order of appetitive behaviors and consummatory acts. Both Tinbergen and G. P. Baerends (1956) have demonstrated that the lawfulness of behavior in intact higher organisms and the neurophysiological events in lower organisms are parallel.

Thus inspired by the work of Lorenz and Tinbergen, ethology began to expand into the neurophysiological bases of behavior. That these neurophysiological bases existed in fact and had a clear correlation with behavioral events was shown by the work of Erich von Holst (1933 *et seq.*), P. Weiss (1941a, b) W. R. Hess (1927, 1949, 1954, 1956), and K. D. Roeder (1955). Von Holst and Hess demonstrated the existence of neurological organization underlying various behavior patterns by stimulating a particular brain region of birds and cats with electrodes. The elicited patterns of behavior in response to electrical brain stimulation were the species-specific behavior patterns which ethologists had already observed in those particular species. Hess's elicitation in integrated threat, fighting, sleeping, and eating behaviors upon electrical stimulation of the cat's brain are examples of the behaviors observed. The *integration* of these behaviors was a particularly important finding; for example, cats not only went to sleep but also searched about for a place to sleep. Other areas of neurophysiological research have included von Holst's studies on the relationship between the rhythms of nervous impulses and of muscular movements, Weiss's proof of central nervous determination of primitive movement coordinations, and Roeder's demonstration that behavior is created spontaneously within the central nervous system. Recently, von Holst and von St. Paul have published a monumental paper on the interaction of different behavior patterns through the method of simultaneous electrical stimulation of adult chicken brains

(1960). Their findings represent a landmark in ethological theory and evidence, and will accordingly be discussed in detail later.

There are many other modern ethologists who have made significant contributions to the growth of their discipline. Indeed, it would be a staggering task to attempt to treat all of them adequately.

Ethological Concepts

FIXED ACTION PATTERNS

The fixed action pattern, or more simply, fixed pattern, is one of the most fundamental concepts of modern ethology. In fact, ethology was founded on the discovery of this phenomenon by Heinroth and Whitman, who were the first ones to describe it.

The fixed action pattern is defined as a sequence of coordinated motor actions that appears without the animal having to learn it by the usual learning processes. The animal can perform it without previous exercise and without having seen another species member do it. The fixed action pattern is *constant in form*, which means that the sequence of motor elements never varies.

These patterns are not equivalent to the well-known reflexes, nor are they chain reflexes; this statement will be discussed in connection with neurophysiological evidence for ethological tenets. There are many differences between the fixed action patterns and reflexes; however, an adequate discussion of these differences is beyond the scope of this paper. It may be mentioned, nevertheless, that the frequency with which the fixed action pattern is performed depends in part on how long it is since it was last performed; this is in accordance with Lorenz's postulation of specific action potential. This is not the case with reflexes. The animal engages in appetitive behavior that ends in the performance of the fixed action pattern, or consummatory act. No such appetitive behavior ending in the discharge of a reflex has been found. What is more, as we shall see later on, rhythmic movements such as those of locomotion are not necessarily equivalent to chain reflexes.

The appearance of such fixed action patterns in animals isolated from their own species is clear evidence of their genetic fixedness. Even though experimentally isolated animals may never have had any experience with the particular objects or situations involved, they will still perform the fixed pattern when the appropriate situation arises, as demonstrated by squirrels that were reared in isolation and were never given any objects to handle. Nevertheless, the squirrels attempted to bury nuts or nut-like objects in a bare floor upon their first encounter with them, making scratching movement as if to dig out earth, tamping the object in the floor with the nose, and, finally, making complete covering movements in the air (Eibl-Eibesfeldt, 1956a).

The fixed action pattern, appearing as it does in animals that have been isolated from their own species and deprived of experience relevant to this behavior, is therefore a constant characteristic of the species in question, being based, presumably, on specific central nervous system mechanisms that are inherited, just as are other morphological and physiological characters. In line with this, they are, furthermore, characteristics of genera and orders right up to the highest taxonomic categories. The fact that they are always to be found in more than one species proves their taxonomic value. They can be used, in fact, to differentiate between very closely related species.

The fixed action patterns are quite resistant to phylogenetic change through evolution, more so than morphological characters. For example, a morphological structure (such as a colored skin patch or an enlarged feather) connected with a fixed action pattern may often appear after the fixed action pattern has come into existence in the species, or the fixed action pattern may remain but the morphological structure may disappear. The first case is illustrated by the mandarin duck's pointing to an enlarged and colored wing feather during courtship. This pointing has derived, through the process of ritualization, from wing-preening, which presumably occurred before the wing feathers had become enlarged and specially colored. The last case is illustrated by the behavioral rudiments that have been observed in animals.

Krumbiegel (1940) compared the behavior of long-tailed and short-tailed monkeys and found that when a long-tailed monkey runs along a branch, its tail moves from the right to the left and back again, thus achieving balance. These same compensatory movements are to be observed in the short stumps of the short-tailed monkeys, even though there is obviously no value at all in these movements for balancing. Similarly, hornless domestic cattle and goats attempt to fight with their heads in the same way as their horned relatives.

Finally, mutant drosophila flies with no wings still perform the wing-preening movements typical of the species (Heinz, 1949).

Not only may the fixed pattern persist even though the relevant morphological structures have disappeared, but it also may persist even though the biologically appropriate situation no longer exists in the normal environment of the species. The injury-feigning ruse of a number of birds when their nest containing young is approached by an intruder or a predator is well known. On the Galapagos Islands, there are no mammalian predators, and most of the birds no longer show this distraction behavior when their nest is approached by man. However, the Galapagos dove still does this, running and fluttering from the nest as if it had a broken wing, in order to distract the attention of the intruder from the nest (Eibl-Eibesfeldt, personal communication).

In the same fashion, a kind of ontogenetic development, similar to Haeckel's well-known "phylogenetic recapitulation"

of organs, has been observed in some cases where a primitive behavior pattern precedes the more recent one during ontogeny of the individual. There are some species of birds (the lark, the raven, and the starling) belonging to the *Passeres* whose original form of ground locomotion was hopping, but that now live on the ground and run. It is most interesting to find that the juveniles of these species hop in biped fashion before they run (Lorenz, 1937).

It is therefore clear that the fixed action patterns are extremely conservative in the evolution of a species. In only one case has rapid phylogentic change in fixed action patterns been observed. This happens in the sexual behavior of closely related species that live in the same territory. In such cases the courtship behavior of these two species must of necessity become differentiated from each other if crossbreeding is not to occur. Thus changes take place in the motor patterns and vocalizations by means of which the sexual partner of the same species is selected during courtship. For example, closely related songbirds inhabiting the same ecological niche, as P. Marler (1957) has shown, have very different songs and courtship movements, whereas other fixed patterns that do not play a role in the ethological barrier between the species have remained the same.

Evolutionary changes that occur in fixed action patterns are similar to those that occur in morphological or physiological characteristics. Thus selection pressure may favor the development of a clear-cut execution of a fixed pattern that has much survival value, or cause it to disappear when it has no survival value. In some cases, of course, behavioral rudiments or vestigial behavior may remain even though there is little survival value.

A phylogenetic change during evolution is the altering of the function of a fixed action pattern in a species that has changed its manner of living. This was demonstrated by one of Tinbergen's group at Oxford, Esther Cullen (1957), who analyzed the behavior of a gull species, the Kittiwake, which now lives on cliffs rather than at the shore. Many fixed patterns changed their function completely, but were still the same in form, so that their homologies with the patterns of the gull group to which this particular species belonged were quite apparent. For example, the young, unlike those of other gulls, cannot run away from strange adults, and consequently have developed an attack-inhibiting appeasement gesture. In related gulls this gesture appears only in sexually mature animals during mating.

Ethologists have postulated that there are two stages in the evolution of motor patterns. In the first, there is a quantitative increase or decrease of motor elements—perhaps actual disappearance in some cases—and in the second, there is a coordinative coupling and disengagement of almost unalterable basic motor units. These basic motor units were shown by Lorenz's film analyses of courtship in ducks. This coupling of previously independent motor elements into a fixed sequence is part of the phylogenetic process that J. S. Huxley, an English naturalist, called ritualization in 1914.

Another phylogenetic process in ritualization is one in which a recently formed fixed pattern may become motivationally autonomous of the situation that originally aroused it, or dependent on another motivation. An example of this process is to be seen in the different forms of the female's "inciting" movement during courtship in different species of swimming ducks (Anatinae). In the original form of this behavior, the female attempts to separate the male from the group by inciting fights between her partner and other males. To do this she runs toward the strange male, but at a certain point fear overtakes her, and she runs back toward her mate. When she is close enough to him, however, aggressiveness again takes hold of her, and she stops and turns toward the strange male. This results in her standing at the point of equilibrium, near her mate, but stretching her neck toward the other male, making

inciting movements. Here the angle between her body and her stretched-out neck is a function of her position and those of the two males. This behavior constitutes the unritualized form of incitement. Now, in some other species, the behavior has become so fixed that the female simply stands near her mate and moves her head back over the shoulder, regardless of where the strange male is. This shows that the movement is now performed solely as a courtship movement by the female. The interpretation that this behavior constitutes ritualized incitement is supported by the fact that still other species perform actions which are intermediate between these two extremes when in a similar situation (Lorenz, 1941).

Still another phylogenetic process in the ritualization of behavior is one in which the fixed pattern is no longer performed in different degrees of intensity, but in one intensity only. Thus the degree of motivation is not expressed in the intensity of the behavior, but in how often the behavior is repeated, much as the urgency of a telephone call may be recognized by the frequency of ringing rather than in loudness. All fixed patterns with a single or typical intensity function as means of communication between species members; selection pressure would in these cases operate to enforce a quite simple and unmistakable form of the movement (Morris, 1957).

Another very interesting evolutionary process in the development of fixed patterns is to be found in fighting behavior between members of the same species. Here actions that injure the opponent have been removed to the end of the sequence of fighting behavior by raising the threshold for its release to a very high level. This results in the development of ceremonial "tournaments" with a very small likelihood of actual bodily harm, a development that has clear survival value to the species, since fighting behavior will maintain its function of spacing out members of a species without causing injury to species members.

The result of ritualization, in summary,

is that actions come to be performed in a mimetically exaggerated way in special situations. The same species may be observed to perform both forms of the fixed action pattern, ritualized and unritualized. As different and related species perform ritualized and unritualized forms of these movement patterns, as well as forms intermediate to these extremes, the homologies between these forms can be used to reconstruct phylogenetic relationships.

During the past few years ethologists have expanded from the phylogenesis of these fixed action patterns to their physiological bases. At the present time very little is known regarding their neuroanatomical bases, but it seems probable that they share a common physiological base, and the investigations so far conducted strongly indicate that they are based on inherited and structured neurophysiological mechanisms. For the time being, nevertheless, the fixed action pattern is defined in purely functional terms.

RELEASERS AND THE INNATE
RELEASING MECHANISM

An animal, like man, does not give a particular response to *all* of the stimuli it perceives; most of them are only *potential* stimuli, to some of which it may learn to respond. Instinctive behavior, in particular, is evoked in response to only a few of the stimuli in an animal's environment; these stimuli are called *sign stimuli,* or *releasers* of the behaviors which they elicit.

An example of these facts is to be found in the behavior of the common tick, which was described in detail by von Uexküll (1909). The tick does not respond to the sight of a host, but when an odor of butyric acid from a mammal strikes the tick's sensory receptors, the tick drops from the twig to the host, finds a spot on the skin which is about 37° centigrade, and begins to drink blood. Only a few stimuli elicit the tick's behavior, this behavior being without doubt innate.

But the simplicity of releasers can sometimes lead animals into grave situa-

tions. For instance, a patient tick climbs up a slippery twig to waylay its prey, a nice, juicy mammal. When it has reached the end of the twig, it is above a rock on which a fat, perspiring man has been sitting. The rock therefore emanates the typical odor of butyric acid, and is just the right temperature. So the tick jumps, and lands on the rock—whereupon, in trying to suck from the rock, it breaks its proboscis.

This description shows clearly that only a few stimuli elicit the tick's behavior, this behavior being without doubt innate.

Another example is the carnivorous water beetle *Dytiscus marginalis*. It does not react to the sight of prey—even though it has perfectly well developed compound eyes, as is easily demonstrated when a tadpole in a glass tube is presented to it —but to the chemical stimuli emanating from the prey through the water. If a meat extract solution is put into the water, the beetle engages in frantic searching behavior, clasping inanimate objects (Tinbergen, 1951). These two examples of the few stimuli that release innate behavior patterns make it easy to understand why a male robin will attack a bundle of red feathers but not a dummy of a male, perfect in all respects except that it lacks the characteristic red breast (Lack, 1939).

Animals react automatically to sign stimuli, with little insight; the behavior is just run off. The lack of insight is well demonstrated by the hen's failure to rescue a chick that it can see struggling under a glass bell, but that it cannot hear. It will come to its rescue immediately, however, if it does not see him but can hear his distress cries (Brückner, 1933).

Sign stimuli, or releasers, furthermore, almost always release only one *reaction,* an example being the fact that the smell of butyric acid can release only jumping in a tick. This property differentiates sign stimuli from an acquired picture, where the response seems to depend on a configurational stimulus or Gestalt complex, which may be so altered by small changes or additions so that the original is not recognized. A tame bird, for example, may become quite frightened when it sees its keeper wear glasses or a hat for the first time. In addition, the response given to an acquired stimulus may be changed; a dog may learn to avoid a particular place instead of approaching it.

Sign stimuli also differ from *Gestalten* in that when several of them (usually attached to the same object) that produce the same response are present, they do not interact in determining the animal's response; instead, their effects are completely additive. This is in contrast to the Gestalt psychologists' view that an object is *more* than the sum of its component parts. The additiveness of releaser stimuli was demonstrated by Seitz (1940) when he studied the fighting response of the male cichlid fish *Astatotilápia Strigigena* (Pfeffer). He found that the following stimuli released fighting behavior: (1) silvery blueness, (2) dark margin, (3) highness and broadness by means of fin erection, (4) parallel orientation to the opponent, and (5) tail beating. All of these are characteristics normal to an intruding and attacking male. Seitz found that each of these, presented singly, would elicit the fighting response about equally. This remarkable finding provides a fundamental distinction between releasers and acquired *Gestalten*, since only the whole is responded to in a *Gestalt*. Furthermore, if two of these stimuli were presented simultaneously, the elicited fighting response was twice as great. The intensity of a reaction, therefore, can depend not only on what sign stimuli are present, but how many are present. Seitz called this phenomenon the "law of heterogeneous summation" *(Reizsummen regel)*.

Weidmann and Weidmann (1958) recently tested the law of heterogeneous summation quantitatively and found it to hold, in most cases, in a strict arithmetical sense. They counted the number of pecks made by black-headed gull chicks, while they were begging, at cardboard models. If they presented a round and a rectangular model to the chick, one would receive more pecks

than the other. But if they made both models red, each received the same increase in the total number of pecks.

Although sign stimuli often consist of a quality such as butyric acid for the tick, or red feathers for the male robin, and differ from *Gestalten* in many ways, most releasers, like *Gestalten*, consist of relational characteristics between stimuli. Indeed, the registration of relationships between stimuli is a fundamental attribute of perception, since the strength or distinctiveness of a perception is to a large part dependent on the contrast or relationship between, or distinctiveness of, stimuli.

For example, a male stickleback reacts with fighting behavior to the red on a rival male. But this red must be on the rival's belly, for if the red is on the back, the stickleback will not attack (Tinbergen, 1951).

Similarly, Tinbergen and Kuenen (1939) showed that the young thrush's gaping response was to a particular stimulus relationship. They constructed a round cardboard model with two different-sized

FIG. 1. The two double-headed models used by Tinbergen and Kuenen in their study of the stimuli eliciting the gaping response in young thrushes. The body of the model on the left is 4 cm.; the body of the model on the right is 8 cm. The small heads are 1 cm.; the large heads are 3 cm. When the left model is presented, the small head is found to elicit gaping, but when the right model is presented, the large head now elicits gaping. This shows that the ratio between the size of the head and of the body is the stimulus quality releasing gaping in young thrushes. (From TINBERGEN, N., and D. J. KUENEN, *Zeitschrift für Tierpsychologie*, 1939, 3, Verlag Paul Parey, Berlin.)

heads attached to it. Tinbergen and Kuenen found that the thrushes directed their gaping toward the larger of the two heads. They then took off the two heads and placed them on a smaller round cardboard. The young thrushes now directed their gaping toward the smaller head, thus showing that it was the relationship between the sizes of the head and body that elicited gaping.

Since releasers can consist of relational qualities, these relations can be made even stronger in some cases through transposition or exaggeration. For instance, Koehler and Zagarus (1937) studied egg recognition on the ringed plover. If a normal egg having dark brown spots on a light brown background was presented together with another egg having black spots on a white background, the birds preferred the black and white eggs, because the spots contrasted more strongly with the background. More remarkable was their preference for abnormally large eggs, even ones they could not sit on. A herring gull behaves similarly (Baerends, 1957, 1959, and Kruijt, 1958). Such stimuli that release a response stronger than that released by the natural stimulus are *superoptimal*, or supernormal.

Magnus (1958) also convincingly demonstrated superoptimality of releasers, this time in the silver-washed fritillary butterfly, *Argynnis paphia L.* Magnus first found that the color yellow-orange, the same as in the female's wings, released courtship responses in the male. The female also flutters its wings, and the resulting alternation between color and dark releases the male's courtship behavior, as Magnus showed by placing yellow-orange and dark strips on a revolving cylinder. Surprisingly, Magnus further found that increasing the speed of the rotating cylinder so that the color and dark alternation was more rapid than the rate used by the female resulted in greater effectiveness in eliciting courtship. The greater the speed of rotation of the cylinder, the greater the courtship responses, right up to the physiologically

demonstrated flicker fusion frequency for the species when the color and dark alternation was so rapid that it could not be seen. This was indeed a very dramatic demonstration of supernormal releasers.

The susceptibility of animals to superoptimal releasers provides us with an insight as to the reason for the development of bizarre morphological structures in some animals such as the peacock. These strange structures are used in courtship of the female. It is clear, also, that parasitic birds capitalize on this phenomenon, since the young parasite is usually larger and more babyish than are the host's own young, so that it is actually preferred, with resultant neglect of the host's own young (Cott, 1940). Heinroth described the situation accurately when he called the young cuckoo a "vice" of its foster parents (1938).

When the different stimuli that act as releasers are examined, it is apparent that they are all very clear and simple in character—the color red on the belly or breast, a head-body size ratio, an odor, a movement, and so on. At the same time, they are unmistakable distinguishing characteristics of the appropriate biological situation—characteristics that are highly improbable in any other biological situation. This fact, when coupled with the selection pressures that must operate so as to bring about the ability to recognize without fail certain biological situations essential for the survival of the individual and of the species, accounts for their reliability in eliciting the required and adaptive response in natural conditions.

Their great simplicity, in fact, means that they can be imitated for certain purposes. The fisherman utilizes a releaser when he places a silvery lure into the water in order to attract and catch a pike (Baerends, 1950). There are some flowers which give off a putrid odor that attracts flies, and fertilization of these flowers is thus carried out by the flies. Still other flowers look like a female bumblebee's body and are fertilized in the male bumblebee's attempt to copulate with it.

Releasers, or sign stimuli, are also used for interspecies communication. An example of this is to be found in the fish symbioses studied by Eibl-Eibesfeldt (1955b). There are certain large species of fish in the Caribbean, the groupers *(Epinephelus striatus)*, that allow their teeth and gills to be cleaned of particles and ectoparasites by the neon goby, *Elacatinus oceanops.* The fish wishing to be cleaned makes a movement inviting the cleaner fish to enter its mouth and pick its teeth, and makes another movement signaling it to come out from the mouth. The principle of imitation is also to be found in this case (Eibl-Eibesfeldt, 1959). These fish do not normally allow any other fish to come near it, and in the Indopacific oceanic regions they permit only fish looking and behaving like cleaners of that area, the *Labroides dimidiatus,* to approach it. However, there is another species, *Aspidontus taeniatus,* which has taken advantage of this by having a certain coloration and by imitating the movements of the cleaner fish. When they come close to the large fish, they fall on it, biting out chunks of flesh, and the fish must flee. However, these parasites do occasionally pick ectoparasites from larger fish.

Now that we have considered the nature of the releaser, or sign stimulus, let us complete the picture by taking a look at the *innate releasing mechanism,* known for short as the I.R.M. As has been earlier mentioned, an inhibitory block has been postulated by Lorenz (1937) and Tinbergen (1950) to prevent the continuous discharge of internally produced energy. The I.R.M. functions to remove this inhibition when it receives sensory impulses arising from a releaser stimulus. This brings us to an important rule in evaluating the relative effectiveness of a given stimulus as a releaser for a fixed action pattern, in the light of the fading of reactivity due to repeated stimulation, and reaction recovery during a period in which no performance of the reaction takes place (see above). If the animal is under low motivation, a strong releaser is required in order to elicit a reaction; whereas if the animal is highly motivated, a weak stimulus is sufficient to elicit a response of the same strength. Therefore, it is necessary to test the potential effectiveness of different releasers in relation to each other. This can be done by making certain that the animal is under the same motivation when exposed to each of them, or by exposing the animal to a standard stimulus just prior to the presentation of the stimulus in question. Thus the difference in responsiveness between the different stimuli and the antecedent standard stimulus is the basis for evaluation. Only in these ways can it be determined whether a stimulus is a normal, subnormal, or supernormal releaser.

The I.R.M. operates as a receptor of key stimuli and must be adapted to the world as it exists; this is necessary to make sure it will respond only to stimuli that unfailingly characterize a particular biological situation, and no other. If a particular response is elicited by several sign stimuli belonging to a certain biological situation, then the presence of most of them in that situation guarantees the elicitation of the response in question. A pike cannot attach any releaser or sign stimuli to the fish on which it preys in order to differentiate it from a fisherman's lure; therefore the species must adapt the I.R.M. accordingly. However, within a species or where interspecies communication takes place, natural selection can quickly result in the evolution of special sign stimuli or releasers that will be understood easily by the reacting animal.

Not only morphological structures but also behavioral patterns performed by another animal may function as releasers, as Tinbergen has shown in his study of the courtship behavior of the three-spined stickleback (1942). In such cases there is a reaction chain, each animal's action serving as a releaser for the other animal's subsequent response. Thus, the appearance of the female initiates the male's zigzag dance toward the nest, which in turn releases a following response in the female. The male, in responce to her having followed him, shows her the nest entrance, and she reacts by swimming into it. On seeing her in the nest, the male touches her tail with a quivering motion, with the result that she lays the eggs and then swims out. The male then swims into the nest and fertilizes the eggs. Reaction chains, where they exist, enable the male to select a female of the same species. As Baerends (1950) points out, they also serve to select fully mature and healthy females, since any others would fail to respond correctly after the first couple of links in the chain.

Another feature of the I.R.M. is that in some cases its selectivity for sign stimuli may increase during the life of the individual. Such a process occurs in all members of the species, not in just one individual.

The increased selectivity may be of either of two types:

1. *Narrowing of the range of stimuli evoking a particular response through the dropping out of individual stimuli.* This occurs by means of habituation or one-trial negative conditioning. For example, a bird becomes habituated to the motion of leaves, other members of its species, etc., with the result that it no longer responds with fright to them. Its fright behavior in the face of predators, however, is absolutely unaffected. Similarly, a toad will at first snap at all small objects, but after a single unhappy experience will avoid bees and wasps.

2. *Selection and strengthening of one releaser out of a large range of potential releasers, with the result that only this releaser is responded to and not any of the others.* This occurs in the socialization process of many animals, and this instance is known as *imprinting.* Soon after hatching, for example, a gosling has the disposition to follow almost any moving object and to behave as if that object were its mother. After this experience only this object, and no other, is treated as if it were the mother. Thus a gosling imprinted to a green box

will not have anything to do with its real mother, but will stay close to the green box. This shows, of course, that the socialization process in the natural situation occurs in the same fashion. The subject of imprinting and its difference from ordinary types of association learning will be discussed in a later section.

In both cases of the increased selectivity of the I.R.M. during the life of the individual, it is clear that it results in behavior which has greater survival value.

SIMULTANEOUS AROUSAL OF DIFFERENT DRIVES

Most often people think of behavior as being influenced by one drive at a time. Actually, however, behavior can most frequently be seen to be influenced by or be a result of more than one activated drive, thus making the analysis of behavior quite complex. There are several types of such behaviors: successive ambivalent behavior, simultaneous ambivalent behavior, redirected behavior, and displacement behavior.

In the case of successive ambivalent behavior, it is seen that the animal alternates between incompletely performed movements belonging to the conflicting drives. When two males of a territory-owning species (such as the stickleback or herring gull) meet each other at the common boundary of their two territories, each is influenced by the other in two ways. First, because the other is so near the territory, the owner is roused to attack. But the stranger also causes hesitance and avoidance, for it is not in the owner's territory, but just outside it, and furthermore in its own territory. Each male is therefore in the same conflict, one which usually finds expression in an ambivalent reaction: attack and retreat in quick and repeated alternation.

Simultaneous ambivalent behavior, however, is also to be found. In such a case both tendencies are simultaneously, rather than alternately, aroused. An example of this is the threat posture of the cat, which according to Leyhausen (1956), results from the animal retreating more rapidly with the front paws than with the rear ones, or advancing with the rear paws while retreating with the front ones. Lorenz (1953) has shown that fear and aggression occur simultaneously in the dog, with at least nine different expressions possible as a result of mixing three different degrees—high, medium, and low—of either drive.

Redirected behavior is another type in which two conflicting behaviors manifest themselves. This occurs when one behavior is inhibited or suppressed by another motivation. For example, an animal feeling aggressive towards a member of its own species (its mate, for instance) may at the same time be inhibited in its attack. Hence, the aggression may be redirected, and the animal will attack another animal or even an object if no third animal is available. Thus, prairie falcons defending their nest from a human intruder may swoop down toward him, but at the last moment fear overtakes the falcon: it makes a sudden swerve to the side and flies to attack bypassing birds.

Since cases in which behavior is determined by only one drive are relatively rare, the different behaviors of animals result from independently varying sets of motivations. In accordance with this knowledge, Oehlert (1958) demonstrated the existence of a mechanism of sex recognition that is widely distributed throughout the animal kingdom. In *Cichlasoma biocellatum* and *Geophagus brasiliensis*, two species of cichlids studied by Oehlert, and perhaps in many other species in which the sexes do not have a distinctive sexual dimorphism, the only sexual difference in behavior consists of the fact that three drives—sex, aggression, and fear—which are always activated simultaneously when two strange fish meet, can be mixed in different ways in males and females. In the males just about every possible mixture and superposition of sexual and aggressive behavior elements can be made, but the flight drive,

even when minimal, will immediately inhibit the sexual drive. In the female, however, flight behavior can mix very easily with sexual behavior, whereas aggressiveness immediately suppresses sexuality. This difference between males and females is enough to guarantee the formation of male-female pairs. In the same way, fear suppresses male sex behavior and aggression inhibits female sex behavior in grouse and crows (A. A. Allen, 1954, and Lorenz, 1931).

Still another type of behavior may occur when two motivations are in conflict with each other. This is the *displacement activity* discovered independently in 1940 by both Tinbergen and Kortlandt. Very often in conflict situations the animal may show behavior patterns that do not belong to either of the two conflicting drives, but that are completely different. At first such "irrelevant" behavior is surprising, but after further study it is found that a particular irrelevant act is often typical of a particular set of conditions. Since the intensity of the displacement act is correlated with strength of the conflicting motivations, Tinbergen proposed that the irrelevant or displacement act is activated by the energy from the conflicting drives. Thus such displacement acts were *allochthonous*, as distinct from the case in which they are motivated by their own drive, when they are *autochthonous*.

For example, fighting domestic cocks may suddenly peck at the ground as if they were feeding (Lorenz, 1935, Tinbergen, 1939). In this case the irrelevant feeding results from a conflict between aggressiveness and fear. Quite often such pecking on the ground has been observed in other birds. The prairie horned lark does this during territorial fights (Pickwell, 1931), and so does the lapwing between attacks of an intruder disturbing it at its nest. Male snow buntings will peck at the ground during boundary disputes (Howard, 1929).

Many other types of displacement activities have been observed. The three-spined stickleback makes nest-building movements (displacement sand digging) during boundary fights with another male (Tinbergen and van Iersel, 1947), and herring gulls pick up nesting material during boundary disputes. Sexual movements such as wing-flapping and gurgling, which normally occur in courtship behavior, are shown by cormorants when fighting, and sky larks burst into violent song just after having escaped from a predator (Tinbergen, 1952). Cormorants also perform sessions of "false brooding" during nest fights (Kortlandt, 1940a), and the avocet may suddenly sit down during exciting hostile encounters (Makkink, 1936). Even sleep may occur as a displacement activity; this was first discovered by Makkink (1936) in the avocet and has been observed since then in various other waterbirds such as the oyster catcher, turnstone, and common sandpiper, and in male snow buntings, always in an aggressive situation.

It is apparent even from this short review of displacement activities that they often occur when the fighting and escape drives are simultaneously aroused. They are also very common in sexual situations. They can, of course, be aroused by combinations of other drives.

From what has been found concerning displacement activities, it is clear that such activities are usually dependent, at least in part, on internal impulses. The so-called innate "comfort movements" such as preening, shaking the feathers, wiping the bill, bathing, and so forth, most often depend on internal impulses and also appear as displacement activities in both hostile and sexual situations. Displacement preening is quite common during courtship, and displacement bathing has been observed regularly in the sheld duck when copulation was interrupted for some reason (Makkink, 1931). Scratching of the fur is a very common displacement activity in mammals up to the primates (Portielje, 1939, and Tinbergen, 1940).

Another fact in considering the nature of displacement activities is that they are more likely to occur when conflicting drives are relatively intense. For example, in the boundary clash between males of territory-owning species, ambivalent behavior consisting of attack and retreat in alternation occurs as long as the conflicting drives of aggressiveness and fear are not too strong. But when these drives are very intense, displacement activities appear. Tinbergen (1952) therefore hypothesized that displacement activities were outlets through which strong but thwarted drives could express themselves in motion.

In sexual situations, displacement activities may occur as a result of sudden cessation of external stimulation emanating from the partner, or from conflict. Also, it has been suggested (Verwey, 1930, Kortlandt, 1940b) that copulation in birds brings about a situation which they normally avoid, that is, bodily contact with another individual. Therefore, the precoition situation may evoke in each individual a tendency to keep away from or to attack the partner as well as the expected one of approach.

However, no experimental evidence has been found that supports Tinbergen's hypothesis. Recently, Andrew (1956), Sevenster (1958) and van Iersel and Bol (1958), by studying grooming in birds, displacement fanning in the three-spined stickleback, and displacement preening in terns, respectively, suggested that inhibitions exerted by one or both of the conflicting systems on an activity are temporarily removed as a result of the conflict between these drives. These authors hypothesize that if the two conflicting motivations are balanced, then not only their own motoric manifestations, but also the inhibiting effect on the third motor pattern is removed.

This new conceptualization agrees with a number of well-known facts regarding displacement activities. For example, displacement activities occur particularly when specific motivations that strongly inhibit other motivations and dominate the entire organism, such as flight, escape, and copulation, come into conflict. Furthermore, the fixed patterns that occur as displacement activities are almost always those that are repeated many times daily and that do not usually require a high motivation level. Also, the form of the displacement movement has often been observed to be correlated with the body position into which an animal is forced by his primary conflict: a movement for which this body position is the basis is made in a large number of cases. This last is a point made by Tinbergen (1952) in connection with his theory.

Sevenster (1958) supported his hypothesis by the finding that the presence of adequate external stimuli can facilitate the appearance of certain types of displacement activities. For example, if food is thrown to fighting cocks, then displacement feeding increases. Sevenster could increase the fanning of the nest by the stickleback as a displacement activity by bringing about the appropriate conflict situation and at the same time maintaining a high CO_2 concentration in the water. Van Iersel and Bol (1958) also found that displacement bill-shaking, which occurs in sandwich terns when in conflict between escape and incubation drives, was increased in rainy weather. These phenomena would be hard to explain if displacement were based only on irradiation of energy, channeled strictly in a certain direction by the structure of the central nervous system.

On the other hand, there are several facts that could be better explained by the earlier hypothesis than by the new theory. The new theory, for example, fails to explain why in the majority of cases where there is a particular conflict, only a particular displacement activity is performed. This is an important point, because in closely related species the same small motor patterns are performed, but in the same conflict situation different specific displacement activities occur. Furthermore, according to the inhibition theory, the *balance* between the two conflicting motivations is responsible for the occurrence of displace-

ment activity, whereas it has been shown that the intensity of the displacement act is proportional to the absolute drive level of the conflicting motivations. Lastly, if the inhibition hypothesis were correct, then displacement activity would have to be performed with the same *irregularity* as its autochthonous forms, as, for instance, in the case of a bird; it does not preen itself ceaselessly when the preening drive is not under inhibition by other drives.

Finally, these different types of mixed-drive behavior—successive and simultaneous ambivalence, redirection and displacement activities—are not mutually exclusive and may often be found to exist in the same behavior sequence. For example, as Baerends (1958) has shown, the courtship of the male cichlid fish, *Cichlasoma meeki*, has successive ambivalence in the zigzag dance (the *zigs* being incipient attacks and the *zags* being incipient leading-to-the-nest), redirection in its incipient attacks toward plants, and displacement activity in a peculiar quivering movement interpreted as displacement digging.

HIERARCHICAL ORGANIZATION
OF BEHAVIOR

Lorenz and Craig distinguished between two types of behavior: the appetitive and aversive behaviors, and the consummatory act. Appetitive behavior consists of initially variable searching behavior that becomes more and more specific until the simpler and more stereotyped consummatory act, in response to a releasing stimulus situation, is performed. Aversive behavior has some similarity with appetitive behavior, but consists of behavior that continues until a disturbing situation is removed, and the animal reaches a state of equilibrium. Here the goal is not the discharge of specific behavior patterns, but the cutting off of appetitive behavior that in this case is undirected locomotion.

The distinction between appetitive behavior and the consummatory act is not an absolute one; there are many forms intermediate to them. But these concepts serve to mark the extremes, since appetitive behavior is variable and plastic, whereas the consummatory act is relatively fixed and stereotyped.

Appetitive behavior is characterized in three ways. The first is by its motor pattern, usually one of locomotion. The others are its orientation component and the stimuli to which the animal is particularly responsive. Since the first and second components may remain the same while the third changes, as seen when a hungry squirrel (1) climbs (2) up trees (3) looking for cones; and when a squirrel motivated to build nests (1) climbs (2) up trees (3) looking for twigs and bark, appetitive behavior is usually classified according to the third component. Therefore, in the first case, the squirrel is showing appetitive behavior for food, while in the second case it is showing appetitive behavior for nesting material.

The consummatory act itself is made in response to one or more releasers and is composed of an orientation component, the *taxis,* and a motor component, the *fixed action pattern.* These two aspects of the consummatory act were pointed out by Lorenz and Tinbergen (1938) during a study of the egg-rolling response of the greylag goose. But before we discuss this, let us briefly examine the nature of the taxes, since the fixed action pattern has already been discussed in detail.

Taxes are oriented locomotory reactions of motile organisms. When exposed to a source of stimulation, the body as a whole, or a particular part, is oriented in line with the source of stimulation. Movement toward the source is said to be positive, while movement away from the source is negative. There are many types of taxes recognized by ethologists, and some of the most important are klinotaxis, tropotaxis, telotaxis, and transverse orientation (Fraenkel and Gunn, 1940).

Klinotaxis consists of the animal traversing a short distance, stopping, making a turning movement from one side to the other, and then finally moving toward one side according to whether it is nearer or farther away from the source of stimulation. The animal then travels a short distance further, and then repeats the whole procedure. In this way an animal gradually gets nearer or farther away from the source of stimulation. Tropotaxis is like klinotaxis except that there are no trial movements, but a gradual turning toward or away from the stimulation. Telotaxis, however, is direct locomotion toward the source of stimulation, without trial movements, and looks as if it were goal-directed. Transverse orientation may or may not involve locomotion, and is illustrated by the light compass reaction shown by bees navigating toward or away from the hive, and by the dorsal light reaction of fishes swimming always belly down, that is, belly away from the light.

Instinctive behavior is complex, being composed of several elements: reflexes, taxes, and fixed action patterns or instinctive movements. In the egg-rolling reaction of the greylag goose we find two separate components in this behavior. If an incubating goose is presented with an egg outside of her nest, she will reach out with her neck toward it and roll it back into her nest with her bill, balancing it in its course with little sideways movements. If, after it has begun this action, the egg is taken away, the goose will continue to perform the action to the very end. However, the bill is moved directly, without the balancing movements, toward the nest. Hence the movement of the bill toward the nest is a pure fixed action pattern, being released but not guided, while the balancing movements are guided by continuous external stimulation from the egg. Tinbergen (1951) has compared the taxic component and the fixed action pattern with the steering and propulsory mechanisms of a ship, respectively.

Another example of the simultaneous presence of fixed action patterns and of taxic movements is to be found in the wing-cleaning behavior of the common fly. The fly moves its legs over and under the wings, making little scrubbing movements. If, however, the wings are removed, the fly still moves its legs around in the region where the wings had been, but will not make the tiny scrubbing movements. This shows that the action of passing the legs over and under the wings is a fixed action pattern, while the little scrubbing movements were guided by the stimulation offered by contact with the wings (Heinz, 1949).

Often the same stimuli both steer and release the reaction, and in some cases the taxic steering component is absent in certain consummatory acts such as swallowing or blinking. Although the distinction between the fixed action pattern and the taxis is not absolute, the isolation of the fixed action pattern has contributed a great deal to the analysis of behavior.

However useful the distinction between appetitive behavior and the consummatory act, the Lorenz-Craig scheme of appetitive behavior leading to the consummatory act has been found to be a rather simplified case. Normally, particular appetitive behavior does not usually end in a consummatory act, but, rather, leads to a stimulus situation that initiates another and more specific appetitive behavior (Baerends, 1941 and 1956, and Tinbergen, 1950). A chain of appetitive behaviors gives rise to a temporal sequence of "moods" or readiness to act, anchored in the central nervous system. We shall illustrate this by considering the reproductive behavior of the male stickleback.

In spring the gradual increase in length of day is responsible for bringing the fish into a reproductive motivation. It does not immediately acquire a red belly, but first begins migrating into shallow fresh water. The rise in water temperature, as it goes further inland, together with the visual stimulation arising from suitable territory consisting of heavily vegetated sites, then releases the entire reproductive behavior. Only then, after it has established its territory, does the male stickleback acquire its characteristic red belly. At this point it be-

gins to react to particular stimuli that previously had no effect on it. If males caught during migration are put together in a bathtub, they all will remain in a school except one who establishes a territory by the drain plug chain. This chain is the only structured element in the bathtub; it is for this reason that a territory is established there. Furthermore, it provides enough territory for only one male. This male will then fight at the appearance of a stranger, begin to build a nest with suitable material, and court passing females. Since the male's behavior depends principally on the stimulus situation, this makes difficult the prediction as to precisely what it will do. Fighting, for example, is released by the stimulus *red belly* on a male intruding into its territory, but it cannot be predicted which of the five known fighting movements will occur, each being, again, dependent on still further and highly specific stimuli. If the stranger bites, the territory owner will bite in turn, or if the stranger beats with its tail, the owner makes the same response. Fleeing will elicit chasing, and threatening will elicit threatening in turn. In summary, the stimuli emanating from suitable territory will activate the fighting, building, and mating drives. The more specific stimulus, *red-bellied male*, activates only a general readiness to fight; the specific movements made are dependent on even more specific stimuli.

Thus one can organize different levels of integrations into a hierarchical system. In this way it is clear that there are chains of behavior tendencies that are connected in higher and lower levels of integration. The adaptive advantages of the mood hierarchy rather than a stereotyped series of single fixed action patterns lie in its adaptability to several situations. For example, a hunting peregrine falcon initially seeks prey of any kind, this behavior being of a rather general appetitive type. If it sees a group of prey birds, it dives down toward them and isolates a single bird from the swarm. If it has met with success, it performs the very specific behavior patterns of killing the prey, pulling out its feathers, and eating it (Tinbergen, 1950). The adaptability of the mood hierarchy lies in the fact that if a falcon should happen to meet a single bird by accident, the previous part of the chain will drop out, and it immediately proceeds to kill, pluck, and eat it.

It seems evident that a structural organization within the central nervous system must exist which parallels the lawfulness of behavior, particularly the mood hierarchy. Tinbergen (1950) has illustrated this in the diagram shown in Figure 2, which, of course, represents only functional units and does not attempt to represent anatomy or localization of functions. The number and kind of appetitive links, as well as the innate releasing mechanisms

(IRM) that respond to certain stimulus situations and the chain of built-in fixed patterns that are also their final goals or consummatory acts, are rigorously derived from empirical observations of behavior.

Close relationships exist between Tinbergen's results and those of P. Weiss (1941b), who showed a similar hierarchical organization of the central nervous system mechanism in motor processes that are almost exclusively below the level of integration of the goal-forming fixed patterns. Since Weiss had specified that the highest level of his hierarchy was the behavior of the animal as a whole, Tinbergen assumed that the two hierarchies were physiologically similar, and therefore he added Weiss's diagram below a horizontal line

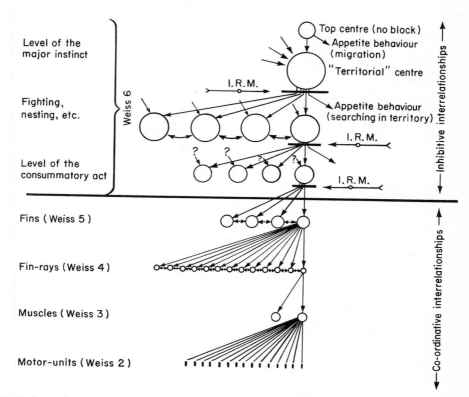

FIG. 2. Tinbergen's diagram of the hierarchical organization of instincts, superimposed on Weiss's diagram of the hierarchical organization of central nervous mechanisms, Weiss's highest level incorporating the same phenomena as those placed in Tinbergen's hierarchy. (From TINBERGEN, N., 1950.)

under his own hierarchical organization, making Weiss's uppermost level equivalent to his own system.

In this scheme Tinbergen ignored a complication that he recognized: some of the same behavior patterns at the lowest level, for instance those of locomotion, can be among the final effecting links in several hierarchical organizations of a higher order as a common final pathway, so that under certain circumstances the chains diverge and then converge again. Tinbergen's results and hypothesis are highly valuable because they provide a link to a real physiology of the central nervous system. Further evidence regarding this will be discussed later when we return to neurophysiological evidence for ethological concepts.

REFERENCES

ALLEN, A. A.   Sex rhythm in the ruffed grouse (*Bonasa umbellus*) and other birds. *Auk,* 1954, **51**, 180–199.

ANDREW, R. J.   Normal and irrelevant toilet behaviour in *Embenza,* Spp. *Brit. J. Anim. Behaviour,* 1956, **4**, 85–96.

BAERENDS, G. P.   Fortpflanzungsverhalten und Orientierung der Grabwespe, *Ammophila campestris* Jur. *Tijdschr. Ent.,* 1941, **84**, 68–275.

BAERENDS, G. P.   Specialization in organs and movements with a releasing function. *Symp. Soc. Exp. Biol.,* 1950, **4**, 337–360.

BAERENDS, G. P.   Aufbau des tierischen Verhaltens. *Kukenthal's Hb. Zool.,* 1956, **10**, 1–32.

BAERENDS, G. P.   The ethological concept "releasing mechanism" illustrated by a study of the stimuli eliciting egg-retrieving in the herring gull. *Anat. Record,* 1957, **128**, 518–519.

BAERENDS, G. P.   Comparative methods and the concept of homology in the study of behaviour. *Arch. Néer. Zool.,* 1958, **13**, Suppl. 1, 401–417.

BAERENDS, G. P.   The ethological analysis of incubation behaviour. *Ibis,* 1959, **101**, 357–368.

BRUCKNER, G. H.   Untersuchungen zur Tiersoziologie, insbesondere der Auflösung der Familie. *Zs. Psychol.,* 1933, **128**, 1–120.

COTT, H. B.   *Adaptive coloration in animals.* London: Methuen, 1940.

CRAIG, W.   Appetites and aversions as constituents of instincts. *Biol. Bull.,* 1918, **34**, 91–107.

CULLEN, ESTHER   Adaptations in the Kittiwake to cliff-nesting. *Ibis,* 1957, **99**, 275–302.

EIBL-EIBESFELDT, I.   Uber Symbiosen, Parasitismus, und andere besondere zwischenartliche Beziehungen bei tropischen Meeresfischen. *Zeit. f. Tierpsychol.,* 1955b, **12**, 203–219.

EIBL-EIBESFELDT, I.   Angeborenes und Erworbenes in der Technik des Beutetötens (Versuche am Iltis, *Putorious putorius* L.). *Z. Säugetierkunde,* 1956a, **21**, 135–37.

EIBL-EIBESFELDT, I.   Der Fisch *Aspidontus taeniatus* als Nachahmer des Putzers *Labroides dimidiatus. Zeit. f. Tierpsychol.,* 1959, **16**, 19–25.

FRAENKEL, G. S., and D. I. GUNN   *The orientation of animals.* Oxford: Clarendon Press, 1940.

HEINROTH, O.   Beiträge zur Biologie, namentlich Ethologie und Psychologie der Anatiden. *Verh. 5th Int. Ornith. Kongr.,* 1910, 589–702.

HEINROTH, O.   *Aus dem Leben der Vögel.* Berlin: Springer, 1938.

HEINZ, H.-J.   Vergleichende Beobachtungen über die Putzhandlungen bei Dipteren im allgemeinen und bei *Sarcophaga carnaria* L. im besonderen. *Zeit. f. Tierpsychol.,* 1949, **6**, 330–371.

HESS, W. R.   Stammganglien-Reizversuche. *Vortrag Dtsch. Physiol. ges. Bonn,* 1927.

HESS, W. R.   *Das Zwischenhirn: Syndrome, Lokalisationen, Funktionen.* Basel: Schwabe, 1949.

HESS, W. R.   *Das Zwischenhirn. Syndrome, Lokalisationen, Funktionen.* Mongr. II. Erweiterte aufl. Basel: Schwabe, 1954.

HESS, W. R.   *Hypothalamus and Thalamus. Experimental-dokumente.* Stuttgart: Thieme, 1956. (Parallel English and German text.)

HOLST, E. v.   Weitere Versuche zum nervösen Mechanismus der Bewegung beim Regenwurm. *Zool. Jb.,* 1933, **53**, 67–100.

HOLST, E. v.   Uber den Prozess der zentralnervösen Koordination. *Pflüg. Arch. ges. Physiol.,* 1935, **236**, 149–158.

HOLST, E. v.   Versuche zur Theorie der Relativen Koordination. *Pflüg. Arch. ges. Physiol.,* 1936a, **237**, 93–121.

HOLST, E. v.   Uber den "Magnet-Effekt" als koordinationender Prinzip im Rückenmark.

Pflüg. Arch. ges. Physiol., 1936b, **237**, 655–682.

HOLST, E. v.   Bausteine zu einer vergleichende Physiologie der lokomotorischen Reflexe bei Fischen. II Mitteilung. *Z. vergl. Physiol.*, 1937a, **24**, 532–562.

HOLST, E. v.   Vom Wesen der Ordnung im Zentralnervensystem. *Naturwiss.*, 1937b, **25**, 625–631, 641–647.

HOLST, E. v.   Die Auslösung von Stimmungen bei Wirbeltieren durch "punktförmige" elektrische Errengung des Stammhirns. *Naturwiss.*, 1957, **44**, 549–551.

HOLST, E. v., and U. v. ST. PAUL   Das Mischen von Trieben (Instinkbewegungen) durch mehrfache Stammhirnreizung beim Huhn. *Naturwiss.*, 1958, **45**, 579.

HOLST, E. v., and U. v. ST. PAUL   Vom Wirkungsgefüge der Triebe. *Naturwiss.*, 1960, **18**, 409–422.

HOLST, E. v., and U. v. ST. PAUL   Electrically controlled behavior. *Sci. Amer.*, 1962, **206**, No. 3, 50–59.

HOWARD, H. E.   *An introduction to the study of bird behaviour.* Cambridge: Cambridge University Press, 1929.

HUXLEY, J. S.   The courtship habits of the great crested Grebe *(Podiceps cristatus);* with an addition to the theory of sexual selection. *Proc. Zool. Soc. London,* 1914, 491–562.

IERSEL, J. v., and A. C. BOL   Preening of two tern species. A study on displacement activities. *Behaviour,* 1958, **13**, 4–89.

KOEHLER, O., and A. ZAGARUS   Beiträge zum Brutverhalten des Halsbandregenpfeifers *(Charadrius h. hiaticula L.). Beitr. Fortpfl.-Biol. Vögel,* 1937, **13**, 1–9.

KORTLANDT, A.   Eine Ubersicht der angeborenen Verhaltensweisen des mitteleuropäischen Kormorans *(Phalacrocorax Carbosinensis),* ihre Funktion, ontogenetische Entwicklung und phylogenetische Herkunft. *Arch. Néer. Zool.,* 1940a, **4**, 401–442.

KORTLANDT, A.   Wechselwirkung zwischen Instinkten. *Arch. Néer. Zool.,* 1940b, **4**, 442–520.

KRUIJT, J. P.   Speckling of herring gull eggs in relation to brood behaviour. *Arch. Néer. Zool.,* 1958, **12**, 565–567.

KRUMBIEGEL, I.   Die Persistenz Physiologischer Eigenschaften in der Stammesgeschichte. *Zeit. f. Tierpsychol.,* 1940, **4**, 249–258.

LACK, D.   The behavior of the robin. II. *Proc. Zool. Soc. London,* 1939, **109**, 200–219.

LEYHAUSEN, P.   Verhaltensstudien an Katzen. Beiheft 2 zur *Zeit. f. Tierpsychologie,* 1956.

LORENZ, K. Z.   Beiträge zur Ethologie sozialer Corviden *J. f. Ornith.,* 1931, **79**, 67–120.

LORENZ, K. Z.   Der Kumpan in der Umwelt des Vogels. *J. f. Ornith.,* 1935, **83**, 137–213, 289–413.

LORENZ, K. Z.   Uber die Bildung des Instinktbegriffes. *Naturwiss.,* 1937, **25**, 289–300, 307–318, 324–331.

LORENZ, K. Z.   Vergleichende Bewegungsstudien an Anatiden. *J. f. Ornith.,* 1941, **89**, 194–294.

LORENZ, K. Z.   Die angeborenen Formen möglicher Erfahrung. *Zeit. f. Tierpsychol.,* 1943, **5**, 335–409.

LORENZ, K. Z.   The comparative method in studying innate behaviour patterns. *Symp. Soc. Exp. Biol.,* 1950, **4**, 221–268.

LORENZ, K. Z.   Die Entwicklung der vergleichenden Verhaltensforschung in den letzten 12 Jahren. *Verh. Dtsch. Zool. ges. Freiburg,* 1952, 36–58. Leipzig: Akad. Verlag. 1953.

LORENZ, K. Z., and N. TINBERGEN   Taxis und Instinkthandlung in der Eirollbewegung der Graugans. *Zeit. f. Tierpsychol.,* 1938, **2**, 1–29.

MAGNUS, D.   Experimentelle Untersuchungen zur Bionomie und Ethologie des Kaisermantels *Argynnis paphia* L. (Lep. Nymph). I. Uber optische Auslöser von Angliegereaktionen und ihre Bedeutung für das Sichfinden der Geschechter. *Zeit. f. Tierpsychol.,* 1958, **15**, 397–426.

MAKKINK, G. F.   Die Kopulation der Brandente *(Tadorna tadorna L.). Ardea,* 1931, **20**, 18–22.

MAKKINK, G. F.   An attempt at an ethogram of the European Avocet *(Recurvirostra avosetta L.)* with ethological and psychological remarks. *Ardea,* 1936, **25**, 1–62.

MARLER, P.   Specific distinctiveness in the communication signals of birds. *Behaviour,* 1957, **9**, 13–39.

MORRIS, D.   "Typical intensity" and its relation to the problem of ritualisation. *Behaviour,* 1957, **11**, 1–13.

OEHLERT, B.   Kampf und Paarbildung bei einigen Cichliden. *Zeit. f. Tierpsychol.,* 1958, **15**, 141–174.

PICKWELL, G. B. The prairie horned lark. *Trans. Acad. Sci. St. Louis*, 1931, **27**, 1–153.

PORTIELJE, A. F. J. Triebleben bzw. intelligente Aeusserungen beim Orang-Utan *(Pongo pigmaeus* Hoppius*). Bijdr. Dierk.*, 1939, **27**, 61–114.

ROEDER, K. D. Spontaneous activity and behavior. *Sci. Mon. Wash.*, 1955, **80**, 362–370.

SEITZ, A. Die Paarbildung bei einigen Cichliden. I. Die Paarbildung bei *Astatotilapia strigigena* (Pfeffer). *Zeit. f. Tierpsychol.*, 1940, **4**, 40–84.

SEVENSTER, P. A causal analysis of a displacement activity. Unpublished, 1958.

TINBERGEN, N. On the analysis of social organization among vertebrates, with special reference to birds. *Amer. Midl. Nat.*, 1939, **21**, 210–234.

TINBERGEN, N. Die Uebersprungbewegung. *Zeit. f. Tierpsychol.*, 1940, **4**, 1–40.

TINBERGEN, N. An objectivistic study of the innate behaviour of animals. *Biblioth. Biother.*, 1942, **1**, 39–98.

TINBERGEN, N. The hierarchical organisation of nervous mechanisms underlying instinctive behaviour. *Symp. Soc. Exp. Biol.*, 1950, **4**, 305–312.

TINBERGEN, N. *The study of instinct.* London: Oxford University Press, 1951.

TINBERGEN, N. "Derived" activities; their causation, biological significance, origin, and emancipation during evolution. *Quar. Rev. Biol.*, 1952, **27**, 1–32.

TINBERGEN, N., and J. VAN IERSEL "Displacement reactions" in the three-spined stickleback. *Behaviour*, 1947, **1**, 56–63.

TINBERGEN, N., and D. J. KUENEN Uber die auslösenden und richtungsgebenden Reizsituationen der Sperrbewegung von jungen Drosseln *(Turdus m. merula* und *T. e. ericetorum* Turton). *Zeit. f. Tierpsychol.*, 1939, **3**, 37–60.

UEXKÜLL, J. v. *Umwelt und Innenwelt der Tiere.* Jena: 1909. Second edition, Berlin, 1921.

VERWEY, J. Die Paarungbiologie des Fischreihers. *Zool. Jb. Physiol.*, 1930, **48**, 1–120.

WEIDMANN, R., and U. WEIDMANN An analysis of the stimulus situation releasing food-begging in the black-headed gull. *Brit. J. Anim. Behaviour*, 1958, **6**, 114.

WEISS, P. Autonomous versus reflexogenous activity of the central nervous system. *Proc. Amer. Phil. Soc.*, 1941a, **84**, 53–64.

WEISS, P. Self-differentiation of the basic patterns of co-ordination. *Comp. Psychol. Monogr.*, 1941b. **17**, 1–96.

WHITMAN, C. O. Animal behavior. *Biol. Lect. Marine Biol. Lab. Wood's Hole, Mass.,* 1898. Boston: 1899. 285–338.

W. H. THORPE

3 Ethology as a New Branch of Biology

W. H. Thorpe, a renowned ethologist of Cambridge University, has done much to bring ethology and comparative psychology together. With O. L. Zangwell, a Cambridge psychologist, he has edited *Current Problems in Animal Behavior* (Cambridge, 1961), and his scholarly *Learning and Instinct in Animals* (Methuen, 1963) is now in its second edition.

The paper that follows was presented at a symposium of marine biologists. In it Thorpe presents a brief history of the development of ethology and reviews ethological research relevant to marine biology.

For more on the development of schooling in fish see reading 55.

The article originally appeared in *Perspectives in Marine Biology*, A. A. Buzzati-Traverso, ed., Berkeley: University of California Press, 1956. Reprinted by permission of author and publisher.

The word ethology is certainly not very new. It was at least in occasional use as a zoölogical term by the end of last century.

But it is now widespread and popular use is certainly something new, and moreover many at least of those who use it are convinced that it denotes a new approach to the study of animal behavior. I propose to start by considering briefly various ways of approaching the study of animal behavior, to inquire how far any of them is new or embodies new techniques, and to consider the prospects for further development and application of such methods in one or two fields of marine biology.

There are three scientific ways of probing into the behavior of animals. Briefly, they may be called the way of the naturalist, the way of the psychologist, and the way of the physiologist. Certainly none of these three ways is new. Let us look at them a little closer and see how they have developed. Before Darwin there was very little of the scientific approach to the study of animal behavior. The physiology of that day had hardly got to the point where behavior as such was coming above its horizon. Similarly, psychology, insofar as it was scientific, was concerned solely with human beings, and naturalist writers were primarily anecdotal. Anyone who doubts this latter statement has only to look at books such as Bingley's *Animal Biography* (1829) and Couch's *Illustrations of Instinct* (1847) to be made aware how little there was, apart from straight-forward descriptions of life history, to interest the modern zoölogist. Even Romanes, writing much later in 1882, shows similar defects, although as a physiologist he was highly and justly valued in his day. So in considering the present position of animal behavior studies, we shall not go far wrong if we start with Charles Darwin.

The publication in 1872 of *The Expression of the Emotions in Man and Animals* was an important milestone in natural history, and ultimately had a big influence on the behavior study that was to come. We will return to that a little later. Let us first consider what was happening in the physiological and psychological spheres. Thomas Willis (1664) was the real father of the concept of reflex as a scientific rather than a philosophical idea, and it would take too long and be too far removed from our pres-

ent interests to attempt to trace the development of this concept, until in the hands of the nineteenth-century Russian physiologists Sechenov, Pavlov, and Bekterev it flowered into a general theory of the origin and development of the fixed inherited behavior patterns of animals. So it was that by the end of the nineteenth century, the physiological view of animal behavior was primarily that of a coördination of a very large number of simple, quick muscular movements, executed in an immediate response to simple environmental stimuli and combinations of such stimuli of varying degrees of complexity. The problem of the adaptation of behavior by the individual organism in response to changing conditions experienced within its life span was largely beyond the scope of physiological theory until Pavlov developed his work on the conditioning of the reflex. Then, for the first time, the reflex theory seemed to be within sight of providing a reasonably complete physiological explanation of animal behavior, and the philosophical idea of reflex, which started with Descartes and had been translated into scientific terms by Whytt, at last came into its own as a major scientific concept. Looking at it in this way, we see the justice of Sherrington's summing up of Pavlov as "Descartes' greatest successor." Perhaps the greatest merit of Pavlov's great contribution was that he isolated by his experimental procedure a single element of behavior, and was able to produce it at will in the laboratory under controlled conditions, to measure its intensity, and to measure the strength of the various stimuli influencing it. The systematic and quantitative study of reflex conditioning has of course given rise to an immense body of knowledge. R. S. Woodworth (1938) justly says, "The conditioned reflex is perhaps no more simple than other types of learned response, and we cannot regard it as an element out of which behaviour is built. But it does open a window into the dynamics of behaviour and it furnishes an outlet for the investigation of the senses of animals." It is hard to exaggerate the importance of this step in the scientific study of animals. But it would be a disservice to a very great physiologist to suggest that study of the conditioned reflex in the original simple sense of both words is the only scientific way of studying the actions of animals. The simplest reflex is in fact now seen as something very different from what it was originally thought to be, as well as much more complicated, and we realize now that instinctive behavior, far from being merely chain reflex, includes characteristics that cannot be derived from reflex in anything like the original sense of the term. Great as was the advance made by Pavlov, we now realize that instinct is more than reflex and learning is more than conditioning, and it is idle to pretend that they are the same.

The nineteenth-century psychologists were, as I have said, solely concerned with human beings, and almost the whole of their outlook and technique was centered upon the problems of the human mind, its feelings and emotions, and did not provide the tools required for the scientific study of animal behavior. But toward the latter part of the nineteenth century, a change began to appear in that psychologists became imbued with the concept of association which had arisen from the philosophical writings of Hobbs, Hume, and James Mill, which were slowly working through two centuries to their theoretical climax as a principle of philosophical associationism or the mechanical compounding of stimuli. Ebbinghaus (1885) was the pioneer in making practical experimental use of these ideas, and his study of human learning of nonsense syllables was an important landmark in the development of the scientific and objective study of human behavior. Thorndike was the first to undertake similar studies with animals. Whether he was influenced by Ebbinghaus or whether he evolved his ideas and methods for himself is not clear, but his studies of the behavior of cats and dogs in puzzle boxes led to a theory of animal behavior which was taken up by Watson, and became known as Behaviorism. This was fundamentally associationist or mechanist in outlook, and prided itself on being purely objective; with the implication perhaps that it was more nearly a physiological than a psychological system. Perhaps we should not have heard so much of Watson's Behaviorism had it not been that, within a few years of its publication, the work of Pavlov and Bekterev began to be known outside Russia, and so, for the first time, there seemed to be a physiological system that could be related in detail to the superficially physiological ideas behind behavioristic psychology. Behaviorism received much violent criticism, not all of it justified; for it was in some ways a laudable attempt to be objective and to purge behavior study of the uncritical anecdotal writing, so much of which was still being passed off as science at the time. But Behaviorism as a general theory of animal behavior was woefully inadequate in its original rather crude form, and in this form its day was short—although it may be said to have given rise by a long process of development, refinement, and extension to the vast system of comparative psychology, which will always be associated with the name of Hull, and may be perhaps not too unfairly paraphrased in the single sentence, "Learning only proceeds when it leads to reduction of need." "Need" in this context is not usually defined, but it is a physiological need that is implied.

The obvious deficiencies of the existing mechanist physiological appproach to the study of animal behavior first became apparent to those workers who were studying the more highly developed perception of animals and man, and so it was that Wertheimer (1912), working on the visual perception of movement, and later his disciples Wolfgang Köhler and Koffka, were led to propound the concepts and theories which in due course came to be known as the Gestalt psychology. These in their turn had a far-reaching influence upon our ideas of animal behavior, and, through a quarter of a century of debate, had, in the form of various field theories, a great influence on the development and fate of Behaviorism itself.

The various schools of workers we have been discussing up to now were concerned almost exclusively with the laboratory approach. Perhaps 95 per cent of the work of physiologists was done with dogs and cats, and 99 per cent of that of the comparative psychologist with the white rat. This being so, it is hardly surprising if the picture of animal nature and behavior which emerged was distorted and incomplete. What had happened to the naturalists? Darwin was a field naturalist; yet, as Elton has shown, his promulgation of the natural-selection theory had the extraordinary result of sending students of terrestrial animals indoors for fifty or more years where, as embryologists, comparative anatomists, and at length comparative physiologists, they attempted to work out with techniques, which at the time were fresh and exciting, the full implications of the new and tremendous generalization. And natural history for the time being suffered much neglect, and it needed the stimulus of a "new" discipline, ecology, to bring naturalists interested in the terrestrial animal and its environment out into the open once again, and to make them observe and experiment in the field. With marine natural history the response was fortunately just the reverse. Darwin's oceanographical speculations offered so much promise to the marine explorer that they were never subject to quite the same danger of becoming purely laboratory zoölogists and indeed his writings gave the impetus for the founding of a number of marine stations. The effect of Darwin's work on that aspect of field natural history which used to be called bionomics until its rebirth as ecology, is seen to be closely paralleled when we look at behavior studies. It is generally true to say that field studies of behavior suffered an even longer neglect, and it was not until the reformulation of our ideas about instinct in 1935 that the field investigation of behavior once again began fully to come into its own. Just as with ecology,

so the adoption of a comparable term, ethology, had an important effect in bringing this about. So we shall see that ethology in some sense represents the rebirth of one-half of a scientific natural history, and although there has been a strong tendency to reserve it for appplication to the particular school of behavior students who happened to be most active in bringing this rebirth about, it is in my view most undesirable to restrict it in this way. The only limitation permissible is one that stresses the fact that both animal ecology and animal ethology are branches of zoölogy, with the implication that the ethologist is looking at his problems from the point of view of one primarily interested in the animal kingdom as a whole, and not as adjunct to the study of human psychology or social relations. So I consider that ethology means the scientific study of animal behavior. And insofar as the vastly greater part of modern experimental psychology is concerned, not with theorizing about emotions, feelings, and states of mind, but with the objective study of behavior, the term can be justifiably used to cover it too.

As usual with new ideas, those about animal behavior and the new attitude accompanying them arose independently with three or four different workers. Some of the essential concepts can be found in the writings of Heinroth in Germany, Wallace Craig and Lashley in America, and Lorenz in Austria but it was only Lorenz who succeeded in welding his concepts together to form a thoroughgoing theory of animal behavior, and consequently he is rightly regarded as the founder of the new movement.

The new workers were concerned primarily with instinct, and it is easy to see the reason for this. Previous to Lorenz' appearance on the scene, hardly any scientific work on the genesis and implications of the elaborate inherited behavior patterns of animals was being carried out. Those groups that might have been expected to have developed scientific studies of instinctive behavior were either halted by an inadequate and misleading theory of instinct, or else were, perhaps for that very reason, busy with other things. The physiologists should, one thinks, have been able to make progress in this field, but they were curiously constrained by the dead hand of Pavlov. Pavlov did in fact widen the use of the term reflex so that it became first synonymous with response, and then practically meaningless. Nevertheless, he handicapped his followers by his retention of it, and by his contention that instincts are nothing but reflexes. He urged indeed that the investigation of instincts was the next important task, but none of his followers heeded this, for the simple reason that the idea of reflex did not alone provide them with the concepts necessary for the work. Perhaps partly for the same reason the "rat psychologists" were devoting all their energies to the study of learning, and the older type of comparative psychologist had, as Lorenz showed, become entangled in a rather stultifying vitalistic approach which in extreme cases tended to look upon "instincts" as something "given," to be accepted as such, and to be impossible of further analysis. Instincts were generally looked upon as directed in some mysterious teleological way toward ends that it was desirable for the race or species should be achieved. Instinct had in fact become something of a dirty word and the reaction of respectable scientific workers to it was to turn up the nose, and change the subject. Lorenz' main argument is that in each example of true instinctive behavior there is a hard core of absolutely fixed and relatively complex automatism, an inborn movement form. This restricted concept is the essence of the instinct itself; it is now usually referred to as the *fixed action* or the *fixed-action pattern*. Such action patterns are items of behavior in every way as constant as are anatomical structures, and potentially just as valuable for phylogenetic and systematic studies. Where such action patterns constitute an end point or climax of either a major or a minor chain of instinctive behavior, they have come to be known

as *consummatory acts*. The internal coördination mechanism of these consummatory acts is assumed to be generating some *Specific Action Potential* (SAP). This is the internal drive, which is of the very essence of the word instinct. Both Lashley and Lorenz had realized that instead of trying to study this mysterious drive itself, and utter vague generalities about tension, nervous energy, and so forth (which were in any case useless both as explanatory concepts and as guides for future research), the way out was to describe and analyze the complex and stereotyped action systems themselves. These and their coördinating mechanisms were assumed to be the fundamental things, and the conviction was felt that a study of the mechanisms themselves might eventually throw further light on the problems of drive and of motivation. Woodworth (1938), in the field of human psychology, had already pointed out that habit mechanisms may become drives, and the similarities between habit and instinct had of course been commented upon by many workers. So it was felt that the *activation* of rigid instinctive actions was the result of the activity of specific mechanisms behind them, and the first thing to do was therefore to make as complete an inventory as possible of these fixed action patterns, study their relation to one another, the circumstances in which they appear, and as far as possible analyze them experimentally into their constituent units.

Although instinct is characterized by an internal drive, and is not simply a response to external stimulation, yet obviously instincts would be useless without an appropriate system ensuring adjustments to the external situation. So we have the concept of the *Innate Releasing Mechanism* (IRM), which assumes that within the central nervous system, there is a series of mechanisms coördinated with the more complex sense organs, which effectively inhibits or blocks all discharges of activity unless the animal encounters the right environmental situation or stimulus to remove or release the block. Furthermore, since, as everyone knows, instinctive behavior is not entirely rigid but is sometimes remarkably adaptable, the distinction was made between the preliminary adjustable introductory phrase of instinct known as *appetitive behavior* and the rigid *consummatory act*. It is in this preliminary, flexible, searching behavior that learning ability is most likely to be manifest, and intelligence has the opportunity to show itself. In a simple animal it may consist of little more than random wandering governed by simple kinesis or taxis as of the hungry wireworm *(Agriotes)*, burrowing at random in search of its food. On the other hand, appetitive behavior may contain subsidiary consummatory acts, and searching behavior of great elaboration. This division into appetitive behavior and consummatory act, while as we now see relative only and not absolute, resulted in substantial experimental advance. One could now plan experiments for the investigation of both fixity and flexibility, whereas before there was no real clue as to how to begin. Moreover, by separating the taxis or steering component of behavior, which in lower invertebrates is largely reflex, from the internally activated locomotory behavior, much of the mystery and confusion associated with complex orientation began to be dispelled, and experiments became far easier and more profitable than before. Another main attraction of the scheme lay in its apparent avoidance of the vitalistic approach; for the objective of the animal is now no longer the attainment of the final biological goal or result, which it is of course inconceivable in most cases that it could know about; rather is it the performance of the rigid consummatory acts themselves. So we have a physiologically reasonable system replacing an obviously untenable vitalistic one. Finally, Lorenz' idea of internal drive, arising from the activation of the specific coördination mechanisms of the consummatory act, but held back by the block or inhibitory action of the innate releasing mechanism until the right *releaser* is encountered, at once attracts the field naturalist. For it supplies a

ready explanation for a vast amount of puzzling behavior—displacement and vacuum activity — which it seems otherwise extremely difficult, if not impossible, to interpret. This theoretical system of instinct led almost directly to the hierarchy scheme of Tinbergen, according to which there are a number of tiers or levels within the total organization which makes up an instinct, and incorporated in each level are one or more innate releasing mechanisms. On the receptor side, these are in some way attuned to the biologically right stimuli or situations in the environment, as for example the appearance of the sexual partner or the specific prey, and are as it were unlocked by the appropriate environmental releasers and only by them, thus allowing behavior to proceed to the levels below only in the biologically right situation. These lower levels in their turn incorporate blocks that, although they remain unmoved, prevent action of these lower centers proceeding. So long as such lower centers remain blocked, the action potential will activate the appetitive behavior — which is directive, in the sense that it tends to bring the animal into the kind of environment where the appropriate releaser is likely to be encountered.

Since this scheme was proposed our ideas on many details of it have changed. The term center is no longer thought of, if indeed it ever was thought of, as a physically localized region in the central nervous system. The blocks are not merely blocks, but more probably antagonistic coördination mechanisms, and the channels represent causal relations of behavior and not nervous communications. Again, appetitive behavior and consummatory act are two extremes of one concept rather than two incompatible systems. Nevertheless, in spite of, or perhaps because of, these modifications, the system seems to be more valuable now in promoting and coördinating research than it has ever been.

Although many of the essential ideas of Lorenz' system can be found in the writings of earlier and contemporary writers, as a system, the whole is new in a number of respects; and it is the new relations, which it displays, rather than the novelty of its separate components which have rendered it so valuable.

The techniques of ethology, insofar as they are new, are extremely simple. From the ethologist's point of view it is important to be able to study closely the whole sequence of acts which constitute an animal's behavior. If we are studying the relation between instinct and learning, we cannot get very far without being able to rear the animal in isolation from its associates, for without this we cannot be sure we are observing the performance of a given act for the first time. Ethology, then, must be done not only in the field but also with tame and captive animals kept in the best and most natural conditions. Again, because the whole sequence of acts must be investigated, it is essential to recognize the same individual animal and observe its behavior for a significant part of its individual life. Therefore, simple forms of individual marking are essential. Since the innate releasing mechanism is one of the most important new concepts put forward, experiments must be carried out with models in which the different components or sign stimuli making up the full releaser can be tested, singly and in combination, on the animal. Since also minute investigation and inventory of the animal's actions are essential, recording by cinematograph, sound-recording apparatus, etc., are necessary.

Let us now look at what is known of the behavior of some typical marine organisms with a view to making some estimate of the future importance of ethological concepts and techniques in marine biology.

Let us first consider the importance and applicability of the main methods and techniques of ethology to problems of marine biology. The technique of individual marking was of course developed by marine biologists well before its use was taken up by naturalists interested in terrestrial organisms. We are due to hear from Dr.

Hasler about the latest developments in the study of the homing and orientation of fishes by this method, and so it would obviously be quite redundant for me to say anything more about it. As far as the other main techniques mentioned, it seems to me that marine biology is on the threshold of very important advances. Although there have been satisfactory sea-water aquaria for a very long time, the recent development of very large aquaria which has taken place both in Florida and California extends the possibilities for the observation of the larger marine animals under reasonably good conditions of captivity beyond the wildest hopes entertained by naturalists a few years ago. It has brought within reach the prospects of extremely interesting work on the behavior and social organization of the smaller Cetacea and the larger fishes, which marine biologists have already begun to exploit with good results.

The simple technique of observation under natural conditions has again been enormously extended by the development of "aqualung" diving and of the underwater television and cinema cameras. A field of almost embarrassing richness for the ethologist, particularly for the ethologist interested in instinctive behavior and social releasers, has thus been opened up. Further ahead, but still to my mind not beyond the foreseeable future, are the prospects of study of the larger and more numerous marine animals by means of radiolocation, echo-sounding, the bathyscaphe, and — is it too fantastic to suggest? — the relatively silent atomic-powered research submarine! It is an amusing thought that perhaps the greatest rival to the latest mode of marine transport as a research tool may in fact turn out to be the most ancient one, namely the raft.

The student of instinct is inevitably attracted to the problems posed by examples of rhythmic behavior, which is apparently unrelated to changes in external stimulation; superficially, at least, such behavior seems to be "instinctive" in both senses: that of being innate and of being driven within. I have in mind particularly work such as that of Batham and Pantin on the inherent activity cycles in the coelenterate *Metridium,* and of Wells and his fellow workers on the internally driven activity cycles of *Arenicola* and other annelids. I should enjoy discussing these, but refrain from doing so, since we are to hear about them from Dr. Pittendrigh, whose remarkable work on the emergence rhythm of *Drosophila* will be fresh in the minds of many of us.

So it seems to me best to restrict my remarks chiefly to the fishes, and to point out one or two of the contexts in which research on fishes has already proved of great importance to ethology, and to suggest a few particularly interesting problems for future study. From the behaviorial point of view, there are three characteristics of the group which appear to be directly significant. First, the elementary social behavior which expresses itself in the formation of schools or shoals; second, the lack of prehensile organs and the small part which manipulation plays in the lives of most fishes—which might be expected to limit their powers of space perception; third, a fact which should tend to counteract this, namely that most fishes are effectively and actively in a three-dimensional world for the greater part, or the whole, of their lives. Where no obstacles are present, as in the open sea, this circumstance may not be particularly significant, but where, as in lakes and littoral forms, there is vegetation and other obstacles to be negotiated, the development of competence in spatial orientation and control must, one would think, be aided very substantially.

Modern ethology has a particular interest in the fishes, for this group has provided material for some basic and highly critical studies on the hierarchical organization of instinctive behavior and on its analysis in terms not of chain reflexes but of reaction chains. Harris and Whiting (1954) have recently confirmed the conclusions of Wintrebert (1920) that the earliest contractions of the skeletal musculature of the embryo dogfish are of almost constant rhythm and entirely myogenic in origin and control. At this stage the active myotomes on the right and left sides behave as two entirely different units. Presently, although the two sides are still independent in frequency and phasing, each side may show sudden changes in frequency; this apparently being evidence of the first participation of the nervous system. Later still, coördination of the two sides appears, suggesting the first development of central nervous excitation and inhibition. From the work of Holst (1935-1937), Lissman (1946), and others it appears that the locomotory movements of the mature fish are not necessarily to be interpreted as pure instincts in the sense that the "locomotory centers" are completely independent of proprioceptive and other peripheral stimulation. Thus any "locomotory drive" which may exist must be the expression of the activity of the sensory-motor coördination system as a whole, not exclusively of the C.N.S. Moreover, the coördination of the various movements into an economical and effective locomotory pattern may well be learned as a result of mechanical necessity, and the drive itself thus be acquired. But leaving aside locomotion itself, we may ask whether there is any behavior more completely inborn.

A very thorough analysis of instinctive behavior has been provided by the work of N. Tinbergen on the mating behavior of the three-spined stickleback (*Gasterosteus aculeatus*). The male must first receive the appropriate internal and external stimuli for setting up a territory, among which stimuli the sight of green vegetation is necessary. He next constructs a nest, in choosing material for which green is again the preferred color (Wunder, 1930), and is then ready to receive and conduct a female thither for the purpose of egg-laying. The male's first reaction, the zigzag dance, is dependent on the sight of a female having the swollen abdomen which shows that she is ready to lay eggs. At this stage the special swimming movements made by the female also play a part. She in her turn reacts to the red color of the male and to his zigzag dance by swimming directly toward him. This action enables him to "lead," which simply consists of swimming rapidly toward the nest. This in turn induces the female to follow and again stimulates the male to the next action, which is to show her the nest entrance by pointing his head at it. And so the chain of behavior patterns of the two individuals proceeds, each one dependent on releasers or sign-stimuli, mostly visual, which are different for each of the links and are essential in order to enable the behavior to proceed to the next action in the series. From an example such as this it will be seen that it is perhaps not the basic *locomotory* movements themselves, but the ground plan of the over-all *coördination* and *orientation* of those locomotory movements that must be inborn.* Some of those movements which are less specifically locomotory can probably also be regarded as inborn; for although they may have been ritualized from locomotory components, they do not themselves seem necessitated by stimuli explicable in terms of the mechanical necessities of the fluid environment. On the contrary, they seem to demonstrate much more clearly the concept of the pure instinct or "erbkoördination." Thus in the case of the three-spined stickleback the characteristic expression of the territorial phase of the reproductive instinct consists of the particular orientation of movements in patrolling and fighting activities. In the next phases it similarly consists largely of correct coördination and orientation of the movements we have just been describing. But since the orientation or taxis component is shown to be such an important part of the instinctive organization, we must inquire as to how much of the releaser system which mediates it is inborn. It now seems fairly clear from the work of Bae-

* Dr. D. Morris tells me that if the normal nest-building pattern is continually interfered with, quite large modifications in orientation may be made.

rends, Seitz, Tinbergen, Morris, and many others that in these fishes the inborn releasers are very simple sign-stimuli. These may be chemical, as Frisch has shown, for the broken cuticle of an injured minnow *(Phoxinus laevis)* may release a chemical substance that causes the school to congregate and immediately go into hiding. The releasers may also include a particular movement—such as the trembling of the courting stickleback or the typical slow, jerky swimming movement characteristic of the cichlid parent leading away its young (Baerends and Baerends-van Roon, 1950). Baerends again has shown that relative size may be an inborn releaser, for in the same cichlids the angle at which the young have to see the parent when following is fixed for a given age, and this probably prevents the young from following objects too small or too large to be a parent.

Besides movement and size, visual releasers display two other features often less easy to evaluate precisely, namely configuration and color. As an example of configuration alone providing a stimulus we may mention the outline of the breeding female stickleback and the threatening attitude adopted by a male at the boundary of his territory and directed toward an intruder of the same sex. This consists of standing in a vertical position, head pointing downward; but it is by no means the configuration only which supplies the stimulus here but probably to an even greater extent the displacement "picking" movements the male continually makes on the floor of the aquarium. In a great many instances configuration is also linked with color. Much of the earlier work on color vision in the fishes is suspect owing to lack of understanding of the difficulties of designing critical experiments, but that color vision does exist in many fishes is now well enough established. An excellent summary of the earlier work will be found in the paper by Warner (1931). Noble and Curtis (1939), in their studies of the jewel fish, found that the young were attracted to red and suggested that this attraction was related to the breeding colors of the adults. The females were found to recognize their own males as individuals by means of the color pattern on the head, for if the whole body of the male except the head were covered, the female still recognized her mate. If, however, the faces were painted and the rest of the body left its natural color, the recognition was no longer shown. The parent fish were found to distinguish their own young from those of other species by the color of the face, for if the young fish were stained an abnormal color, they were rejected by their parents. These authors succeeded in inducing *Hemichromis* to rear the young of *Cichlasoma bimaculatum* and produced evidence that the color preference of these young was very largely learned. That conditioning in the early life can affect the response to colors of several species of cichlids seems to be fairly clear both from the work of Noble and Curtis and from Baerends and Baerends-van Roon. But there seems little doubt, from the work of the latter authors, that in some species there is a strong inborn preference for a particular color and this preference can be affected only very slightly by experience. Seitz (1940), studying the genus *Tilapia* (mouth-breeders in which there is a marked difference between the reproductive color patterns of male and female), has shown that simple models do not release courting in the male, which apparently has a very detailed and presumably conditioned knowledge of female characters. It is assumed that this learning process can take place in the schools of immature fishes showing markings very similar to the color pattern of the ripe female. The *Tilapia* male, however, apparently cannot recognize the reproductive markings of a male of its species, nor indeed can the female, for a male that assumes this color immediately isolates itself in a territory. In *Astatotilapia* also Seitz found that fighting could be released by quite simple models and both male and female in this genus possess an inborn knowledge of the form and probably the color pattern of the

male. But although, as such studies show, learning abilities may play an important part even in such closely organized instinctive behavior chains as these, nevertheless extraordinarily few cases have as yet been investigated. There is an immense field of work now open to the student both of marine and fresh-water forms.

The schooling behavior of fishes is certainly one of the most characteristic features of the life of the group, and a study of its course naturally leads on to the investigation of visual releasers; for it is clear that vision is the chief sense governing social behavior in this group. Critical studies of social behavior have long been under way in this country, particularly by Parr, Breder, and his associates at the Marine Laboratory at Bimini in the Bahamas. It was my good fortune to visit this station four years ago and see something of its work in progress, but I feel sure that many of you here are quite as familiar with it as I am, so I shall pass it over lightly. But I think we can summarize the subject very briefly by saying that although there is abundant evidence for the development of the schooling response by a learning process, it is in most cases extremely difficult to distinguish between the effect of this and the possibility that an inborn recognition of the species pattern is slowly maturing. Most young fish school heterogeneously and very strongly; an aquarial life of a few months as an adult is often sufficient to inhibit this, and it would seem fairly clear that the concepts both of learning and of maturation are necessary to account for the many variations of behavior which have been described. The schooling is of interest also in that it seems to be such a distinct behavior pattern, and one not necessarily linked with any of the main instinctive urges. I feel convinced that one must at present regard it as evidence of a distinct social instinct, sufficient in itself and in some species at least, independent of the instincts of feeding and reproduction—although no doubt likely to be valuable in both these connections. This is an important conclusion for our science, for ethologists, notably Tinbergen, have been reluctant to allow the existence of social instinct in its own right. So I should like to see much more investigation directed toward unraveling the complex interrelations of inborn and learned responses in the schooling behavior of fish. I also hope that the new techniques in marine biology will soon give us more information about the survival value of school formation. The advantages of schooling for fish with poor vision might well be that the species is safer in a group since many pairs of eyes are better than one; but is there a real advantage when it comes to feeding behavior? One would like to know whether species that feed on large particles, which have to be searched for but when found can provide food for many individuals, may be more successful when hunting in groups; just as the feeding flock is an efficient technique for birds that have to survive the nonbreeding season under hard conditions. There is already impressive evidence that fish learn more rapidly and efficiently when the individuals are grouped (Welty, 1934).

The territorial behavior of fishes is another subject that strikes me as particularly promising for future investigation. The term "territory" should strictly be reserved for a defended area, and as far as I know, the evidence for area defense by fish in the nonreproductive state is still somewhat inconclusive. It is certainly an important aspect of the biology of inshore fishes. Territory holding, as apart from territorial defense, is common in fresh-water fishes, and is certainly very obvious in many marine species that dwell in nooks and crannies of coastal rocks and coral reefs. The evidence that territorial recognition is normally based on vision is so overwhelming that it need hardly be discussed, but of course there are exceptions, particularly among fresh-water fish living in very turbid water. It is interesting that the electric fishes *Gymnarchus* (Lissmann, 1958) can use their electric organs and electric sensitivity to aid territorial recognition. The tendency

to take up residence in a particular spot, even though the fish is not in the reproductive phase, is of course already well known to aquarists, and there is evidence (Braddock, 1949) that prior residence in an area gives an individual of the species *Platypoecilus maculatus* greater potentiality for dominion over its fellows than it would otherwise have. The effect is mainly upon the initial contacts with other individuals, and tends to fade as time passes. The exploits of aqualung divers have already indicated how widespread is this habit of establishing nonreproductive territories, and the workers at the Lerner Marine Station at Bimini are familiar with the extraordinary spectacle of subtropical reef fishes in the marine enclosures seeking out the same "sleeping places" night after night.

This matter of territory recognition is of theoretical importance, because so many of the observations are difficult to explain without assuming a general exploratory tendency and an ability as a result of this tendency to acquire a general knowledge of the immediate environment, a knowledge that could hardly be achieved except by a process that, when displayed in the laboratory by a rat in a maze, we call "latent learning." Perhaps such a general knowledge of an area is shown more strikingly by *Bathygobius soporator* than by any other known fish. This species inhabits tidal pools. Aronson (1951) finds that the fish are so well orientated that they are able to jump from pool to pool at low tide without running any significant risk of finding themselves on dry land. Evidence seems to force us to the provisional conclusion that these gobies swim over rock depressions and hollows at high tide, and thereby acquire an astonishingly detailed memory of the general features and topography of a limited area around the home pool. They are able to utilize this memory when the tide is low and the depressions are turned into tidal pools; for when the fish are restricted to these, they must, if they travel at all, jump from pool to pool.

I linked territorial learning of a fish to

some examples of the more complex behavior shown by rats when tested with the maze and detour techniques. Mazes have of course been used for the investigation of fish behavior for a considerable time, and Spooner in 1937 carried out an elaborate piece of research into the learning of detours by wrasse (Ctenolaborus rupestris). Spooner emphasizes that the learning displayed by the fish could not be explained on any simple association hypothesis, but involved a synthesizing or organizing process occurring in the sensory centers which was the expression of the discrimination of some relation in the external situation not previously apprehended. Since Spooner's work there have been many other studies that have reinforced this general conclusion.

Learning abilities of this kind could hardly be occurring if the animals were not showing something that can only be described as a general curiosity about the environment, and the observations of many naturalists suggest that this is indeed a feature of much fish behavior. But we badly need more information, and in particular we want to know how far any such curiosity extends and what objects and circumstances set limits to it. No animal displays an absolutely general curiosity: we always find that some types of stimulation are more "interesting" and attractive than others, and learning the topography and other characteristics of an environment is always governed in some degree by an inborn tendency to pay attention to particular kinds of objects, or to those kinds of objects in a particular setting. Here is a promising field for further investigation.

Learning abilities of this kind are of course very closely related to the basic powers of perception, particularly visual perception, and to the possibilities of coördinating and effectively synthesizing these complex perceptions.

There has been a good deal of work on visual configurational learning in fishes, particularly with goldfish. Goldsmith (1914) and Maes (1930) produce good evidence

of an ability to recognize both size and shape, and Herter (1929, 1930, 1937) was highly successful in training minnows and other species to discriminate between different shapes (circles, squares, triangles, crosses, etc.) as well as between the same figures at different sizes. Meesters showed that sticklebacks trained to distinguish a triangle from a square continued to do so correctly when the figures were turned through an angle up to 30°. When the rotation was 45° the discrimination was greatly reduced and above 45° it was lost entirely. These and other experiments showed that the figure-background relation was of great importance for the fish and there was no complete abstraction such that the figure could be recognized in any orientation. Experiments showed that "wormlike" figures differing in the number and sharpness of their curves could be well distinguished. Rowley (1934) found that he could train goldfish to distinguish between circles whose diameters differed by only 3 millimeters. Proof of such precise perception of size differences invites investigation of the fishes' response to the standard visual illusions such as the Muller Lyer illusion, etc. Herter (1930) has carried out such experiments successfully and finds that the response of the fish to the illusion is very similar to that of man.

Perkins and Wheeler (1930) and Perkins (1931) found that goldfish could learn to choose one of three absolute light intensities. At first the fishes usually had a preference for the minimum light intensity and could then transpose both up and down the intensity scale without further training. They were also able to choose one light on the basis of its relationship to two others when the intensities as well as the positions were changed after each trial. Schiller (1933) claimed to have demonstrated "intersensorial transposition" in minnows, but I know of no confirmation or repetition of his extraordinarily interesting work. Fish trained to the brighter or darker of two lights were then found to choose the "brighter" or "darker" of two smells (indol "dark"; ketone-musk "bright"). Controls appeared adequate and the effect was found to last for sixteen days. Perkins and Wheeler arrived at the curious conclusion that a constantly changing pattern of light intensities is learned more quickly than is a stereotyped pattern, and conclude that their experimental results demand an interpretation of the behavior of the goldfish in terms of insight rather than trial and error. They seem to have good grounds for suggesting that the volleys by which the learning curves ascend are objective pictures of the way the maturation of the learned pattern takes place in the individual animals. In all their work they found that the goldfish was responding to a total situation "in accordance with the law of configuration."

These evidences of insight learning which fish display are further discussed by Herter (1953), who suggests that some of them at least are examples of "preadaptation." He points out that fish often display abilities in the realms of sense physiology and psychology of which they can make no use in their natural life. As a particular instance of this he cites the fact that the crepuscular fish Amiurus nebulosus have quite good optical capacity for differentiating forms and are also able to respond to colors even though, under natural conditions, they can hardly ever use these abilities for orientation. He suggests that this preadaptation is a general feature of fish learning abilities, and although some of the examples he cites, such as the high ability to distinguish different complex sounds (e.g., different human voices), may be seen in a different light now that we know more about the sound production of fish, yet, in general, his conclusions seem to carry much weight. In this connection he quotes Buddenbrock (1937) to the effect that the sensitivity of the sense cell is usually greater than the apparent biological importance of the stimuli concerned would warrant. It does indeed seem to be a general feature of animal life that the precision and sensitivity of sense organs is higher than the environment would appear to justify. This fact poses a serious problem for students of evolution, since it is not easy to account for such perfection on the basis of natural selection alone. However, the answer may be that the nature of sensory nervous mechanisms is such that to achieve full efficiency at the normal level of stimulation, the threshold must be much lower.

Before leaving the subject of form vision it is interesting to note that Sperry and Clark (1949) have demonstrated interocular transfer of visual discrimination habits in the goby (Bathygobius soporator). Fish were trained, against the initial preference, to swim toward smaller, higher, and less bright-colored of two lures simultaneously presented. Blinkers of tantalum foil were used to occlude the vision of one eye and evidence was found that the nervous system of this fish can easily mediate interocular transfer in some individuals but not in all. Thus after a minimum of 120 trials, they found that out of 16 cases 5 showed excellent or good transfer, 4 a lesser degree of transfer, and the remaining 7 little or none. In other experiments it was found that when habits were learned with both eyes uncovered, learning and retention had not been confined to one dominant eye. This is in marked contrast to what was found in some earlier experiments with pigeons.

Social facilitation and imitation.—What has already been said about schooling will have made clear that there is much behavior suggesting social facilitation in fishes. Gudger (1944) has given a number of interesting records of follow-my-leader behavior in both swimming and leaping fish, although in most of these cases no particular advantage appears to accrue from the behavior. Breder and Halpern say that it is common knowledge among aquarists that in order to get a fish to feed it is often necessary to show it a companion feeding, a companion that need not necessarily be of the same species. Baerends and Baerends-van Roon (1950) report that the cichlids they had kept appeared to live in schools till they reached maturity and that it was typical of those schools that the members continually showed a preference to perform the same action simultaneously. "Sometimes they are all engaged in foraging on the bottom, and then again we will find them all scraping *algae* from the glass walls, floating quietly in the water, or lying together on the bottom. That they can experience the same emotional reaction simultaneously is illustrated by the following observations on *Tilapia natalensis*. These fish, when immature and living in schools, show either a pattern of vertical bars or two longitudinal bands. The latter pattern they assume when not disturbed, the former when they feel anxiety. Now, as soon as we brought a small *Hemichromis* into a tank containing a school of *Tilapias* showing the longitudinal bands, all at once assumed the cross bands. From this we conclude that they all became anxious irrespective of whether they individually had been affected or not. When living together in a territorial society such sharp, simultaneous reactions to events in a certain territory do not occur." The most careful experiments on the group learning of fishes have been those of Welty (1934). He found that a maze was learned by goldfish more quickly when they were grouped than when they were isolated. Putting a trained fish in the maze will speed up the learning of untrained fish. This group facilitation is attributed to three related causes: (1) group cohesion based on vision, (2) mass-habituation (which the author describes as "interreassurance"), and (3) group-interaction stimulating exploratory activity. However, none of these three categories can be considered as evidence of true imitation; rather they are three special cases of social facilitation. Welty, however, has some further observations rather more puzzling. Thus, for instance, he found that a goldfish learns to run a simple maze more rapidly after having seen another goldfish run it. This seems to be owing (a) to reassurance that the stimulus

was not followed by harmful results, so that there was a mutual quietening effect, and (b) to learning, through visual cohesion, to move forward at the time the stimulus was presented. Untrained fishes were sometimes seen even to precede the trained fish in moving toward the stimulus in their respective chambers. It seems fairly clear that this latter group of observations, (b), can again be explained as social facilitation together with local enhancement. There does, however, remain a doubt as to the first class, (a), of observations. This, at first sight, seems to be owing to an appreciation by one fish of the lack of harmful results subsequent to the behavior of the other fish. If this could be established it would seem to be evidence of true imitation, but there seems to remain the possibility that the quiet behavior of the fish being tested had a quietening effect on its associate. Morrow (1948) considers that the shape of Welty's learning curves indicates typical trial-and-error learning, which would not be expected if imitation were actually in operation. Welty also found that numbers of goldfish *retain* motor responses better than do isolated fishes, but the explanation of this retention is not understood. Besides these and many similar experiments with goldfish, Welty found that paradise fish (*Macropodus opercularis*), the zebra fish (*Brachydanio rerio*), and shiners (*Notropis atherinoides*) eat more per fish when in groups than when kept singly. Welty's work on the superiority of groups of fishes over single fishes in maze-learning experiments has been confirmed by Greenberg (1947) in work with the green sunfish (*Lepomis cyanellus*). He found that the biggest individual tends to be the leader, although leadership at the maze shifted at almost every trial. Subordinates appear to lessen tension among territory-holding fishes, and removal of the "omega" from aquaria with three territories increased aggressive behavior among those remaining, whereas the introduction of a new fish led to their attacking it instead of one another.

Before leaving the subject of the evidence for psychologically higher types of behavior in fish, I would like to make a brief reference to behavior we describe colloquially as play. Behavior that appears playlike can often be seen in fishes, particularly in nest building—as in the stickleback (Iersel, 1953)—but there seems good reason for thinking that many such examples represent only the simplest transference activity, and do not require any concepts as elaborate and subtle as those implied by the term play. But there do seem to be some well-authenticated examples of what seem like true play in addition. Thus Brahm has a long account of the apparently playful squirting of water by "shooters" *(jaculator)* at an aquarium keeper personally known to them. Such a record may savor too much of anecdote and I may be thought unwise to quote it. But many other naturalists and psychologists have described other examples suggestive of true play and some of these accounts seem sufficiently precise to suggest that a critical investigation of the subject in fish would be well worthwhile.

In what I have said, I have cast a brief glance at a few types of investigation which seem to me to be particularly promising for ethologists who have at their disposal the facilities and techniques supplied by the modern marine biological station. But I could have chosen many other examples for mention, and it has largely been a matter of personal choice and interest. I hope, however, I have said enough to show that ethology, although only new in a rather limited and special sense of the word, has great significance for the future of marine biology, and I hope that this conference may be a means of securing coöperation and understanding between the two groups of investigators.

REFERENCES

ARONSON, L. R., 1951   Orientation and jumping behaviour in the gobiid fish *Bathygobius soporator*. *Am. Mus. Novitates.* **1486:** 1–22.

BAERENDS, G. P., and J. M. BAERENDS-VAN

ROON, 1950   An introduction to the ethology of cichlid fishes. *Behaviour Supplement.* **1:** 1–243.

BINGLEY, W., 1829   *Animal biography*, 7th ed.; London, Ribington. 4 vols.

BRADDOCK, J. C., 1949   The effect of prior residence upon dominance in the fish *Platypoecilus maculatus. Physiol. Zool.* **22:** 161–169.

BUDDENBROCK, W. VON, 1937   *Grundriss der vergleichenden Physiologie.* 2d ed.; Berlin, Borntraeger. Vol. 1, 567 pp.

COUCH, J., 1847   *Illustrations of instinct.* London, John Van Voorst, 343 pp.

DARWIN, C., 1872   *The expression of the emotions in man and animals.* London, John Murray. 387 pp.

EBBINGHAUS, H., 1885   *Uber das Gedachtnis: Untersuchungen zur experimentellen Psychologie.* Leipzig. (Translated as *Memory: a contribution to experimental psychology.*) New York, Teachers' College, 1913.

GOLDSMITH, M., 1914   Reactions physiologiques et psychiques des poissons. *Bull. Inst. Gen. Psychol.* **14:** 97–239.

GREENBERG, B., 1947   Some relations between territory, social hierarchy and leadership in the green sunfish *(Lepomis cyanellus). Physiol. Zool.* **20:** 267–299.

GUDGER, E. W., 1944   Fishes that swim heads to tails in single file. *Copeia.* **1944:** 152–154.

HARRIS, J. E., and H. P. WHITING, 1954   Control of rhythmical activity in the skeletal muscle of the embryonic dogfish. *J. Physiol.* **124:** 63.

HERTER, K., 1929   Dressurversuche an Fischen. *Z. vergl. Physiol.* **10:** 688–711. Akademie Verlag, Berlin.

HERTER, K., 1930   Weitere Dressurversuche an Fischen. *Z. vergl. Physiol.* **11:** 730–748.

HERTER, K., 1937   *Dressur der Ellritze (Phoxinus laevis) auf verschieden gross optische Signale.* (Hochschulfilme C. 178, quoted Herter, 1940).

HERTER, K., 1953   *Fie Fischdressuren und ihre sinnephysiologischen Grundlagen.* Berlin, Akademie Verlag, 326 pp.

HOLST, E. VON, 1935-1937   Vom Wesen der Ordnung im Zentralnervensystem. *Naturwiss.* **25:** 625–631, 641–647.

IERSEL, J. J. A. VAN, 1953   An analysis of the parental behaviour of the male three-spined stickleback. *Behaviour Suppl.* III: 1–159.

LISSMANN, H. W., 1946 The neurological basis of the locomotory rhythms in the spinal dogfish (*Scyllium canicula, Acanthias vulgaris*). I. Reflex behaviour. II. The effect of de-afferentiation. *J. Exp. Biol.* **23**: 143–161, 162–176.

LISSMANN, H. W., 1958 (Untitled; in press.)

MAES, R., 1930 La vision des formes chez les poissons. *Ann. Soc. R. Zool. Belg.* **60**: 103–130.

MORROW, J. E., 1948 Schooling behaviour in fishes. *Quart. Rev. Biol.* **23**: 27–38.

NOBLE, G. K., and B. CURTIS, 1939 The social behaviour of the jewel fish, *Hemichromis bimaculatus*, Gill. *Amer. Mus. Nat. Hist. Bull.* **76**: 1–46.

PERKINS, F. T., 1931 A further study of configurational learning in the goldfish. *J. Exp. Psychol.* **14**: 508–538.

PERKINS, F. T., and R. H. WHEELER, 1930 Configurational learning in the goldfish. *Comp. Psychol. Monogr.* 7, No. 31, 50 pp.

ROWLEY, J. B., 1934 Discrimination limens of pattern and size in the goldfish *Carassius auratus*. *Genet. Psychol. Monogr.* **15**: 245–302.

SCHILLER, P. VON, 1933 Intersensorielle transposition bei Fischen. *Z. vergl. Physiol.* **19**: 304–309.

SEITZ, A., 1940 Die Paarbildung bei einigen Cichliden. I. Die Paarbildung bei Astatotilapia strigigena. *Z. Tierpsychol.* **4**: 40–84.

SPERRY, R. W., and E. CLARK, 1949 Interocular transfer of visual discrimination habits in a teleost fish. *Physiol. Zool.* **22**: 372–378.

SPOONER, G. M., 1937 The learning of detours by wrasse (*Ctenolabris rupestris* L.). *J. Mar. Biol. Assoc.* **21**: 497–570.

WARNER, L. H., 1931 The problem of colour vision in fishes. *Quart. Rev. Biol.* **6**: 329–348.

WELTY, J. C., 1934 Experiments on group behaviour of fishes. *Physiol. Zool.* **7**: 85–127.

WERTHEIMER, M., 1912 Experimentelle Studien über das Sehen von Bewegung. *Z. Psychol.* **61**: 161–265.

WINTREBERT, P., 1920 La contraction rhythmée aneurale des myotemes chez les embryons de sélaciens. *Arch. Zool. exp. gen.* **60**: 221–245.

WOODWORTH, R. S., 1938 *Experimental psychology*. New York, Columbia Univ. Press, 889 pp.

WUNDER, W., 1930 Experimentelle Untersuchungen am Dreistachligen Stickling (*Gasterosteus aculeatus*) während der Laichzeit. *Z. Morph. ü Ök. Tiere.* **16**: 453–498.

FRANK A. BEACH

4   The Descent of Instinct

Frank A. Beach here reviews the history of the "instinct" concept. After evaluating its usefulness, Beach proposes that the term be dropped.

How would an ethologist answer these criticisms of the "instinct" concept?

For more information on the inheritance of audiogenic seizures, see reading 8. Reading 21 is concerned with the kind of prenatal influences discussed by Beach.

This article originally appeared in the *Psychological Review*, 1955, 62, 401–410. It is reprinted by permission of the author and the American Psychological Association.

"The delusion is extraordinary by which we thus exalt language above nature:— making language the expositor of nature, instead of making nature the expositor of language" (Alexander Brian Johnson, *A Treatise on Language*).

The basic ideas underlying a concept of instinct probably are older than recorded history. At any rate they are clearly set forth in the Greek literature of 2500 years ago. They have been controversial ideas and they remain so today. Nevertheless, the instinct concept has survived in almost complete absence of empirical validation. One aim of the present article is to analyze the reasons for the remarkable vitality of a concept which has stood without objective test for at least two millenia. A second objective is to evaluate the concept as it relates to a science of behavior.

Origins in Philosophy and Theology

The concept of instinct evolved in relation to the broad problems of human destiny, of Man's place in nature, and his position in this world and the next. From the beginning, instinct has been defined and discussed in terms of its relation to reason and, less directly, to the human soul.

During the fourth century B.C. the Greek philosopher Heraclitus declared that there had been two types of creation. Men and gods were the products of rational creation, whereas irrational brutes comprised a separate category of living creatures. Heraclitus added the observation that only gods and men possess souls. The close relation between rational powers and possession of a soul has been reaffirmed time and again during the ensuing 2500 years. Heraclitus did not advance the concept of instinct but he laid the groundwork for its development.

Stoic philosophers of the first century A.D. held that men and gods belong to one natural community, since they are rational beings. All animals were specifically excluded since they are not creatures of reason and even their most complex behavior takes place "without reflection," to use the words of Seneca. This stoical taxonomy was both flattering and convenient since, according to the tenets of this school, members of the natural community were forbidden to harm or enslave other members. It is significant that neither Heraclitus

nor the Stoics based their conclusions upon objective evidence. Their premises concerning the psychology of animals were not derived from empirical observation; they were demanded by assumption of the philosophical position that animals lack a rational soul.

Aristotle, who was more of an observer than a philosopher, was of a different mind. In *Historia Animalium* Man is placed at the top of Scala Natura (directly above the Indian elephant), and is accorded superior intellectual powers, but none qualitatively distinct from those of other species.

In the thirteenth century Albertus Magnus composed *De Animalibus*, based chiefly upon the writings of Aristotle but modifying the Aristotelian position where necessary to conform to Scholastic theology. Albertus removed Man from the natural scale, holding that he is unique in possessing the gift of reason and an immortal soul. Animals, lacking reason, "are directed by their natural instinct and therefore cannot act freely."

St. Thomas Aquinas, student of Albertus, supported his teacher's distinction between men and animals. Animals possess only the sensitive soul described by Aristotle. The human embryo is similarly endowed, but the rational soul is divinely implanted in the fetus at some time before birth.[*] The behavior of man therefore depends upon reason, whereas all animals are governed by instinct. Like the Stoic philosophers, the Scholastics were unconcerned with factual evidence. Their emphasis upon instinctive control of animal behavior was dictated by a need of the theological system, and in this frame of reference instinct was a useful concept.

Roughly four centuries after the time of St. Thomas Aquinas, René Descartes and his followers aggressively restated the existence of a man-brute dichotomy. The

[*] It is not irrelevant to point out that weighty disputation concerning the exact age at which the soul enters the fetus retarded the advancement of embryological knowledge during its seventeenth century beginnings.

bare facts of the Cartesian position are common knowledge, but for the purpose of the present argument it is important to ask why Descartes felt so strongly about the matter—felt compelled to hold up man as the Reasoner, at the same time insisting that all other living creatures are only flesh-and-blood machines. The explanation stands out in the following quotation:

"After the error of atheism, there is nothing that leads weak minds further astray from the paths of virtue than the idea that the minds of other animals resemble our own, and that therefore we have no greater right to future life than have gnats and ants" (René Descartes, *Passions of the Soul*).

From Albertus to Descartes the argument runs clear. The theological system posits a life after death. Hence the postulation of the soul. But mere possession of a soul is not enough. Each man must earn the right of his soul's salvation. This in turn depends upon reason, which man exercises in differentiating good from evil, behavior which is sinful from that which is not. An afterlife is man's unique prerogative; no animals share it. They have no souls and therefore no need to reason. But how are the complex and adaptive reactions of subhuman creatures to be explained if not by reason, foresight, volition? They are comfortably disposed of as products of instincts with which the Creator has endowed all dumb brutes.

That the thirteenth-century point of view persists today is shown by the following quotation:

In animals there are only instincts, but not in man. As St. Thomas points out, there cannot be any deliberation in a subrational being (even though we may get the impression that there is). . . . Instincts in animals seem to operate according to the pattern of physical forces, where the stronger always prevails; for animals are utterly devoid of the freedom which characterizes man. . . . That is why when one studies human behavior one must rise above the purely animal pattern and concentrate upon those two

faculties, intellect and will, which separate man from animal (Msgr. Fulton J. Sheen, *Peace of Soul*).

To summarize what has been said thus far, it appears that the descent of the instinct concept can be traced from early philosophies which set man apart from the rest of the living world and sought for him some divine affinity. This was achieved by claiming for man alone the power of reason. By a process of elimination the behavior of animals was ascribed to their natural instincts. During the Middle Ages this dichotomous classification became a part of Church doctrine, with the result that possession of reason and of a soul were inextricably linked to the hope of eternal life. Prescientific concepts of instinct were not deduced from the facts of nature; they were necessitated by the demands of philosophical systems based upon supernatural conceptions of nature.

Early Scientific Usage

When biology emerged as a scientific discipline, there was a general tendency to adopt the prescientific point of view regarding instinct. Some exceptions occurred. For example, Erasmus Darwin's *Zoonomia* expressed the theory that all behavior is a product of experience, but this point of view was subsequently disavowed by the grandson of its sponsor. Charles Darwin made the concept of instinct one cornerstone of his theory of evolution by means of natural selection.

To bridge the gap of the Cartesian man-brute dichotomy, and thus to establish the evolution of mind as well as structure, Darwin and his disciples amassed two types of evidence. One type purported to prove the existence of human instincts; the other pertained to rational behavior in subhuman species. The idea of discontinuity in mental evolution was vigorously attacked, but the dichotomy between instinct and reason was never challenged.

The nineteenth-century literature on

evolution shows plainly that the concept of instinctive behavior was accepted because it filled a need in the theoretical system, and not because its validity had been established by empirical test.

Contemporary psychologists such as Herbert Spencer were influenced by the evolutionary movement, and the idea of an instinctive basis for human psychology became popular. William James, in Volume II of his *Principles*, insisted that man has more instincts than any other mammal. McDougall's widely read *Social Psychology* listed human instincts of flight, repulsion, parental feeling, reproduction, self-abasement, etc. Woodworth, Thorndike, and other leaders agreed that much of human behavior is best understood as an expression of instinctive drives or needs.

One of the difficulties with such thinking is that it often leads to the nominal fallacy—the tendency to confuse naming with explaining. Some psychological writers were guilty of employing the instinct concept as an explanatory device, and the eventual result was a vigorous revolt against the use of instinct in any psychological theory.

The Anti-instinct Revolt

Dunlap's 1919 article, "Are there any instincts?" (5), was one opening gun in the battle, but the extreme protests came from the most radical Behaviorists as represented by Z. Y. Kuo, who wrote on the subject, "A psychology without heredity" (18). For a while the word "instinct" was anathema, but the revolt was abortive, and there were three principal reasons for its failure.

First, Kuo denied instinct but admitted the existence of unlearned "units of reaction." By this phrase he meant simple reflexes, but in using it he set up a dichotomy of learned and unlearned behavior which was fatal to his basic thesis. It merely shifted the debate to arguments as to the degree of complexity permissible in an unlearned response, or the proportion of a

complex pattern that was instinctive. The second error consisted essentially of a return to the position taken by Erasmus Darwin at the close of the eighteenth century. Having averred that the only unlearned reactions consist of a few simple reflexes, the opponents of the instinct doctrine invoked learning to explain all other behavior. This forced them into untenable positions such as that of maintaining that pecking behavior of the newly-hatched chick is a product of head movements made by the embryo in the shell, or that the neonatal infant's grasp reflex depends upon prenatal exercise of this response. The third loophole in the anti-instinct argument derived from a dualistic concept of the hereditary process. Admitting that genes can affect morphological characters, and simultaneously denying that heredity influences behavior, opponents of instinct were hoist by their own petard. If the physical machinery for behavior develops under genetic control, then the behavior it mediates can scarcely be regarded as independent of inheritance.

It is important to note that this war over instinct was fought more with words and inferential reasoning than with behavioral evidence. It is true that a few individuals actually observed the behavior of newborn children or of animals, but most of the battles of the campaign were fought from the armchair in the study rather than from the laboratory.

Current Thought in Psychology

Although there are militant opponents of the instinct doctrine among present-day psychologists, it is undoubtedly correct to say that the concept of instincts as complex, unlearned patterns of behavior is generally accepted in clinical, social, and experimental psychology. Among experimentalists. Lashley suggested that instinctive behavior is unlearned and differs from reflexes in that instincts depend on "the pattern or organization of the stimulus," whereas reflexes are ilicited by stimulation of localized groups of sensory endings (19).

Carmichael (3) expressed agreement with G. H. Parker's statement that human beings are "about nine-tenths inborn, and one-tenth acquired." Morgan (20) studied food-hoarding behavior in rats, and concluded, "since it comes out spontaneously without training, it is plainly instinctive." The following quotation reveals that some modern psychologists not only embrace the concept of instinctive behavior, but consider it a useful explanatory device.

"Of the theories of hoarding which have been advanced, the most reasonable one in terms of recent data is that the behavior is instinctive . . ." (28).

At least three serious criticisms can be leveled against current treatment of the problem of instinctive behavior. The first is that psychologists in general actually know very little about most of the behavior patterns which they confidently classify as instinctive. In his paper, "The experimental analysis of instinctive activities," Lashley mentions the following 15 examples:

1. Eating of Hydra by the Planarian, Microstoma.

2. Nest-building, cleaning of young and retrieving by the primiparous rat.

3. Restless running about of the mother rat deprived of her litter.

4. Homing of pigeons.

5. Web-weaving of spiders.

6. Migratory behavior of fishes.

7. Nest-building of birds, including several species.

8. Mating behavior of the female rat in estrus.

9. Dancing reactions of the honeybee returning to the hive laden with nectar.

10. Visual reactions of rats reared in darkness.

11. Responses of the sooty tern to her nest and young.

12. Reactions of the seagull to artificial and normal eggs.

13. Sexual behavior of the male rat.

14. Mating responses in insects.

15. Mating responses in domestic hens.

It is a safe guess that most American psychologists have never observed any of these patterns of behavior. At a conservative estimate, less than half of the reactions listed have been subjected to even preliminary study by psychologically trained investigators. The significance of this criticism lies partly in the fact that those psychologists who *have* worked in the area of "instinctive" behavior tend to be more critical of the instinct concept than are those who lack first-hand knowledge of the behavioral evidence.

Relevant to the criticism of unfamiliarity is the fact that the degree of assurance with which instincts are attributed to a given species is inversely related to the extent to which that species has been studied, particularly from the developmental point of view. Before the development of complex behavior in human infants had been carefully analyzed, it was, as we have seen, a common practice to describe many human instincts. Longitudinal studies of behavior have reduced the "unlearned" components to three or four simple responses not much more complex than reflexes (4).

The second criticism is that despite prevailing ignorance about the behavior which is called instinctive, there is strong pressure toward premature categorization of the as yet unanalyzed patterns of reaction. The history of biological taxonomy shows that the reliability of any classificatory system is a function of the validity of identification of individual specimens or even populations. Unless the systematist is thoroughly familiar with the characteristics of a given species, he cannot determine its proper relation to other groups. Similarly, until psychologists have carefully analyzed the salient characteristics of a given pattern of behavior, they cannot meaningfully classify or compare it with other patterns.

The third criticism of current treatment of instinctive behavior has to do with the classificatory scheme which is in use. When all criteria which supposedly differentiate instinctive from acquired responses are critically evaluated, the only one which seems universally applicable is that instincts are unlearned (21). This forces psychology to deal with a two-class system, and such systems are particularly unmanageable when one class is defined solely in negative terms, that is, in terms of the absence of certain characteristics that define the other class. It is logically indefensible to categorize any behavior as unlearned unless the characteristics of learned behavior have been thoroughly explored and are well known. Even the most optimistic "learning psychologist" would not claim that we have reached this point yet. At present, to prove that behavior is unlearned is equivalent to proving the null hypothesis.

Perhaps a more serious weakness in the present psychological handling of instinct lies in the assumption that a two-class system is adequate for the classification of complex behavior. The implication that all behavior must be determined by learning or by heredity, neither of which is more than partially understood, is entirely unjustified. The final form of any response is affected by a multiplicity of variables, only two of which are genetical and experiential factors. It is to the identification and analysis of all of these factors that psychology should address itself. When this task is properly conceived and executed there will be no need nor reason for ambiguous concepts of instinctive behavior.

Genes and Behavior

Experimental investigation of relationships between gentical constitution and behavior was exemplified by the pioneering studies of Yerkes (30), Tryon (27), and Heron (12). Interest in this area has recently increased, and a large number of investigations have been summarized by Hall (11) who anticipates a new interdisciplinary science of psychogenetics.

As Hall points out, the psychologist interested in examining gene-behavior relations has several approaches to choose from. He can compare the behavior of different inbred strains of animals currently available in the genetics laboratory. He can cross two strains and study the behavior of the hybrids. Selective breeding for particular behavioral traits is a well-established technique. The behavioral effects of induced mutations have as yet received very little attention but should be investigated.

It is known that selective breeding can alter the level of general activity (23), maze behavior (12), emotionality (9), and aggressiveness (17) in the laboratory rat. Inbred strains of mice differ from one another in temperature preference (13), aggressiveness (24), and strength of "exploratory drive" (26).

Various breeds of dogs exhibit pronounced differences in behavioral characteristics. Some are highly emotional, unstable and restless; whereas others are phlegmatic and relatively inactive (7). Special breeds have been created by selective mating to meet certain practical requirements. For example, some hunting dogs such as the foxhound are "open trailers." While following a fresh trail they vocalize in a characteristic fashion. Other dogs are "mute trailers." The F_1 hybrids of a cross between these types are always open trailers although the voice is often that of the mute trailing parent (29).

Inbreeding of domestic chickens for high egg production has produced behavioral deficiencies of various kinds. Although hens of some lines are excellent layers, they have almost totally lost the normal tendency to brood the eggs once they have been laid (15). The maternal behavior of sows of different inbred lines of swine is strikingly different. Females of one line are so aggressively protective of their young that they cannot be approached during the lactation period. Sows of a second genetical line possess such weak maternal interest that they frequently kill their litters by stepping or lying on the young (14).

Study of the effects of controlled breeding cast doubt upon the validity of any classificatory system which describes one type of behavior as genetically determined and another is experientially determined. For example, by manipulating the genotype it is possible to alter certain types of learning ability. As far as present evidence can show, the influence of genes on learning is as important as any genetical effect upon other behavior patterns commonly considered instinctive. There is no reason to assume that so-called instinctive reactions are more dependent upon heredity than noninstinctive responses; hence genetical determination is not a differentiating criterion.

The Meaning of Genetical Determination

Behavior which is known to vary with the genotype is often incorrectly defined as "genetically determined" behavior. Although we can show a correlation between certain genes and particular behavior patterns, this is of course no proof of a causal relationship. Many other genes and nongenic factors are always involved in such correlations. This point is nicely illustrated by a series of experiments on audiogenic seizures in mice.

Susceptibility to fatal seizures is high in some inbred strains and low in others (10). When a high-incidence and low incidence strain are crossed, the susceptibility of the F_1 generation is intermediate between those of the parental strains. So far the evidence strongly supports the conclusion that seizure incidence is genetically determined. However, the incidence of seizures can be altered without changing the genetic constitution.

This is accomplished by modifying the prenatal environment. Fertilized eggs recovered from the tubes or uterus of a female of one strain and introduced into the uterus of a female of a different strain will sometimes implant normally and produce viable young. This has been done using seizure-susceptible females as donors and seizure-resistant females as hosts. Under such conditions the genetical characteristics of the young are unaltered, but their susceptibility to fatal seizures is lower than that of their own genetic strain and higher than that of the "foster" mothers in whose uteri they developed (8).

Studies of this sort emphasize the important but often neglected fact that postnatal behavior is affected by factors acting upon the organism before birth. As Sontag has pointed out, this is true of human beings as well as lower species.

Fetal environment may play a part in determining characteristics of the physiological behavior of any newborn infant. We are too often inclined to neglect this source of modification of physiological potential. Too frequently we think of the individual as beginning life only at birth. Yet because it is during the period of intrauterine life that most of the cells of the vital organs are actually formed, it is during this period that "environmental" factors such as nutrition, oxygen, mother's hormones, etc. are most important in modifying their characteristics (25, p. 482).

Another fundamental principle illustrated by the results of transplanting fertilized ova is that the uniformity of behavior which characterizes highly inbred strains of animals cannot be ascribed solely to homozygosity, but depends as well upon *minimal variability of the prenatal environment*. More broadly conceived, this principle implies that behavioral similarities and differences observable at birth are in part a product of intrauterine effects.

If forced to relinquish the criterion of genetical control, proponents of the instinct doctrine fall back upon the criterion of the unlearned nature of instinctive acts. Now learning is a process occurring through time, and can only be studied by longitudinal analysis. If instinctive acts are unlearned, their developmental history must differ in some significant fashion from that of a learned response.

The Ontogeny of Behavior

No bit of behavior can ever be fully understood until its ontogenesis has been described. Had psychologists always recognized this fact, much of the fruitless debate about unlearned behavior could have been avoided.

Perhaps the most widely cited psychological experiment on development and instinctive behavior is that of Carmichael, who studied the swimming behavior of larval amphibians (2). He reared embryos in a solution which paralyzed the striped muscles but permitted normal growth. Animals that were thus prevented from practicing the swimming response were nevertheless capable of normal swimming when placed in pure water. These findings are often offered as proof of the claim that swimming is instinctive. However, to demonstrate that practice is not essential for the appearance of a response is only the beginning of the analysis. This point is clearly illustrated by certain observations of insect behavior.

Gravid female moths, *Hyponomenta padella*, lay their eggs on the leaves of the hackberry plant and die shortly thereafter. The eggs hatch, the larvae eat the leaves and eventually become mature. Females of this new generation in turn select hackberry leaves on which to deposit their eggs. Another race of moths prefers apple leaves as an oviposition site. The difference between the two races has been perpetuated, generation after generation, for many centuries. It would appear to be the example par excellence of a genetically controlled behavior trait. But such an explanation is insufficient.

When eggs of the apple-preferring type are transferred to hackberry leaves, the larvae thrive on the new diet. Thirty per cent of the females developing from these larvae show a preference for hackberry leaves when it comes time for them to deposit their eggs (16).

The evidence is of course incomplete.

Why only 30 per cent of the insects show a reversal of preference is not clear. It would be illuminating if the same experimental treatment could be repeated on several successive generations. Nevertheless it appears likely that the adult moth's choice of an oviposition site is influenced by the chemical composition of the food consumed during the larval period (6). If this interpretation is correct, the data illustrate the fact that a complex behavior pattern may be "unlearned" and still depend upon the individual's previous history.

Comparable examples can be found in the behavior of vertebrates. Stereotyped patterns of behavior appear with great regularity in successive generations under conditions in which practice plays no obvious role. Nonetheless such "species-specific" responses may be dependent upon previous experience of the organism.

The maternal behavior of primiparous female rats reared in isolation is indistinguishable from that of multiparous individuals. Animals with no maternal experience build nests before the first litter is born, clean the young, eat the placenta, and retrieve scattered young to the nest (1). However, pregnant rats that have been reared in cages containing nothing that can be picked up and transported do not build nests when material is made available. They simply heap their young in a pile in a corner of the cage. Other females that have been reared under conditions preventing them from licking and grooming their own bodies fail to clean their young at the time of parturition (22).

There are undoubtedly many adaptive responses which appear *de novo* at the biologically appropriate time in the absence of preceding practice, but the possibility remains that component parts of a complex pattern have in fact been perfected in different contexts. Whether or not this is the case can only be determined by exhaustive analysis of the ontogeny of the behavior under examination. Nonetheless, to define behavior as "unlearned" in the absence of such analysis is meaningless and misleading.

Summary and Conclusions

The concept of instinctive behavior seems to have originated in antiquity in connection with attempts to define a clear-cut difference between man and all other animals. Human behavior was said to be governed by reasoning, and the behavior of animals to depend upon instinct. In his possession of the unique power of reason, man was elevated above all other creatures, and, incidentally, his use of them for his own purposes was thus morally justified.

Christian theologians adopted this point of view and averred that man was given the power of reason so that he could earn his own salvation. Similar privileges could not logically be accorded to lower animals. Therefore they were denied reason and their behavior was explained as a product of divinely implanted instincts. In both sacred and secular philosophies the concept of instinct served a practical purpose, although in no instance was there any attempt to validate it by examination of the empirical evidence.

The concept gained a central position in scientific thinking as a result of the Darwinian movement. Proponents of the evolutionary theory accepted uncritically the assumption that all behavior must be governed by instinct or by reasoning. Their aim was to demonstrate that animals can reason and that men possess instincts. The same dichotomy has persisted in experimental psychology. Attempts to eliminate the instinct concept were unsuccessful because those who made the attempt accepted the idea that all behavior is either acquired or inherited.

No such classification can ever be satisfactory. It rests upon exclusively negative definitions of one side of the dichotomy. It obscures the basic problems involved. It reflects an unnaturally narrow and naive conception of factors shaping behavior.

To remedy the present confused situation it is necessary first to refrain from premature classification of those kinds of behavior that are currently defined as unlearned. Until they have been systematically analyzed it will remain impossible to decide whether these numerous response patterns belong in one or a dozen different categories.

The analysis that is needed involves two types of approach. One rests upon determination of the relationships existing between genes and behavior. The other consists of studying the development of various behavior patterns in the individual, and determining the number and kinds of factors that normally control the final form of the response.

When these methods have been applied to the various types of behavior which today are called "instinctive," the concept of instinct will disappear, to be replaced by scientifically valid and useful explanations.

REFERENCES

1. BEACH, F. A.: The neural basis of innate behavior. I. Effects of cortical lesions upon the maternal behavior pattern in the rat. *J. comp. Psychol.*, 1937, **24**, 393–436.

2. CARMICHAEL, L.: The development of behavior in vertebrates experimentally removed from the influence of external stimulation. *Psychol. Rev.*, 1927, **34**, 34–47.

3. CARMICHAEL, L.: The growth of sensory control of behavior before birth. *Psychol. Rev.*, 1947, **54**, 316–324.

4. DENNIS, W.: Infant development under conditions of restricted practice. *Genet. psychol. Monogr.*, 1941, **23**, 143–189.

5. DUNLAP, K.: Are there any instincts? *J. abnorm. Psychol.*, 1919–20, **14**, 35–50.

6. EMERSON, A. E.: Ecology, evolution and society. *Amer. Nat.*, 1943, **77**, 97–118.

7. FULLER, J. L., and J. P. SCOTT: Heredity and learning ability in infrahuman animals. *Eugenics Quart.*, 1954, **1**, 28–43.

8. GINSBURG, B. E., and R. B. HOVDA: On the physiology of gene controlled audiogenic seizures in mice. *Anat. Rec.*, 1947, **99**, 65–66.

9. HALL, C. S.: The inheritance of emotion-ality. *Sigma Xi Quart.*, 1938, **26**, 17–27.

10. HALL, C. S.: Genetic differences in fatal audiogenic seizures between two inbred strains of house mice. *J. Hered.*, 1947, **38**, 2–6.

11. HALL, C. S.: The genetics of behavior. In S. S. Stevens (Ed.), *Handbook of experimental psychology*. New York: Wiley, 1951.

12. HERON, W. T.: The inheritance of maze learning ability in rats. *J. comp. Psychol.*, 1935, **19**, 77–89.

13. HERTER, K.: Die Beziehungen zwischen Vorzugstemperatur und Hautbeschaffenheit bei Mausen. *Zool. Anz. Suppl.*, 1938, **11**, 48–55.

14. HODGSON, R. E.: An eight generation experiment in inbreeding swine. *J. Hered.*, 1935, **26**, 209–217.

15. HURST, C. C.: *Experiments in genetics*. Cambridge: Cambridge Univer. Press, 1925.

16. IMMS, A. D.: *Recent advances in entymology*. Philadelphia: Blakiston's Sons, 1931.

17. KEELER, C. E., and H. D. KING: Multiple effects of coat color genes in the Norway rat, with special reference to temperament and domestication. *J. comp. Psychol.*, 1942, **34**, 241–250.

18. KUO, Z. Y.: A psychology without heredity. *Psychol. Rev.*, 1924, **31**, 427–451.

19. LASHLEY, K. S.: Experimental analysis of instinctive behavior. *Psychol. Rev.*, 1938, **45**, 445–471.

20. MORGAN, C. T.: The hoarding instinct. *Psychol. Rev.*, 1947, **54**, 335–341.

21. MUNN, N.: *Psychological development*. New York: Houghton Mifflin, 1938.

22. RIESS, B. F.: The isolation of factors of learning and native behavior in field and laboratory studies. *Ann. N. Y. Acad. Sci.*, 1950, **51**, 1093–1102.

23. RUNDQUIST, E. A.: The inheritance of spontaneous activity in rats. *J. comp. Psychol.*, 1933, **16**, 415–438.

24. SCOTT, J. P.: Genetic differences in the social behavior of inbred strains of mice. *J. Hered.*, 1942, **33**, 11–15.

25. SONTAG, L. W.: The genetics of differences in psychosomatic patterns in childhood. *Amer. J. Orthopsychiat.*, 1950, **20**, 479–489.

26. THOMPSON, W. R.: The inheritance of behaviour: behavioural differences in fifteen mouse strains. *Canad. J. Psychol.*, 1953, **7**, 145–155.

27. TRYON, R. C.: Genetics of learning ability in rats. *Univer. Calif. Publ. Psychol.*, 1929, **4**, 71–89.

28. WADDELL, D.: Hoarding behavior in the Golden Hamster. *J. comp. physiol. Psychol.*, 1951, **44**, 383–388.

29. WHITNEY, L. F.: Heredity of trail barking propensity of dogs. *J. Hered.*, 1929, **20**, 561–562.

30. YERKES, R. M.: The heredity of savageness and wildness in rats. *J. anim. Behav.*, 1913, **3**, 286–296.

R. A. HINDE and N. TINBERGEN

5   The Comparative Study of Species-Specific Behavior

The study of evolution has much to contribute to our understanding of the determination of behavior. Conversely, behavioral studies have frequently contributed to the solution of evolutionary puzzles. The evolution of behavior is, however, a difficult area for research. Behavior, quite obviously, does not fossilize. Although it is possible to make reasonable guesses about the gross behavior patterns of extinct species on the basis of fossil remains, these are of little help in tracing the evolution of a particular behavior pattern.

A more fruitful approach is to study the behavior of closely related existing species. Data from such studies sometimes permit inferences concerning the behavior of the common ancestor. The biological adaptiveness of the behavior patterns is always an important consideration in these studies.

In this reading, two noted ethologists describe the methods and problems in the study of the evolution of behavior. Examples are presented from the evolution of courtship and threat displays in birds. The reading originally appeared as Chapter 12 in *Behavior and Evolution* edited by Anne Roe and G. G. Simpson and published by Yale University Press in 1958. It is reprinted here by permission of authors and publisher. Other chapters in *Behavior and Evolution* are suggested for further reading.

Introduction. Aims and Methods

AIMS

Species-specific behavior is in part the product of evolutionary processes. Likewise, the behavior of a species must influence the course of its evolution. These two interrelated problems — the influence of evolutionary processes on behavior and of behavior on evolution—comprise a large field about which little is yet known. This chapter is concerned mainly with the first, namely how behavior changes in evolution. It is also confined primarily to behavior which is more or less characteristic of the species, and thus discusses only one aspect of the whole problem.

METHODS

In studying evolution, the ethologist is in a different position from the morphologist. Direct evidence about the ancestral species, which morphologists can obtain from paleontology, is not available; and ontogenetic evidence has so far been little help, though it may be more widely used in future. Comparison between living taxonomic units is thus the only method available, and this is naturally indirect. However, by comparing the behavior traits of species whose phylogenetic relationships are established, it is possible to make hypotheses about the probable origins of that behavior, and thus about the course of its evolution.[*] In doing this, the ethologist must start by relying on the currently accepted classification of the group he is studying. This is usually satisfactory, but sometimes the results of behavior study clash with the classificatory scheme previously in use. In such cases a reappraisal of all characters, morphological and behavioral, may lead to a revision of the classification. Circular arguments are thus avoided by the same method that is used by comparative morphologists, namely the use of independent sources of evidence about the systematic relationships of the species studied.

Use of the comparative method in studying the evolution of behavior then involves several distinct steps. First, formal similarities in the behavior patterns of the species concerned must be recognized. Since the species are believed to be closely related on other grounds, such similarities suggest that the behavior elements have a

[*] The use of the comparative method in the study of behavior owes much to the pioneering studies of Whitman (1919), Heinroth (1911, 1928) and Lorenz (1935, 1939, 1941). Among the groups now being studied are salticid spiders (Crane, 1948–50), grasshoppers (Jacobs, 1950; Faber, 1953), mantids (Crane, 1952), *Drosophila* (Spieth, 1950, 1952), spider wasps and digger wasps (Evans, 1953, 1955), fiddler crabs (Crane, 1941), cichlid fish (Seitz, 1940, 1941, 1949; Baerends and Baerends, 1950), sticklebacks (Tinbergen, e.g. 1951; van Iersel, 1953; Morris, 1958), ducks and geese (Heinroth, 1911, 1928; Lorenz, 1941), fringilline and cardueline finches (Hinde, 1953, 1954, 1955, 1956; Marler, 1956), old world buntings (Andrew, 1956b), estrildine finches (Morris, in press), and gulls (Goethe, 1937; Tinbergen, 1953; Tinbergen and Broekhuysen, 1954; Moynihan, 1955a; Cullen, 1957).

common evolutionary origin. However, similarity between behavior elements does not necessarily mean identity,† for minor differences between species will occur. Examination of these differences, together with evidence about the causation and function of the behavior elements, enables hypotheses to be erected about which behavior form is the more primitive (i.e. phylogenetically older). This in turn permits hypotheses about the probable origins of the behavior elements, and the differences between their present condition and their probable origin can be described. The result is a tentative description of the way the behavior has changed in evolution; this is the most that can be expected from descriptive comparative studies.

A knowledge of the probable course of evolution prompts further enquiry as to why evolution has taken that course and not some other. It is thus desirable to know whether the changes are adaptive and can have been brought about by selection. This involves a study of the survival value of the behavior elements and of the interspecies differences, as well as further investigation into the causal and functional relationships between the behavior elements.

SELECTION OF CHARACTERS FOR STUDY

As in morphology, successful use of the comparative method depends on the selection of the characters to be compared. A major problem is one of level of complexity: how far is the behavior to be analysed before its parts are compared? Both because there is no direct evidence about the

† The precise meaning to be attached to "similarity" will vary with the nature of the behavioral character and the diversity of the taxonomic group. Since the gaps between the units within a taxonomic group are usually smaller than the gaps between groups, "similar" usually means less different within the group than between the group and other groups. A comparable difficulty of course arises in morphological work and is met in the same way.

behavior of extinct forms, and because convergences are widespread, most of the studies made hitherto have dealt with relatively small behavior elements within groups of closely related species. The conclusions drawn from such studies thus refer at most to microevolution. Although quite complex behavior traits, such as the communal nesting habits of the Crotophaginae (Davis, 1942) and the parasitic habit in cuckoos (Friedmann, 1929), have sometimes been used successfully in comparative work, the results of such studies are often difficult to assess until a further analysis of the characters has been undertaken.

Ultimately it will be desirable to make comparative studies not only of overt behavior but also of the causal mechanisms underlying it. However, since the motor patterns are directly observable, it is these which have been studied most often. Heinroth and Whitman were among the first to point out that species-characteristic movements (the "fixed action patterns") can be isolated from the total motor behavior, and the results obtained by many later workers have confirmed the value of these for comparative work.

One further point about the selection of characters for comparative study must be discussed. All characters of the living animal, behavioral and morphological, are products of environmental factors as well as of inherent potentialities. The student of evolution must therefore always ensure that the differences he is investigating are in fact indicative of genetic diversity and not merely of dissimilar environments. Special care is needed in behavior studies because of the plasticity introduced by learning processes.

In the past, as Lehrman (1953), Beach (1955), and others have pointed out, ethologists have often been too ready to assume that learning does not enter into the development of "instinctive" patterns. (But see also Koehler 1954). Recently, for instance, it has been shown that an inexperienced ring dove (*Streptopelia risoria*) will not walk up to its chick in order to feed it: this has to be learned (Lehrman, 1955). Similarly, Craig (1912) showed that drinking is not elicited in young doves by the sight of water; the response to the visual characteristics of water has to be conditioned.

On the other hand, the opposite tendency has also occurred: many authors have overestimated the part played by learning and underestimated the widespread occurrence of "unlearned" behavior. To cite but two examples, Sauer's (1956) very detailed observations on *Sylvia borin* show that the complete repertoire of species-characteristic movements and calls is performed by birds raised without their parents. Second, female canaries which have never manipulated anything but fine grain show all the movements of nest building before they have had material to build with, and treat such material appropriately as soon as it is presented. Of course such observations do not show that learning processes do not enter into the development of the elements of the behavioral patterns in question, but only that the species-characteristic patterns develop and are given appropriately in the absence of example or reward.

However, for the present purpose the relevant problem is not whether a given character is independent of learning or not but whether and to what extent behavioral differences between species are due to hereditary differences, that is whether they are innate.‡ This can be decided by raising two species in the same environment: if

‡ Some semantic clarification is perhaps required here. In the past the term "innate" has been applied in ethology to both characters and the differences between characters. Various critics (Beach, 1955; Lehrman, 1953; Spurway, 1953) have pointed out that the application of the term to characters is misleading, since these are the result of continuous interaction between environment and inherent potentialities throughout development. In this paper, therefore, "innate" is applied only to differences (Tinbergen, 1955).

specific differences persist, then these must ultimately be due to hereditary differences. For instance, the Heinroths (1928) have given numerous examples of interspecific differences in behavior which persist even in individuals reared in the same artificial environment. To cite another example, great tits (*Parus major*) or blue tits (*Parus caeruleus*) taken from the nest eight days after hatching and reared by hand deal with large food items (e.g. mealworms) by placing them under their feet and pecking at them. The use of the feet appears first, in an incomplete form, at about seventeen days, and learning clearly enters into its perfection. Chaffinches bred from eggs which were hatched and reared for eight days by tits, and subsequently fed by hand, only rarely use the foot in feeding.§ Thus this difference in the use of the foot is basically hereditary, even though learning plays an important part in its development.

This exemplifies a principle of great importance: many of the differences between species do not lie in the first instance in stereotyped behavior sequences but consist in the possession of a propensity to learn. Thus the production of the species-characteristic song by chaffinches (*Fringilla coelebs*) depends on learning from other singing males, but a chaffinch will not imitate any sound it hears—only those having certain characteristics in common with normal chaffinch song (Thorpe, 1954, 1956; see also Heinroth, 1928; Sauer, 1954). However, although the ontogeny of behavioral characters is as yet largely unexplored, there is a wealth of material showing that interspecies differences in motor patterns of the kind most commonly used in comparative studies are almost invariably innate. On the other hand, differences in responsiveness to releasing stimuli are sometimes due to conditioning and sometimes innate. A check on the relative roles of inherent and environmental factors

§ Of course the intra-egg environment differed, but even this is presumably ultimately largely under genetic control.

in the production of interspecies differences is thus even more necessary when comparing responsiveness than when comparing motor patterns.

The Evolution of Courtship and Threat Displays in Birds

To exemplify the use of these methods in comparative work we will now consider some of the conclusions reached about the evolution of the threat and courtship displays of birds. Courtship behavior has been much used in comparative studies because of the relatively stereotyped postures involved and the extent of interspecies diversity.

A PRELIMINARY CAUSAL ANALYSIS
OF THE DISPLAYS

It is first necessary to consider some results obtained in the causal analyses of such displays. Recent studies of both fishes and birds have shown that a threatening animal has two incompatible tendencies: to attack its rival and to flee from it. Similarly a courting bird has three incompatible tendencies: to attack, flee from, and behave sexually toward its mate (e.g. Tinbergen, 1952, 1953; Hinde, 1952, 1953). The nature of the behavior shown at any stage in the courtship depends on the strengths and relative strengths of these conflicting tendencies.

Among fishes and birds species differ in the relative importance of these tendencies. In some the male is markedly aggressive to the female throughout the reproductive season (e.g. three-spined stickleback, *Gasterosteus aculeatus*, Tinbergen and van Iersel, in preparation; river bullhead, *Cottus gobio*, Morris, 1954b), while in others he is afraid of her most of the time (e.g. chaffinch, *Fringilla coelebs*, Hinde, 1953; Marler, 1956; zebra finch, *Poephila guttata*, Morris, 1954a). Among many passerines the male is dominant early in the season and the female later, the time at which the change in dominance occurs varying between species: as the relative strengths

of these tendencies change, there are correlated changes in the courtship displays (Tinbergen, 1953; Hinde, 1955). In a few species the male's tendencies to attack and flee are relatively insignificant and the courtship is primarily a result of sexual thwarting (e.g. Mexican swordtail, *Xiphophorus helleri*, Morris, 1955). Among fringilline and cardueline finches most of the components (e.g. wing raising, tail spreading, etc.) of the courtship displays are associated with one or the other of these three tendencies. The relations between display components and tendencies are similar in all the species and interspecific hybrids so far studied, and are probably widespread among passerines. The species differences in display thus lie primarily in the relative intensities of components.

THE EVOLUTIONARY ORIGIN OF
DISPLAY MOVEMENTS

Comparison of the display movements of related species leads to the establishment of homologies. Behavior elements from the different species can thus be grouped together as having a similar evolutionary origin. Examination of the diversity shown by the homologous elements, coupled with the results of causal and functional analyses, provides indications of the evolutionary origins of the movements. This method has so far revealed three primary sources of display movements. From these the displays as seen today have become elaborated, presumably through the action of selection on genetic variability.

1. Intention movements. These are the preparatory and incomplete movements which often appear at the beginning of an activity; for instance, a bird about to fly crouches, raises its wings and tail, withdraws its neck, and then reverses these movements as it springs off. Many avian displays have been elaborated from such movements (Daanje, 1950).

2. Displacement activities. This term is used here in a broadly descriptive sense for activities which appear at first sight irrelevant in the situation in which they occur;

for instance, the bill wiping, preening, and feather movements which often appear during avian courtship (Tinbergen, 1952). Their causation is still poorly understood, but there seems little doubt that many displays have been elaborated from them. In each case the evidence that present-day display postures have evolved from these sources is comparative. Often the display movement can be compared with the unritualized movement as it occurs in the same species. In other cases species can be found in which the evolutionary changes undergone by a particular display movement are relatively slight, and which therefore form a link between the highly elaborated cases and their presumed source.

3. Redirection activities. When the expression of behavior toward the object which elicited it is inhibited, it is sometimes redirected onto another object. Thus the aggressive behavior of the male blackheaded gull, elicited by its mate, is often redirected onto other nearby gulls (Moynihan, 1955a, 1955b).

Sometimes a display posture of one type becomes secondarily modified into another. Thus some threat postures, themselves derived from intention movements, have become secondarily modified for courtship. Here the evidence is partly comparative and partly ontogenetic; in the chaffinch the threat behavior of the male toward the female changes gradually into courtship as his sexual tendency increases (Marler, 1956).

ELABORATION OF DISPLAY MOVEMENTS
IN EVOLUTION

When the evolutionary origins of the display movements have been provisionally identified, the changes which they have undergone in evolution can be described. Although the precise ways in which intention movements and displacement activities have become elaborated into display are still imperfectly understood, some principles are becoming clear (Tinbergen, 1954).

1. Development of conspicuous structures and further correlation of the movement with the structures. Most display movements show off a conspicuous structure. Although it is often found that a similar movement shows off quite different structures in related species, so that the movement appears to be primary and the structure secondary, there has probably always been a parallel elaboration of structure and movement. Thus among tits (*Parus* spp.) there is a correlation between the degree of elaboration of the "head-up" threat posture and the development of a conspicuous throat and breast coloration (Hinde, 1952). Further, the blue tit (*Parus caeruleus*), in which the head-up posture is relatively inconspicuous, makes much use of a head-forward posture in reproductive fighting, and can raise the cheek feathers in a special way to make this conspicuous (Tinbergen, 1937).

2. Schematization of the movement. Usually the actual nature of the movement itself becomes changed in the course of evolution. The changes which occur have been classified by Daanje (1950) as follows:

a. Exaggeration of certain components of the movement. Thus the magpie (*Pica pica*) makes exaggerated tail movements in display. These represent an elaborated form of the up-and-down tail movements before flight and probably serve as a social releaser.

b. Changes in absolute and relative thresholds of components. This may result in marked accentuation of one component of, for instance, an intention movement of take-off and a virtual suppression of others. Similar changes result in the movement becoming increasingly stereotyped, a given intensity of response being elicited by a wider range of strengths of the eliciting factors. As we have seen, in many finches and other passerines the various components of the displays are linked with one or other of the conflicting tendencies. There have so far been no studies in other groups to determine how far relative changes in the components of the displays are related to changes in the associated tendencies.

c. Changes in the coordination of components. Thus a component of the first stage of taking off (e.g. crouching) may be combined with one from the springing-off phase (e.g. tail lowered).

The above three categories are, of course, to be regarded only as a means of classifying the changes that can be observed. The changes in the mechanisms underlying them are still unknown, and it seems unlikely that the categories have any causal validity. All the changes in the movements and the accompanying structures can be understood as adaptations to the signal functions|| of the movement; they make it more conspicuous and, in some cases, more different from other movements. The genetic changes involved are undoubtedly rather complex: the displays of cardueline F_1 interspecies hybrids are intermediate between those of the parents (Hinde, 1956a; see also the detailed work of Clark, Aronson, and Gordon, 1954, on Xiphophorin fishes), and most plumage characters conspicuous in display are polygenic (references in Hinde, 1956b).

3. Emancipation. In addition to the changes in absolute and relative thresholds mentioned above, it has been suggested that there are more marked motivational changes such that the movement comes in evolution to be governed by causal factors different from those which governed it originally. Although such changes may be important in some groups (e. g. Lorenz, 1951), their general importance is not yet established. Thus it has recently been suggested that the feather postures of birds, much used in display and always apparently well correlated with one or other of the tendencies underlying it, may be under the same type of autonomic control as when they are used for cooling or warm-

|| The diverse functions which displays may cover, and the ways in which signal movements have been elaborated to serve these functions, have been reviewed recently by Baerends (1950) and Tinbergen (1954).

ing (Andrew, 1956a; Morris, 1956). Even courtship feeding, which seems to be a clear-cut case of emancipation from parental/juvenile to sexual behavior (for the female may beg while actually holding food in the beak), may in fact be partly a secondary result of other (e.g. dominance) changes such that common factors between the parental and sexual situations are introduced.

THE FUNCTION OF DISPLAY

Now that we have made a provisional sketch of the evolutionary radiation of display movements within a group of closely related species, it remains to assess their functional significance. Here it is necessary to consider the biological significance both of the differences between a given display movement and its origin and of the differences (and similarities) between the displays of the present-day forms. The principal functions of the displays used in fighting and courtship have recently been reviewed by Tinbergen (1954), and will be mentioned only briefly here:

1. Fighting. Displays reduce the amount of actual combat and help to limit fighting to intraspecific encounters.

2. Courtship. (a) Synchronisation of the behavior of the sexes. This may be long term, involving, for instance, hormonal changes (Craig, 1911; Matthews, 1939), or short term, synchronising the mating activities of the pair. (b) Orientation. Some displays have primarily a guiding function (for instance the song of many passerines, the nest site display of the great tit and other hole-nesting species). The highly coloured patches round the genitalia of many baboons and chimpanzees may guide the male to the female's copulatory organs. (c) Suppression of nonsexual responses. "Submissive" postures in passerines help to suppress the aggressive behavior of the mate. (d) Maintenance of reproductive isolation. Thus sympatric closely related species of birds usually differ markedly in display, color, or song (Huxley, 1942; Skutch, 1951).

As Lorenz has pointed out, all these functions require that the display should be effective in eliciting responses in other individuals. This has led to progressive adaptation for signaling. Apart from this, divergence between species is enhanced by the need for maintaining reproductive isolation. This does not mean, however, that selection acting through the disadvantageous consequences of hybrid pairings is the only cause of evolutionary divergence in displays. Since the various characters of an animal are developmentally, causally, and also functionally interrelated, selection for change in any one character will have repercussions on many others. Thus not all differences in displays are necessarily the product of selection for divergence in the displays themselves (see below; Hinde, 1955; Mayr et al., 1956; Cullen, 1957).

The Extent of Interspecies Differences in Behavior

In general, the behavior of closely related species is more similar than that of distantly related ones. To mention but one example of this well-known fact, all gulls feed their chicks by regurgitating food and presenting it in their bills, carduelines by regurgitation into the gape of the young, *Parus* spp. by dropping insects and so forth directly onto the gape of the young without previously swallowing them themselves. On the other hand, there are constant differences even between closely related species: thus the alarm calls of all gulls are a series of staccato cries, but the number, pitch, and frequency of the calls varies between species.

The nature and extent of such interspecies differences very often seem to be adaptive. For instance, the motor patterns used in maintenance activities such as preening, bathing and feeding, and in nest building, are closely similar in all carduelines so far studied. All species use the head-forward threat posture, though there are slight interspecies differences in the

relative intensities of components. In song and courtship, however, the interspecies differences are conspicuous, a fact presumably related to their function in promoting reproductive isolation. In general it is in the earlier phases of courtship that interspecies differences are most marked; the female's soliciting posture and the copulatory behavior of the male vary little among species. This suggests that it is these earlier phases of courtship—i.e. pair formation and the immediately subsequent period—which are most important in effecting reproductive isolation.

Supporting evidence for this conclusion is given by the fact that if pair formation is forced under conditions of captivity breeding success of mixed pairs between closely related species may be comparable with that of pure species. Similar generalizations could be made for other groups of closely related species. Thus where the motor patterns of courtship, song, and so on play a role in maintaining reproductive isolation there has been selection for interspecies divergence (Huxley, 1942). Usually, however, the color patterns shown off by the displays have diverged more than the displays themselves (Morris, 1954a; Hinde, 1956b); and this in its turn implies that the releasers for courtship behavior have diverged more than the motor patterns. In other spheres, also, the stimuli eliciting the behavior show greater interspecies divergence than the motor patterns. Thus the behavior used in hunting for, catching, preparing, and swallowing food is usually similar in closely related species, but there is seldom much overlap in the kind of food eaten (references in Lack, 1954). However, in cases where one species is exploiting a food niche different from those of its relatives there may also be marked divergence in the method of hunting (contrast, for instance, the avocet, *Recurvirostra avosetta*, with other waders). Interspecies differences in the eliciting stimuli are the rule in other aspects of behavior which have important ecological implications. Often, as with habitat selection, this is probably the direct result of selection for interspecies divergence.

Convergence in behavior can be seen in the feeding behavior of unrelated species exploiting similar niches, for example fly-catchers (*Muscicapidae*), drongos (*Dicruridae*), and some American warblers (*Compsothlypidae*); swifts (*Apodidae*) and swallows (*Hirundinidae*). Among display postures, the wide-spread distribution of the head-forward threat among passerines probably indicates that it is primitive and not the result of convergence, but since interspecific disputes over food, roosting sites, and so forth often arise there may have been selection against divergence. Further, since there are selective forces governing the precise way in which intention movements and displacement activities are elaborated into displays, some degree of convergence in the broader features of the displays of unrelated species is to be expected. Among vocal utterances, Marler (1955) has shown that the similarities among the "flying predator" alarm calls of many passerines are probably due to convergence toward a pattern which is difficult for a hawk to locate. Marler also gives an important discussion of many of the selective factors affecting animal calls.

Convergence in color patterns is of course common in predominantly cryptic species. Occasionally unrelated species show some degree of convergence toward conspicuous patterns which are presumably particularly effective in display; e.g. the great tit, Java sparrow (*Padda oryzivora*), and white-cheeked bulbul (*Pycnonotus leucogenys*).

The Use of Characters of Behavior in Systematics

In spite of their ephemeral nature, characters of behavior have been used successfully in studies of the systematics of a number of groups. The problems involved are parallel to those entailed in the use of morphological characters.

It is of course necessary to choose characters in which the interspecies differences are innate. Next, the characters must have an interspecies variability suitable for the particular problem. In general, those which have been either markedly conservative or divergent within a group are of little use for assessing relationships within that group, though characters which are conservative within a group may be useful for assessing the relationship of that group with others. For instance, the various *Parus* species all nest in holes and use moss for nest construction, differing in these characters from the other genera frequently included in the Paridae: these characters could thus be used to characterize the genus but would be useless for elucidating relationships within it (Hinde, 1952). Threat postures, and some courtship displays, on the other hand, are very valuable in studying relationships between closely related species or genera but are too divergent for determining relationships between families. The precise patterns of "tail flicks" made by passerine birds when moving through foliage and so forth have proved to be rather conservative within families, and can therefore provide useful evidence in assigning genera to families and in assessing relationships between families (Andrew, 1956c).

As with morphological characters, it is not desirable to use characters which change rapidly and could have been acquired independently in different groups for establishing phylogenetic relationships: when unrelated species acquire superficially similar characters, they may have different origins. However, if the character is analyzed sufficiently, the danger of false homologizing disappears. It is extremely difficult to find characters where there is no danger of convergence. Although, as Lorenz claimed, the courtship postures of birds depend on an "inherited" convention among the members of the species and are thus especially useful for systematic work, even in these movements convergences are by no means absent. There must be some reason for the elaboration of this intention movement other than its being a social signal, and the most effective type of ritualization will depend upon the context. The dangers of being misled by convergent characters can of course be reduced by making comparisons first between species believed to be closely related on other grounds: similarities then found are reasonably likely to be due to homologies.

It is often difficult to assess the systematic significance to be attached to behavioral characteristics because functional relations between characters are frequently more difficult to trace than those between morphological ones (Hinde, 1955). For instance, in passerine birds, selection for territorial behavior, distinctive song, sexual dimorphism in color and behavior, and suppression of male aggressiveness in courtship may all be linked, so that a trend in the direction of one of them will influence the selective advantages of all the others.

An excellent example of the ramifying effects of selection of one characteristic throughout the whole adaptive complex is given by the work of E. Cullen on the kittiwake (*Rissa tridactyla*); we are grateful to her for allowing us to quote her unpublished work. Kittiwakes are the only gulls that select steep cliffs for breeding. This enables them to nest out of reach of both mammalian and avian predators. The following characteristics of the kittiwake are undoubtedly connected with this: (1) They are extremely tame while on the ledges, as shown by their very short fleeing distance and the high threshold of the alarm call. (2) They do not attack predators as other gulls do. (3) They defecate just over the rim of the nest (other gulls walk or fly several yards from the nest), and as a result the nest, though not itself fouled, is extremely conspicuous, the whole rim being white. (4) Neither the eggs nor the chicks are camouflaged. (5) The egg shells are not carried off after hatching, and their white inner surface contributes still more to making the nest conspicuous. (6) The chicks do not run when alarmed, and

are thus protected from falling over the cliff. (7) Regurgitated food is not dropped on the ground (nest), so that fouling of the nest is avoided. (Unlike other gulls, which leave the nest soon after hatching, young kittiwakes stay on the nest until fledging.) (8) Prior to building the nest itself, kittiwakes construct a mud platform which broadens and flattens the narrow and often slanting substrate. This involves collecting of mud and trampling it down by "foot paddling." (9) In a contest over food the young bend the head away from the attacker, instead of either fighting back or fleeing as other gulls do; this head bending stops the attack. The gesture also exposes the black neckband. Neither the movement nor the band is found in chicks of other gulls.

Many of the difficulties involved in the use of behavioral characters in systematics can be avoided by a broad approach: the importance of a knowledge of the natural history of the animal and of the causation and function of the behavior cannot be overemphasised.

Conclusion

We see, then, that the comparative study of behavior can yield the same type of results as comparative anatomy—a tentative description of the course evolution has taken. Furthermore, in both cases the method depends basically on the establishment of homologies, that is the grouping together of elements having a common evolutionary origin. The fertility of the comparative method is, however, enormously enhanced when it is coupled with studies of function and causation. These enable us to distinguish between homology and convergence, give us insight into the origin and later adaptation of "derived" movements, and permit a more accurate description of the true innate differences between species.

All this work, tentative though it may be, provides the necessary basis for an attack on the ultimate problem of the dynamics of behavior evolution. Comparative study itself cannot contribute directly to the solution of this problem, but as a phase of research it is indispensable; it alone can supply us with a formulation of the problems to be solved.

REFERENCES

ANDREW, R. J., 1956a Some remarks on behaviour in conflict situations, with special reference to *Emberiza* spp. *Brit. J. Anim. Behav.*, **4**, 41–5.

ANDREW, R. J., 1956b The aggressive and courtship behaviour of certain *Emberizinae*. *Behaviour*, **10**, 255–308.

ANDREW, R. J., 1956c Intention movements of flight in certain passerines, and their use in systematics. *Behaviour*, **10**, 179–204.

BAERENDS, G. P., 1950 Specializations in organs and movements with a releasing function. In *Physiological mechanisms in animal behaviour*. Sympos. Soc. Exp. Biol., No. 4. Cambridge, Eng., Cambridge Univ. Press, pp. 337–60.

BAERENDS, G. P., and J. M. BAERENDS, 1950 An introduction to the ethology of cichlid fishes. *Behaviour*, Suppl. 1, pp. 1–242.

BEACH, F. A., 1955 The de-scent of instinct. *Psychol. Rev.*, **62**, 401–10.

CLARK, E., L. R. ARONSON, and M. GORDON, 1954 Mating behaviour patterns in two sympatric species of Xiphophorin fishes: their inheritance and significance in sexual isolation. *Bull. Amer. Mus. Nat. Hist.*, **103** (2), 135–225.

CRAIG, W., 1911 Oviposition induced by the male in pigeons. *J. Morphol.*, **22**, 299–305.

CRAIG, W., 1912 Observations on doves learning to drink. *J. Anim. Behav.*, **2**, 273–9.

CRANE, J., 1941 Crabs of the genus *Uca* from the West Coast of Central America. *Zoologica*, **26**, 145–208.

CRANE, J., 1948–50 Comparative biology of salticid spiders at Rancho Grande, Venezuela. *Ibid.*, Vols. 33–5.

CRANE, J., 1952 A comparative study of innate defensive behaviour in Trinidad mantids. *Ibid.*, **37**, 259–93.

CULLEN, E., 1957 Adaptations in the kittiwake to cliff-nesting. *Ibis*, **99**, 275–302.

DAANJE, A., 1950 On the locomotory movements of birds, and the intention movements derived from them. *Behaviour*, **3**, 48–98.

DAVIS, D. E., 1942 The phylogeny of social nesting habits in the Crotophaginae. *Quart. Rev. Biol.*, **17**, 115–34.

EVANS, H. E., 1953 Comparative ethology and systematics of spider wasps. *Syst. Zool.*, **2**, 155–72.

EVANS, H. E., 1955 An ethological study of the digger wasp, *Bembecinus neglectus*, with a review of the ethology of the genus. *Behaviour*, **7**, 287–304.

FABER, A., 1953 *Laut und Gebärdensprache bei Insekten*. Staatl. Museum für Naturkunde in Stuttgart.

FRIEDMANN, H., 1929 *The cowbirds*. Springfield-Baltimore, Thomas.

GOETHE, F., 1937 Beobachtungen und Untersuchungen zur Biologie der Silbermöwe auf der Vogelinsel Memmertsand. *J. f. Ornithol.*, **85**, 1–119.

HEINROTH, O., 1911 Beiträge zur Biologie, namentlich Ethologie und Physiologie der Anatiden. *Verh. 5 Int. Ornithol. Kongr.* Berlin.

HEINROTH, O., and M. HEINROTH, 1928 *Vögel Mitteleuropas*. Berlin.

HINDE, R. A., 1952 The behaviour of the great tit, and some other related species. *Behaviour*, Suppl. 2, pp. 1–201.

HINDE, R. A., 1953 The conflict between drives in the courtship and copulation of the chaffinch. *Ibid.*, **5**, 1–31.

HINDE, R. A., 1954 The courtship and copulation of the Greenfinch. *Ibid.*, **7**, 207–32.

HINDE, R. A., 1955 A comparative study of the courtship of certain finches. *Ibis*, **97**, 706–45; **98**, 1–23.

HINDE, R. A., 1956a The behaviour of certain cardueline interspecies hybrids. *Behaviour*, **9**, 202–13.

HINDE, R. A., 1956b Breeding success in cardueline interspecies pairs and an examination of the hybrids' plumage. *J. Genetics*, **54**, 304–10.

HUXLEY, J. S., 1942 *Evolution: the modern synthesis*. London, Allen & Unwin.

IERSEL, J. J. A. VAN, 1953 An analysis of the parental behaviour of the male three-spined stickleback. *Behaviour*, Suppl. 3, pp. 1–159.

JACOBS, W., 1950 Vergleichende Verhaltensstudien an Feldheuschrecken. *Z. f. Tierpsychol.* **7**, 169–216.

KOEHLER, O., 1954 Review of Lehrman (1953) in *ibid.*, **11**, 330–34.

LACK, D., 1954   *The natural regulation of animal numbers.* London, Oxford Univ. Press.

LEHRMAN, D. S., 1953   A critique of Konrad Lorenz' theory of instinctive behaviour. *Quart. Rev. Biol.,* **28**, 337–63.

LEHRMAN, D. S., 1955   The physiological basis of parental feeding behaviour in the ring dove *(Streptopelia risoria). Behaviour,* **7**, 241–86.

LORENZ, K., 1935   Der Kumpan in der Umwelt des Vogels. *J. f. Ornithol.,* **83**, 137–213, 289–413.

LORENZ, K., 1939   Vergleichende Verhaltensforschung. *Zool. Anz.,* Suppl. Band. **12**, 69–102.

LORENZ, K., 1941   Vergleichende Bewegungsstudien an Anatinen. *J. f. Ornithol.,* **89**, Sonderheft, 19–29.

LORENZ, K., 1950   The comparative method in studying innate behaviour patterns. In *Physiological mechanisms in animal behaviour.* Sympos. Soc. Exp. Biol., No. 4. Cambridge, Eng., Cambridge Univ. Press, pp. 221–68.

LORENZ, K., 1951   Uber die Entstehung auslösender "Zeremonien." *Die Vogelwarte,* **16**, 9–13.

MARLER, P., 1955   The characteristics of some animal calls. *Nature,* **176**, 6.

MARLER, P., 1956   The behaviour of the chaffinch. *Behaviour,* Suppl. 5.

MATTHEWS, L. H., 1939   Visual stimulation and ovulation in pigeons. *Proc. Roy. Soc. London,* Series B., **126**, 557–60.

MAYR, E., R. J. ANDREW, and R. A. HINDE, 1956   Die systematische Stellung der Gattung *Fringilla. J. f. Ornithol.,* **97**, 258–73.

MORRIS, D., 1952   Homosexuality in the ten-spined stickleback *(Pygosteus pungitius). Behaviour,* **4**, 233–62.

MORRIS, D., 1954a   The reproductive behaviour of the zebra finch *(Poephila guttata),* with special reference to pseudofemale behaviour and displacement activities. *Ibid.,* **6**, 271–322.

MORRIS, D., 1954b   The reproductive behaviour of the river bullhead *(Cottus gobio)* with special reference to fanning activity. *Ibid.,* **7**, 1–32.

MORRIS, D., 1955   Courtship dance of the swordtail. *Aquarist,* **19**, 247–9.

MORRIS, D., 1956   The feather postures of birds and the problem of the origin of social signals. *Behaviour,* **9**, 75–113.

MORRIS, D., 1958   The reproductive behaviour of the ten-spined stickleback *(Pygosteus pungitius* L.). *Ibid.,* Suppl. 6, pp. 1–154.

MOYNIHAN, M., 1955a   Some aspects of reproductive behaviour in the blackheaded gull *(Larus ridibundus)* and related species. *Ibid.,* Suppl. 4, pp. 1–201.

MOYNIHAN, M., 1955b   Remarks on the original sources of displays. *Auk,* **72**, 240–6.

SAUER, F., 1954   Die Entwicklung der Lautäusserung vom Ei ab schalldichtgehaltener Dorngrasmücken. *Z. f. Tierpsychol.,* **11**, 10–23.

SAUER, F., 1956   Ueber das Verhalten junger Gartengrasmücken *Sylvia borin* (Bodd.) *J. f. Ornithol.,* **97**, 156–89.

SEITZ, A., 1940–41   Die Paarbildung bei einigen Cichliden. *Z. f. Tierpsychol.,* **4**, 40–84; **5**, 74–101.

SEITZ, A., 1949   Vergleichende Verhaltensstudien an Buntbarschen. *Ibid.,* **6**, 202–35.

SKUTCH, A. F., 1951   Congeneric species of birds nesting together in Central America. *Condor,* **53**, 3–15.

SPIETH, H. T., 1950   Mating behaviour and sexual isolation in the *Drosophila virilis* species group. *Behaviour,* **3**, 105–45.

SPIETH, H. T., 1952   Mating behaviour within the genus *Drosophila (Diptera). Bull. Amer. Mus. Nat. Hist.,* **99**, 401–79.

SPURWAY, H., 1953   Territory and evolution in sticklebacks. Penguin *New Biology,* **4**, 33–43.

THORPE, W. H., 1954   The process of song-learning in the chaffinch, as studied by means of the sound spectrograph. *Nature,* **173**, 465.

THORPE, W. H., 1956   *Learning and instinct in animals.* London, Methuen.

TINBERGEN, N., 1937   Über das Verhalten kämpfender Kohlmeisen. *Ardea,* **26**, 222–3.

TINBERGEN, N., 1948   Social releasers and the experimental method required for their study. *Wilson Bull.,* **60**, 6–52.

TINBERGEN, N., 1951   *The study of instinct.* London, Oxford Univ. Press.

TINBERGEN, N., 1952   Derived activities; their causation, biological significance, origin and emancipation during evolution. *Quart. Rev. Biol.,* **27**, 1–32.

TINBERGEN, N., 1953   *The herring gull's world.* London, Collins.

TINBERGEN, N., 1954 The origin and evolution of courtship and threat display. In A. C. Hardy, J. S. Huxley, and E. B. Ford, eds., *Evolution as a process*. London, Allen & Unwin.

TINBERGEN, N., 1955 Psychology and ethology as supplementary parts of behaviour. In *Group processes*, Trans. 1st Conf. Sponsored by Josiah Macy, Jr., Foundation.

TINBERGEN, N., and G. J. BROEKHUYSEN, 1954 On the threat and courtship behaviour of Hartlaubs' gull. *Ostrich*, 25, 50–61.

WEIDMANN, U., 1955 Some reproductive activities of the common gull, *Larus canus* L. *Ardea*, 43, 85–132.

WHITMAN, C. O., 1919 *The behaviour of pigeons*. Carnegie Inst. Wash. Publ., No. 257, 1–161.

section two

BEHAVIOR GENETICS

Behavior genetics is a relatively new, but rapidly growing, branch of the science of animal behavior. As the name implies, the concern is with the effects of genotype on behavior. But it should be noted at once that the behavior geneticist is not studying instinct, as classically defined. Instead he is concerned with the role that genetic differences play in the determination of *behavioral differences* within a population. An example may clarify this distinction. Suppose that all females of a given bird species build identical nests, in identical ways, at a precise time of the year. This would suggest a challenging series of studies for those interested in the development of such an extremely stable behavioral sequence. But, since there are no behavioral differences to work with, the techniques of behavior genetics could not be used. On the other hand, if a variety of nests is built, in different ways, and at different times of the year, the raw material for behavior-genetic investigations exists. By appropriate breeding experiments, the behavior geneticist could study the effects of genotype on the behavioral differences in nest building.

The behavior geneticist, then, requires variation in the traits he studies. Traits, whether morphological, physiological, or behavioral, vary within a population in two major ways. First, they may vary *qualitatively*, that is, in a discontinuous fashion. This means that the organisms can be placed in mutually exclusive categories on the basis of the trait. Examples are red and white flowers, straight and curled *Drosophila* wings, normal and frizzled chicken feathers. Such qualitatively varying traits were studied by Mendel as he established the principles of genetics.

Second, traits may be said to vary *quantitatively*, or continuously, over a broad range within a population. Height and weight offer good examples. Such traits usually can be shown to result from the interaction of many genes with each other and with the environment. A branch of genetics, known as "quantitative genetics," studies such traits, primarily through the use of complex statistical procedures. Because most behavioral traits vary quantitatively rather than qualitatively, the techniques of quantitative genetics are used frequently in behavior genetics.

In most experiments it is possible to specify two classes of variables: independent and dependent. An independent variable is systematically changed by the experimenter; it is varied *independently* of the other variables in the experiment. (These "other variables," ideally, are controlled. They are held as constant as possible for all groups throughout the course of the experiment.) A dependent variable is that which is under investigation, that which is being measured. Most hypotheses state that changes in an independent variable will result in changes in a dependent variable. Thus most experiments can be entitled: The Effects of . . . (Independent Variable) on . . . (Dependent Variable). In experiments in behavior genetics, genotype is usually the independent variable, and some measurable aspect of behavior is the dependent variable. Obviously, if genotype is to be used as an independent variable, the experimenter must be able to manipulate and vary it while holding other variables constant.

The two most frequently used methods of manipulating genotype are selective breeding and the use of inbred strains. In a typical selection experiment, males and females with high values of the trait in question are mated. At the same time, other males and females with low scores are mated. Genetic effects on behavior are demonstrated if discrete populations result from several generations of selective breeding.

A different experimental design is used if the population consists of inbred strains. Inbreeding is defined as the mating of close relatives, usually brothers and sisters. The objective of inbreeding is not to arrive at a particular value for a particular trait as in selective breeding, but rather to establish the highest possible degree of *homozygosity* in the population. Chromosomes usually occur in pairs so that each gene has a "partner" at the corresponding locus of the homologous chromosome. "Homozygosity" simply means that the members of each pair of genes are identical; if gene A occurs on one chromosome its partner must also be gene A. Inbreeding produces genetically similar animals, so that all like-sexed members of an inbred strain have the same, or nearly the same, genotype. The members of the strain may then be described as genetically *homogeneous*.

The degree of genetic control offered by inbred strains has proven extremely useful in many different areas of research. Inbred strains of mice have been particularly important in behavior-genetic experiments. For this reason, reports of experiments that used mice as subjects were selected for this section (readings 8–11). These papers illustrate part of the broad range of behaviors that are affected by genotype *within a single species.*

The two review papers (readings 6 and 7) that begin the section provide a degree of balance by describing a variety of experiments on many different species.

Suggestions for Further Reading:

DAVID, P. R., and L. H. SNYDER, "Some Interrelations between Psychology and Genetics," Chapter 1, Volume 4 of S. Koch, ed., *Psychology: A Study of a Science*. New York: McGraw-Hill, 1962.

FALCONER, D. S., *Quantitative Genetics*. New York: Ronald Press, 1960.

FULLER, J. L., and W. R. THOMPSON, *Behavior Genetics*. New York: Wiley, 1960.

GERALD McCLEARN

6   The Inheritance of Behavior*

The following reading is part of a chapter in which McClearn reviewed studies on the inheritance of behavior in men and animals. The section concerned with animals is reprinted here. The emphasis is on studies done prior to 1930, with a briefer treatment of later work. More detailed information on audiogenic seizures and alcohol preference is found in readings 8 and 9, respectively; reading 18 is concerned with biochemistry and behavior.

Reprinted from Chapter 4 of *Psychology in the Making* edited by Leo Postman. New York: Knopf, 1962, with the permission of the author and the publisher.†

Animal Research

SELECTION

Selection for learning performance. The animal researcher is able to make use of techniques not available to those work-

* The author is indebted to Drs. D. S. Falconer, J. Hirsch, R. C. Roberts, and C. Stern for their helpful advice and criticism. They are, of course, blameless for any remaining errors. This chapter was completed while the author was a National Academy of Sciences-National Research Council Senior Postdoctoral Fellow in Physiological Psychology, at the Institute of Animal Genetics, Edinburgh, Scotland.

† The quotations by John B. Watson are from *Behaviorism*. Copyright 1924, 1925, by The People's Institute Publishing Company, Inc.; Copyright 1930, Revised Edition, W. W. Norton & Company, Inc. Copyright 1952, 1953, by John B. Watson. Reprinted by permission of W. W. Norton & Company, Inc., New York, N. Y.

ing with humans. One of the most important of these is artificial selection.

Selection by natural agencies was, of course, the central theme of Darwin's theory, and "artificial" selection by man, as we have seen, has been a practical art for centuries. The Mendelian discoveries and later developments permitted a more rational approach to the practical aspects of plant and animal breeding, and allowed the development of selection procedures as scientific devices for elucidating genetic mechanisms. If the phenotypic differences shown in a population are determined to any appreciable extent by genotypic differences, a selection program in which animals from one extreme are mated together and animals from the other extreme are likewise mated together, may be expected over a number of generations to result in the establishment of two distinct lines, differing substantially in the characteristic.

On the other hand, as Johanssen had shown with his beans, if the differences in the original population are due solely to environmental differences, such a selection procedure would have no effect. Thus the success of a selective breeding program demonstrates that at least some of the phenotypic variance in the original population was due to genotypic differences.

Tolman's initial study. The application of selective breeding to problems of the inheritance of behavior was reported in 1924 by E. C. Tolman. We may reasonably infer the indirect influence of J. McK. Cattell in this work, since Tolman credited Professor Warner Brown, who had been one of Cattell's doctoral students, with providing the original impetus for the study. It is also of interest that Barbara Burks was involved in the statistical evaluation of the results.

Tolman saw the genetic approach, and selective breeding particularly, as a tool for "dissecting" behavioral characteristics:

The problem of this investigation might appear to be a matter of concern primarily for the geneticist. Nonetheless, it is also one of very great interest to the psychologist. For could we, as geneticists, discover the complete genetic mechanism of a character such as maze-learning ability—i.e., how many genes it involves, how these segregate, what their linkages are, etc.—we would necessarily, at the same time, be discovering what psychologically, or behavioristically, maze-learning ability may be said to be made up of, what component abilities it contains, whether these vary independently of one another, what their relations are to other measurable abilities, as, say, sensory discrimination, nervousness, etc. The answers to the genetic problem require the answers to the psychological, while at the same time, the answers to the former point the way to those of the latter [1924, p. 1].

As his own contribution toward this end, Tolman began with a diverse group of eighty-two rats, which were assessed for learning ability in an enclosed maze. Using as a criterion for selection "a rough pooling of the results as to errors, time, and number of perfect runs," nine male and nine female "bright" rats were selected and mated with each other. Similarly, nine male and nine female "dull" rats were selected to begin the "dull" line. The offspring of these groups comprised the first selected generation. These animals were then tested in the maze and selection was made of the brightest of the bright and the dullest of the dull. These selected animals were mated brother by sister to provide the second selected generation of "brights" and "dulls."

The results were quite clear in the first generation, with the bright parents having bright progeny, and the dull parents dull progeny. The difference between "brights" and "dulls" decreased, however, in the next generation, primarily because of a drop in efficiency of performance of the bright strain. These second-generation results were, of course, disappointing, and Tolman examined several possible explanations. In the first place, the particular maze used turned out to be a not particularly reliable measuring instrument. Secondly, it was suggested that the mating of brother with sister might have led to what was known as inbreeding degeneration—a phenomenon quite commonly encountered in genetic work.

To facilitate further investigation, an automatic, self-recording maze was developed by Tolman in collaboration with Jeffress and Tryon (1929). With the new maze, which provided superior control of environmental variables and which proved to be highly reliable, Tryon began the selection procedure again, starting with a large and highly heterogeneous "foundation stock" of rats. The energies of Tolman himself were taken up in the development of his theory of learning, and he did no further actual experimentation on behavioral genetics. Nevertheless, he made a continuing contribution to the field by insisting on the importance of heredity in his well-known HATE (Heredity, Age, Training, Endocrine, drug, vitamin conditions) list of individual-difference variables.

Tryon's and Heron's studies. Tryon's (1940) results are shown in Figure 1. It is clear that two different lines were established, one clearly superior to the other in terms of errors made in learning the maze. In fact, by generation 7 there was practically no overlap between the distributions for the two groups. The dullest bright rats were about equal to the brightest dull rats.

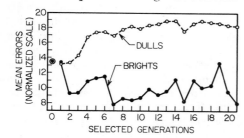

FIG. 1. The results of Tryon's selective breeding for maze-brightness and maze-dullness. (From data provided through the courtesy of R. C. TRYON.)

Heron (1935, 1941), at about the same time, was also selectively breeding for maze performance, beginning with a different foundation population and using a different (but also automatic) maze. This study also yielded two clearly distinct strains. Yet another successful program of selection for maze ability has been reported by Thompson (1954). In this study the rats were presented with the Hebb-Williams set of tasks, which increase systematically in complexity, thus providing a closer analogue to human intelligence tests than did the previous studies using only one maze pattern.

Selection for other behavioral characteristics. Selection has also been applied to phenotypes other than maze performance. Rundquist (1933) selected for active and inactive strains of rats, using the number of revolutions in a rotating cage as the selection criterion. Hall (1938) used selection to derive an "emotional" and a "nonemotional" strain of rats, where emotionality was defined in terms of defecation and urination in a brightly illuminated

open-field test. More recently, Broadhurst (1958a) has reported another successful selection program for these behaviors. Frings and Frings (1953) have successfully developed several strains of mice which differ in susceptibility to sound-induced convulsive seizures and also in the pattern of the seizure, and Nachman (1959) has selectively bred for saccharin preference in rats.

In a different phylum, Hirsch and Boudreau (1958) have developed two strains of Drosophila, characterized by different intensities of light-approaching tendencies.

FURTHER RESEARCH ON BEHAVIORALLY SELECTED STRAINS

By their success, the selection studies have demonstrated that hereditary differences were important contributors to the individual differences in behavioral phenotypes displayed in the foundation stocks with which the studies began. By reasonable inference, these conclusions may be extended to heterogeneous populations in general. In addition, the strains which were developed in the course of the breeding programs have proved to be of the greatest importance to subsequent research. Several examples may be taken from work with Tryon's and Heron's animals.

Tryon's strains. Tryon (1940) bred his "bright" rats with "dull" rats, and the resulting F_1 generation was tested in the maze. These animals were intermediate to the parent strains and, from this and other evidence, Tryon concluded that a multiple factor genetic system determined rat maze-learning ability. Krechevsky (1933) tested Tryon "brights" and "dulls" in a situation which offered both visual and spatial cues, and found that animals of the bright strain tended to respond to spatial cues, whereas the dull rats responded to visual cues. This outcome is in accord with the fact that the selection measure employed by Tryon was spatial maze performance. The question remained as to whether the "brights" were generally superior, or superior only in this specific type of situation. Searle (1949) examined this point directly by subjecting "brights" and "dulls" to a battery of tests which measured learning under hunger motivation, learning under escape-from-water motivation, activity, and emotionality. The "brights" learned better than the "dulls" in the hunger-motivation problems, whereas the "dulls" were superior to the "brights" in the escape-from-water situations. Furthermore, "brights" were more active in the maze but less active in rotating wheels. Other differences were found with respect to emotionality. "Brights" were more "emotional" in open spaces, while "dulls" displayed emotional behavior with respect to certain of the mechanical features of the maze. The selection program had quite obviously resulted in strains which differed from each other in complex ways—not simply in ability to learn a pattern of responses in the maze. In selective breeding, characteristics other than those deliberately sought may fortuitously become associated in the developing lines. It is not possible, therefore, without further research, to determine which of the constellation of behavior differences between strains are fundamental to the principal behavior difference, and which are only incidental.

Genes, enzymes, and learning. Krech, Rosenzweig, Bennett, and collaborators (Krech *et al.*, 1954, 1956; Rosenzweig *et al.*, 1956, 1958a, 1958b) have systematically investigated the relationship among genes, brain biochemistry, and behavior in descendants of the original Tryon strains, which have been maintained without selection from the twenty-first generation to the present. In a number of learning situations the descendants of the "brights" have proved to be less stereotyped and more flexible in behavior than the "dull" descendants. It has also been shown that the "brights" have a higher level of cholinesterase (ChE) activity in the cerebral cortex. This enzyme, ChE, determines the rate of breakdown of acetylcholine (ACh), which is involved in neural transmission. Krech

et al. (1956) proposed that the greater ChE activity in the "brights" reflected greater ACh activity, and that this was related to greater efficiency of neural transmission. However, these authors recognized the possibility of fortuitous association, and undertook to determine if in the present case the relationship between the characters was only a matter of chance.

One approach was to mate animals from the separate strains to obtain an F_1, and then to mate the F_1 animals *inter se* to obtain an F_2. In the F_2 there will be genetic reassortment. If there is no genetic communality underlying the two traits, then the correlation between them should be zero. If the traits have common genetic bases, in whole or in part (or if there is linkage among relevant genes), there should be a correlation in the F_2. With reference to the present problem, there should be a negative correlation between ChE activity and the number of errors made. The actual outcome of this test, however, was a *positive* correlation in F_2— the animals with the greater ChE activity tended to make more errors (Rosenzweig *et al.*, 1958b).

Another approach was to breed selectively for cholinesterase activity, without regard to any behavioral characteristics. Again, the results were contrary to the initial hypothesis. The animals selected for high ChE activity performed more poorly, on the whole, than did those selected for low ChE activity. These results have suggested that

... among strains or individuals the levels of ACh and ChE are determined by independent genetic mechanisms. In this case, raising the level of ChE activity and leaving ACh unaltered may cause too rapid a breakdown of ACh for efficient synaptic transmission. Behavioral selection, as in Tryon's case, may have been made for both ACh and ChE. To be certain about the level of ACh metabolism at the synapse will require measurement of both ACh and ChE in the same subjects [Rosenzweig *et al.*, 1958b].

Recently reported results are congruent with this hypothesis (Rosenzweig *et al.*, 1960).

Heron's strains. Heron's strains were also subjected to further investigation. Harris, for example (1940), showed that the learning curve of the Heron "dulls" dropped from an initially high error score to about the chance level of 50 per cent correct responses. This was shown to be due to a decreasing tendency to make repeated entries into the same incorrect alley. The "dulls" never did learn to select the correct alley of the two alternatives at each choice point, but simply learned not to repeat errors. The "brights," on the other hand, showed a systematic increase in percentage of correct choices of the proper alleys. The Heron "brights" were also found to show a higher rate of bar-pressing in a Skinner box (Heron and Skinner, 1940), and a faster speed of running the maze than the "dulls" (Harris, 1940).

COMPARISONS OF STRAINS
NOT BEHAVIORALLY SELECTED

In addition to the study of strains deliberately selected for behavioral differences, a very substantial number of researches have taken advantage of the existence of other strains, derived in the most part without regard to their behavioral characteristics. These studies have differed from each other in several ways. Some have consisted solely of comparisons between two, or among several, strains. For such studies, the logic has been as follows. If two strains of animals of different origins have been maintained separately, with no matings between the strains having occurred, one may safely presume that the strains differ genetically. (Indeed, under such circumstances, it would not be possible for the strains to retain genetic identity). Therefore, if the compared strains differ in behavior, and the environmental circumstances are similar, one may presume that the genetic differences account for the behavioral differences. Nothing whatever is revealed concerning the nature of the genetic differences. In other cases, the strains have been mated to provide F_1 and further generations, sometimes with the purpose of determining the presence of segregating Mendelian genes, but more often to examine the means and variances of the derived generations with respect to the parent strains. From the study of derived generations, it is frequently possible to determine something about the nature of the genetic mechanism.

In the earlier work, particularly, it was possible to make only rather vague distinctions between the strains. Thus "tame" laboratory rats were compared to "wild" rats, and many of the mouse strains compared were simply stocks from different pet shops, different laboratories, or even different trapping sites. Gradually, however, the maintenance and breeding of laboratory animals became more systematic. In the case of mice, for example, a vigorous program of selection, largely for tumor characteristics, provided a number of discrete identifiable strains. In many cases, furthermore, the selected strains were subjected to intense inbreeding, which has the effect of greatly reducing genetic variability within the strains. The obtained (relative) genetic uniformity enormously facilitates genetic interpretation of results. The gradual adoption of these inbred strains has been one of the principal advances of methodology in strain-comparison studies.

Earlier rodent research: rodent "temperament." One of the earliest studies on strain differences was that of Yerkes (1913), who compared tame and wild rats for savageness, wildness, and timidity. These characteristics were inferred from the observable behaviors of biting, gnashing of teeth, squeaking, jumping, hiding, excited running, urination, defecation, cowering, and trembling, exhibited when the animals were taken from the cage. Rating scales from 0 to 5 were established to describe the degree of the trait exhibited by each rat, and Yerkes claimed high reliability for the observations. The observations were made on wild and tame rats, on the F_1 obtained from mating tame female with wild male rats, and F_2 descendants. The wild rats received ratings of 3, 4, or 5, indicating high expressions of all three characteristics. The tame rats received ratings of 0 or 1. Most of the F_1 animals obtained high ratings, but there was a moderate spread, with some F_1 animals being found in almost every category. In the F_2, the average rating was lower and the variability was greater than in the F_1. In this study, Mendelian-like categories, such as timid vs. non-timid, or savage vs. non-savage, were not used. The use of rating scales acknowledged the quantitative variation of the traits being investigated, but with the work of Fisher and Wright still some years in the future, Yerkes had to content himself with the assertion, "The results . . . prove conclusively that savageness, wildness, and timidity are heritable behavior-complexes. It is hoped that the further study of these characteristics in the third generation hybrids, and in special matings from the first and second generation hybrids, may yield more definite results concerning the modes of transmission" (1913, p. 296).

A closely related study on mice, undertaken by Coburn (1922) at the suggestion of Yerkes, was completed in 1914, although it was not published for a number of years. Utilizing behavioral indices very much like those used by Yerkes with rats, Coburn examined wildness and savageness of wild mice, tame mice, and the subsequent F_1 and F_2 generations. For both wildness and savageness, the F_2 generation had a greater variability than the F_1. The tame mice all scored 0 on a Yerkes-type scale, and the wild mice all scored 4 or 5. The restriction of each character to 5 grades, which imposes a perhaps artificial upper and lower limit, makes comparison of the parental and F_1 variabilities difficult, but the greater variability of the F_2 generation was taken by Coburn to support a multiple-factor interpretation of the inheritance of both wildness and savageness.

Yerkes, in obtaining his F_1, had mated tame females with wild males, and the possibility existed that the outcome would have been different had wild females been mated with tame males. In the first place, the behavior of the tame mother might have provided quite different environmental stimulation to the young during their development than would a wild mother. In the second place, the relevant genes might be located on the X chromosomes, in which case the male offspring would receive all the determining genes from their mother. Obviously, in this case, the "reciprocal crosses" would be expected to differ. Coburn tested these possibilities in his mice by obtaining F_1's from both crosses: wild males with tame females and tame males with wild females. No differences were found in the behavior of the offspring of these reciprocal crosses. The factors determining wildness, savageness, and tameness thus are evidently not located on the sex chromosomes, and the behavior of the mothers of different strains (or the quality of their milk, etc.) does not provide environmental stimulation which differentially affects the phenotype.

The Wistar rats. Over a period of years, the Wistar Institute had developed an inbred strain of rats with brains of somewhat less than normal weight, and J. H. Donaldson of the Institute had suggested to J. B. Watson, of Johns Hopkins University, that the strain might be deficient in ability to acquire habits. Watson encouraged Basset to investigate the matter. Two learning problems were used. The first was the Watson circular maze, and the second was a problem box in which a treadle had to be pressed to give access to food. These problems were presented to animals of the low brain weight group, and also to a control group of "normal" brain weight, and it was concluded that the rats with less than normal brain weight were slightly inferior to the normal controls (Basset, 1914).

While Basset's work was in progress, the Wistar Institute also suggested a cooperative research program to R. M. Yerkes of Harvard. Yerkes undertook some preliminary studies, and then turned the problem over to a colleague, Mrs. Yerkes. In a footnote to the paper, R. M. Yerkes describes his interest in the research (and incidentally anticipated the later findings of Searle in regard to the Tryon strains).

In suggesting to Mrs. Yerkes a comparative study of stock and inbred rats, I expressed especial interest in the attempt to analyze "the temperament" of the animals, for certain previous observations in comparison with those reported by Basset had convinced me that crude measurements of modifiability, if directly compared, might lead to seriously misleading conclusions because of differences in timidity, savageness, aggressiveness, sensibility, etc., in the two groups of organisms under observation [A. W. Yerkes, 1916, p. 267].

The Watson circular maze was again employed, along with the Yerkes brightness discrimination box. On the basis of the small number of animals available, it was concluded that the Wistar animals were somewhat inferior to normal control animals. The former were generally slower than the latter, and this was believed to be due to timidity.

Utsurikawa (1917) at Harvard, presumably under the influence of Yerkes, compared the Wistar rats with a control group, some of which were obtained from a Miss Lathrop, and some of which were from a second Wistar stock. A number of differences were described, with the Wistar animals being less active than the control animals, more prone to bite, more responsive to auditory stimulation, and more "timid," in that they retreated to the back of the cage as the experimenter approached. These results, in general, confirmed the work of A. W. Yerkes, who had used a control group of similar constitution with which to compare her Wistar rats.

In 1929 Crozier and Pincus presented the first of a series of studies on the inheritance of geotropic orientation in rats. It was found that three strains of rats differed in the angle of orientation adopted in climbing an inclined plane. It was shown, furthermore, that the relationship of orientation angle to steepness of the incline differed among the strains. In various F_1 and backcross-generation tests, it was concluded that variability of response, as well as magnitude of response, was inherited (Crozier and Pincus, 1932).

Learning by mice. Meanwhile, Bagg had made a study of strain differences in learning by mice. The influence of Cattell is acknowledged by Bagg: "In the work here described an attempt has been made to apply the methods of genetics to the study of conduct. Such work was begun by Professor J. McKeen Cattell some fifteen years ago, but the results obtained by him and his students were not published and the problem was given to me" (1916, p. 222). The initial report of this study was made in 1916, and a later report, on an increased number of subjects, was presented in 1920. Albino and colored mice (mainly yellow) were presented with two learning situations, a two-choice position discrimination problem and a multiple-choice problem. A considerable strain difference was found, with the yellow mice being poorer learners. In analyzing the records of mice within the same families, Bagg was unable to find any particular resemblance. However, it was noted that the quick learners exhibited a high degree of flexibility of behavior, as reflected in their quick mastery of the discrimination problem when the situation was reversed, and the formerly incorrect response was made correct. This relatively greater flexibility was later found in "bright" rats, as noted above.

It should also be noted that Bagg, in a limited way, had applied some artificial selective breeding in his research. Two exceptionally poor learners of the yellow strain were mated, and their offspring proved to be greatly inferior to the white mice.

Another study on mouse learning was soon presented by Vicari (1921). The maze was an adaptation of the Cattell-designed maze used by Bagg, and two different strains of mice were employed—the Japanese Waltzer and the Bagg albino.

Both of these strains had been inbred for nine or more years, and consequently could be expected to be relatively uniform genetically.

Several measures of performance were used—the number of errorless trials, the number of consecutive errorless trials, and the running time. With respect to the first two measures the strains were quite similar, but the Japanese waltzers showed much longer running times than the Bagg albinos.

Turning to the F_1 hybrids, a surprising result is found: 10 percent of the mice in this generation made more perfect trials than any parent in either parent race; some individuals excel all those in the parent races in the number of consecutive perfect trials; and the time averages, instead of being intermediate between those of the parent races, are considerably lower, lower even than the averages for the albinos [Vicari, 1921, p. 132].

Thus, hybrid vigor was identified in a behavioral characteristic.

A subsequent report (Vicari, 1929) gave the results for four highly inbred mouse strains, their F_1's and F_2's. In addition to the Japanese waltzing mice and the Bagg albino strain, this study included a dark brown strain and a brown strain with abnormal eyes (the eye abnormality being due to a mutation experimentally induced by X-rays and involving defects ranging from reduction in size to absence of one or both eyes).

In examining the learning curves for reaction time, Vicari found it possible to identify three types of curves: Type I, a flat curve, e.g., the dark brown animals' curve in Figure 2; Type II, a gradually descending curve, e.g., the Bagg albino curve in Figure 2; and Type III, a descending-ascending curve which was displayed only by the Japanese waltzers. When waltzers were mated with Bagg albinos, the Type II curve characteristic of the albinos was found for the F_1 and F_2. The F_1 animals were faster than either parent, and the F_2 animals were intermediate to the

parents. When albinos were mated with dark brown, the dark browns' Type I curve appeared in F_1. This outcome is shown in Figure 2. The average F_2 curve also resembled a Type I, but was irregular. Closer inspection led to the conclusion that thirty-five F_2 animals showed Type I and eleven showed Type II—very nearly a 3 : 1 Mendelian ratio!

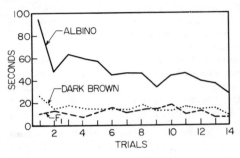

FIG. 2. Different types of learning curve for running time for two mouse strains and their F_1. (After VICARI, 1929.)

Finally, crossing abnormal-eyed mice, characterized by a Type I curve but with generally high reaction time, with a dark brown, also with a Type I curve but much lower reaction time, gave an F_1 which was faster than either parent during the last half of the testing period—once again Vicari had found hybrid vigor. The F_2 resembled the dark brown parental strain.

In all three crosses the F_1 curve fell closest to the curve of the fastest parent, suggesting dominance of fast reaction time over slow reaction time. The hybrid vigor in the waltzer albino F_1, followed by intermediacy of the F_2, and the greater variance of F_2 relative to F_1, suggested that these two strains differed in respect to multiple factors. For the albino $\times$ dark brown cross, where a 35 : 11 F_2 ratio was found, Vicari proposed that the parent strains differed with respect to only one gene.

Generally speaking, the examination of individual family pedigrees gave results in accord with these interpretations.

The Dawson study. In 1932 Dawson reported another mouse study, dealing with what was termed wildness and tameness. Two parental strains were obtained: one, the wild strain, consisted of laboratory-reared descendants of wild trapped mice which were easily excited, resisted handling, and were prone to bite. The other, tame stock consisted of relatively placid, easily handled mice obtained from various sources. From these strains, reciprocal F_1, F_2, and backcross generations were obtained.

The behavior measured was the time required for a mouse to traverse an enclosed runway approximately twenty-five feet long. Wild animals ran the runway much more quickly than did the tame animals. No difference was found between reciprocal F_1's, and the F_1 mean speed was nearly equal to that of the wild parents. The F_2 mean speed was slightly less than that of the F_1, but closer to the wild mean than to the tame mean, and F_2 variability was greater than F_1 variability. The backcross of F_1 to wild produced animals which ran as rapidly as the wild parents, and the backcross to tame gave animals which ran almost as slowly as the tame parents.

Dawson concluded from these results that the genes for "wildness" (as defined) were almost completely dominant, and that no maternal effect existed. Examination of the results for the sexes separately gave no evidence of sex linkage. Two to three gene pairs were estimated to account for the difference between tame and wild.

Dawson also applied selective breeding within strains for four generations. The fastest of the wild were mated, and the slowest of the tame were mated. This selection had no effect on the wild line, but produced progressively slower animals in the tame line. This result amply demonstrates that considerable genetic variability existed in the original tame stock, a fact which renders interpretation of the results somewhat ambiguous.

Recent mouse research. Thus far, we have seen the procedure of strain comparison utilized in studies on learning and various attributes of "wildness" of rats and

mice. In subsequent years there was a marked increase in the types of behavior pattern investigated and also some improvement in the breadth of coverage of other species. The large number of researches which have been performed makes it impossible to do more than briefly list some representative examples.

Aggressiveness. Scott (1942) found a strain of mice designated C3H to be more likely to initiate aggression than were C57BL mice. Ginsburg and Allee (1942), however, showed that males of the C57BL strain were superior to C3H in ability to win fights. The role of environment was also considered in this study, and it was found possible to make a given mouse either more or less aggressive by subjecting it to a systematic series of victories or defeats. Fredericson (1952) then showed that foster rearing of C57BL and BALB/c animals did not affect their aggressive behavior. Ecological implications of strain differences in aggressiveness were pointed out by Calhoun (1956), who placed small samples of mice in rooms containing food and a water supply and numerous nesting boxes. C57BL mice were placed in one room and DBA/2 mice in another. The DBA/2 mice were much less successful than the C57BL in reproducing themselves under these conditions. At least part of the difference was attributed to the fact that DBA/2 animals fought more often and more intensely than the C57BL animals. Occasionally, an aggressive DBA/2 was even found to attack a female, something which was never observed in the C57BL colony. Generally, the C57BL's appeared more adaptable to the environment, making quicker use of new food and nesting material, and, in respect to fighting behavior, the C57BL pattern tended to become one of threats and retreats, or relatively mild pushing about. Among the DBA/2's, on the other hand, the dominant male vigorously attacked subordinate males at every opportunity.

The mouse has also been featured in studies on exploratory or locomotor activity. Fredericson (1953) showed that, in an enclosed area, C57BL mice were more prone than C3H or C Bagg albino mice to leave the area adjacent to the wall and to go to the center of the field. Thompson (1953) tested a number of inbred strains on several behavior traits, including the amount of locomotor activity displayed in an apparatus which contained numerous barriers. C57BL and C57BR sublines were very active, while BALB/c mice and mice of an A strain were very inactive. Other strains were more or less intermediate. The same general ranking of strain activity was later found (Thompson, 1956) in a Y maze, and in several other types of apparatus (McClearn, 1959), showing that the behavioral differences were not an idiosyncratic result due to the peculiarities of any one apparatus situation.

Learning. Relatively few of the more recent studies have been concerned with learning in mice. King and Mavromatis (1956) found C57BL mice to condition more rapidly than BALB/c mice in a shock-avoidance situation, but the BALB/c mice relearned more rapidly. Other studies (McClearn, unpublished data) have shown C57BL to be about equal to BALB/c mice in maze and discrimination learning, and both of these strains are superior to C3H animals. Denenberg (1959) has reported a difference between the conditioning rates of two C57 sublines which had been separated for approximately thirty generations. The genetic changes which have occurred during this interval are probably quite small relative to the total genotype, and the results appear to indicate, therefore, that changes in a relatively small number of genetic factors may appreciably influence learning ability.

Alcohol preference. Strain differences have also been shown in alcohol preference when animals were given a choice between plain water and a 10 per cent alcohol solution (McClearn and Rodgers, 1959). C57BL mice gradually come to drink most of their daily consumption from the alcohol bottle, while animals from the A, DBA, and BALB/c strains almost completely abstain. F_1's between C57BL and the non-preferring strains show a mean preference higher than that of the non-preferring parent strain, but considerably lower than that of the C57BL strain (McClearn and Rodgers, 1961).

Audiogenic seizures. Another area in which mouse studies have made important contributions is that of the genetics of audiogenic seizures. Hall (1947) reported that DBA mice were much more prone to convulsive seizures than were C57BL mice, when presented with a loud auditory stimulus. In analyzing the responses of F_1, F_2, and backcross animals, derived from these parent strains, Witt and Hall (1949) concluded that susceptibility to seizure was determined by a single autosomal dominant gene. Ginsburg, Miller, and Zamis (1950) mated a different C57BL subline to DBA and found that the seizure incidence of the F_1 was intermediate. In the F_2, seizure incidence was about three-fourths of that in F_1. These authors took these data to indicate the presence of two or more non-dominant alleles. It was further found that different sublines of DBA had different degrees of susceptibility, and that the F_1's and F_2's derived from crossing these sublines with C57BL mice also differed. Ginsburg (1954) has emphasized, on the basis of differential response to various metabolites, that different genotypes underlie the seizure proneness of several susceptible strains which he has investigated. Fuller, Easler, and Smith (1950) also rejected the single-gene explanation in favor of a multiple-factor hypothesis.

Recent rat research: hoarding, activity, and emotionality. In an investigation of rats, Stamm (1954) demonstrated large differences among three strains in food-hoarding behavior. The F_1 between a high-hoarding and low-hoarding strain hoarded as much as the high-hoarding parent strain, and a backcross of F_1 to the low-hoarding strain was intermediate between these two groups (Stamm, 1956). Broadhurst (1958b) studied five rat strains, including the three used by Stamm, in respect to locomotor activity and emotionality, as defined by defecation. Clear strain differences were found in both types of behavior, which were not, however, significantly correlated with each other. In comparing the strain characteristics with Stamm's results, a correlation between hoarding tendency and defecation was found.

Carr and Williams (1957) have also reported differences in locomotor (exploratory) behavior in an investigation of three rat strains.

Domestication, hormones, and behavior. A number of studies have compared the inbred Wistar albino rats with wild rats, in attempts to identify endocrine changes associated with the process of domestication. Hatai (1914) showed that wild Norway rats had heavier adrenals and gonads, but smaller hypophyses than the Wistar. No strain differences, however, were found in thyroid weight. King and Donaldson (1929) compared a group of gray rats, which had been in captivity for ten generations, with both wild animals and with the Wistar strain. Behaviorally, the gray line had become somewhat less savage, but were still less tame than the Wistars. Relative to the wild rats, the hypophyses, adrenals, and gonads of the gray rats were heavier, lighter, and equal, respectively. Relative to the Wistar strain animals, these glands were lighter, heavier, and heavier, respectively. In general, the results suggested a change in endocrine pattern of the gray rats toward that of the Wistars. Farris and Yeakel (1945) utilized the criteria of tendency to defecate and/or urinate in an illuminated field in an effort to objectify the behavioral differences between wild and Wistar rats, and found the latter group to display much less emotional elimination.

Richter (1952) compared a line descendant from the original Wistar strain with rats trapped in the wild, and reported smaller adrenals, larger hypophyses, and more quickly developing gonads in the domesticated animals. Richter regards the changes as due to natural and artificial selection in the laboratory setting, where there is protection against predators, and an advantage given to the more fertile, milder, and "better-adjusted" rats. The argument is extrapolated to man, and evidence of similar changes during human "domestication" is presented (Richter, 1952, p. 283).

The general impression from the above studies is that laboratory selection, acting upon polygenic systems, has gradually altered the endocrinic basis of behavior described as indicating tameness. Keeler and King (1942), however, have summarized "character sketches" of various mutant stocks, and concluded that tameness may be accomplished by a mutant coat-color gene. Reservations concerning this interpretation have been expressed by Scott and Fredericson (1951).

Audiogenic seizures. Rats have also been employed in the study of susceptibility to audiogenic seizure. Strain differences have been found (Farris and Yeakel, 1943; Maier, 1943), and various experiments were oriented toward the problem of determining the number of genes involved. As was true in the case of the mouse research on this topic, the interpretation changed from a simple dominant hypothesis (Maier and Glaser, 1940) to a multiple-factor hypothesis (Maier, 1943; Finger, 1943). Hall (1951), in reviewing these researches, has taken the view that ambiguity in this case was due to the lack of genetic homogeneity within the strains employed.

Myers' study. We may close the consideration of studies comparing strains of rats with the remarkable investigation of Myers (1959). In this experiment, which dealt with shock-avoidance learning, there were five variables: type of stimulus (CS) (buzzer vs. tone); type of response (pressing a bar vs. rotating a wheel); time of testing (day vs. night); shock condition (floor and three walls shocked vs. floor and all four walls including manipulandum [bar or wheel] shocked); strain of animal

(Sprague-Dawley vs. Wistar). When the data were analyzed in terms of the relative increase in responses, above operant level, during the period between CS and shock, a bewildering array of interactions emerged. When the manipulandum was not shocked, Sprague-Dawley rats were superior to Wistar rats when a tone CS was employed, but were inferior when a buzzer was used. Furthermore, under this condition, both strains performed better during the day testing when tone CS was used, but more poorly when buzzer CS was used. However, when the manipulandum was shocked, differences between day and night testing were greatly reduced. The Wistars' performance to tone CS was better than the Sprague-Dawleys', but for buzzer CS conditions, strain differences were very small. Myers presented an ingenious explanation, based on an assumed strain difference in emotional startle responses to the manipulandum, with the level of such responses increasing at night in both strains. Whether or not this explanation proves ultimately to be correct, the empirical data have provided an admirable demonstration of the subtle ways in which genotypic differences may interact with environmental variables.

Research on other species. Sex drive was found to differ among males of different guinea-pig strains (Valenstein *et al.*, 1954), and it was demonstrated that the administration of sex hormones to previously castrated animals did not eliminate the strain differences (Riss *et al.*, 1955). Furthermore, the effectiveness of various conditions of social experience upon subsequent sexual behavior was found to vary from strain to strain (Valenstein *et al.*, 1955).

In rabbits, strain differences have been reported in nest-building behavior (Sawin and Crary, 1953), and in aggression (Denenberg *et al.*, 1958).

In mice of the genus *Peromyscus*, the study of various species and subspecies has revealed differences in climbing and jumping ability (Horner, 1954), in maternal behavior (King, 1958), in activity on an elevated maze (King and Shea, 1959), and in habitat selection (Harritt, 1952). In some instances the various subspecies or races are interfertile, and F_1 animals can be obtained for study. For example, Harritt (1952) mated *Peromyscus maniculatus bairdi*, which selected an artificial grass environment rather than an artificial tree-trunk environment, with *Peromyscus maniculatus gracilis*, which preferred the tree-trunk habitat. The F_1 results suggested dominance of the genetic factors determining grass preference, for the F_1 showed a strong preference for this type of habitat.

The well-established dog breeds have also provided valuable research material. James (1941) studied the behavior of dogs of a number of breeds in classical Pavlovian conditioning situations. Many animals were found to fall in one of two extreme behavior types: excitable or lethargic. Many others were intermediate. Some breeds were almost exclusively of one behavior type. For example, Basset hounds were all lethargic and German shepherds were all excitable. Five Basset hound-shepherd F_1's were also studied, and were found to be intermediate. In seven F_2 animals the entire range from one extreme type to the other was displayed.

In other dog studies, breed differences have been shown in the development of dominance hierarchies (Pawlowski and Scott, 1956), response to different modes of rearing (Freedman, 1958), spontaneous activity (Anderson, 1939), "emotional behavior" (Mahut, 1958), trainability (Fuller, 1955), specific behavior characteristics such as trailbarking propensity (Whitney, 1932), and aggression (Fuller, 1953).

Whereas research on mammals has been predominant, some investigations have been made of other taxonomic groups. Hinde (1956), for example, investigated various threat, submission, and courtship behavior patterns in canaries, goldfinches, and green finches, and in F_1's derived from these species. In those instances where both parents possessed the behavior pattern, it was found to be unchanged in the F_1. When only one parent showed the behavior, or when it was shown in different degrees in the two parents, expression was intermediate in the F_1.

Differences in behavior among several Drosophila species have been intensively investigated from the point of view of the reproductive isolation of one species from another (see Spieth, 1958; Santibañez and Waddington, 1958; Manning, 1958). Another example of insect research is provided by Rothenbuhler (1958), who found one inbred line of honey bees which quickly removed diseased brood from the comb, and another line which did not. The F_1 resembled the last-named line, indicating that the "hygienic" behavior pattern is recessive.

The above must be regarded as only a sample of the literature available, but will perhaps serve to illustrate that clear evidence of genetic influence has been obtained in a wide variety of behavior patterns and at various phylogenetic levels.

The search for single gene effects. In view of the history of genetics it is understandable that in many of the pioneer behavioral studies rather persistent attempts were made to interpret the results in accord with simple Mendelian hypotheses. It is, of course, legitimate, and, indeed, obligatory, to examine any results to determine if they are susceptible to a single-locus interpretation. In the earlier discussion of genetic principles, however, it was pointed out that the dependence of most behavior patterns upon many integrated organ systems makes a polygenic hypothesis *a priori* more likely. In fact, we have seen that many of the simple interpretations had to give way later to polygenic ones. On the other hand, the success of the human researches in establishing the simple genetic basis of some mental-deficiency syndromes provides a reminder that single genes, strategically located in the causal paths leading to a phenotype, may produce large effects. Similar reminders are available in the mouse literature, particularly in the studies on neurological and labyrinthine disorders.

Waltzing and other "neurological mutants." As a matter of fact, some of the very earliest behavioral genetics studies dealt with one of these conditions, which is known as "waltzing." Waltzing is a periodic, extremely rapid whirling movement, and was characteristic of a strain of mice called "Japanese waltzing" or "Japanese dancing" mice. The syndrome also includes head-shaking and deafness.

Von Guaita reported (1898, 1900) that mating waltzers with normal albino mice yielded offspring which did not show the waltzing characteristic. Darbishire (1904) also mated waltzers with normal albinos in a study aimed at determining if coat color and waltzing were inherited in a Mendelian manner. Two hundred and three F_1 offspring were obtained, none of which waltzed. When the F_1 animals were mated to other F_1 animals, the resulting F_2 consisted of 458 non-waltzers and 97 waltzers. Darbishire concluded that, while waltzing was recessive in good Mendelian fashion in the F_1, the F_2 results were too discrepant from the expected 3 : 1 ratio to support the notion of Mendelian segregation. In general, from the waltzing and coat-color data, Darbishire upheld the biometrical insistence on a form of blending inheritance, and denied the "purity of gametes."

In 1907 R. M. Yerkes published a book devoted to a description of the behavior and capabilities of the Japanese waltzing mouse. With respect to waltzing behavior, Yerkes noted that one line of waltzers tended to whirl to the left while another line consisted of left-whirlers, right-whirlers, and mixed-direction whirlers. He suggested that the "pure" waltzer inherited a tendency to whirl to the left, and that this tendency was obscured in the one line because its ancestry included some nonwaltzing mice. No attempt was made to relate this suggestion to Mendelian genetics, although Darbishire's results and Bateson's Mendelian interpretation of them had been considered earlier in the book.

Later research (summarized in Grüneberg, 1952) has made it clear that waltzing is a Mendelian recessive condition, and that the discrepancies in F_2 ratio, such as were noted by Darbishire, are due to reduced viability of the homozygous animals, which results in the death of some of this group before they can be classified.

A number of other mutants have been found which give rise to waltzer-like symptoms (e.g., jerker, fidget, shaker), thus illustrating that similar phenotypes can result from the action of different genes.

Other "neurological" conditions, involving, variously, muscular tremor, incoordination, abnormal posture, head-shaking, and deafness or auditory hypersensitivity have also been described as single-gene effects.

Drosophila mating. Insect research has provided more examples of single-gene effects. Several studies (e.g., Reed and Reed, 1950; Merrell, 1953) have shown that some conditions determined by a single gene lower mating activity in Drosophila. Bastock's (1956) research provides an illustration of this type of experiment. It had long been known that mutant yellow males were less successful in mating than were normal males. Bastock's aim was to determine if this fact was due to a behavioral difference which resulted from the presence of the yellow gene, which is a sex-linked recessive. Thus it was important to obtain normal and yellow males which were highly similar in other genetic respects. To accomplish this, heterozygous females were mated to yellow brothers. The male offspring of this cross were yellow and normal in equal numbers, and other genetic differences could be expected to be randomly distributed between the two color groups.

The normal courtship pattern of the male Drosophila includes a bout of wing vibration, which evidently provides important stimuli which are detected by the female antennae. It was found that the duration of the wing vibration bouts by yellow males is shorter than normal, and this behavioral difference reduces the effectiveness of the courtship of the yellows.

THE LAMARCKIAN ISSUE

In general, the researches on behavioral genetics have not been particularly involved in the development of concepts within the field of genetics itself. The overall picture is rather one of the application of already demonstrated principles and techniques to the particular subject matter of behavior. With respect to the question of the inheritance of acquired characteristics, however, the behavioral studies formed an important part of the evidence, and were centrally involved in the controversy which took place. We have seen that the Mendelian theory posited a "purity of the gametes" which was incompatible with the idea that acquired traits could be transmitted. Nonetheless, "Lamarckism" persisted obstinately and was repeatedly put forward in spite of much contradictory evidence. The first negative study in behavior was provided by Yerkes (1907) in his work, *The Dancing Mouse.* One male and one female from each of two lines was taught a black-white discrimination, and they were then mated. From their litters, one male and one female were chosen for training, and were then mated, and so on for a total of four generations. There was no indication that the offspring benefited in learning ability by having parents, grandparents, and even great-grandparents who had learned the problem. "There is absolutely no evidence of the inheritance of this particular individually acquired form of behavior in the dancer" (p. 283).

Griffith (1922) reported an experiment in which white rats were rotated day and night in revolving cages for several months. When the animals were released from the cages, they showed marked changes in posture and a characteristic circling movement. When these affected animals were mated with normal rats, some offspring were found who displayed disequilibration. Detlefson (1923, 1925) soon reported similar results. A number of defects of these studies were pointed out by later workers, the most compelling of which was the possibility that the animals had contracted a middle ear disease, affecting the labyrinthine mechanism. The accumulation of animal waste during the uninterrupted rotation of the cages would be favorable to the spread of a disease organism. In the matings the infection could be transmitted by parents to offspring, and a superficial appearance of "inheritance" would be given.

In the face of these and other objections (see Munn, 1950, p. 40), the Griffith and Detlefson studies came to be regarded generally as inconclusive.

Pavlov's announcement. A new round in the controversy was dramatically begun by Pavlov, who stated in 1923 during a lecture tour in the United States:

The latest experiments (which are not yet finished) show that the conditioned reflexes, *i.e.,* the highest nervous activity, are inherited. At present some experiments on white mice have been completed. Conditioned reflexes to electric bells are formed, so that the animals are trained to run to their feeding place on the ringing of the bell. The following results have been obtained.

The first generation of white mice required 300 lessons. Three hundred times was it necessary to combine the feeding of the mice with the ringing of the bell in order to accustom them to run to the feeding place on hearing the bell ring. The second generation required, for the same result, only 100 lessons. The third generation learned to do it after 30 lessons. The fourth generation required only 10 lessons. The last generation which I saw before leaving Petrograd learned the lesson after 5 repetitions. The sixth generation will be tested after my return. I think it very probable that after some time a new generation of mice will run to the feeding place on hearing the bell with no previous lesson [1923, pp. 360–1].

Thus could conditioned reflexes, through a Lamarckian mechanism, be converted into unconditioned reflexes!

Contradictory evidence. Just a few months later, two reports contradictory to

Pavlov's results were announced. Vicari (1924), using mice, and MacDowell (1924), using rats, found no evidence that offspring of maze-trained ancestors learned the maze with any more facility than did their ancestors. Another negative report came from Sadovnikova-Koltzova, who examined her data on rats' maze performance and concluded that ". . . we see that the teaching of parents did not increase the abilities of the offspring" (1926, p. 316).

McDougall felt that Darwinian natural selection was not sufficient to account for the evolutionary process, and that the Lamarckian principle had to be invoked. Pavlov's results were a bit too good to be true, so McDougall had attempted to replicate them, with no success. He had therefore written Pavlov concerning the matter, and Pavlov had replied, ". . . briefly stating that he no longer held his deductions from his experiments to be valid" (McDougall, 1927, p. 271). Anrep, who translated Pavlov's work into English, also told McDougall that Pavlov had authorized him to make a retraction in the forthcoming *Conditioned Reflexes.* This was duly made in a footnote as follows:

Experiments . . . upon hereditary facilitation of the development of some conditioned reflexes in mice have been found to be very complicated, uncertain and moreover extremely difficult to control. They are at present being subjected to further investigation under more stringent conditions. At present the question of hereditary transmission of conditioned reflexes and of the hereditary facilitation of their acquirement must be left entirely open [Pavlov, 1927, p. 285].

Razran (1958) informs us that there is no evidence that Pavlov carried out his announced intention to repeat the experiment, and the whole topic is conspicuously absent from Pavlov's later publications.

McDougall's research. McDougall persevered, however, and undertook a long-term investigation with Wistar strain rats. The learning situation employed consisted of three parallel alleys in a water tank. The animals were placed in the center alley, and upon swimming its length could choose to turn either right or left into one of the side alleys. Each side alley contained an escape platform and could be illuminated or left dim. The dim alley was the correct path. The platform in the illuminated alley was electrified so that the rat would receive an electric shock if it attempted to escape the water by that route. Each generation was obtained by supposedly random selection from the preceding generation. The principal results were a decrease in the number of errors made in the thirty-four successive generations, and the gradual development of "photophobia." The results were interpreted as demonstrating the inheritance of characteristics acquired by the experience of the ancestors (McDougall, 1927, 1930, 1938; Rhine and McDougall, 1933).

Criticisms appeared at once (Hazlitt, 1927; Crew, 1930), directed primarily to procedural matters. One of these criticisms suggested that there had been non-deliberate selection of faster learning animals as parents. Furthermore, McDougall had unfortunately failed to maintain an untrained control group from the same initial stock as the trained group, but had relied upon animals newly imported to his laboratory for control observations. McDougall challenged some of the criticisms, and undertook to select for *poorer* learning ability. There was still improvement over a number of generations.

Attempts to replicate McDougall's results. The issue was of such importance that two repetitions of the costly experiment were attempted. Crew (1936) also began with Wistar strain rats, and used an apparatus similar to McDougall's. In this study, however, a control line was maintained from the outset. Some of the control animals were tested in each generation to provide data for comparison with the trained line, and other control line animals were retained, untrained, to provide the next generation. In the trained line, of course, all animals were trained. Over eighteen generations, Crew (1936) found no convincing evidence of a decrease in errors among the trained line, and they were, in fact, not different from the untrained controls. In both groups there were wide fluctuations from generation to generation.

Agar and collaborators (1948) likewise started with Wistar rats, used an apparatus similar to McDougall's, and maintained a control line. In this experiment a progressive improvement did occur over twenty-eight generations in the trained group, but this was followed by a worsening in performance from the twenty-eighth to the thirty-sixth generation. More important, the results were remarkably paralleled by the control group, in which the parents of each successive generation *had never been trained.*

It is not possible to establish definitely exactly what accounts for McDougall's results, but the failure of Crew's and Agar's attempts to replicate them casts serious doubt on the validity of the Lamarckian explanation, and various alternative explanations have been advanced. The small size of the breeding population, for example, could lead to inbreeding depression, and all the cited researches agree that less vigorous animals learn more quickly in this particular situation. Small breeding populations are also susceptible to genetic drift, so that over a period of time a line could change quite considerably in genetic constitution, even in the absence of any selection. The possibility of gradual and systematic change in environmental conditions of rearing and testing during the many years involved in such an experiment is another important possibility.

Failures to demonstrate unambiguously the Lamarckian phenomenon, and the great successes of the genetical theory which presupposes absence of Lamarckian effects, have brought Lamarckism into general disrepute in modern genetics. The only notable exception is provided by Russian Lysenkoism. One very recent line of research, moreover, has shown how apparent transmission of acquired characters may be due to subtle selection for modifying genes (Waddington, 1957).

SUMMARY OF ANIMAL RESEARCH

The general picture presented by animal behavioral genetics is of a discipline which has established a base of operations by the demonstration of genetic influence in a wide variety of behaviors and in diverse animal species. Over and above the establishment of the simple fact of genetic contribution, some progress has been made in determining the mode of gene action. In some cases it has been possible to demonstrate single-gene effects. In some polygenic characters, descriptions of additive effects or of partial average dominance are available. There have also been advances in describing the causal processes between genes and behavioral characters.

In terms of application of current genetic theory and procedure, behavioral genetics lags behind. For example, one of the central concepts of modern genetics is that of *heritability*, which is defined as the ratio of the variance attributable to additive gene effects to the total phenotypic variance. This quantity represents the genetic contribution which is "useful" in the sense that it provides for firm prediction of the outcome of various matings (e.g., in a selection program). Effects due to dominance and epistasis, which are, to be sure, genetic, are dependent upon the vagaries of combinations of genes, and consequently are less predictable. As yet, only a few studies have attempted to estimate heritabilities of behavioral traits (Hirsch and Boudreau, 1958; Broadhurst, 1959). Further development of behavioral genetics will require the precise estimation of the heritabilities of a broad range of behavior patterns.

Again, it is rather remarkable that in animal work, where the technique could be most appropriately applied, there has been so little work on correlations among relatives. Only one study in which correlations were the chief concern (Burlingame

and Stone, 1928) has come to the author's attention. Other techniques have also remained untried. For example, a very recent publication by Broadhurst (1959) provides the first example of the use of diallele crossing in studying behavioral traits. In this procedure F_1's are obtained among a number of inbred strains, and the results provide estimates of heritability and description of the relative contributions of additive, dominance, and epistatic effects.

Another technique only recently introduced to behavioral genetics is that of chromosome analysis in Drosophila (Hirsch, 1962). In this technique specific chromosomes may be combined in desired combinations, and the contributions of each chromosome to a particular type of behavior can be assessed.

It seems reasonable to judge that the foundation of behavioral genetics is now sufficiently stable to permit the future course of research to be more detailed and refined explorations of the dynamics of genetic determination of behavior.

Behavioral Genetics and Psychology

To this point, little has been said of the relationship which studies in behavioral genetics have had to psychology in general. To a considerable extent, of course, developments in behavioral genetics were directed by contemporary trends in psychology. The great concern with the inheritance of learning ability in animals, for example, reflects the dominant role which learning theory has played in psychology. Furthermore, the techniques which could be utilized in the study of the genetics of behavior have depended upon the refinements and improvements in psychological procedures. The Watson circular maze gave way to the multiple T-maze; assessment of intelligence in humans was made ever more precise as new instruments were developed, and so on.

The reciprocal influence, that of behavioral genetics upon developments within psychology as a whole, has been limited by the predominantly environmentalistic orientation which has characterized psychological theory.

From the beginning, there have been vigorous opponents to any suggestion that the composition of a man's chromosomes could have any determining effect upon his intelligence, personality, emotional stability, or any other "mental or moral" characteristic. There ensued an intense debate, which has come to be known as the nature-nurture controversy.

In all controversies of this type, apparently, the motivations of the opposing teams are diverse and various, and this is clearly true of the nature-nurture debate. For some, religious convictions may have played a predominant role in shaping opinions. Political attitudes were also undoubtedly involved. Are not all men created equal? This was a self-evident truth to the signers of the Declaration of Independence. Arguments that some men are inherently wiser than others have appeared to some to be inimical to the democratic ideal, and to imply the rightness of a rule by the elite. The dominant political philosophy of a large part of Western culture during much of the nature-nurture controversy has insisted, on the contrary, that education and socioeconomic reform can improve the lot of individuals and thereby the stature of a culture. Pastore (1949) has presented a detailed defense of the thesis that sociopolitical allegiances have played a major role in determining opinion on this issue. In the late 1930's and the 1940's, particularly, the horror at the results of the Nazis' perverted application of their pseudogenetics of race differences led to a strong bias against any suggestion of inheritance of mental characteristics.

Another factor which presumably acted to reduce interest in psychological genetics was the dampening of the ardor of eugenicists. As newly discovered genetic principles were brought to bear on the proposals of eugenics, it became clear that some of the early hopes for quick improvement in human welfare through genetic alteration were overly optimistic. Since eugenic considerations had directly or indirectly motivated much of the human research, it was inevitable that the disenchantment would have an adverse effect on the vigor with which studies on behavioral genetics were conducted. (See Scheinfeld, 1958, for a discussion of changing views in eugenics.) Furthermore, as we have seen, there is considerable room for differences in interpretation of the evidence, especially in the case of the human data.

But the most important factor was no doubt the development of the "behavioristic" point of view which assumed a dominating role in the developing discipline of psychology, particularly in America. With J. B. Watson as the prime mover, behaviorism developed as a protest against all forms of introspective psychology. Mental states, consciousness, mind, will, imagery—all became taboo. Stimulus and response were the only acceptable explanatory terms.

The instinct doctrine, which had been brought to its culmination by McDougall (1908), was also attacked by behaviorists as being redundant and circular. Instincts had been thought of as inherited patterns of behavior in contrast to learned behavior, and with the rejection of instincts, the whole notion of heredity influencing behavior was cast into discard. The burden of explaining individual differences fell completely to environmental factors.

So let us hasten to admit—yes, there are heritable differences in form, in structure . . . These differences are in the germ plasm and are handed down from parent to child. . . . But do not let these undoubted facts of inheritance lead us astray as they have some of the biologists. The mere presence of these structures tells us not one thing about function. . . . Our hereditary structure lies ready to be shaped in a thousand different ways—the same structure—depending on the way in which the child is brought up [Watson, 1930, p. 97].

Objectors will probably say that the behaviorist is flying in the face of the known facts of eugenics and experimental evolution—

that the geneticists have proven that many of the behavior characteristics of the parents are handed down to the offspring. . . . Our reply is that the geneticists are working under the banner of the old "faculty" psychology. One need not give very much weight to any of their present conclusions. We no longer believe in faculties nor in any stereotyped patterns of behavior which go under the names of "talent" and inherited capacities" [p. 99].

Our conclusion, then, is that we have no real evidence of the inheritance of traits. I would feel perfectly confident in the ultimately favorable outcome of careful upbringing of a *healthy, well-formed* baby born of a long line of crooks, murderers and thieves, and prostitutes. Who has any evidence to the contrary? [p. 103].

Then came the familiar and frequently quoted challenge:

I should like to go one step further now and say, "Give me a dozen healthy infants, well-formed, and my own specified world to bring them up in and I'll guarantee to take any one at random and train him to become any type of specialist I might select—doctor, lawyer, artist, merchant-chief and, yes, even beggar-man and thief, regardless of his talents, penchants, tendencies, abilities, vocations, and race of his ancestors." I am going beyond my facts and I admit it, but so have the advocates of the contrary and they have been doing it for many thousands of years [p. 104].

Woodworth (1948) has pointed out that this extreme environmentalism was not a necessary consequence of the behavioristic philosophical position, and suggests that Watson's stand was taken, in part at least, "to shake people out of their complacent acceptance of traditional views" (1948, p. 92). For whatever reason Watson sought to exorcise genetics from psychology, he succeeded to a remarkable degree, and the position taken in his *Behaviorism* soon became the "traditional view" which was "complacently accepted" by the majority of psychologists.

It is quite apparent from the account given above that this majority view was not without opposition. In fact, since Watson's pronouncement, no single year has passed without publication of some evidence showing it to be wrong. Collectively, these researches have demonstrated the important role of the genotype in many kinds of organism and in many varieties of behavior pattern. From the accumulated evidence, it is obvious that genetic differences are fundamental to individuality, in behavior as well as in physical characteristics.

It would be rash to predict in any detail the effect which the implications of this generalization will have upon psychology in the future. It does appear, however, from a striking increase in the rate of publications in the past decade, that a growth of interest is under way. The hope might be expressed that this growing interest presages a general understanding of the fallacy of the nature-nurture dichotomy, and an acknowledgment of the mutual, interacting, and co-operative roles played by the genes and by environmental agencies in shaping psychological characteristics.

REFERENCES

AGAR, W. E., R. H. DRUMMOND, and O. W. TIEGS Third report on a test of McDougall's Lamarckian experiment on the training of rats. *J. exp. Biol.*, 1948, **25**, 103–22.

ANDERSON, O. D. The spontaneous neuromuscular activity of various pure breeds of dog and of inter-breed hybrids of the first and second generation. *Amer. J. Physiol.*, 1939, **126**, 422–3.

BAGG, H. J. Individual differences and family resemblances in animal behavior. *Amer. Nat.*, 1916, **50**, 222–36.

BAGG, H. J. Individual differences and family resemblances in animal behavior. *Arch. Psychol.*, 1920, **6**, 1–58.

BASSET, G. C. Habit formation in a strain of albino rats of less than normal brain weight. *Behav. Monogr.*, 1914, **2**, 1–46.

BASTOCK, M. A gene mutation which changes a behavior pattern. *Evolution*, 1956, **10**, 421–39.

BROADHURST, P. L. Studies in psychogenetics: The quantitative inheritance of behaviour in rats investigated by selective and crossbreeding. *Bull. Brit. psychol. Soc.*, 1958a, 34, 2A (Abst.).

BROADHURST, P. L. Determinants of emotionality in the rat: III. Strain differences. *J. comp. physiol. Psychol.*, 1958b, 51, 55–9.

BROADHURST, P. L. Application of biometrical genetics to behaviour in rats. *Nature*, 1959, 184, 1517–18.

BURLINGAME, M., and C. P. STONE Family resemblance in maze-learning ability in white rats. *Yearb. Nat. Soc. Stud. Educ.*, 1928, 27 (I), 89–99.

CALHOUN, J. B. A comparative study of the social behavior of two inbred strains of house mice. *Ecol. Monogr.*, 1956, 26, 81–103.

CARR, R. M., and C. D. WILLIAMS Exploratory behavior of three strains of rats. *J. comp. physiol. Psychol.*, 1957, 50, 621–3.

COBURN, C. A. Heredity of wildness and savageness in mice. *Behav. Monogr.*, 1922, 4, 1–71.

CREW, F. A. E. Lamarckism. *Eugen. Rev.*, 1930, 22, 55–9.

CREW, F. A. E. A repetition of McDougall's Lamarckian experiment. *J. Genet.*, 1936, 33, 61–101.

CROZIER, W. J., and G. PINCUS Analysis of the geotropic orientation of young rats. *J. gen. Physiol.*, 1929, 13, 57–119.

CROZIER, W. J., and G. PINCUS Certain principles of physiological genetics. *Proc. 6th Int. Congr. Genetics*, 1932, 2, 31–2.

DARBISHIRE, A. D. On the result of crossing Japanese waltzing with albino mice. *Biometrika*, 1904, 3, 1–51.

DAWSON, W. M. Inheritance of wildness and tameness in mice. *Genetics*, 1932, 17, 296–326.

DENENBERG, V. H. Learning differences in two separated lines of mice. *Science*, 1959, 130, 451–2.

DENENBERG, V. H., P. B. SAWIN, G. P. FROMMER, and S. ROSS Genetic, physiological and behavioral background of reproduction in the rabbit. IV. An analysis of maternal behavior at successive parturitions. *Behaviour*, 1958, 13, 131–42.

DETLEFSEN, J. A. Are the effects of long-continued rotation in rats inherited? *Proc. Amer. Phil. Soc.*, 1923, 62, 292–300.

DETLEFSEN, J. A. Inheritance of acquired characters. *Physiol. Rev.*, 1925, 5, 244–78.

FARRIS, E. J., and E. H. YEAKEL The sus-

ceptibility of albino and gray Norway rats to audiogenic seizures. *J. comp. Psychol.*, 1943, 35, 73–80.

FARRIS, E. J., and E. H. YEAKEL Emotional behavior of gray Norway and Wistar albino rats. *J. comp. Psychol.*, 1945, 38, 109–18.

FINGER, F. W. Factors influencing audiogenic seizures in the rat. II. Heredity and age. *J. comp. Psychol.*, 1943, 35, 227–32.

FREDERICSON, E. Reciprocal fostering of two inbred mouse strains and its effects on the modification of inherited aggressive behavior. *Amer. Psychologist*, 1952, 7, 241–2 (Abst.).

FREDERICSON, E. The wall-seeking tendency in three inbred mouse strains (*Mus musculus*). *J. genet. Psychol.*, 1953, 82, 143–6.

FREEDMAN, D. G. Constitutional and environmental interactions in rearing of four breeds of dogs. *Science*, 1958, 127, 585–6.

FRINGS, H., and M. FRINGS The production of stocks of albino mice with predictable susceptibilities to audiogenic seizures. *Behaviour*, 1953, 5, 305–19.

FULLER, J. L. Cross-sectional and longitudinal studies of adjustive behavior in dogs. *Ann. N. Y. Acad. Sci.*, 1953, 56, 214–24.

FULLER, J. L. Hereditary differences in trainability of purebred dogs. *J. genet. Psychol.*, 1955, 87, 229–38.

FULLER, J. L., C. EASLER, and M. E. SMITH Inheritance of audiogenic seizure susceptibility in the mouse. *Genetics*, 1950, 35, 622–32.

GINSBURG, B. E. Genetics and the physiology of the nervous system. *Proc. Ass. Res. Nerv. Ment. Dis.*, 1954, 33, 39–56.

GINSBURG, B. E., and W. C. ALLEE Some effects of conditioning on social dominance and subordination in inbred strains of mice. *Physiol. Zool.*, 1942, 15, 485–506.

GINSBURG, B. E., D. S. MILLER, and M. J. ZAMIS On the mode of inheritance of susceptibility to sound-induced seizures in the house mouse (*Mus musculus*). *Genetics*, 1950, 35, 109 (Abst.).

GRIFFITH, C. R. Are permanent disturbances of equilibration inherited? *Science*, 1922, 56, 676–8.

GRÜNEBERG, H. *The genetics of the mouse*, 2nd ed. The Hague: Martinus Nijhoff, 1952.

HALL, C. S. The inheritance of emotionality. *Sigma Xi Quart.*, 1938, 26, 17–27.

HALL, C. S. Genetic differences in fatal audiogenic seizures between two inbred strains of house mice. *J. Hered.*, 1947, **38**, 3–6.

HALL, C. S.   The genetics of behavior. In S. S. Stevens (ed.), *Handbook of experimental psychology.* New York: John Wiley and Sons, 1951, 304–29.

HARRIS, R. E.   An analysis of the maze-learning scores of bright and dull rats with reference to motivational factors. *Psychol. Rec.*, 1940, **4**, 130–6.

HARRITT, T. V.   An experimental study of habitat selection by prairie and forest races of the deer mouse *Peromyscus maniculatus. Contr. Lab. Vert. Biol.*, University of Michigan, 1952, **56**, 53.

HATAI, S.   On the weight of some of the ductless glands of the Norway and of the albino rat according to sex and variety. *Anat. Rec.*, 1914, **8**, 511–23.

HAZLITT, V.   Professor McDougall and the Lamarckian hypothesis. *Brit. J. Psychol.*, 1927, **18**, 77–86.

HERON, W. T.   The inheritance of maze learning ability in rats. *J. comp. Psychol.*, 1935, **19**, 77–89.

HERON, W. T.   The inheritance of brightness and dullness in maze learning ability in the rat. *J. genet. Psychol.*, 1941, **59**, 41–9.

HERON, W. T., and B. F. SKINNER   The rate of extinction in maze-bright and maze-dull rats. *Psychol. Rec.*, 1940, **4**, 11–18.

HINDE, R. A.   Breeding success in cardueline interspecies pairs and an examination of the hybrids' plumage. *J. Genet.*, 1956, **54**, 304–10.

HIRSCH, J.   Individual differences in behavior and their genetic basis. In Bliss, E. (Ed.), *Roots of behavior.* New York: Harper & Brothers, 1962.

HIRSCH, J., and J. C. BOUDREAU   Studies in experimental behavior genetics: I. The heritability of phototaxis in a population of *Drosophila melanogaster. J. comp. physiol. Psychol.*, 1958, **51**, 647–51.

HORNER, B. E.   Arboreal adaptations of *Peromyscus,* with special reference to use of the tail. *Contr. Lab. Vert. Biol.*, University of Michigan, 1954, **61**, 1–85.

JAMES, W. T.   Morphological form and its relation to behavior. In C. R. Stockard, *The genetic and endocrinic basis for differences in form and behavior.* Philadelphia: Wistar Institute, 1941, 525–643.

KEELER, C. E., and H. D. KING   Multiple

effects of coat color genes in the Norway rat with special reference to temperament and domestication. *J. comp. Psychol.*, 1942, **34**, 241–50.

KING, H. D., and H. H. DONALDSON   Life processes and size of the body and organs of the gray Norway rat during ten generations in captivity. *Amer. Anat. Mem.*, 1929, **14**, 106.

KING, J. A.   Maternal behavior and behavioral development in two subspecies of *Peromyscus maniculatus. J. Mammal.*, 1958, **39**, 177–90.

KING, J. A., and A. MAVROMATIS   The effect of a conflict situation on learning ability in two strains of mice. *J. comp. physiol. Psychol.*, 1956, **49**, 465–8.

KING, J. A., and N. J. SHEA   Subspecific differences in the responses of young deermice on an elevated maze. *J. Hered.*, 1959, **50**, 14–18.

KRECH, D., M. R. ROSENZWEIG, E. L. BENNETT, and B. KRUECKEL   Enzyme concentrations in the brain and adjustive behavior-patterns. *Science*, 1954, **120**, 994–6.

KRECH, D., M. R. ROSENZWEIG, and E. L. BENNETT   Dimensions of discrimination and level of cholinesterase activity in the cerebral cortex of the rat. *J. comp. physiol. Psychol.*, 1956, **49**, 261–8.

KRECHEVSKY, I.   Hereditary nature of "hypotheses." *J. comp. Psychol.*, 1933, **16**, 99–116.

McCLEARN, G. E.   The genetics of mouse behavior in novel situations. *J. comp. physiol. Psychol.*, 1959, **52**, 62–7.

McCLEARN, G. E., and D. A. RODGERS   Differences in alcohol preference among inbred strains of mice. *Quart. J. Stud. Alcohol*, 1959, **20**, 691–5.

McCLEARN, G. E., and D. A. RODGERS   Genetic factors in alcohol preference of laboratory mice. *J. comp. physiol. Psychol.*, 1961, **54**, 116–19.

McDOUGALL, W.   *An introduction to social psychology.* London: Methuen, 1908.

McDOUGALL, W.   An experiment for the testing of the hypothesis of Lamarck. *Brit. J. Psychol. (Gen. Section)*, 1927, **17**, 267–304.

McDOUGALL, W.   Second report on a Lamarckian experiment. *Brit. J. Psychol. (Gen. Section)*, 1930, **20**, 201–18.

McDOUGALL, W.   Fourth report on a Lamarckian experiment. *Brit. J. Psychol.*, 1938, **28**, 321–45, 365–95.

MacDowell, E. C.   Experiments with rats on the inheritance of training. *Science*, 1924, **59**, 302–3.

Mahut, H.   Breed differences in the dog's emotional behaviour. *Canad. J. Psychol.*, 1958, **12**, 35–44.

Maier, N. R. F.   Studies of abnormal behavior in the rat: XIV. Strain differences in the inheritance of susceptibility to convulsions. *J. comp. Psychol.*, 1943, **35**, 327–35.

Maier, N. R. F., and N. M. Glaser   Studies of abnormal behavior in the rat: V. The inheritance of the "neurotic pattern." *J. comp. Psychol.*, 1940, **30**, 413–18.

Manning, A.   An evolutionary approach to the study of behaviour. *Proc. Roy. phys. Soc. Edinburgh*, 1958, **27**, 1–5.

Merrell, D. J.   Selective mating as a cause of gene frequency changes in laboratory populations of *Drosophila melanogaster*. *Evolution*, 1953, **7**, 287–96.

Munn, N. L.   *Handbook of psychological research on the rat*. Boston: Houghton Mifflin Co., 1950.

Myers, A. K.   Avoidance learning as a function of several training conditions and strain differences in rats. *J. comp. physiol. Psychol.*, 1959, **52**, 381–6.

Nachman, M.   The inheritance of saccharin preference. *J. comp. physiol. Psychol.*, 1959, **52**, 451–7.

Pastore, N.   *The nature-nurture controversy.* New York: Kings Crown, 1949.

Pavlov, I. P.   New researches on conditioned reflexes. *Science*, 1923, **58**, 359–61.

Pavlov, I. P.   *Conditioned reflexes.* Trans. G. V. Anrep. New York: Oxford University Press, 1927.

Pawlowski, A. A., and J. P. Scott   Hereditary differences in the development of dominance in litters of puppies. *J. comp. physiol. Psychol.*, 1956, **49**, 353–8.

Razran, G.   Pavlov and Lamarck. *Science*, 1958, **128**, 758–60.

Reed, S. C., and E. W. Reed   Natural selection in laboratory populations of *Drosophila*. II. Competition between a white-eye gene and its wild type allele. *Evolution*, 1950, 4, 34–42.

Rhine, J. B., and W. McDougall   Third report on a Lamarckian experiment. *Brit. J. Psychol.*, 1933, **24**, 213–35.

Richter, C. P.   Domestication of the Norway rat and its implication for the study of genetics in man. *Amer. J. hum. Genet.*, 1952, 4, 273–85.

Riss, W., E. S. Valenstein, J. Sinks, and W. C. Young   Development of sexual behavior in male guinea pigs from genetically different stocks under controlled conditions of androgen treatment and caging. *Endocrinology*, 1955, **57**, 139–46.

Rosenzweig, M. R., D. Krech, and E. L. Bennett   Effects of pentobarbital sodium on adaptive behavior patterns in the rat. *Science*, 1956, **123**, 371–2.

Rosenzweig, M. R., D. Krech, and E. L. Bennett   Brain enzymes and adaptive behaviour. *Ciba Foundation Symposium* on the *Neurological basis of behaviour*, 1958a, 337–55.

Rosenzweig, M. R., D. Krech, and E. L. Bennett   A search for relations between brain chemistry and behavior. *Psychol. Bull.*, 1960, **57**, 476–92.

Rosenzweig, M. R., D. Krech, E. L. Bennett, and C. Longueil   Strain differences of rats in behavior and brain chemistry. Paper delivered at APA, Washington, Sept., 1958b.

Rothenbuhler, W. C.   Genetics of a behavior difference in honey bees. *Proc. 10th Internat. Congr. Genetics*, 1958, **2**, 242.

Rundquist, E. A.   Inheritance of spontaneous activity in rats. *J. comp. Psychol.*, 1933, **16**, 415–38.

Sadovnikova-Koltzova, M. P.   Genetic analysis of temperament in rats. *J. exp. Zool.*, 1926, **45**, 301–18.

Santibañez, S. K., and C. H. Waddington   The origin of sexual isolation between different lines within a species. *Evolution*, 1958, **12**, 485–93.

Sawin, P. B., and D. D. Crary   Genetic and physiological background of reproduction in the rabbit. II. Some racial differences in the pattern of maternal behavior. *Behaviour*, 1953, 6, 128–46.

Scheinfeld, A.   Changing attitudes toward human genetics and eugenics. *Eugenics Quart.*, 1958, **5**, 145–53.

Scott, J. P.   Genetic differences in the social behavior of inbred strains of mice. *J. Hered.*, 1942, 33, 11–15.

Scott, J. P., and E. Fredericson   The causes

of fighting in mice and rats. *Physiol. Zool.*, 1951, **24**, 273–309.

SEARLE, L. V.   The organization of hereditary maze-brightness and maze-dullness. *Genet. Psychol. Monogr.*, 1949, **39**, 279–325.

SPIETH, H. T.   Behavior and isolating mechanisms. In A. Roe and G. G. Simpson (Eds.), *Behavior and evolution.* New Haven: Yale University, 1958, 363–89.

STAMM, J. S.   Genetics of hoarding: I. Hoarding differences between homozygous strains of rats. *J. comp. physiol. Psychol.*, 1954, **47**, 157–61.

STAMM, J. S.   Genetics of hoarding: II. Hoarding behavior of hybrid and backcrossed strains of rats. *J. comp. physiol. Psychol.*, 1956, **49**, 349–52.

THOMPSON, W. R.   The inheritance of behaviour: behavioural differences in fifteen mouse strains. *Canad. J. Psychol.*, 1953, **7**, 145–55.

THOMPSON, W. R.   The inheritance and development of intelligence. *Proc. Ass. Res. Nerv. Ment. Dis.*, 1954, **33**, 209–31.

THOMPSON, W. R.   The inheritance of behavior: activity differences in five inbred mouse strains. *J. Hered.*, 1956, **47**, 147–8.

TOLMAN, E. C.   The inheritance of maze-learning ability in rats. *J. comp. Psychol.*, 1924, **4**, 1–18.

TOLMAN, E. C., R. C. TRYON, and L. A. JEFFRESS   A self-recording maze with an automatic delivery table. *Univ. California Publ. Psychol.*, 1929, **4**, 99–112.

TRYON, R. C.   Genetic differences in maze-learning ability in rats. *Yearb. Nat. Soc. Stud. Educ.*, 1940, **39** (I), 111–19.

UTSURIKAWA, N.   Temperamental differences between outbred and inbred strains of the albino rat. *J. Anim. Behav.*, 1917, **7**, 111–29.

VALENSTEIN, E. S., W. RISS, and W. C. YOUNG   Sex drive in genetically heterogeneous and highly inbred strains of male guinea pigs. *J. comp. physiol. Psychol.*, 1954, **47**, 162–5.

VALENSTEIN, E. S., W. RISS, and W. C. YOUNG   Experiential and genetic factors in the organization of sexual behavior in male guinea pigs. *J. comp. physiol. Psychol.*, 1955, **48**, 397–403.

VICARI, E. M.   Heredity of behavior in mice. *Yearb. Carnegie Inst. Washington*, 1921, 132–3.

VICARI, E. M.   The non-inheritance of the effects of training. *Science*, 1924, **59**, 303.

VICARI, E. M.   Mode of inheritance of reaction time and degrees of learning in mice. *J. exp. Zool.*, 1929, **54**, 31–88.

VON GUAITA, G.   Versuche mit Kreuzungen von verschiedenen Rassen der Hausmaus. *Ber. Nat. Ges.*, Freiburg, 1898, **10**, 317–32.

VON GUAITA, G.   Zweite Mitteilung über Versuche mit Kreuzungen mit verschiedenen Rassen der Hausmaus. *Ber. Nat. Ges.*, Freiburg, 1900, **11**, 131–8.

WADDINGTON, C. H.   *The strategy of the genes.* New York: The Macmillan Company, 1957.

WATSON, J. B.   *Behaviorism.* New York: Norton and Co., 1924. Rev. ed. 1930.

WHITNEY, L. F.   Inheritance of mental aptitudes in dogs. *Proc. 6th Internat. Congr. Genet.*, 1932, **2**, 211–12 (Abst.).

WITT, G., and C. S. HALL   The genetics of audiogenic seizures in the house mouse. *J. comp. physiol. Psychol.*, 1949, **42**, 58–63.

WOODWORTH, R. S.   *Contemporary schools of psychology*, rev. ed. New York: Ronald Press, 1948.

YERKES, A. W.   Comparison of the behavior of stock and inbred albino rats. *J. Anim. Behav.*, 1916, **6**, 267–96.

YERKES, R. M.   *The dancing mouse.* New York: The Macmillan Company, 1907.

YERKES, R. M.   The heredity of savageness and wildness in rats. *J. Anim. Behav.*, 1913, **3**, 286–96.

JERRY HIRSCH

7   Behavior Genetics and Individuality Understood*

In this article, Jerry Hirsch attacks the "uniformity assumption" and the
environmental approach of modern behaviorism. He points out the importance
of individual differences in behavior and how they have been either ignored or
"averaged out" in many experiments. Hirsch then discusses the meaning of "normality" and the great improbability of any two individuals, except identical
twins, having the same genotype. The article concludes with a brief review of
some of the author's important research on *Drosophila* and with a frank discussion
of race differences.

Hirsch makes the important point that heritability "is a property of populations and never of traits." An example may serve to clarify this statement.

Heritability may be briefly defined as the proportion of trait variance that
is due to genetic variance in the population. ("Variance" is used here in its
statistical sense: σ^2. Students unfamiliar with this term should consult an introductory text in statistics.) One formula for heritability is written as:

$$h^2 = \frac{\sigma_g^2}{\sigma_g^2 + \sigma_e^2}$$

where

σ_g^2 = genetic variance
σ_e^2 = environmental variance
$\sigma_g^2 + \sigma_e^2$ = the total variance of the population, or σ_p^2.

Heritability, or h^2, is thus seen to have possible values in the range 0 to 1.0.
Zero heritability means that none of the variation in the population is due to
genetic variation. On the other hand, if $h^2 = 1.0$, all of the population variation
is accounted for by genetic variation.

Now suppose we take two groups of mice, one a highly inbred strain and the
other a genetically heterogeneous wild strain. We put both groups in a water
tank and measure swimming speed. The inbred strain averages twenty units with
a standard deviation of 2; the total variance for this group is thus 4. What is the
heritability (if we assume 100 percent homozygosity in our inbred strain)? The
answer is *zero*. Because there is no genetic variation, all the variance must be
due to the environment.

The wild strain also averages twenty units, but the variance is ten. If we take

* This article derives partly from discus-
sions presented in 1959 at the symposium
"Roots of Behavior," program of the American
Psychiatric Association at the Chicago meeting
of AAAS; in 1960 at the American Orthopsy-
chiatric Association symposium "Genetics of
Mental Disease"; and in 1961 at a symposium,
"Expanding Goals of Genetics in Psychiatry,"
of the Department of Medical Genetics, New
York State Psychiatric Institute.

the variance of the inbred strain as an estimate of σ_e^2, we can calculate h^2 for the wild strain to be 0.60. So we see that the heritability of the trait "swimming speed" varies with the population.

This article originally appeared in *Science*, **142**, pp. 1436–1442, 13 December 1963. Copyright 1963 by the American Association for the Advancement of Science. Reprinted by permission of the author and the American Association for the Advancement of Science.

Behaviorism's Counterfactual Dogma Blinded the Behavioral Sciences to the Significance of Meiosis

Individual differences are no accident. They are generated by properties of organisms as fundamental to behavioral science and biology as thermodynamic properties are to physical science. Much research, however, fails to take them into account. The behavioral sciences have attempted to erect a superstructure without paying sufficient attention to its foundation. A uniformity of expression over individuals, and even across species, has too often been assumed for behaviors under study. The uniformity assumption is explicitly incorporated into a spate of mathematical models that have been developed to formalize the study of behavior: Bush and Mosteller (1), for example, built theirs for "organisms that can be considered 'identical' at the start of an experiment. . . ." Rosner (2) speaks of "a fundamental attitude" which keeps psychophysics (3) "oriented toward the sources of uniformity in behavior." In this article I consider some effects that such assumptions about heredity, individuality, and behavior have had on the behavioral sciences.

THREE APPROACHES TO BEHAVIOR

In the study of behavior, three points of view can be distinguished. (i) Only common properties of behavior are studied among individuals and species. (ii) Only common properties of behavior are studied among individuals, while both similarities and characteristic differences are studied among species. (iii) Similarities and differences are studied among individuals, populations, and species.

The first view prevails when an organism is used as a tool for studying behavioral correlates of stimulus conditions, reinforcement schedules, deprivation regimens, pharmacological agents, or physiological mechanisms. It is hopefully assumed that the form of any relation observed—for example, that between stimulus and response —will have universal generality. The organism's role is essentially that of an analyzer, like the role of the Geissler tube in physics. In their illuminating discussion "The misbehavior of organisms," the Brelands (4), drawing on over 14 years of faithful application of the methods and assumptions of behaviorism, show that behaviorism also assumes "that the animal comes to the laboratory as a virtual *tabula rasa*, that species differences are insignificant, and that all responses are about equally conditionable to all stimuli." They relate (4), a history of "egregious failures" which they feel "represent a clear and utter failure of conditioning theory."

From the second viewpoint the behavior of animals is as characteristic of their species as is their form. This view prevails in ethologically oriented studies—for example, studies of such instincts as reproductive, parental, or territorial behavior. All members of a species are assumed to manifest a given behavior pattern, in some typical way. In Mayr's cogent analysis (5) this represents typological thinking whose replacement "by population thinking is perhaps the greatest conceptual revolution . . . in biology."

The third approach characterizes behavior genetics: the study of the relations between the genetic architecture of a taxon and the distributions of its behavioral phenotypes. It employs the methods of both the behavioral sciences and genetics.

The growth of this field can be attributed to protest against the counterfactual uniformity postulate, combined with the realization that we can now have a description and analysis of behavior based on a deeper understanding of the materials on which the behavioral sciences make their observations.

The key to our present understanding of the structure of life came during the first half of this century, from investigations of transmission cytogenetics (6) and population cytogenetics (7). Through study of cell division and reproduction (mitosis, meiosis, and fertilization), together with statistical analysis of variations in the expression of traits among offspring of specified matings, transmission cytogenetics gave us our first picture of the fundamental units of life (genes and chromosomes) and of the variation-generating probability mechanism (meiosis) by which lawfully combined random samples of these units are passed on from parents to offspring. Through study of (i) the distributions of genes in populations, (ii) the mechanisms responsible for both stability and change in gene frequencies, and (iii) the role of such mechanisms in evolution, population cytogenetics has given us some understanding of ensembles of these units that comprise the gene pools of populations and species—the taxa that are natural units of evolution.

UNDERSTANDING INDIVIDUALITY

The phenotype (appearance, structure, physiology, and behavior) of any organism is determined by the interaction of environment with its genotype (the complete genetic endowment). Each genotype is the end product of many mechanisms which promote genotypic diversity in populations.

Ordinarily members of a cross-fertilizing, sexually reproducing species possess a diploid, or paired, set of chromosomes. Most species whose behavior we study are sexually dimorphic. The genetic basis of this dimorphism resides in the distribution of the heterosomes, a homologous pair of sex chromosomes (XX) being present in the mammalian female and an unequal pair (XY), in the mammalian male. Sexual dimorphism guarantees that any population will be variable to the extent of at least two classes. Whether sex-chromosome or other genotypic differences are involved in any particular behavior remains an empirical question to be investigated separately for every population. It can no longer be settled by dogmatic attitudes and assumptions about uniformity.

Chromosomes other than sex chromosomes are called autosomes. Every autosome is normally represented by a homologous pair whose members have identical genetic loci. Alternative forms of a gene any of which may occupy a given locus are termed alleles. If an individual receives identical alleles from both parents at homologous loci, he is said to be homozygous for that gene. If he receives two alleles that differ, however, he is said to be heterozygous for that gene. The process by which a gene changes from one allelic form to another is called mutation.

When a gene is represented in the population gene pool by two allelic forms, the population will be genotypically polymorphic to the extent of at least three classes. That is, individuals may be homozygous for either of two alleles or heterozygous for their combination.

Study of populations has revealed that often extensive series of alleles exist for a locus. Well-known examples are the three (actually more) alleles at the ABO-blood locus in man and a dozen or more alleles at the white-eye locus in *Drosophila*. Benzer (8), in his study of the internal genetic architecture of *one* "gene" with a corresponding physical structure of probably less than 2000 nucleotide pairs, the *r*II region of the T_4 bacteriophage, found 339 distinguishable mutational sites, and he expects to eventually find some 428. There is no reason to believe that we shall find less complexity in cellular organisms as further refinement increases the resolving power of our techniques for analyzing them. In general, for each locus having n alleles in the gene pool, a population will contain $n(n + 1)/2$ genotypic classes. Mutation insures variety in the gene itself.

Sexual reproduction involves meiosis—a complex cellular process resulting in a meristic division of the nucleus and formation of gametes (reproductive cells) having single genomes (a haploid chromosome set). One homolog in every chromosome pair in our diploid complement is of paternal origin and the other is of maternal origin. In meiosis, the homologs of a pair segregate and a gamete receives one from each pair. The assortment to gametes of the segregating homologs occurs independently for each pair. This process insures diversity because it maximizes the likelihood that gametes will receive unique genomes. For example, gametogenesis in *Drosophila willistoni* produces eight alternative gametic genomes, which, if we represent the three chromosome pairs of this species by Aa, Bb, and Cc, we designate ABC, ABc, AbC, aBC, Abc, aBc, abC, abc. In general, n pairs of chromosomes produce 2^n genomes (if we ignore the recombination of gene linkages that actually occurs in crossover exchanges between chromosomes). Man, with 23 chromosome pairs, produces gametes with any of 2^{23} alternative genomes. This makes vanishingly small the chances that even siblings (other than monozygotes) will be genetically identical. Since the gamete contributed by *each* parent is chosen from 2^{23} alternatives, the probability that the second offspring born to parents will have exactly the same genotype as their firstborn is $(\frac{1}{2}^{23})^2$, or less than 1 chance in over 70 trillion! The probability that two unrelated individuals will have the same genotype, then, is effectively zero (9).

The argument for the genotypic uniqueness of members of populations is even more compelling, since other conditions also contribute to diversity. So, it is clear, the organisms which the behavioral sciences study are intrinsically variable be-

fore they undergo differentiating experiences. The mechanisms responsible for this variety are mutation, recombination, and meiosis. Add to these individual experience, and it becomes evident why individuals differ in behavior. In fact, the more reliable our methods of observation become, the more evident will this variety be.

THE ABNORMALITY OF THE NORMAL

For Watson, its founder, behaviorism was "a natural science . . . [whose] closest scientific companion is physiology. . . . It is different from physiology only in the grouping of its problems, not in fundamentals or in central viewpoint" (*10*). Assumptions about the uniformity and normality of material under investigation are often made in physiology, the science after which, more than any other, experimental psychology has attempted to pattern itself. We may, therefore, get a better grasp of the individuality-uniformity distinction by examining the differences between organisms whose behavior is studied by behavioral scientists and systems whose functioning is studied by physiologists.

Since the two disciplines are working at distinctly different levels of biological organization, the meaning of "normality" as operationally determined by them is quite different. Physiologists choose a normal organism to work with—one that looks healthy and does not appear unusual —and study one or more of its systems, such as the adrenals, gonads, or other endocrines, or regions of the nervous system. Either pre- or postexperimentally, anatomical, histological, or biochemical verification is made of the normality of the material under study, and sometimes of related or adjacent functions to boot. In the behavioral sciences we choose normal-appearing organisms to study too. We rarely perform biopsies unless there is a specific physiological interest, in which case we operate as the physiologist does.

Physiological systems are variable, not uniform. Williams (*11*) amply documents this and points out that implicit in our use of "normal" is reference to some region of a distribution arbitrarily designated as not extreme—for example, the median 50 percent, 95 percent, or 99 percent. We choose such a region for every trait. Among n mathematically independent traits—for example, traits dependent on n different chromosomes—the probability that a randomly selected individual will be normal for all n traits is the value for the size of that region raised to the nth power. Where "normal" is the median 50 percent and $n = 10$, on the average only 1 individual out of 1024 will be normal (for ten traits). When we consider at one time the distributions throughout a population of large numbers of physiological systems, we should expect negative deviates from some distributions to combine with positive deviates from others, both kinds of extreme deviates to combine with centrally located ones, and deviates of similar algebraic sign and magnitude to combine. Each individual's particular balance of physiological endowments will be the developmental result of the genotype he draws in the lotteries of meiosis and the mating ritual. Because of crossing over, most genes assort independently. Hence, we cannot expect high correlations among the systems they generate.

If, underlying every behavior, there were only a single such system—for example, if the male "sexual drive" were mainly dependent on the seminal vesicles (12) or if escape behavior were mainly dependent on the adrenals—then the same kind of distribution might be expected for both the behavior and the underlying system. Whatever uniformity might exist at one level would be reflected at the other. The last few decades of research on the biological correlates of behavior have made it increasingly clear that behavior is the integration of most of these systems rather than the expression of any one of them. Therefore, there is little reason to expect that the many possible combinations and integrations of those systems that go to make up the members of a population will yield a homogeneously normal distribution of responses for many behavioral measures. An organism richly endowed with the components of one subset of systems and poorly endowed with those of another is not to be expected to behave in the same manner as an organism with an entirely different balance of endowments. The obviousness of this fact is well illustrated by the differences in behavior among the various breeds of dogs and horses.

REDUCTIONISM

Another conviction, strongly held by some, is that *real* explanations must be reductionistic. Those who hold this view in its most extreme form assert that no behavior can be understood until its physical basis has been unraveled. And the search for the physical basis proceeds along physiological, biochemical, biophysical, or genetical lines, depending on the skills and predilections of the investigators.

In laboratory experiments, some rats learn mazes more readily on the basis of visual cues while others do better with predominantly kinesthetic cues (13). The kinds of differences in organization that can coexist as alternative forms within a species, as well as some relations between one behavior and the component subsystems that are alternative possibilities, have been further revealed in a series of studies of the effects of domestication. In some domesticated rats, activity in a revolving drum was controlled by the gonads: control rats had daily activity scores as high as 18,000 revolutions, while gonadectomized rats scored only a few hundred revolutions. Cortisone therapy restored a high activity level in the gonadectomized rats. When the same experiment was repeated on wild Norway rats, however, the presence or absence of gonads made no detectable difference in measured activity. Further study of differences between these domesticated and wild rats revealed larger adrenals in the wild rats and larger gonads in the domesticated (14). So it appears that activity may be under the control of adrenal output in one case and gonadal output in the other —that behavior is not a univocal index to an organism's balance of endowments. The fallacy of reductionism lies in assuming a one-one relation between different levels of organization. With degeneracy already demonstrated in the genetic code of messenger RNA base triplets for the amino acids of proteins, we should be surprised not to find it at the levels of complexity we are considering. (15).

BEHAVIORISM AND INTROSPECTION

According to my naive picture, the pyramid of sciences forges links of knowledge "out" from the periodic table: on the one hand, "down" into atomic structure through advances in physics; on the other, "up" into life through the genetic code and organic structure by advances in biophysics and biochemistry. The place of the behavioral sciences in the outline of that pyramid has been clearly demarcated for some time (16). Our models and assumptions must be consistent with the knowledge that is burgeoning at other levels. This means doing our homework and learning (17) about developments in fields which may once have seemed remote from behavior, but which clearly are not. Unfortunately, we are still plagued by a legacy of pseudo-problems which, like MacArthur's old soldier, seem to be slowly fading away instead of discreetly dying.

Recently, in *Science* (18), immediately following Wilkin's exposition (19) of his magnificent work on nucleic acids that led to the Watson-Crick model, Skinner heeded a call to issue "a restatement of radical behaviorism. . . ." It may be recalled that behaviorism bears its title to call attention to the fact that it studies behavior objectively rather than mind subjectively. Under Watson, in 1913, it wished to distinguish itself from unreliable (?) introspectionist psychology, whose findings lacked intersubjective agreement. Under Skinner, 50 years after, it is still worried

about "the dimensions of the things studied by psychology and the methods relevant to them."

Starting from the uniformity assumption, the introspectionists were attempting to study the generalized human mind by analyzing the contents of their own consciousness. Of course, the study of mind through analysis by different individuals of the contents of their consciousness inevitably revealed individual differences. Under a given set of stimulating conditions, different people reported different sensations. According to Boring (20) "there is always to be remembered that famous session of the Society of Experimental Psycologists in which Titchener, after hot debate with Holt, exclaimed: 'You can see that green is neither yellowish nor bluish!' and Holt replied: 'On the contrary, it is obvious that a green is that yellowish-blue which is just exactly as blue as it is yellow.' That impasse was an ominous portent . . ."

In over 50 years no one has suggested that Titchener and Holt might *both* have been making reliable observations. The event Boring bemoans would not be looked upon as an "impasse" that represents "an ominous portent" by a behavioral science that understands the structure of the materials it studies. Until recently, some of our best information on the assignment of genes to human chromosomes came from introspective behaviorial observation. We know that genes affecting red-green color discrimination are carried on the X chromosome. We know it because some people fail to report differences in sensation easily observed by others, and the determining factors are transmitted to sons by mothers but never by fathers. Furthermore, Graham (21) has made excellent use of the introspections of one individual whose two eyes receive different color sensations from the same stimulus. Wouldn't it have been of great interest to learn how colored stimuli appeared to other members of the Titchener and Holt families? How many more potentially fruitful leads have been lost in the behavioral sciences because of rigid adherence to the counterfactual uniformity assumption?

Now, what was really wrong with introspection? Is there any other method by which Penfield could have made the startling discovery that apparently long-forgotten experiences remain stored in specific regions of our brain? He succeeded in restoring "lost" memories to introspectively observed consciousness by electrical stimulation of appropriate regions of exposed human brains (22). If the behaviorists had scrutinized the assumptions, which they shared with introspective psychology, they might not have been so quick to condemn its method. Every method has limitations, which it behooves its users to understand.

BEHAVIOR GENETICS

There now exists a substantial and rapidly growing literature on the behavior genetics of many organisms, from *Drosophila* to man—what Tryon (23) calls "the basic science of individual differences." It comes from research far less hampered by unsound premises. In Fuller and Thompson's useful summary (24) we can see "its documentation of the fact that two individuals of superficially similar phenotype may be quite different genotypically and respond in completely different fashion when treated alike." This field, like others, is passing through stages.

The goal of the early work was a genetics *of* behavior. It took a while to learn that heritability is a property of populations and never of behaviors: the relation between behavioral variation and relevant genetic variation is never constant. It must be measured in specific populations under specific conditions, because it varies with both. Tolman (24), Tryon (24), and Heron (24) each measured individual differences in rats' ability to learn and then, by selective breeding, produced strains of "maze-bright" and "maze-dull" rats. Hall (24) and Broadhurst (24) selected for differences in emotional responses. Analogous studies have been made of performance on an animal "intelligence test" (25).

Many strains of small mammals (mice, hamsters, rats, guinea pigs, and rabbits) are maintained under varying inbreeding regimens for purposes of medical and other research. When different strains within a species are compared, it actually becomes a challenge *not* to find differences in one or more behaviors. When strain comparisons are followed by appropriate genetic crosses, genetic correlates of behavioral differences are demonstrated. Such experiments have been performed for a large variety of behaviors: alcohol preference (26), hoarding (24), mating competition (24), susceptibility to audiogenic seizure (24), exploratory tendency (24), and various learning measures (24).

Paralleling the animal research are studies of human pedigrees, studies of family resemblances, twin comparisons, population surveys, and studies of race differences. Again, heritabilities have been demonstrated for many behaviors; for example, nature-nurture ratios were computed for intelligence-test and personality-test performance. Kallmann and his associates have pioneered, and others have joined, in collecting an impressive body of evidence on genetic factors in schizophrenia and other psychopathologies (27).

In 1963, with the wisdom of hindsight, we can ask why so many demonstrations were necessary. Should it not have been common knowledge that within each population the variation pattern for most traits will be conditioned by the nature of the gene pool, and that this will differ among populations? The answer lies in one phrase: the heredity-environment controversy.

The "opinion leaders" (28) of two generations literally excommunicated heredity from the behavioral sciences. Understandably, they objected to amateurish labeling of behaviors as instincts without proper experimental analyses. Also, they were repelled by the pseudogenetics of Hitler and other purveyors of race prejudice (29). On the other hand, impressed with the power of conditioning *procedures*, they proclaimed their faith in analysis of experience as the starting point for behavioral science —as though experience, like the Cheshire Cat's grin, could exist without the organism. "Our conclusion . . . is that we have no real evidence for the inheritance of traits," said Watson *(10)*. While acknowledging that there are heritable differences in form and structure, he claimed there is no evidence that those differences are related to function, because "hereditary structure lies ready to be shaped in a thousand different ways" *(30)*. Behaviorism still makes the gratuitous uniformity assumption that all genetic combinations are equally plastic

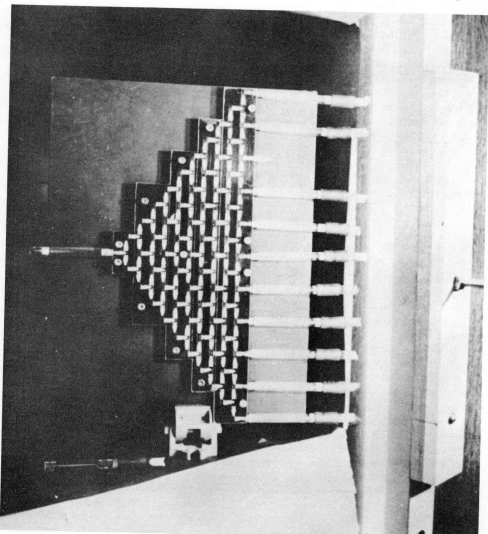

FIG. 1. Vertical ten-unit plastic maze facing a fluorescent tube. Squads of flies introduced in the vial at left are collected from the vials at right. They are attracted through the maze by the odor of food and by light. Small trap-like funnels, having a larger opening continuous with the alley surfaces and a small one debouching in midair, discourage backward movement in the maze. [HIRSCH (51).]

and respond in like fashion to environmental influences (31).

We are now in a more fruitful period. Experimental analysis is yielding information about genes and chromosomes and how they act. The way is open to understanding molecular—ultimately submolecular (32)—mechanisms and to following metabolic pathways between genes and phenotypes. In the honey bee, Rothenbuhler (24) found that resistance to foulbrood disease (a bacterial infection of the larvae) depends on homozygosity of the worker bees for recessive alleles of at least two genes: one which enables them to uncap compartments containing infected larvae and another which enables them to remove those larvae from the hive (33).

Médioni (34), in his studies of phototaxis (light-oriented locomotion) in *Drosophila*, employed genetic, physiological, and stimulus variables in an exquisitely detailed analysis articulating relations between components of behavior, components of the organism, and stimulus properties of the environment. Behaviorally, phototaxis is resolvable into five components: (i) a photopositive phase; (ii) a sensory adaptation factor [Viaud's *capacité photopathique* (35)]; (iii) an exploratory phase; (iv) a photokinetic factor; and (v) a photoinhibition phase. The interplay of the behavioral components depends on (i) the intensity and wavelength of light, (ii) the differential effects of stimulation through the ocelli and through the compound eyes, (iii) sex, and (iv) genetic background and geographical region of racial origin. Races in 17 regions of the Northern Hemisphere, from Japan across Eurasia to America, arrange themselves into two distinct North-South clines, an Eastern and a Western, in which light preference diminishes with latitude of origin.

Our laboratory has made the most detailed analysis, to date, of relations between the genome and a behavioral phenotype in studies of geotaxis (gravity-oriented locomotion) in *Drosophila*. Behavioral distributions for populations are obtained in the

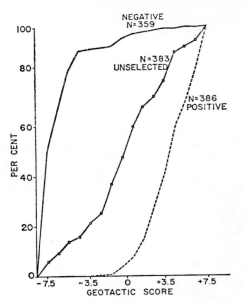

FIG. 2. Cumulated percentages of animals (males and females) that received geotactic scores in a 15-unit maze, from an unselected foundation population (middle curve) and from the two selected strains (outer curves). [Hirsch and Erlenmeyer-Kimling (52).]

apparatus shown in Figure 1. Selective breeding from a geotactically and genetically heterogeneous foundation population has produced the two strains shown in Figure 2, which have diametrically opposite response tendencies. Other methods produced three populations differing with respect to both degree and kind of similarity in chromosome constitution among their members. Two parameters of their behavioral distributions were thus controlled. The least dispersion occurred in the population in which all members carried two of the three large chromosomes in identical form. The other two populations, differing from each other with respect to the single chromosome distributed in identical form to all their members, differed in central tendency but not in dispersion, which was twice that of the first population. Figure 3 shows, for this model situation, the kind of prediction and control that an understanding of popu-

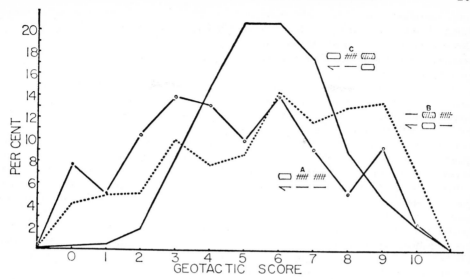

FIG. 3. Distributions of geotactic scores in a ten-unit maze for males of three populations (described in text). (Rectangles) Chromosomes carried in identical form by all members of a population; (dashes) chromosomes varying at random; (hatching) heterozygosity; (half-arrowhead) the Y chromosome of males. (In Fig. 2 the abscissa scale was reversed and the zero point was shifted to the center of the distribution.) [HIRSCH (51).]

lation structure and its genetic basis may yield.

Erlenmeyer-Kimling's subsequent chromosome analysis shows that genes influencing the response to gravity are distributed throughout the genome. The first two chromosomes in the unselected foundation population contribute to positive geotaxis, and the third to negative. Selection pressure both enhances and reduces their effects, depending on the direction of selection (36).

At the molecular level, an exciting development is the measurement, by Hydén and Egyházi (37), of changes, with learning, in the RNA base ratios in nuclei of specific mammalian nerve cells and in their glia. This work, if confirmed, represents a major advance in our search for the physical basis of experience. Hydén's speculative, but interesting, suggestion is that the electrical disturbance of the nerve impulse releases, in some as yet unspecified way, a repressed region of chromosomal DNA. This DNA henceforth produces, on demand, its characteristic RNA to code the protein that facilitates forward transmission of the particular temporal pattern of electrical frequencies that first released the DNA. This suggestion is the first to be made that appears capable of reconciling the universal feature of improvement with practice with the idiosyncratic features of individual performance. In this schema the individuality encoded in the chromosomal DNA of each genotype at meiosis and fertilization is propagated directly into the learning and memory mechanism by means of the established sequence of DNA producing RNA producing protein. Such a schema could thus accommodate the distributions of individual differences invariably found in studies of learning and memory.

The study of man is also moving beyond the stage of wondering whether we can find a heritability for this or that behavior. Phenylpyruvic oligophrenia, a form of mental deficiency accompanied by a high concentration of phenylpyruvic acid in the urine, had early been traced to a gene-controlled enzymatic deficiency in phenylalanine metabolism *(27)*. Now, Down's syndrome (mongolism) has been associated with the presence of extra chromosomal material *(24)*.

Human populations are dimorphic for taste sensitivity to certain bitter compounds. Different races show different distributions with respect to this trait, as well as to almost every other trait that has been genetically analyzed. On the basis of behavioral observations indicating that an individual's ability to taste certain compounds depends upon the presence of his own saliva, Cohen and Ogdon *(38)* suggested that components of the saliva might play a critical role in tasting ability. Lately, Fischer and his coworkers *(39)* have shown in vitro that the bitter-tasting thioureas are oxidized faster by the saliva of nontasters than by that of tasters. Presumably, at low concentrations so much of the compound is oxidized in a nontaster's mouth that the few molecules which might reach their receptor sites remain undetectable. Furthermore, Fischer and his associates have now confirmed Cohen and Ogdon's finding that, in order to taste certain compounds at all, even a taster requires the presence of his own saliva. Superficially at least, it appears that saliva, like many body tissues, cannot be transplanted. A valuable observation here would involve an exchange of saliva between identical twins, who are presumably alike in body chemistry.

The ramifications of the taster phenomenon appear to be legion. There is a significantly higher incidence of nontasting of the bitter compounds among persons with nodular goitre *(40)*, among patients with congenital athyreotic cretinism, and among parents of the latter as well *(41)*. In another study *(42)* it was found that, among 38 parents of children with Down's syndrome, none was able to taste quinine. Furthermore, all but one of the fathers in that sample were unable to taste a bitter thiourea. Finally, a correlation exists between taste sensitivity and dislike of foods: the more sensitive tasters find more foods objectionable *(43)*.

RACE DIFFERENCES

A problem of continuing social importance, for an understanding of which most behavioral scientists have lacked a proper conceptual basis, is the question of race differences. To the liberals this question has been a continuing source of embarrassment *(44)*. They have made little progress in answering it since the signing of our Constitution and Bill of Rights, when it was *asserted* that all men are created equal. To the prejudiced the question has presented no difficulties, because they *know* other races are inferior to their own; this seems as obvious to them as the flatness of the earth did to our ancestors.

This question appears in another perspective when it is examined in the light of current knowledge of population structure. Dobzhansky *(45)* has clearly called attention to the difference between equality and identity. Genotypic uniqueness creates biochemical individuality. Without enforcing conformity—irrespective of heredity, training, or ability—a democratic ethico-social system offers to all equality of opportunity and equal treatment before the law. Genetics explains both individual and population uniqueness. Even though reproductively isolated populations belong to the same species and have the same genes, the relative frequencies of different alleles of genes in their gene pools are almost certain to differ. Mutations and recombinations will occur at different places, at different times, and with differing frequencies. Furthermore, selection pressures will also vary *(46)*. In analyzing data from such populations we have learned to ask, not whether they are different, but, rather, in what ways they differ.

Races are populations that differ in gene frequencies. Observations on populations are summarized in distributions, so often assumed to be normal *(47)*. When we add the assumption of common variance, or make transformations to obtain it, the data fit into the ever popular analysis-of-variance models. *The* difference between two populations must then be a difference between means, because the assumptions of normality and homogeneity of variance for the model leave no other property with respect to which the distributions can differ. The final step in this fantastic chain of reasoning has recently been taken in *Science* by Garrett (48). He ignores individual differences and claims that wherever two populations differ on some scale of measurement, no matter how vague, any individual from the population with *the* higher mean is better than any individual in the other population, and that intermarriage will "be not only dysgenic but socially disastrous"!

Distributions have other properties, such as dispersion, skewness, and kurtosis (peakedness), and no single one is exclusively important. Where these other properties have been examined, the inadequacy of a preoccupation with the central tendency and a hasty assumption of normality has been easy to document (49). There is no reason to expect two populations with different heredities and different environments to have precisely the same distribution for any trait. We can expect to find varying combinations of similarities and differences in the several properties of distributions when we compare different populations for a given trait, or any set of populations for different traits. Furthermore, the number of traits for which we could make comparisons is effectively unlimited, and many of the traits will be uncorrelated (11). Again, a lack of intrinsic correlation would come as no surprise to a behavioral science that understands its materials, because traits are the developmental result of thousands of genes, most of which, because of crossing over, sooner or later undergo independent assortment.

For ease of exposition, I have not considered environment in discussing race. Certainly, it is no less important than genetic endowment. The ontogeny of a responsible and effective citizen requires prolonged socialization, highly dependent upon the socializing agency. A genotype must have an environment in which to develop a phenotype. But the same genotype can produce quite different phenotypes, depending on the environments in which it may develop. Furthermore, a given environment can nurture quite different phenotypes, depending on the genotypes which may develop there. This fact is attested daily by parents and teachers who find that a method of tuition admirably successful with one child may be worthless with another, who nevertheless can learn by a different method. So, while environment makes an undeniably important contribution to the particular values obtained in phenotypic measurements, consideration of particular environments should not change our general picture of population structure. Without an appreciation of the genotypic structure of populations, the behavioral sciences have no basis for distinguishing individual differences that are attributable to differences in previous history from those that are not, and no basis for understanding any differences whatsoever where there is a common history.

CONCLUSIONS AND SUMMARY

Traditionally, many behavioral scientists have assumed that individuals start life uniformly alike, and that individual differences result only from differentiating experiences. To assume this is as contradictory to the established fact of uniqueness at conception as to assume that entropy is as likely to decrease as it is to increase. Recognition of the contradictory nature of this assumption does not make the role of experience in ontogeny any less important, but we now realize that the effects of experience are conditioned by the genotype. Therefore, a careful reconsideration of our statistical tools, experimental methods, theoretical models, and research goals is in order.

Many problems that have generated violent controversy now appear in totally different perspective. Introspection may provide a legitimate probe into subjective experience, without requiring intersubjective agreement. The concept of a normal individual has no generality. The outlook for understanding the physical basis of behavior has never been more promising. Awareness that a multiplicity of variable systems comprise its substrate, however, emphasizes the integrity and importance of the different levels of biosocial organization at which the several sciences work. In place of reductionism, we may now think of studying correlations between phenomena, reliably observed and analyzed at various levels, and of assessing the correlations over an ever-widening range of conditions. The controversial aspects of the heredity-environment question and of the race-differences question arise from failure to understand the genetics of individual and population differences and the rationale of their statistical analysis (50).

REFERENCES

AND NOTES

1. BUSH, R. R., and F. MOSTELLER: *Stochastic Models for Learning* (Wiley, New York, 1955).
2. ROSNER, B. S.: In *Psychology: A Study of a Science*, S. Koch, Ed. (McGraw-Hill, New York, 1962), vol. 4, p. 299.
3. Psychophysics is the study of changes in response associated with changes in physically specified stimuli.
4. BRELAND, K., and M. BRELAND: *Am. Psychologist* **16**, 681 (1961).
5. MAYR, E.: *Animal Species and Evolution* (Harvard Univ. Press, Cambridge, 1963), p. 5.
6. MORGAN, T. H., A. H. STURTEVANT, H. J. MULLER, and C. B. BRIDGES: *The Mechanism of Mendelian Heredity* (Holt, New York, 1915).
7. DOBZHANSKY, T.: *Genetics and the Origin of Species* (Columbia Univ. Press, New York, ed. 2, 1941).

8. BENZER, S.: *Proc. Natl. Acad. Sci. U. S.* **47**, 403 (1961); S. BENZER and S. P. CHAMPE: *Ibid.* p. 1025; S. P. CHAMPE and S. BENZER: *Ibid.* **48**, 532 (1962).
9. HIRSCH, J.: In *Roots of Behavior*, E. Bliss, Ed. (Hoeber, New York, 1962), p. 6. This calculation has provoked intense resistance. Its implications for well-encrusted modes of thinking in the "establishment" of the behavioral sciences are clearly most unwelcome. In an already legendary correspondence (part of which Mosteller circulated privately without informing me), F. Mosteller and J. Tukey independently attempted to disprove it. Both mathematicians overlooked the simple empirical fact that two sexes are required to produce children in the human species. Of course, my calculation is most conservative: assuming 10,000 human genes and an average of four alleles each gives ten combinations per locus and the astronomical number of $10^{10,000}$ potential human genotypes!
10. WATSON, J. B.: *Behaviorism* (Univ. of Chicago Press, Chicago, new ed., 1959), pp. 11, 103.
11. WILLIAMS, R. J.: *Biochemical Individuality* (Wiley, New York, 1956); *Science* **126**, 453 (1957); R. J. WILLIAMS, R. B. PELTON, and F. L. SIEGEL: *Proc. Natl. Acad. Sci. U. S.* **48**, 1461 (1962).
12. BEACH, F. A., and J. R. WILSON [*Proc. Natl. Acad. Sci. U. S.* **49**, 624 (1963)] have demonstrated that this is not the case.
13. KRECHEVSKY, I.: *J. Comp. Psychol.* **16**, 99 (1933).
14. RICHTER, C. P.: *J. Natl. Cancer Inst.* **15**, 727 (1954).
15. PERUTZ, M. F.: *Proteins and Nucleic Acids Structure and Function* (Elsevier, Amsterdam, 1962); R. V. ECK: *Science* **140**, 477 (1963).
16. WILLIAMS, R. J.: *Science* **124**, 276 (1956); R. W. GERARD: *Behavioral Sci.* **3**, 137 (1958).
17. GLASS, B.: In *Expanding Goals of Genetics in Psychiatry*, F. J. Kallmann, Ed. (Grune and Stratton, New York, 1962), p. 259.
18. SKINNER, B. F.: *Science* **140**, 951 (1963).
19. WILKINS, M. F. H.: *Ibid.*, p. 941.
20. BORING, E. G.: *Am. J. Psychol.* **59**, 173 (1946).
21. GRAHAM, C. H., and Y. HSIA: *Proc. Am. Phil. Soc.* **102**, 168 (1958).

22. PENFIELD, W.: *Proc. Natl. Acad. Sci. U. S.* 44, 59 (1958).

23. TRYON, R. C.: *Am. Psychologist* 18, 134 (1963).

24. FULLER, J. L., and W. R. THOMPSON: *Behavior Genetics* (Wiley, New York, 1960), p. 38.

25. THOMPSON, W. R., and A. KAHN: *Can. J. Psychol.* 9, 173 (1955).

26. McCLEARN, G. E., and D. A. RODGERS: *Quart. J. Studies Alc.* 20, 691 (1959).

27. KALLMANN, F. J.: Ed., *Expanding Goals of Genetics in Psychiatry* (Grune and Stratton, New York, 1962).

28. G. LINDZEY's phrase (private communication).

29. STEWARD, J. H.: *Science* 135, 964 (1962).

30. WATSON, J. B.: *Behaviorism* (People's Institute Publishing Co., New York, 1925), p. 77.

31. The irresistible attraction that these ideas have had in the behavioral sciences seems all the more appalling today when one reads the excellent systematic exposure of the "fallacies" of behaviorism published in 1930 by Jennings, a well-known and highly respected scientist of that period. [H. S. Jennings, *The Biological Basis of Human Nature* (Norton, New York, 1930); I thank Professor Donald D. Jensen of Indiana University for directing me to Jennings.] What is more, Watson had read Jennings. He cites those parts of the book that suit his purposes (see 10).

32. SZENT-GYÖRGYI, A.: *Introduction to a Submolecular Biology* (Academic Press, New York, 1960); M. KASHA and B. PULLMAN: Eds., *Horizons in Biochemistry Albert Szent-Györgyi Dedicatory Volume* (Academic Press, New York, 1962).

33. To demonstrate the independence of the second gene, Rothenbuhler opens compartments for bees that cannot open them themselves.

34. MÉDIONI, J.: Thesis, University of Strasbourg (1961), partially summarized in *Ergeb. Biol.* 26, 72 (1963).

35. VIAUD, G.: *J. Psychol. Normale et Pathologique* 42, 386 (1949).

36. ERLENMEYER-KIMLING, L., and J. HIRSCH: *Science* 134, 1068 (1961); J. HIRSCH and L. ERLENMEYER-KIMLING: *J. Comp. Physiol. Psychol.* 55, 722 (1962).

37. HYDÉN, H., and E. EGYHÁZI: *Proc. Natl. Acad. Sci. U. S.* 48, 1366 (1962); 49, 618 (1963).

38. COHEN, J., and D. P. OGDON: *Science* 110, 532 (1949).

39. FISCHER, R., and F. GRIFFIN: *Behavior Genetics Symposium, 17th International Congress of Psychology Washington, D. C.* (1963).

40. HARRIS, H., H. KALMUS, and W. R. TROTTER: *Lancet* 1963-II, 1038 (1949); F. D. KITCHEN, W. HOWEL-EVANS, C. A. CLARKE, and R. B. McCONNELL: *Brit. Med. J.* 1959, 1069 (1959).

41. SHEPARD, T. H.: *J. Clin. Invest.* 40, 1751 (1961).

42. FISCHER, R., A. R. KAPLAN, F. GRIFFIN, and D. W. STING: *Am. J. Mental Deficiency* 67, 849 (1963).

43. FISCHER, R., F. GRIFFIN, S. ENGLAND, and S. M. GARN: *Nature* 191, 1328 (1961).

44. *Science* 134, 1868 (1961).

45. DOBZHANSKY, T.: *ibid.* 137, 112 (1962).

46. POST, R. H.: *Eugenics Quart.* 9, 131 (1962).

47. MINCKLER, L. S.: *Science* 133, 202 (1961).

48. GARRETT, H. E.: *ibid*, 135, 982 (1962); S. GENOVÉS, *ibid.* p. 988.

49. YAMAGUCHI, H. G., C. L. HULL, J. M. FELSINGER, and A. I. GLADSTONE: *Psychol. Rev.* 55, 216 (1948); J. HIRSCH: *Am. J. Orthopsychiat.* 31, 478 (1961).

50. I am indebted to E. R. Hilgard for suggesting that I write this article and to the following for commenting on a draft of the manuscript: E. W. Caspari, J. Cohen, D. E. Dulaney, Nikki Erlenmeyer-Kimling, R. W. Frankmann, L. J. Goldsmith, D. A. Hamburg, R. C. Hostetter, C. L. Hulin, L. G. Humphreys, H. L. Jacobs, R. Kesner, G. Ksander, G. E. McClearn, J. E. McGrath, O. H. Mowrer, F. H. Palmer, D. Rosenthal, S. Ross, Leigh M. Triandis, P. Tyler, and M. W. Weir. This work is partially supported by a National Science Foundation grant (G-21238) to the Center for Advanced Study in the Behavioral Sciences, Stanford, Calif.

51. HIRSCH, J.: *J. Comp. Physiol. Psychol.* 52, 304 (1959).

52. HIRSCH, J.: and L. ERLENMEYER-KIMLING: *Science* 134, 835 (1961).

JOHN L. FULLER, CLARICE EASLER,
and MARY E. SMITH

8 Inheritance of Audiogenic Seizure Susceptibility in the Mouse

Audiogenic seizures have been the object of a great deal of study in recent years. This reading is concerned with possible genetic mechanisms underlying the inheritance of such seizures. The very important concept of *threshold* is discussed, and a theoretical model for the inheritance of seizure susceptibility is presented. The authors point out that a polygenic system operating near a threshold can sometimes produce proportions that mimic the results expected on the basis of a simpler genetic hypothesis. Appropriate backcrosses are necessary to test for such effects.

The strains designated in this reading as dba subline 2 and C57 Black subline 6 are now called DBA/2 and C57BL/6.

John L. Fuller has made many outstanding contributions to animal behavior. With W. R. Thompson he wrote *Behavior Genetics*, cited above, a most thorough review of the methods and results of this important area of research.

This reading originally appeared in *Genetics*, 1950, 35, 622–632. Reprinted by permission of authors and publisher.

Hall (1947) has reported a remarkable difference between dba and C57 black mice in their susceptibility to audiogenic seizures. When dba mice are placed in a metal tub and stimulated by the sound of a doorbell, the majority undergo violent tonic-clonic seizures which are usually fatal. The incidence of such seizures in the C57 black strain is very low. These convulsions appear to be similar to audiogenic seizures occurring in rats, which have been recently discussed by Finger (1947). Similar convulsions have been reported in Peromyscus (Dice 1935; Watson 1939) where susceptibility has been considered due to recessive genes. In 1949 Witt and Hall attributed seizure susceptibility in the house mouse to a single dominant gene which they called *As*. This hypothesis was based upon the results of the F_1, F_2 and the two backcross generations. Only their "critical backcross" of $F_1 \times$ C57bl non-reactors by C57bl failed to accord with

their single dominant gene hypothesis. Twenty-five percent of these animals underwent mild convulsive behavior which the authors attributed to minor modifying genes. Ginsburg, Miller and Zamis (1950) have postulated two or more non-dominant factors, including a single major gene essential for seizure susceptibility.

The clearcut strain difference makes these animals admirably suited for investigations of physiology of convulsions, and the physiological genetics of susceptibility. Ginsburg and Hovda (1947) in the course of studying the metabolic differences between strains, noted that one strain of dba's recovered from seizures more readily than the regular Jackson Laboratory stock of dba's. These animals were descended from a female which had developed in the uterus of a C57bl female following an ovum transfer. They suggested that a non-genic maternal influence might affect recovery. The experiments described in this paper were initiated to test this hypothesis by comparing reciprocal crosses. The preliminary results were not in accordance with the single dominent gene hypothesis, and a series of experiments was initiated on the factors producing variability in the risk of convulsions in hybrids.

Methods

The subjects of this experiment were C57 black subline 6 Jax mice descended by brother-sister matings from Witt and Hall's original strain. The dba mice were of subline 2 and had been inbred for over 50 generations. Witt and Hall used dba subline 1, and it has been shown that the authors' subline has an even higher susceptibility than Hall's original stock.

The stimulation method used was identical to that of Witt and Hall except that behavior observations were not made for a two-minute period following bell ringing, and each animal, provided it survived that long, was exposed on five successive days (instead of four) to two minutes of bell ringing. The mice were 30 days of age on the first trial day except for F_2 animals which were started on Mondays at an age of 29 to 35 days.

Our index of seizure susceptibility differs from that of Witt and Hall. These investigators classified each animal as a "reactor" or "non-reactor." A "reactor" was defined as an animal which convulsed on any one of its four trials. Their tables show 93.3 percent of the dba stock to be "reactors," and 94.7 percent of the C57 black stock to be "non-reactors," while the F_1 mice included 94.5 percent of reactors. These figures indicate that the convulsion phenotype does not always follow the genotype, and that a classification of genotypes on their basis cannot be expected to be accurate to better than ±5 percent. It seems to be more satisfactory to define seizure susceptibility in terms of the risk of an induced convulsion during a standard exposure. This risk cannot be determined on one individual, but it can be calculated for populations of different genotypes. Since the percentage of convulsions is usually highest on first exposure, the first exposure seizure risk is the best single index of susceptibility. In estimating this value all convulsions of any degree of severity are included, but preconvulsive activity, such as hopping or wild circling, is not. The percentage of seizures among survivors of the first trial on successive trials is of physiological and genetic interest, particularly when dealing with genetically heterogeneous groups such as the F_2, F_3 and backcrosses.

Reciprocal Cross and Sex Differences

The principal results of this investigation are summarized in Table 8-1, which gives the percentage of convulsions and of deaths for each group of mice studied. No statistically significant differences have been found between reciprocal crosses and they have been grouped together in all summarizing tables. There are nine possible pairings of male and female subjects with the same genetic background. If the comparison is based upon the percentage of "reactors" (Witt and Hall's criterion), males have a higher percentage in three pairings, females in three, and the remaining three cases are equal. If the comparison is based upon first trial seizure risk, the males are higher in five cases, females in two, and two are equal. The most extreme sex differences are found in the $F_1 \times C57$ black backcross and F_1 hybrids. In the latter group females showed a higher susceptibility than males. This particular group of mice appears to be exceptional and will be discussed below. In fact, a repeat sample of F_1's included on the last line of Table 8-1 shows a strong reversal of the sex difference. The effect of sex on susceptibility appears to be influenced by the genotype of the individual. It is unimportant in genotypes with very high or very low susceptibility, and influential in genotypes of moderate susceptibility.

TABLE 8-1

Incidence of convulsions (C) and death (D) from convulsions in dba, C57bl, and hybrids

FEMALE P	MALE P	SEX	PERCENT CONVULSERS N	PERCENT CONVULSERS %	TRIAL 1 N	TRIAL 1 %C	TRIAL 1 %D	TRIAL 2 N	TRIAL 2 %C	TRIAL 2 %D	TRIAL 3 N	TRIAL 3 %C	TRIAL 3 %D	TRIAL 4 N	TRIAL 4 %C	TRIAL 4 %D	TRIAL 5 N	TRIAL 5 %C	TRIAL 5 %D	TRIALS 1–5 N	TRIALS 1–5 %C	TRIALS 1–5 %D	D/C ×100	% SURVIVORS
dba	dba	F	41	100	41	98	85	6	83	33	4	100	100				1	0	0	45	96.1	80.4	87.0	0.0
dba	dba	M	54	100	54	100	87	7	100	57	3	33	33	2	50	50	20	50	5	67	94.0	79.1	84.7	2.0
F₁	dba	F	59	97	59	90	54	27	33	19	22	41	5	21	48	5	17	47	0	148	60.8	26.3	43.2	32.3
F₁	dba	M	69	93	69	87	61	27	70	22	21	57	10	19	58	10	7	29	0	152	74.3	33.5	45.1	24.6
dba	F₁	F	31	94	31	97	65	11	55	27	8	38	8	8	63	13	10	40	20	65	66.2	37.0	55.8	22.6
dba	F₁	M	32	100	32	97	47	17	59	30	12	75	8	11	73	9	15	40	0	82	75.7	29.3	28.7	25.0
dba	C57	F	25	76	25	32	16	21	10	0	21	33	19	17	47	12	17	29	0	99	31.3	10.1	32.0	60.0
dba	C57	M	25	52	25	20	12	22	18	14	19	26	5	18	22	6	15	60	13	101	22.3	7.9	35.4	68.0
C57	dba	F	25	84	25	48	20	20	20	10	18	56	6	17	53	12	18	22	6	104	45.8	12.8	27.9	52.0
C57	dba	M	25	64	25	28	8	23	26	13	20	45	10	18	22	0	22	14	7	94	29.9	7.7	25.7	68.0
C57	F₁	F	49	37	49	18	10	44	2	2	43	5	2	42	4	0	42	8	0	220	8.2	4.1	50.0	79.6
C57	F₁	M	35	37	35	29	20	28	11	4	27	11	7	25	3	3	30	8	0	140	13.5	7.1	52.5	71.5
F₁	C57	F	37	24	37	16	14	32	9	3	31	0	0	31	9	5	21	0	0	161	6.2	4.3	71.0	81.2
F₁	C57	M	30	37	30	30	23	23	4	4	22	5	0	22	32	3	36	5	0	104	11.8	7.6	64.3	70.0
F₁	F₁	F	55	69	55	60	29	39	41	5	37	30	3	37	24	10	26	31	6	204	40.7	10.3	25.3	61.8
F₁	F₁	M	57	70	57	60	40	33	27	9	30	17	3	29	0	0	12	12	0	175	33.1	17.1	51.7	45.6
C57	C57	F	25	0	25	0	0	25	0	0	25	0	0	25	0	0	25	0	0	125	0	0	—	100.0
C57	C57	M	25	0	25	0	0	25	0	0	25	0	0	25	0	0	25	0	0	125	0	0	—	100.0
(dba)[b]	(C57)	M	73	79[a]	79	74	51	17[a]	6[a]	0[a]	17[a]	12[a]	6[a]	16[a]	13[a]	0[a]	16[a]	31[a]	0[a]	104[a]	35.6[a]	21.2[a]	59.6[a]	42.1[a]
(C57)	(dba)	F																						

[a] Based upon a subsample of 38 F₁ animals.
[b] This is referred to as the "repeat" F₁.

TABLE 8–2

Summary of selected results by genetic groups.

GROUP	N	PERCENT CONVULSERS 5 TRIALS	PERCENT[a] "REACTORS" WITT & HALL 4 TRIALS	TRIAL 1 %C	TRIAL 1 %D	TRIAL 1 D/C	PERCENT SURVIVORS 5 TRIALS
dba	96	100	93.3±4.7	99	86±3.5	87±3.5	1
$F_1 \times$ dba	191	95 ±1.6	90.9±6.1	92±2.0	57±4.6	62±3.7	27 ±3.2
F_1 "original"	100	68 ±4.7	90.5±3.3	32±4.7	14±3.5	44±8.8	62 ±4.9
F_1 "repeat"	73	79[b]±6.6	90.5±3.3	74±4.9	51±5.8	69±6.3	42[b]±8.0
F_2	112	70 ±4.3	77.3±5.0	60±4.6	35±4.5	58±6.0	53 ±4.7
$F_1 \times$ C57bl	151	34 ±3.8	52.8±6.0	23±3.4	16±3.0	70±7.7	76 ±3.5
C57bl	50	0	5.3±3.6	0	0	0	100

a Data from Witt and Hall (1949).
b Based upon a subsample of 38 cases.

The Single Dominant Gene Hypothesis

If the sexes and reciprocal crosses are combined, as in Table 8–2, it is possible to compare these results with those of Witt and Hall. The two parent strains which were used differ more widely than those of Witt and Hall, and all hybrids except the $F_1 \times$ dba have a lower percentage of "reactors" than these authors obtained. It should also be noted that hybrids which would be expected to behave like dba's under the single dominant gene hypothesis ($F_1 \times$ dba and F_1) actually differ considerably, particularly if death-convulsion ratios and percentages of survivors of five trials are taken into consideration.

Both the "original" and "repeat" samples of F_1 are intermediate in susceptibility between the parental strains. It is probable that the repeat group is more representative of the total F_1 population. The original F_1 sample is exceptional in having a higher susceptibility in females than in males, in not showing the highest seizure incidence on the first trial, and in not fitting into the progression of susceptibility indices. If the F_1 repeat group replaces the original sample, indices of susceptibility are seen to decrease regularly in relation to the proportion of dba genes

contained in each group. The single dominant gene hypothesis may be formally tested by calculating χ^2 for the F_2 and $F_1 \times$ C57bl groups on the assumption that all animals carrying this gene will convulse within five trials and 99 percent of them will convulse on the first trial.

The values marked with asterisks are significant at better than the 1 percent level, so that the dominant gene hypothesis may be rejected for this particular cross.

We may now examine the evidence as it relates to the number of genes involved. Will a single gene producing high susceptibility in homozygous animals and moderate susceptibility (74 percent) in heterozygous animals explain the results? In calculating expected values under this assumption the F_1 repeat group is taken as the standard for the heterozygote. The calculations may be summarized as follows:

Except for the first trial seizure risk for the $F_1 \times$ C57, the calculated and observed risks do not differ more than might be explained by errors of random sampling and the occurrence of modifying genes. The assumption of a single major partially-dominant convulsing gene is not contraindicated by these data.

As Wright (1934) has pointed out, however, the occurrence of expected ratios

GROUP	CONVULSE WITHIN 5 TRIALS				CONVULSE ON FIRST TRIAL		
	N	EXPECTED	OBSERVED	χ^2	EXPECTED	OBSERVED	χ^2
F_2	112	84	78	1.72	83	66	13.41°
$F_1 \times$ C57bl	151	75.5	51	14.9°	75	35	43.7°

	GENOTYPES	FIRST TRIAL SEIZURE RISK CALCULATED	OBSERVED
$F_1 \times$ dba	1/2 AA, 1/2 Aa	$(99+74)/2 = 86.5$	92 ± 2.0
F_2	1/4 AA, 1/2 Aa, 1/4 aa	$(99+2(74)+0)/4 = 61.8$	60 ± 4.6
$F_1 \times$ C57bl	1/2 Aa, 1/2 aa	$(74+0)/2 = 37.0$	23 ± 3.3

		CALCULATED TOTAL CONVULSIONS	OBSERVED
$F_1 \times$ dba	1/2 AA, 1/2 Aa	$(100+79)/2 = 89.5$	95 ± 1.8
F_2	1/4 AA, 1/2 Aa, 1/4 aa	$(100+2(79)+0)/4 = 64.5$	70 ± 4.6
$F_1 \times$ C57bl	1/2 Aa, 1/2 aa	$(79+0)/2 = 39.5$	34 ± 3.9

in the F_1, F_2, and backcross generations is not a certain proof of single gene control. An attempt was made to utilize Wright's procedure for estimation of the number of genes involved, by comparing the percentages of 1) non-convulsions, 2) convulsions and recovery, and 3) convulsions with death, in the various populations. The method proved inapplicable because of the fact that some populations include too few members in some of the three classes. Also, evidence described below favors a hypothesis that death from convulsions does not merely result from a more severe convulsion or a greater seizure susceptibility. The strongest evidence in favor of a multiple gene hypothesis is the fact that three matings of non-convulsing F_2 animals yielded an F_3 which is practically identical in seizure risk to the $F_1 \times$ C57bl group. This small sample (n=17) includes two subjects dying on the first trial, nine resisting five trials, one which recovered five times from severe convulsions, and five others which convulsed at least once. Certainly genes lowering resistance were well distributed in this group selected on the basis of successfully withstanding five exposures without convulsions. The results are most simply interpreted by a multiple factor hypothesis under which the number of susceptibility genes determines seizure risk. Animals in the F_2 having low genetic seizure risk may produce offspring with a high risk through segregation and recombination. Very large samples of F_2 and F_3 subjects must be available, however, to provide a critical test for the number of gene pairs involved, because of the fact that in low dilution there is at present no way to distinguish these genes. In fact, the detailed genetics must await a method of classifying phenotypes which is based upon a quantitative unit of susceptibility, not a simple dichotomy into convulser or non-convulser.

The Physiological Gradient of Susceptibility

It has been shown above that there is no simple correspondence between genotype and phenotype in respect to audiogenic seizure incidence. This is well demonstrated in the genetically homogeneous F_1 which is extremely variable in seizure susceptibility. Furthermore, seizure susceptibility is not constant in one animal from day to day. One mouse may resist four exposures and die on the fifth, another may convulse and recover on the second exposure and be resistant on four other trials, while still another convulses and recovers five times. If one interprets the data from a statistical point of view, it must be concluded that the genotype actually determines the proportion of time during which an individual is susceptible. Mice of our dba subline 2 strain are almost always susceptible, the C57 blacks practically never susceptible, and the F_1's susceptible somewhere between 32 percent and 74 percent of the time. The extreme variability of the F_1's is, in fact, predictable on the basis of the hypothesis that what appears to be a character of alternative expression is in reality a quantitative character which varies over a wide range. The assay of this character by bell ringing merely divides the group into animals above and below a threshold at the moment of testing. Thus, the mode of inheritance appears to parallel that found by Wright (1934) for polydactyly and Wright and Wagner (1935) for otocephaly in the guinea pig, and by Heston (1942a and b) for lung cancer in mice. Audiogenic seizure susceptibility differs from these examples because no gross structural changes have been found, nor is any individual absolutely committed to a definite position on the scale. Susceptibility may shift up and down in an apparently random manner during the five day test period. However, this shifting apparently occurs within genetically prescribed limits which are the same for all members of the same genotype. In the repeat F_1 group the probability of not seizing on the first trial is 0.26 and of not seizing on any one of trials 2 to 5 is 0.85. The probability of not seizing on any trial is $0.26 \times 0.854 = 0.222$. The expected number of non-convulsers in 5 trials for the sample of 38 is 8.36, and the observed value, 8, is not significantly different.

If the non-genetic factors operate in a random manner, each genotype should include members grouped symmetrically

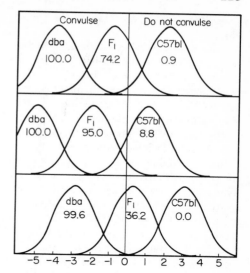

FIG. 1. Changes in convulsive risk on first trial (figures under curves) associated with conditions shifting physiological susceptibility by one standard deviation. The abscissa is a scale of physiological susceptibility. Each genotype is assumed to vary normally about some point on this scale. The convulsive risk is dependent upon the proportion of the curve to the left of an arbitrary threshold. (a) The upper section represents the situation in the 'repeat' F_1; (b) the middle section approximates the results obtained by Witt and Hall; (c) the lower section approximates the results in the authors' 'original' F_1.

about a mean value of susceptibility. The curves of figure 1 express these relationships graphically. The abscissae represent differences of susceptibility in units of the standard deviation (t units), while the ordinates are arbitrarily drawn so that the area under each curve equals unity.

A genotype with a convulsive risk of 50 percent would have its midpoint at zero on the scale; genotypes with less resistance will have their midpoints in the negative region. At any moment in time a cross section of the genotype will yield seizure susceptible animals in proportion to the portion of the area under the curve lying to the left of the threshold. Individual animals, however, at different points in time shift their relationship to the threshold.

External conditions such as temperature, and the degree of restraint or mechanical agitation have been shown in preliminary experiments to affect seizure susceptibility. Such factors may be considered to move the population as a whole to the right or left along the susceptibility axis. Figure 1 demonstrates that changes of this sort influence the seizure risk of F_1 hybrids much more than the parent strains. The parents are assumed to be 6 t units apart and the F_1 to be exactly intermediate. The "normal" position of the F_1 in figure 1a is based upon the repeat F_1 sample. A convulsant agent is assumed in figure 1b to shift all curves to the left by one unit; and in figure 1c an anticonvulsant agent shifts them all one unit to the right. The parental values are arbitrarily selected, as the data to locate them exactly are not available. The striking fact is that a change which greatly affects the hybrid is relatively unimportant to the parents. This accords with the observed agreement between investigators with respect to the susceptibility of the parent strains, and the variability between different samples of the hybrids.

The writers are unable to explain the discrepancy between their own "original" and "repeat" F_1 groups. The procedure for each was supposed to be the same, though the testing was done by a different person in a different room at a different time of year. Presumably some subtle environmental influence was responsible. Figures 1a and 1c approximately represent the two samples. Figure 1b approximates the Witt and Hall data which were obtained from a different subline of the dba strain.

Comparison of Convulsion Risk and Death Risk

In the discussion of results thus far, only the incidence of convulsions has been considered. The hybrids, however, differ from the dba stock in another particular,

the ability to recover from an induced seizure. Eighty-seven percent of convulsing dba's die on the first trial, and only one percent survive five trials. The dba backcross has nearly as high a convulsion risk as the dba, but only 62 percent of the first trial convulsers die, and 27 percent survive five trials. Data for the other hybrids are included in Table 8–1.

The lowered death rate could be due to 1) less severe convulsions, 2) to an increased stress resistance in the hybrids, derived presumably from the C57bl line, and 3) to a combination of these factors. The fact that the first trial death/convulsion ratio is so constant in the hybrids, although the incidence of seizures varies widely, is evidence in favor of a separate gene system influencing stress resistance. It is impossible to secure direct evidence on the ability of C57 blacks to recover from audiogenic seizures, since the incidence is so low. However, convulsions can be induced in C57 black mice by applying alternating current to the head. Electrogenic convulsions have many features in common with audiogenic convulsions, and in some strains of mice frequently result in death (Stone, Eady, and Hanty 1949). Mr. A. J. Coulombre, working in the authors' laboratory, has determined the death/convulsion ratio in C57bl mice at 30-40 days of age. Twelve mice given 7.5 milliamperes through electrodes applied to their ears convulsed, and five died. Although the sample is small, the rate of recovery from E.C.S. in C57bl appears to be definitely higher than the rate of recovery of dba mice from audiogenic seizures, and is comparable to the rate of recovery in dba×C57 hybrids. Furthermore, observation indicates that animals may recover from long severe seizures, and die from seizures of apparently lesser intensity. Only mild forms of seizure involving hind limb paralysis without falling on the side never result in death.

Further evidence of independence of susceptibility and recovery has been obtained from a study of seizure latency. The

TABLE 8–3

Distribution of seizure latencies for first three trials.

GROUP	LATENCY IN SECONDS										N	M
	0–9	10–19	20–29	30–39	40–49	50–59	60–69	70–79	80–89	90–99		
dba	1	20	3	32	43	9	—	—	—	—	108	35.8±1.2
$F_1 \times$ dba	2	24	12	83	90	29	9	—	—	—	249	38.9±0.8
F_1	—	—	1	2	12	44	15	3	—	1	78	55.2±1.1
F_2	2	1	—	16	47	13	2	1	—	—	82	43.6±1.1
$F_1 \times$ C57	—	—	—	2	18	14	8	4	2	—	48	54.5±1.7
Total	5	45	16	125	210	109	34	8	2	1	565	—

interval between the onset of each convulsion and the beginning of the stimulus was recorded to the nearest second. The distribution of latencies is given in Table 8–3. It is clear that the seizure latencies in the F_1 and $F_1 \times$ C57 are significantly higher than in dba or $F_1 \times$ dba. The two latter groups have a bimodal distribution of latencies, and there is a hint of bimodal-

ity in the F_2. The cause of this bimodality in the highly inbred parental strain presents an interesting problem for future experimentation. The data of Table 8–3 are wholly consistent with the hypothesis that average seizure latency is an index of physiological susceptibility to audiogenic seizures. The distribution of the latencies is consistent with the hypothesis that the

TABLE 8–4

Analysis of variance of seizure latency according to genetic group and outcome of convulsions.[a]

	dba		F_1		W	D
	n_1	$\bar{x}_1$	n_2	$\bar{x}_2$		
Recover	27	34.4	59	54.7	18.52	20.3
Die	117	34.7	45	53.7	32.50	20.0

[a] In the analysis of variance calculated below $\bar{x}$ and D have been coded by dividing by 5. Correction for disproportion in the subclass numbers has been made according to Snedecor (1946, p. 284).

SOURCE OF VARIATION	d.f.	SUM OF SQUARES (UNCORRECTED)	CORRECTION FOR DISPROPORTION	MEAN SQUARE
Genetic	1	921.61	147.84	773.77
Outcome	1	156.43	147.84	8.59
Interaction	1			0.80
Individuals	246	1152.16		4.68

F (for genetic variance) = 773.77/4.68 = 165.33 (significant at better than 1%)
F (for outcome) = 8.59/4.68 = 1.83 (not significant)
F (for interaction) = 0.80/4.68 = 0.17 (not significant)

[a] Additional cases have been added to those reported in Table 8–3 so that the numbers and means differ slightly. With respect to seizure latency the "original" and "repeat" F_1 samples are the same.

dba parent contributes genes reducing latency and the C57 parent contributes genes increasing latency. When these genes produce latencies of more than 80 seconds, convulsions seldom result. Hence the seizure latency of the C57 backcross is essentially the same as the F_1, although the seizure risk is much less.

Is seizure latency also related to death risk? An analysis of variance according to the genotype and outcome was carried out with the dba and F_1 hybrids. The results, summarized in Table 8–4, show that only the difference between genotypes is significant, and there is no relationship between fatal or non-fatal outcome and latency. Convulsion risk and death risk once a convulsion is initiated depend upon different physiological mechanisms.

Discussion

The findings reported here provide a basis for reconciling divergent results on the seizure susceptibility of dba and C57bl hybrids. Although the conclusions presented here regarding the type of genic control of susceptibility differ from those of Witt and Hall, their data are perfectly consistent with the hypothesis presented. Subline differences may be expected to shift populations along the axis of physiological susceptibility, and the effect upon seizure risk will depend upon the particular region in which the shift occurs. Another probable cause of variation in results with hybrids, is the expected greater sensitivity of genotypes near the threshold to environmental influences. Evidence has been presented to show that such influences may be subtle, and hard to detect even when all ordinary precautions are taken.

The clear separation of seizure risk and death risk is of importance in considering the significance of experiments on the physiology of seizures. Ginsburg and coworkers (1947) have reported several agents which protect against death without altering seizure incidence. It is almost certain that these operate on the recovery mechanism rather than on the physiological gradient of susceptibility postulated in this paper. Since the protective agents are related to modification of brain metabolism, it is probable that resistance to death from seizure depends upon the ability of the brain to sustain metabolism during the anoxia produced by the cessation of respiration at the climax of the convulsion.

The only clue to the nature of the physiological gradient of susceptibility is in the relationship of susceptibility and seizure latency. If one assumes that impulses entering the central nervous system over the auditory nerve cause the accumulation of a substance or produce a polarized state, then differences in the rate of removal or destruction of the substance or leakage of electric charges would have an effect on the amount of time needed to reach a threshold. If the rate of destruction were sufficiently rapid the threshold would never be attained. Further speculation is of little value until experiments are designed to test this hypothesis.

Summary and Conclusions

1. A study of audiogenic seizure susceptibility has been made in hybrids between dba subline 2 and C57bl subline 6.

2. Susceptibility to sound induced convulsions is probably due to multiple factors although the F_1 and F_1 backcross generations contain susceptible animals in proportions which approach those which would be expected on the basis of a single gene showing incomplete dominance.

3. The gene system producing susceptibility determines the position of an animal on a physiological gradient of susceptibility.

4. The ability to recover from a sound-induced seizure is also inherited, but is independent of seizure susceptibility.

5. The latency of seizure onset is related to convulsion risk, but not to death risk.

REFERENCES

DICE, L. R., 1935   Inheritance of waltzing and of epilepsy in mice of the genus *Peromyscus. J. Mammal.* **16**: 25–35.

FINGER, F. W., 1947   Convulsive behavior in the rat. *Psych. Bull.* **44**: 201–248.

GINSBURG, B. E., and R. B. HOVDA, 1947   On the physiology of gene controlled audiogenic seizures in mice. (Abstract.) *Anat. Rec.* **99**: 65–66.

GINSBURG, B. E., D. S. MILLER, and M. J. ZAMIS, 1950   On the mode of inheritance of susceptibility to sound induced seizures in the house mouse *(Mus musculus). Genetics* **35**: 109. (Abstract.)

GINSBURG, B. E., SHERMAN ROSS, M. J. ZAMIS, and A. PERKINS, 1947   Some effects of 1(+) glutamic acid on sound induced seizures in mice. *J. comp. physiol. Psych.*

HALL, C. S., 1947   Genetic differences in fatal audiogenic seizures between two inbred strains of house mice. *J. Hered.* **38**: 2–6.

HESTON, W. E., 1942   Genetic analysis of susceptibility to induced pulmonary tumors in mice. *J. nat. Cancer Inst.* **3**: 69–78.

HESTON, W. E., 1942   Inheritance of susceptibility to spontaneous pulmonary tumors in mice. *J. nat. Cancer Inst.* **3**: 79–82.

SNEDECOR, G. W., 1946   *Statistical Methods.* Fourth Edition. xvi+485 pp. Ames, Iowa: College Press.

STONE, C. P., H. R. EADY and G. T. HANTY, 1949   Possible genetic differences in the mortality of mice from electroconvulsive shocks. *J. comp. physiol. Psych.* **42**(5): 427–428.

WATSON, M. L., 1939   *The inheritance of epilepsy and of waltzing in Peromyscus.* Contr. Lab. of Vertebrate Genetics, Univ. Michigan, 1939, No. 11.

WITT, G., and C. S. HALL, 1949   The genetics of audiogenic seizures in the house mouse. *J. comp. physiol. Psych.* **42**: 58–63.

WRIGHT, SEWALL, 1934   The results of crosses between inbred strains of guinea pigs differing in numbers of digits. *Genetics* **19**: 537–551.

WRIGHT, SEWALL, and K. WAGNER, 1934   Types of subnormal development of the head from inbred strains of guinea pigs and their bearing on the classification and interpretation of vertebrate monsters. *Amer. J. Anat.* **54**:(3) 383–447.

GERALD McCLEARN and
DAVID A. RODGERS

9   Genetic Factors in Alcohol Preference of Laboratory Mice*

Previous studies by McClearn and Rodgers have demonstrated that inbred strains of mice, given a choice between a solution of ten percent ethyl alcohol and water, differ in their preference for the ethyl alcohol solution. This reading carries the genetic analysis several steps further. Again we find that a behavioral trait seems to be under the control of a polygenic system.

Original reference: *Journal of Comparative and Physiological Psychology,* 1961, **54**, 116–119. Reprinted by permission of the authors and the American Psychological Association.

* This research was supported by National Science Foundation Grant G4574. We are also indebted to the Cancer Research Genetics Laboratory of the University of California, Berkeley, for provision of facilities.

In a previous study (McClearn & Rodgers, 1959), it was shown that inbred strains of mice differ in the proportion of 10% ethyl alcohol solution they ingest when offered a choice between the alcohol solution and water. Specifically, C57BL/Crgl animals showed preference for the alcohol solution, whereas C3H/Crgl/2, A/Crgl/2, BALB/cCrgl, and DBA/2NCrgl animals showed strong preference for water. Subsequent unpublished evidence indicates that the A/Crgl is also a non-alcohol-preferring strain.

A number of pilot studies have since been carried out as an initial phase of exploration into the genetic mechanisms underlying the differences in alcohol preference. The results of these studies, although based on limited numbers of animals varying somewhat in age, further document the importance of genotype in alcohol preference of the mouse and provide some evidence concerning the mechanisms involved.

Method

SUBJECTS

The Ss used are described in Table 9–1. (For brevity, the abbreviation "Crgl" in the strain designations, which identifies the strains as those maintained by the Cancer Research Genetics Laboratory, University of California, Berkeley, will be omitted hereafter. The strain designations used here follow the recent recommendations of the Committee on Standardized Genetic Nomenclature for Mice [*Cancer Research,* 1960, **20**, 145-169]. The strains here designated as C3H/Crgl/2 and A/Crgl/2 were designated C3H/2Crgl and A/2Crgl in our 1959 report.) In Experiment A, the animals were F_1's between the alcohol-preferring C57BL strain and several low alcohol-preference strains: C3H/2, A/2, BALB/c, and DBA/2N. In Experiment B, reciprocal F_1's were obtained between the C3H/2 and the C57BL strain. The Ss of

TABLE 9–1

Number, age, and parentage of Ss

STUDY	GENERATION	FEMALE PARENT	MALE PARENT	N ♂	N ♀	AGE AT TESTING (DAYS)
A	F_1	C57BL	C3H/2	2	3	270
	F_1	A/2	C57BL	4	4	237–265
	F_1	BALB/c	C57BL	4	4	213–262
	F_1	C57BL	DBA/2N	4	4	211–275
B	F_1	C57BL	C3H/2	3	3	142
	F_1	C3H/2	C57BL	3	3	191–205
C	Double cross	BALB/c × C3H/2	C57BL × DBA/2N	3	3	85
	Double cross	C57BL × DBA/2N	BALB/c × C3H/2	11	8	85
	Double cross	C3H/2 × DBA/2N	BALB/c × C57BL	1	5	85
	Double cross	A/2 × DBA/2N	BALB/c × C3H/2	4	7	85
D	Parent	C57BL	C57BL	12	10	312–352
	Parent	A	A	7	9	308–357
	F_1	C57BL	A	6	16	294–339
	F_2	C57BL × A	C57BL × A	10	12	307–341
	Backcross	C57BL × A	C57BL	6	12	299–341
	Backcross	C57BL × A	A	6	8	307–338

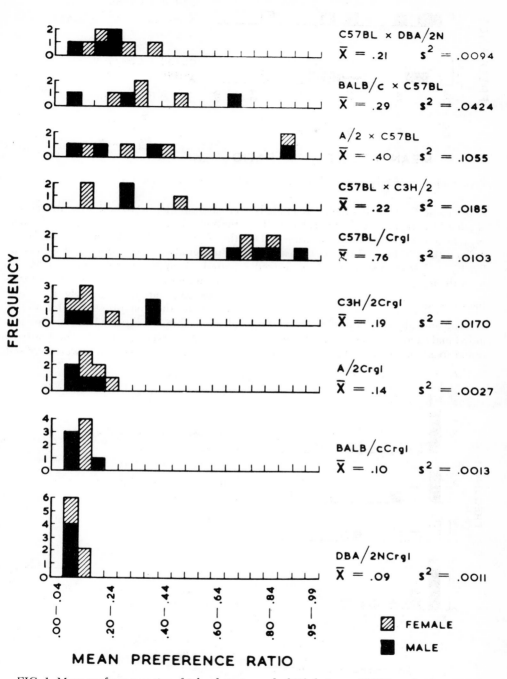

FIG. 1. Mean preference ratios of inbred strains and of F_1's between C57BL and other strains.

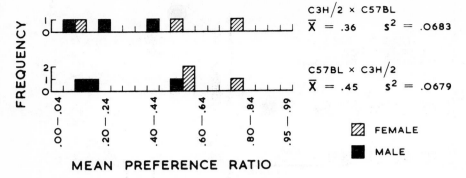

FIG. 2. Mean preference ratios of reciprocal F_1's between C3H/2 and C57BL.

Experiment C were double-cross animals obtained by the matings of hybrid animals, as indicated in Table 9–1. Experiment D utilized the C57BL and the A strains, plus F_1, F_2, and backcross generations derived from them.

PROCEDURE

The animals were housed for testing in individual cages with a standard laboratory ration available ad lib. Water and a 10%

ethanol solution were both available ad lib. through drinking tips extending through the cage tops. The drinking bottles were 25-ml. graduated cylinders, and were supported at approximately 45° angles by wooden racks above the cages. For 14 successive days, at approximately the same time daily, the quantities of water and of alcohol solution consumed during the previous 24 hr. were recorded. The positions of the cylinders in each cage were reversed

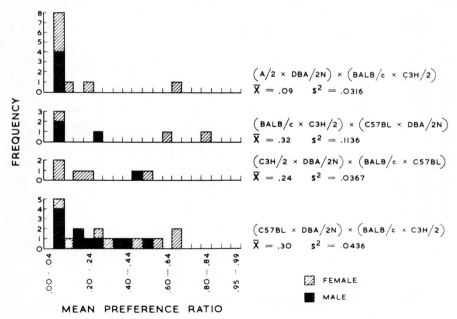

FIG. 3. Mean preference ratios of double-cross groups. Top distribution shows groups without C57BL genes. Bottom three distributions show groups which contain C57BL genes.

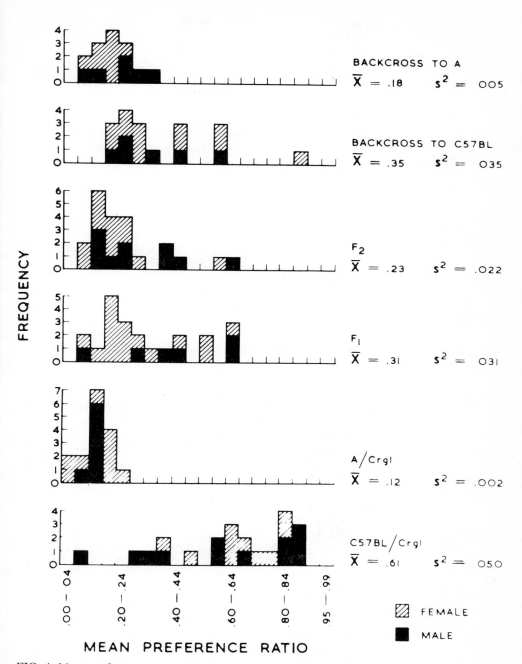

FIG. 4. Mean preference ratios of C57BL and A parent strains, and the F_1, F_2, and backcross generations.

after the sixth and tenth days in Experiment A and after every third day in Experiments B, C, and D. For each animal, a daily preference ratio score was obtained by determining the percentage of the total liquid consumption which was from the alcohol solution bottle—i.e.:

$$\frac{\text{alcohol solution consumed}}{\text{water consumed} + \text{alcohol solution consumed}}$$

Thus, high values indicate alcohol preference and low values indicate water preference. The mean of the daily preference ratio over the 14-day test period was then taken to provide a mean preference ratio for each animal.

Results and Discussion

The results of Experiments A, B, C, and D are shown in Figures 1, 2, 3, and 4, respectively. Figure 1 also includes information concerning the previously reported results from the C57BL, C3H/2, A/2, BALB/c, and DBA/2N strains.

The effectiveness of the genetic factors characteristic of the C57BL genome in determining preference for alcohol is shown by several of the results. In Experiment A, the C57BL × DBA/2N, BALB/c × C57BL, and A/2 × C57BL F_1's are all significantly higher ($p < .05$) in mean alcohol preference than the respective non-alcohol-preferring parent strains. The particular small sample of C57BL × C3H/2 F_1's in Experiment A does not show a significantly higher alcohol preference than the C3H/2 parent strain. In the larger sample of C57BL × C3H/2 and C3H/2 × C57BL tested in Experiment B, however, the mean alcohol preference is significantly higher than that of the C3H/2 strain in Experiment A and does not differ significantly from that of the C57BL × C3H/2 group of Experiment A. The mean of the F_1's between C57BL and C3H/2, combining the data of Experiments A and B, is signifi-

cantly higher than the mean of the C3H/2 group. All F_1's are significantly lower in mean alcohol preference than the C57BL strain. The data thus indicate that all F_1's between the C57BL and the low-preference strains tested show intermediate preference.

The reciprocal crosses of Experiment B permit one type of assessment of maternal effects. C57BL × C3H/2 and C3H/2 × C57BL animals have the same genotype (except for the strain origin of the Y chromosomes of the males), but the former differ from the latter in having developed from C57BL ova, in having developed in C57BL uteri, and in having been reared by C57BL mothers. The lack of significant differences ($t = 0.6$) demonstrates that these maternal variables had little differential influence on alcohol preference. This conclusion, strictly speaking, applies only to F_1's between C57BL and C3H/2. Further studies, such as cross fostering or ova transplants, would provide further information about maternal effects.

The Ss of Experiment C were obtained for the primary purpose of establishing a genetically hetergeneous foundation stock from which selective breeding could be undertaken. The results from these animals, however, are pertinent to the present topic in that they further demonstrate the effect of C57BL genes in determining alcohol preference. One sample of 31 mice (the bottom three subgroups in Fig. 3) was constituted from C57BL, DBA/2N, C3H/2, and BALB/c strains, whereas the other sample of 11 animals was constituted from A/2, DBA/2N, C3H/2, and BALB/c strains. In animals of the first group, the theoretical range of the percentage of total genetic material that is of C57BL origin is from 0 to 50, with intermediate percentages likely. This group has a higher alcohol preference than does the second group, in which none of the genetic material is of C57BL origin. In the latter group, there is only one animal that can be described as alcohol-preferring. There is a possibility that this animal's alcohol preference is determined by a unique combination of genetic factors from the four genome sources. Alternatively, the phenotype may be due to the action of some environmental agency.

In Experiment D, generations beyond the F_1 were used in an attempt to perform a more detailed genetic analysis. The A strain is shown to have low preference, and the results for the C57BL strain of this study generally confirm previous results in showing high mean preference. The variance of the present sample of C57BL animals, however, is significantly greater than that previously found, and there is one C57BL mouse which must be described as "nonpreferring." In all obvious respects, the circumstances of rearing and testing the animals in Experiments A and D were similar, so the differences in C57BL variance are not easily attributed to any specific environmental factor. There is, likewise, no good explanation for the "nonpreferring" individual C57BL mouse. A remote possibility, almost negligibly small, is that the animal is a mutant. Another possibility is that the assumption of homozygosity at all relevant loci is not completely valid for the C57BL strain, and that the alcohol preference of this particular animal is the result of an unusual recombination of alleles. The most plausible interpretation, however, appears to be that some unknown environmental circumstance, such as, for example, an "accident" during prenatal development or the effects of a previous or current undetected illness, affected the animal's alcohol preference.

In the F_1 between C57BL and A, as in the F_1's of Experiments A and B, the mean alcohol preference is significantly greater than that of the nonpreferring parent strain, and significantly less than that of the C57BL parent strain. The hypothesis that the genes act additively, on the average, cannot be rejected, since the mean of the parent means falls within the 95% confidence interval of the F_1 mean. It is apparent that the relevant C57BL alleles, on the average, are neither completely dominant nor completely recessive to the corresponding alleles of the other strains.

The difference between the mean alcohol preferences of the backcross groups is in accord with the general expectation that the group in which there is a higher proportion of C57BL genes, B(C57), should show higher mean preference than the group with the lower proportion, B(A).

On any simple genetic model, the F_2 is expected to have a greater variance than the F_1. In the present case, that outcome is not obtained. The failure of the F_2 variance to exceed the F_1 variance is not easily explained, and makes difficult any further interpretation with respect to heritability, proportional contribution of additive, dominance, and epistatic components, and relative contributions of genetic and environmental factors. Nevertheless, since the relative excess of F_2 variance over F_1 variance tends to decrease as the number of relevant loci increases, other things being equal, the present results strongly suggest that a polygenic system, rather than a single locus, is involved. This suggestion is reinforced by the failure to recover extreme high scores in F_2.

There are suggestions of sex differences in some of the groups tested, particularly in Experiments B and C. However, the sex difference over all of the groups is not significant (Chi square computed by comparing the number of males to the number of females showing above-median preference within their own genetic group equals 1.24, 1 df). It is thus apparent that a sex difference in alcohol preference is not a general phenomenon, although future research may of course reveal such differences to exist in some strains or crosses.

It is apparent that much further work will be required to elucidate the genetic mechanisms that underlie the choice by a mouse of alcohol solution or water. The results to date, however, have clearly shown that genetic constitution is a critical variable.

Even before a more complete description of the genetic mechanism is available,

it should be noted that the genetic manipulability of alcohol preference provides
a promising approach to the problem of
determining the physiological and behavioral causes and concomitants of alcohol
preference.

Summary

C57BL/Crgl mice prefer 10% alcohol
solution to water, whereas C3H/Crgl/2,
A/Crgl, A/Crgl/2, BALB/cCrgl, and
DBA/2NCrgl mice prefer water. F_1's between C57BL and the non-alcohol-preferring strains show higher mean alcohol
preference than their nonpreferring parent
strain, but less than that of the C57BL
strain. The lack of differences between
reciprocal crosses of C57BL and C3H/2
suggests that maternal effects are either
not present or are not of major importance.

The effect of C57BL genes is also
shown by the fact that genetically heterogeneous groups possessing C57BL genes
have higher mean preference than genetically heterogeneous groups without
C57BL genes. Backcrosses of C57BL $\times$
A F_1's to C57BL and to A differ in the expected direction, but the F_2 variance, contrary to expectation, is not greater than the
F_1 variance. The evidence is interpreted as
indicating a polygenic system.

REFERENCE

McClearn, G. E., and D. A. Rodgers Differences in alcohol preference among inbred strains of mice. *Quart. J. Stud. Alcohol,*
1959, **20**, 691–695.

JAN H. BRUELL

10   Inheritance of Behavioral and Physiological Characters of Mice and the Problem of Heterosis*

The findings presented in this reading exemplify an important contribution of
behavior genetics to the study of evolution. Bruell finds support for the suggestion that biologically adaptive traits will show heterotic inheritance, whereas
traits that are biologically neutral will show intermediate inheritance. The study
also suggests that the degree of heterosis is inversely proportional to the degree
of relationship of the parents. Another important contribution is the demonstration that one cannot speak of "dominance," "intermediate inheritance," or
"heterosis" on the basis of a single cross. For example, five of thirty-one hybrid
groups scored below the mid-parent in exploration, but twenty-one hybrid groups
scored above the highest scoring parent. Thus, the author can speak of over-all

* Paper read at the "Refresher Course in
Behavior Genetics" organized by Ernst Caspari
for the American Society of Zoologists during
the 130th meeting of the American Association
for the Advancement of Science in Cleveland,
Ohio, December 27, 1963.

From the Behavior Genetics Laboratory,
Department of Psychology, Western Reserve
University, and Highland View Hospital. The
experimental work reported in this paper was
supported in part by Grant G-14410 from the
National Science Foundation; Grant HE-07216
from the National Heart Institute, U. S. Public
Health Service; and a grant from the Cleveland Foundation.

heterotic inheritance of exploration; whereas, if the study had included only one cross, he might have decided that exploration was inherited in an intermediate fashion. The closely reasoned "Discussion" section of this paper deserves careful reading.

Reference: *American Zoologist*, 1964, **4**, 125–138. Reprinted by permission of the author, the editor: Ernst Caspari, and the publisher.

Heterosis has been studied extensively in plants and animals (Gowen, 1952; Cold Spring Harbor, 1955) but there exist few behavior genetic studies of it (Fuller and Thompson, 1960). I will present results of several behavior genetic studies demonstrating heterotic inheritance of some forms of mouse behavior. Two examples of intermediate nonheterotic inheritance of physiological characters of mice will also be given. The empirical part of the paper will be followed by a discussion of some current views regarding the genetics and evolution of heterosis. My aim will be to show that it is possible to study the mode of inheritance of behavioral traits, and that the study of behavioral heterosis and behavioral inbreeding depression may contribute to the study of evolution.

Heterosis is a descriptive term used to designate the relative positions on a measuring scale occupied by an F_1 hybrid and its inbred parents. Figure 1 shows a meas-

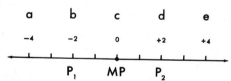

FIG. 1. Represented is a measuring scale and positions on this scale occupied by two inbred strains, P_1 and P_2. The point midway between the parents, the so-called midparent (MP), is also shown. Marked by letters above the scale are positions which may be occupied by F_1 hybrid offspring of the parent strains. Inheritance is called intermediate if the F_1 hybrid scores in position (c), heterotic when the F_1 mean falls into any other place. It is customary to speak of hybrid vigor when the hybrid scores outside the range bracketed in by the parents, e.g., in position (a) or (e). The letters correspond to those given in Table 10–4 and the text.

uring scale, and two points on it occupied by inbred parent strains P_1 and P_2. The position midway between the parents is called midparent, MP. The F_1 hybrids resulting from cross $P_1 \times P_2$ can occupy any position on the measuring scale. If the F_1 mean coincides with the midparent, one speaks of intermediate inheritance; if it occupies any other position on the scale, inheritance is called heterotic.

Method

SUBJECTS

More than 4,000 mice belonging to 13 inbred strains, and 31 populations of F_1 hybrids were tested. These strains and strain crosses are listed in Tables 10–1 and 10–2. Each inbred strain is listed by its standard name (Committee, 1960) and a two digit code number. F_1 hybrids are indicated by combinations of these code numbers, e.g., an F_1 hybrid derived from the mating of an A/J dam (01) to a C57Bl/10 (05) sire, is named 0105. The reciprocal hybrid derived from the mating of an 05 ♀ to an 01 ♂ is called 0501.

Our colony of inbred strains was set up in 1958. At that time the Jackson Laboratories, Bar Harbor, Maine, supplied us with pedigreed breeder pairs belonging to strains 01–05, and 07–09. Breeder pairs of strains 06, and 10–13 were kindly supplied to us by Dr. Edwin P. Les of the Jackson Laboratories. All strains except 06, 11, and 12, were highly inbred. For purposes of this study it is important to note certain blood ties existing among the inbred strains we used. All 13 strains can be traced back to a few, presumably unrelated, ancestral groups, namely, H. J. Bagg's albinos, C. C. Little's albinos, DBA, and C57, and J.

Furth's AKR and RFM (Committee, 1960; Russel and Gerald, 1958).

Descendants of Bagg's albinos. In 1913 H. J. Bagg obtained albino mice from a dealer in Ohio. These are among the ancestors of strain 01-A/J, 03-Balb/c, 04-C3H, 10-SEC/1, 12-HRS, and 13-SEC/2. A/J mice stem from a mating of an albino from Bagg's colony to an albino of Little. C3H mice are derived from a cross between a Bagg albino and a DBA of Little. Finally, Balb/c mice are descendants of Bagg's albinos. After Balb/c had reached a high degree of inbreeding, E. Green crossed a Balb/c to an NB mouse from his colony and obtained SEC mice which gave rise to two sublines, SEC/1 and SEC/2. Green also mated a Balb/c to a hairless mouse which he had obtained from H. R. Chase and thus started the HRS strain.

Descendants of Little's DBA. These mice had been bred by Little since 1909 and used in coat color experiments. The 08-DBA/1 mice used in this study are descendants of these mice. A cross between a DBA mouse and a Bagg albino started the 04-C3H strain.

Descendants of Little's C57. All C57 mice are descendants of one pair of mice which Little obtained from A. E. C. Lathrop in 1921. The 05-C57B1/10 and 07-C57L mice are bred by the Jackson Memorial Laboratory. The 06-C57B1/6 were produced by E. Russel by placing the a^t gene from a mouse of H. R. Chase on a C57B1/6 background by seven generations of backcrossing. The line was then continued by E. Les by forced heterozygosis in brother $\times$ sister matings of type $a^t a \times aa$ for another seven generations before we received a breeder pair from Les. Our data are based on scores of both C57Bl/6 $a^t a$ and aa mice.

The 11-C57B1/6 $A^y a$ strain was also developed by E. Russel. In this case she placed the A^y gene of a mouse from H. B. Chase's colony on a C57B1/6 background by 12 generations of backcrossing. The line was then continued by E. Les by forced heterozygosis in brother $\times$ sister

matings of type $A^y a \times aa$ for four generations before we received a breeder pair from Les. Our data are based on scores of 11-C57B1/6 aa animals only. No yellow animals were included.

Furth's AKR and RFM. The 02-AKR and the 09-RFM strains were developed by J. Furth for leukemia research prior to 1930. AKR are high leukemia mice while RFM are a low leukemia strain. These mice presumably are not related to each other or any of the other strains used in this study.

In our laboratory, matings were between siblings only, and exact records of matings and births of litters were kept. The choice of the inbred strains used in this study was not guided by specific knowledge of their behavior. The F_1 crosses between the inbreds were also made without special consideration of the behavioral performance of the parent strains.

The animals were housed on cedar shavings in aluminum baking pans covered with wire mesh. The size of these cages was $9\frac{5}{8}'' \times 5\frac{1}{2}'' \times 2\frac{3}{4}''$. Except during testing, all animals had free access to Purina Mouse Breeder Chow and water. The temperature in animal quarters and testing rooms was kept at $73°$ F $\pm 3°$. Rooms were ventilated, but humidity was not controlled. The lights remained turned on 12 hours per day. All animals were handled at regular intervals, about every seven to twelve days when they were transferred to a clean cage. Young were weaned when one month old and litter mates of the same sex were kept in the same cage until they reached the testing age of 80 to 100 days. The plan was to test all animals during their fourth month of life. However, when many animals reached testing age simultaneously, testing of some of them had to be postponed; others again, had to be tested before they were 90 days old.

Tests continued throughout 1960 and 1961. The testing of the various strains and crosses did not follow any predetermined pattern. Animals were tested as they reached testing age: this could occur during any season or month of the two year testing program. All animals that became available during these two years were tested and are included in this report.

APPARATUS AND PROCEDURE

Exploratory Behavior. Mice placed in a strange environment behave as if exploring it. To obtain a measure of such activity we placed mice individually in a four compartment maze. As the mouse moved from one compartment of the maze to another, it interrupted a light beam and activated a photorelay and counter. The exploration score for an animal consisted of the total count registered in ten minutes of testing. A photograph of the apparatus was published elsewhere (Bruell, 1962).

Other Tests. Results of other behavioral and physiological tests will be presented in the next section and necessary details regarding subjects and procedure will be given there.

Results

EXPLORATORY BEHAVIOR

Means and standard deviations for females and males of the 44 genotypes

tested are given in Tables 10–1 and 10–2. These data will permit the reader, depending on his special interests, to carry out various correlations and tests of significance. For purposes of this presentation, however, only the means given in the two tables will be used. They will be treated as if they were scores for individual mice, albeit scores based on N repeated measurements. Thus the data are comparable to a set of scores obtained by measuring exploratory behavior of 44 sibling pairs. Thirteen of those pairs were inbred (Table 10–1) and 21 were hybrid organisms (Table 10–2). Some of the inbred animals were the mothers or sires of the hybrids. And some of the hybrids were related to each other, for example, F_1 0103 and F_1 0105 hybrids were half siblings; they had the same 01-A/J mother but different sires.

Inspection of Tables 10–1 and 10–2 did not reveal a significant difference between the exploration scores for females and males. The correlation of 0.834 between the two sets of scores was highly significant (42 degrees of freedom, P < .001). The overall mean for females did not differ from that for males; the average score for both sexes was 168. The identity

TABLE 10–1

Exploratory behavior in 13 inbred strains of mice

CODE NUMBER AND NAME OF STRAIN		N ♀	N ♂	FEMALES Mean	FEMALES S.D.	MALES Mean	MALES S.D.
01	A/J	70	65	132	27.68	125	26.74
02	AKR	47	60	178	48.01	176	66.05
03	Balb/c	54	47	168	30.90	152	36.24
04	C3H	69	80	109	36.63	118	41.24
05	C57BL/10	60	52	155	30.23	146	31.26
06	C57BL/6 $a^t a$	80	81	161	39.59	165	43.51
07	C57L	27	33	181	42.17	171	35.99
08	DBA/1	92	96	144	39.06	156	44.56
09	RFM	52	47	195	57.46	182	39.80
10	SEC/1	117	129	167	38.57	172	40.96
11	C57BL/6 aa	68	74	162	46.89	148	45.02
12	HRS Hr hr	36	27	173	47.65	175	37.75
13	SEC/2	84	69	168	42.10	169	44.42

TABLE 10–2

Exploratory behavior in 31 F₁ hybrid groups of mice

GENOTYPE[a]	N		FEMALES		MALES	
	♀	♂	Mean	S.D.	Mean	S.D.
0103	12	19	143	20.49	132	21.12
0104	19	31	144	38.13	155	38.52
0105	28	27	139	33.63	138	19.10
0106	48	63	159	30.68	148	37.30
0110	38	49	153	40.80	153	38.94
0301	38	42	140	24.60	147	30.38
0304	26	26	175	44.06	167	32.17
0306	34	27	203	34.71	185	45.45
0308	10	12	190	20.95	221	15.91
0310	26	23	180	54.72	171	35.57
0401	25	37	152	38.25	159	43.61
0405	42	57	171	38.43	179	31.24
0501	32	27	145	24.12	134	21.82
0502	62	53	192	42.40	186	36.77
0504	35	40	144	26.46	160	42.01
0506	42	43	191	51.08	163	43.07
0508	54	47	179	39.20	206	28.53
0509	49	42	195	56.49	189	41.15
0510	62	41	195	55.50	190	51.72
0511	12	15	147	28.93	142	33.45
0601	71	109	150	37.11	156	36.17
0603	83	65	182	45.48	185	50.00
0604	16	21	174	41.39	200	33.79
0605	73	71	178	52.51	173	37.20
0705	57	67	191	42.77	181	37.87
0803	12	11	208	33.53	199	33.30
0805	19	16	207	33.47	199	32.34
0806	11	10	186	47.36	211	21.10
1001	61	55	145	50.00	170	50.10
1003	79	82	181	39.10	185	39.19
1005	39	52	179	66.12	174	48.11

a Explanation of code number: Inbred strains are designated by two digit numbers as shown in Table 10–1. The code number for hybrids combines the parental two digit numbers into four digit numbers. The first two digits indicate the strain of the inbred mother, and the third and fourth digits indicate the strain of the inbred sire. For example, F_1 (0103) = F_1 (A/J ♀ × Balb/c ♂).

TABLE 10-3

Exploratory behavior: Comparison of inbred parents with hybrid offspring

			PARENTS NOT RELATED				
GENOTYPE	DAM	SIRE	LP	MP	HP	$\overline{F}_1$	$\overline{F}_1-HP$
0105	132	146	132	139.0	146	138.5	−7.5
0106	132	165	132	148.5	165	153.5	−11.5
0306	168	165	165	166.5	168	194.0	26.0
0308	168	156	156	162.0	168	205.5	37.5
0405	109	146	109	127.5	146	175.0	29.0
0501	155	125	125	140.0	155	139.5	−15.5
0502	155	176	155	165.5	176	189.0	13.0
0504	155	118	118	136.5	155	152.0	−3.0
0508	155	156	155	155.5	156	192.5	36.5
0509	155	182	155	168.5	182	192.0	10.0
0510	155	172	155	163.5	172	192.5	20.5
0601	161	125	125	143.0	161	153.0	−8.0
0603	161	152	152	156.5	161	183.5	22.5
0604	161	118	118	139.5	161	187.0	26.0
0803	144	152	144	148.0	152	203.5	51.5
0805	144	146	144	145.0	146	203.0	57.0
0806	144	165	144	154.5	165	198.5	33.5
1005	167	146	146	156.5	167	176.5	9.5
Mean	151.2	150.6	140.6	150.9	161.2	179.4	18.2

			PARENTS RELATED				
GENOTYPE	DAM	SIRE	LP	MP	HP	$\overline{F}_1$	$\overline{F}_1-HP$
0103	132	152	132	142.0	152	137.5	−14.5
0104	132	118	118	125.0	132	149.5	17.5
0110	132	172	132	152.0	172	153.0	−19.0
0301	168	125	125	146.5	168	143.5	−24.5
0304	168	118	118	143.0	168	171.0	3.0
0310	168	172	168	170.0	172	175.5	3.5
0401	109	125	109	117.0	125	155.5	30.5
0506	155	165	155	160.0	165	177.0	12.0
0511	155	148	148	151.5	155	144.5	−10.5
0605	161	146	146	153.5	161	175.5	14.5
0705	181	146	146	163.5	181	186.0	5.0
1001	167	125	125	146.0	167	157.5	−9.5
1003	167	152	152	159.5	167	183.0	16.0
Mean	153.5	143.4	136.5	148.4	160.4	162.2	1.8

			OVERALL				
Mean	152.1	147.6	138.9	149.9	160.9	172.2	11.3

of means and the high correlation between female and male scores enabled us to simplify the data. Instead of considering $F_1 ♀$ and $F_1 ♂$ means separately, their average was used in all computations. For example, for genotype F_1 0103 the average exploration score was $\overline{F}_1 = (143 + 132)/2 = 137.5$.

The data are presented again in Table 10–3. Entered in the left hand columns are the mean exploration scores for the parents of each hybrid. In the MP (for midparent) column are the averages of the parental scores, and in the F_1 column the average scores (♀ + ♂)/2, for F_1 hybrids. The correlation between the midparental values and the F_1 scores was computed and found to be 0.543 and significant (29 degrees of freedom, P < .01). Figure 2 presents this relation.

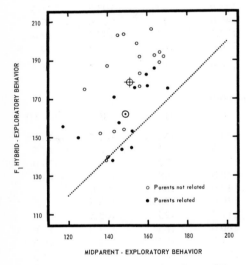

FIG. 2. Heterotic inheritance of exploratory behavior in mice. Relation between midparental score (P ♀ + P ♂)/2, and F_1 score (F_1♀ + F_1♂)/2. Shown are means for 18 groups of F_1 hybrids whose parents belonged to inbred strains derived from unrelated stock, and means for 13 F_1 groups whose inbred parents were related. The mean for "related hybrids" shown by a bull's-eye, differed significantly from the mean for "unrelated hybrids" shown by a cross. Note that most hybrids scored above the diagonal "midparent line".

Table 10–3 shows that only 5 out of 31 groups of hybrid mice (0105, 0501, 0103, 0301, and 0511) scored below the midparent, and only one (0511) below the lower scoring parent, LP. On the other hand, 21 groups scored higher than the higher scoring inbred parent, HP. Thus, overall, we can speak of heterotic inheritance of exploratory behavior. As a group, hybrid mice tended to explore more than their inbred parents.

This general relationship is also indicated in Figure 2. Shown is a scatter diagram in which the mean performance of each F_1 hybrid group (♀ + ♂)/2, is plotted against the average performance of its midparent, (P ♀ + P ♂)/2. The diagonal line shown in Figure 2 represents what may be called the midparent line. An F_1 score that coincided with the midparent would be plotted on that diagonal, and F_1 groups that scored above their respective midparents would be indicated by data points above the line. As can be seen, most F_1 groups scored above the midparent line. They thus demonstrated what, in the discussion, will be referred to as "population heterosis."

Table 10–3 and Figure 2 were designed to make one further point. The 31 hybrid groups were subdivided into 18 groups whose parents had no blood ties, and 13 F_1 groups, which, according to the history of inbred strains given above, shared some ancestors. Figure 2 shows that the data points for hybrids whose parents are related lie closer to the midparent line than those for not related hybrids. And the last column of Table 10–3 shows that the average difference between the F_1 mean and the mean for the higher scoring parent, HP, was 18.2 for the not related "hybrids," and only 1.8 for "related" hybrids. These two averages differed at the .001 level of significance.

OTHER BEHAVIOR GENETIC STUDIES

Elsewhere (Bruell, 1964) I studied inheritance of spontaneous running in activity wheels in the same group of 4,000 mice

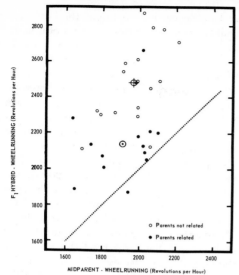

FIG. 3. Heterotic inheritance of wheel running in mice. Shown are the same 31 groups of F₁ hybrids as in Figure 2. Note that most hybrids scored above the diagonal "midparent line", and that again "unrelated" hybrids deviated more from the midparent than "related" hybrids. Means for related and unrelated hybrids are indicated by the bull's-eye and cross respectively.

as used here. Figure 3 summarizes the results of that study. We see that wheel-running is inherited in heterotic fashion, and that again hybrids whose parents were related displayed less heterosis than those whose parents were unrelated.

Collins (1963, and 1964) has studied avoidance conditioning in five inbred strains of mice (A/J, Balb/c, C3H, C57BL/10, DBA/1) and all 20 F₁ hybrids resulting from the systematic crossing of these strains. He showed that the mode of inheritance of learning in an avoidance conditioning situation is heterotic. Hybrids learned faster than their midparents.

In yet unpublished studies with the same 4,000 mice used in the present research, I found that hybrid mice climb down a pole on which they are placed somewhat faster than their midparents. They also emerge from a dark tunnel into a lighted open field more readily than their

inbred parents. In both tests then, the behavior measured is inherited in heterotic fashion. The situations but not the results just summarized were described elsewhere (Bruell, 1962).

INHERITANCE OF SERUM
CHOLESTEROL LEVEL

To illustrate intermediate inheritance, I have to turn to two physiological characters, serum cholesterol level and hematocrit values in mice. Serum cholesterol level was studied in the same 5 inbred strains and 20 F₁ hybrid groups as used by Collins (1963, 1964). The results of this study were reported elsewhere (Bruell, 1963b) and are summarized in Figure 4. Each point in Figure 4 is based on 48 inbred animals and 24 hybrids. As can be seen, hybrids scored above and below the midparent, and the mean score for all hybrids, indicated by a cross in Figure 4, did not differ from the average of all midparents. Statistical analysis of the results (Bruell, 1963b) indicated clearly nonheterotic inheritance of serum cholesterol level in mice.

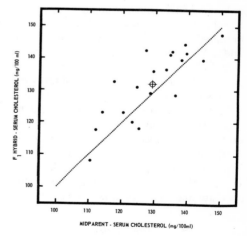

FIG. 4. Intermediate inheritance of serum cholesterol in mice. The mean for F₁ hybrids, indicated by the cross, does not deviate significantly from the mean of all midparents. The graph is based on data presented elsewhere (BRUELL, 1963b.)

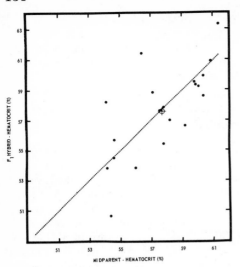

FIG. 5. Intermediate inheritance of hematocrit per cent. The mean for F_1 hybrids did not differ from the mean for all midparents. The graph is based on unpublished original data.

INHERITANCE OF HEMATOCRIT PERCENT

Figure 5 summarizes yet unpublished data on inheritance of hematocrit in mice. The term hematocrit, or hematocrit per cent, refers to the relative proportions of red blood cells and serum in a sample of blood. The data shown in Figure 5 were obtained from the same five inbred strains and 20 F_1 hybrid groups as used in the serum cholesterol study. Again we see, and statistical analysis of the data confirms the impression, that in mice, on the average, inheritance of hematocrit is intermediate.

In this section several examples of heterotic and intermediate inheritance of quantitative characters of mice were given. The remainder of this paper will deal with current theoretical views regarding intermediate and heterotic inheritance.

Discussion

Two phenomena reported above stood out. First, we observed that one and the same trait, e.g., exploratory behavior, displayed intermediate inheritance in some strain crosses, and heterotic inheritance in

others. Secondly, we found that different traits manifested different modes of inheritance. That is, if one disregarded single crosses and considered the average result of all strain crosses, some traits showed intermediate, and others showed heterotic inheritance. Thus, in broad outline, we will have to discuss two problems which I would like to call (i) the problem of single cross heterosis, and single cross intermediate inheritance; and (ii) the problem of population heterosis, and population intermediacy. In my treatment of the subject I will try to present current views concerning heterosis as I understand them. There exists no generally accepted theory of heterosis. Yet, as I read the record of theoretical discussions (Mather, 1949; Gowen, 1952; Cold Spring Harbor, 1955 and 1959; Lerner, 1958; Falconer, 1960; Mayr, 1963), there exists a high degree of unanimity as to its probable causes. The reader who desires to gain a deeper understanding of quantitative inheritance and heterosis may want to study Falconer's (1960) *Introduction to Quantitative Genetics*, the most readable and explicit monographic treatment of the subject to date. And readers interested in evolutionary aspects of heterosis are directed to Mayr's (1963) recent treatise on evolution. It will be quite apparent that I have drawn heavily on ideas and concepts expounded in these two books.

Genetic theories of heterosis differ in details but they all assume that complex quantitative characters are determined by many pairs of genes. There exists no wheel running gene, or exploration gene, or pole climbing gene, but a large number of gene pairs, collectively called a polygenic system, determine each of these complex quantitative traits. Each constituent gene pair of the system either moves the individual up or down the scale on which the quantitative character is measured, and the genotypic value of an individual is determined by the sum of all trait increasing and trait decreasing gene pairs he carries.

Coupled with this polygenic hypothesis

TABLE 10–4

Polygenic model of intermediate and heterotic inheritance

	PARENTS		F_1 HYBRIDS				
	P_1	P_2	(a)	(b)	(c)	(d)	(e)
A	$+1$	-1	-1	$+1$	$+1$	$+1$	$+1$
B	-1	$+1$	-1	-1	$+1$	$+1$	$+1$
C	-1	$+1$	-1	-1	-1	$+1$	$+1$
D	-1	$+1$	-1	-1	-1	-1	$+1$
Value[a]	-2	$+2$	-4	-2	0	$+2$	$+4$

[a] The midparental value, $(P_1 + P_2)/2$, is $(-2 + 2)/2 = 0$, thus, on a descriptive level, inheritance is intermediate in case (c), and heterotic in all other cases. The model, however, shows clearly that on the genotypic level the same genetic mechanism accounts for both intermediate and heterotic inheritance. The letters designating hybrids correspond to those shown in Figure 1.

is the notion that the single gene pairs making up the polygenic system display all the phenomena known from classical genetics, in particular, dominance and recessiveness. Consider two inbred strains P_1 and P_2, and assume that the phenotypic value of P_2 exceeds that of P_1, as shown in Table 10–4 and Figure 1. According to the polygenic hypothesis this must be due to the fact that the effects of trait increasing plus genes outweigh the effects of trait decreasing minus genes in P_2 more than they do in P_1. In Table 10–4, in extreme oversimplification of an actual situation, it is assumed that the quantitative trait under consideration is determined by gene pairs at four loci, A, B, C, and D. The genotypic value of an individual depends on the sum of the values of the four trait determining gene pairs he carries. The genotypic value of P_1 is -2, and that of P_2 is $+2$. Thus the value of the midparent, not shown in Table 10–4, is 0.

Table 10–4 indicates schematically five types of F_1 hybrids, which could result from a mating of P_1 to P_2. Since P_1 and P_2 carry differing alleles at four loci, four heterozygous gene pairs are created when their gametes join. In Table 10–4 it is assumed that in each of the heterozygous gene pairs one of the genes is dominant over the other. In case (a) all the trait decreasing minus genes are dominant over the trait enhancing plus genes, and in case (e) all trait increasing plus genes are dominant. In these two cases, the genotypic values of the hybrids deviate most from their midparent (Figure 1). Cases (b) and (d) are less extreme because, in these instances, at some loci the minus gene is dominant over the plus gene, and at other loci the plus gene is dominant over the minus gene. Case (c) represents the unique case in which the effects of minus genes which are dominant over plus genes is exactly balanced by the effects of plus genes which are dominant over minus genes. In this particular case the genotypic value of the F_1 hybrid corresponds to the value of the midparent. In essence then, according to the theory embodied in Table 10–4, the genetic mechanisms underlying intermediate inheritance are the same as those underlying heterotic inheritance.

At this point a possible source of misunderstanding must be removed. In Table 10–4, to simplify matters, all plus and minus gene pairs were assigned the same absolute value of one. Thus it must be stated explicitly that gene pairs affecting quantitative traits may have major, intermediate, and minor effects; that is, some will affect the phenotype of an individual more, and others less. It is possible to deduce certain features of quantitative inheritance from the model just presented. Which set of trait-determining genes an individual draws from the gene pool is a matter of chance. The likelihood that two individuals would draw the same sample of genes is extremely small. Similarly, the likelihood that two inbred strains would carry the same set of genes determining a quantitative trait is quite remote. This now, however, must not be taken to mean that two genotypically different strains must differ phenotypically. It should be obvious that different combinations of plus and minus genes can result in the same phenotype. Phenotypic identity in the same environment does not indicate necessarily genotypic identity. Borrowing and distorting a familiar term, we can say that in the case of quantitative traits we often will deal with genocopies.

A consequence of the phenotypic similarity or identity of genotypically differing strains is that the phenotype of inbred parents cannot serve as a reliable guide to prediction of the phenotype of their hybrid offspring. The phenotype of the parents does not enable us to predict how they will "combine." The "combining ability" of inbred strains must be established empirically in each case. Even if we dealt with two pairs of inbred parents where $P_1 = P_1'$, and $P_2 = P_2'$, the hybrids resulting from the cross $P_1 \times P_2$ could differ very much from the hybrids resulting from cross $P_1' \times P_2'$. Considering this we are not surprised to have found that one and the same trait in some strain crosses was inherited in an intermediate fashion, while in other crosses it showed varying degrees of heterosis. This is what could have been predicted from the theoretical model presented here, and this is what we observed.

Several variations and refinements of this theory have been proposed. The theory, as presented, explains intermediate and heterotic inheritance entirely in terms of dominance. Refinements of the theory, without denying the importance of dominance, point to other forms of intra-allelic interaction and to interallelic interaction as affecting mode of inheritance. Thus they assume that at some loci neither allele is dominant over the other, and that at such

loci the genotypic value of the heterozygous gene pair is intermediate to that of the homozygous parental gene pairs. We would deal here with single-locus intermediacy, and such loci could account in part for intermediate inheritance. Other theories point to the well established fact that at some loci the genotypic value of the heterozygous gene pair exceeds that of either of the parental homozygotes. Such single locus heterosis or overdominance, as it is commonly called, could account in part for heterotic inheritance. Finally, theories include epistasis, that is, interallelic interactions among the mechanisms which may contribute to heterotic inheritance. While all these mechanisms must be considered in a comprehensive theory of quantitative inheritance, they do not alter basically the simplified model illustrated in Table 10–4, and it is this model primarily that we will examine in more detail here.

INTERMEDIATE INHERITANCE AS A POPULATION PHENOMENON

So far we have dealt with the possible results of single strain crosses of type $P_1 \times P_2$. We turn now to the statistical phenomena which are encountered when many inbred strains are crossed and when the resulting F_1 hybrids are compared with their parents. Under these conditions two phenomena can occur and have been observed by us. The average of all F_1 means can coincide with the average of all midparent values, or it may deviate significantly from it. In the latter case we will speak of "population heterosis," and in the former instance of "population intermediacy" or intermediate inheritance as a population phenomenon.

We will deal with intermediate inheritance first. Two examples of it were given above. We found that serum cholesterol level and hematocrit percent were inherited in intermediate fashion in mice. We have seen that in these two instances some F_1 hybrid groups showed intermediate inheritance and others negative or positive heterosis, so that the population of F_1 hybrids as a whole displayed intermediate inheritance. Hybrids as a group did not display "hybrid vigor," and inbreds, when compared with their hybrid offspring, were not "depressed"; they did not show "inbreeding depression" as far as serum cholesterol or hematocrit percent were concerned. With these observations in mind, let us speculate about attributes of the gene pool from which the founders of the inbred strains we dealt with might have drawn their genes.

Our observations lead us to postulate three characteristics of such a gene pool. We will assume that (i) the gene pool contained many plus (+) and many minus (−) genes; that (ii) some of the genes were dominant (D), and others were recessive (R); and that (iii) extreme minus or plus genes, whether dominant or recessive, were less frequent than genes with small negative or positive effects. In other words, disregarding the magnitude of genes, we assume that D+, D−, R+, and R− genes were equally represented in the gene pool. Figure 6a represents a gene pool with these three characteristics. If we clearly visualize such a pool, it is easy to see how intermediate inheritance as a population phenomenon follows from it.

Consider first single individuals drawing their genes from that pool. Since quantitative traits are based on many genes, it is unlikely that any one individual would draw only minus or plus genes, or only dominant or recessive genes from the pool. Thus extreme phenotypes would be rare, and their uncommonness would be a direct function of the number of genes determining the quantitative character under consideration. In spite, or because of the multitude of genes determining a trait, most individuals would resemble each other and approach closely the average phenotype of the population.

What would happen if such individuals were used for inbreeding, and if, subsequently, the resulting inbred strains were crossed? Two consequences can be listed. (i) In separate brother × sister lines dif-

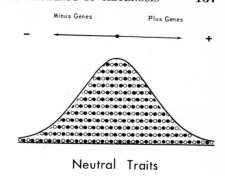

Neutral Traits

o   Dominant Genes

•   Recessive Genes

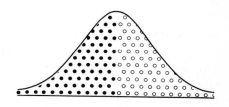

Selected Traits

FIG. 6. Models of Gene Pools. (a) Neutral Traits. Model represents pool of genes for quantitative trait which has not been subjected to selection. Dominant and recessive plus and minus genes are equally represented in the pool. Extreme trait-increasing or trait-decreasing genes are less frequent than genes with small effects. (b) Selected Traits. Trait has adaptive value, and thus was exposed to selection. Dominant minus genes are eliminated from the pool. Most trait-decreasing genes are recessive, and most trait-increasing genes are dominant.

ferent genes would become fixed, but each line or strain would get its share of D+, D−, R+, and R− genes. To be sure, because of errors of sampling, some strains would carry more D+ genes than others, or more D−, R+, or R− genes. And thus single strains would differ from each other and deviate in an upward or downward direction from the mean value of the base population from which the founders of the inbred strains were drawn. But the average value of all inbred strains would equal the mean value of the wild base population.

Inbreeding would not lead to "inbreeding depression." (ii) When such inbred strains were crossed, all hybrid genotypes shown in Table 10–4 would result. However, since most parent strains would transmit to their offspring some plus and some minus, some dominant and some recessive genes, the genotypes of hybrids would tend to resemble those represented under (b), (c), and (d) in Table 10–4. And the mean value of all F_1 hybrid groups would not differ from the average of all midparents. While single crosses would display negative or positive heterosis, in the population of F_1 hybrids as a whole inheritance would be intermediate.

POPULATION HETEROSIS

In the preceding section we started with actual experimental observations of intermediate inheritance in a population of F_1 hybrids, and we inferred from it characteristics of the gene pool from which the genes controlling serum cholesterol level and hematocrit percent in mice may have been drawn. Let us repeat this procedure here when dealing with population heterosis. Several examples of it were given. We saw that inheritance of exploratory behavior, wheel running, avoidance conditioning, and other behavior traits were heterotic. We found that a population of F_1 hybrid groups deviated significantly from the average of all their midparents. As a group, hybrids scored above their midparents; they displayed what is commonly referred to as "hybrid vigor." By contrast, inbred strains as a group scored lower than their hybrid offspring; the inbred parent strains showed "inbreeding depression."

The data on exploratory behavior (Table 10–3, and Figure 2), and wheel running (Figure 3; and Bruell, 1964) permit us to make even more specific statements. They suggest that the degree of heterosis depends on the number of heterozygous gene pairs a hybrid carries. This conclusion is based on the following argument: Consider two quite unrelated inbred strains. Chances are that in the course of

inbreeding they become homozygous for different alleles at most loci. When such strains are crossed, maximum heterozygosity will be achieved. Now think of two related inbred strains. To be related means to have a certain number of genes in common, and, in the case of related inbred strains, it means that the strains are quite likely to be homozygous for the same genes at some loci. If then such related inbred strains are crossed, the hybrid offspring will carry fewer heterozygous gene pairs than hybrids resulting from the crossing of unrelated strains. We found that "related hybrids" showed less heterosis than "unrelated hybrids," and we can attribute this to the differential number of heterozygous gene pairs possessed by related and unrelated hybrids.

What do these empirical findings tell us about the gene pool of the base population from which the inbred strains originated? In a single cross, according to the model presented in Table 10–4, a hybrid will score above the midparent if most of his plus genes are dominant over his minus genes. In other words, positive heterosis depends on a preponderance of D+ over D− genes, and in the extreme case illustrated by case (e) in Table 10–4, all dominant genes are D+, and all recessive genes are R−. If then in a series of strain crosses we observe positive heterosis of varying degrees, we can hypothesize two characteristics of the gene pool from which the founders of the inbred strains drew their genes. We can assume that (i) the gene pool contained mostly D+ and R− genes; and that (ii) extreme D+ and R− genes were less frequent than D+ and R− with small positive and negative effects. A gene pool having these two characteristics is represented in Figure 6b.

Let us examine whether a gene pool with the characteristics shown in Figure 6b can account for population heterosis and inbreeding depression. To simplify discussion, let us consider genes at one locus only. Two types of alleles are found in the pool, namely, D+ and R− alleles.

Let us designate D+ alleles by the capital letter A, and R— alleles by small a. And let us assume, as indicated in Figure 6b, that A and a occur with equal frequencies. Then, by random sampling, three genotypes will be generated in predictable proportions, namely, ¼ AA, ½ Aa, and ¼ aa.

Suppose that the genotypic value of $aa = -10$, and that the value of $AA = +10$. Because of dominance of A over a, the genotypic value of the heterozygous gene pair Aa will be $+10$ also. The contribution of these three gene pairs, occurring in the indicated proportions, to the mean value of the wild base population will be $(0.25)(-10) + (0.50)(+10) + (0.25)(+10) = +5$. What will happen if individuals are drawn at random from this base population and inbred? As a result of inbreeding only two genotypes will persist, namely, AA and aa homozygotes. They will be equally represented among inbred strains, so that their contribution to the average value of the population of inbred strains will be $(0.50)(+10) + (0.50)(-10) = 0$. In other words, as far as locus A is concerned, the average genotypic value of inbreds will be lower than the average genotypic value of a wild population containing homozygotes and heterozygotes. On the other hand, when the inbreds are crossed, ¼ AA, ½ Aa, and ¼ aa hybrid groups will result, and the average genotypic value of the hybrid groups will return to the average value of the wild base population. To summarize, the average value of inbred populations will be "depressed" when compared with the average value of hybrid populations. Or, looking at it from the vantage point of inbreds, hybrids, on the average, will be superior to them; they will display heterosis.

Note, however, that if we consider the situation at one locus only, single crosses of inbreds may result in hybrids whose genotypic value corresponds to the low genotypic value of aa homozygotes, and no F_1 hybrid will score above the highest scoring AA homozygote. In actual experimental work, however, we often encounter populations of F_1 hybrids where not a single hybrid resembles its lower scoring parent (e.g., Bruell, 1964), or where many hybrids score above their higher scoring parent (see Table 10–3), thus displaying what is commonly referred to as hybrid vigor. The phenomenon is readily explainable if we assume, as we did all along, that quantitative traits are determined by genes at several loci. Consider case (e) in Table 10–4. Inbred strains P_1 and P_2 both carry trait decreasing homozygous R— genes and trait increasing D+ genes. When P_1 and P_2 are crossed, the trait reducing homozygous R— gene pairs carried by each parent are complemented by D+ genes carried by the other parent. Thus, in the hybrid, only the trait raising D+ genes are expressed in the phenotype, and the hybrid when compared with his inbred parents displays hybrid vigor (Table 10–4, and Figure 1, case e); on the other hand, the parents show inbreeding depression. This, in a few words, is the essence of the so-called "complementary dominance theory" of hybrid vigor and inbreeding depression, and it is worth noting that this theory makes assumptions about the gene pool of a population which correspond to those presented in Figure 6b. However, instead of speaking of D+ and R— genes, in the context of the complementary dominance theory, we usually speak of beneficial dominant and deleterious recessive genes.

Let us pause and summarize the salient points of this discussion: We noted that some quantitative traits, e.g., serum cholesterol level and hematocrit percent in mice, are inherited in intermediate fashion if a population of F_1 hybrid groups is considered. And we found that other traits, e.g., exploratory behavior and wheel running in mice, displayed population heterosis. From this we inferred that genes controlling traits inherited in intermediate fashion must have been drawn from a different gene pool than genes controlling traits manifesting population heterosis. We then developed hypotheses regarding the differing characteristics of the two gene pools, and showed how the hypothesized features of the pools could account for the empirical findings. We now must go one step further in our inquiry and ask this question: granted that two kinds of gene pools exist, how did they come about? What was their evolution?

EVOLUTIONARY CONSIDERATIONS

It is probably fair to say that in treatments of quantitative genetics more pages have been devoted to heterotic than intermediate inheritance. I have given "equal time" to both phenomena because, so it seems, both are the manifestations of the same genetic mechanisms and environmental forces. Discussion, however, may profitably proceed from what is accepted as likely by many to what is treated by few.

It is widely accepted that heterotic inheritance is characteristic of those traits which contribute to the fitness of organisms, and thus have been subjected to pressures of selection. When the complementary dominance hypothesis states that dominant genes are beneficial, and recessive genes, carried in double dose, are deleterious, it obviously refers to genes which increase or decrease the biological fitness of an organism; genes which either raise or lower the chances of an organism to reproduce successfully and to propagate its kind. Such plus and minus genes can be dominant or they can be recessive. All four types of genes, D+, D−, R+, and R− genes occur, and as such there is no reason why, when a gene mutates and a new allele arises, this allele should be an R− rather than D−, or D+ rather than R+. Why then are there more deleterious recessive R− genes than deleterious dominant D− genes? The answer is simple: D− genes, by virtue of being expressed in the phenotype, are rapidly eliminated by natural selection. On the other hand R− genes elude natural selection when carried in heterozygous state. Therefore we find in wild populations only few D− genes,

while most wild populations are apt to be burdened by a heavy "mutational load"; they are likely to harbor many R− genes. And it is this imbalance between D− genes and R− genes which accounts for the twin phenomena of inbreeding depression and heterosis. The decreased vitality of inbreds and the vigor of hybrids are both a consequence of the natural selection which prevailed in the wild base population from which the founders of the inbred strains were drawn. Natural selection removed from the gene pool of the wild base population most D− genes, thus establishing a pool schematically represented by Figure 6b.

The foregoing considerations seem to imply that intermediate inheritance will be characteristic of quantitative traits which neither increase nor lessen the fitness of the organism possessing them, and thus traits which have not been subjected to selection. While some authors doubt that any character of an organism is absolutely neutral from an evolutionary point of view, there exist certainly traits which are for all practical purposes neutral or at least less contributing to fitness than others (Falconer, 1960; Mayr, 1963). Presumably such traits also depend on dominant and recessive genes which increase or decrease their phenotypic expression. However, because of the selective neutrality of such traits, the genes controlling them will all be preserved in the population: D− genes will have the same chance to persist as D+ genes, and R+ genes will not be favored over R− genes. The expected outcome of such circumstances is a gene pool represented by Figure 6a. An excellent and much more explicit presentation of similar ideas is contained in the last chapter of Falconer's (1960) book.

The essential point of this presentation is that population intermediacy and population heterosis can be understood only in terms of evolutionary processes, namely, an interaction between hereditary endowment of a population, that is, its gene pool, and environmental pressures. The gene pool is generated by random mutational processes, and it is shaped by selection. A trait that has not been subjected to selection reveals during inbreeding the random distribution of accidents of mutation. It shows intermediate inheritance, and the population mean remains constant during inbreeding and crossing. Similarly, a trait that was exposed to selection, that is, a trait whose gene pool was systematically culled by environmental forces discloses its evolutionary past during inbreeding. Its population mean decreases during inbreeding and increases during crossing. It manifests inbreeding depression and hybrid vigor.

Not essential to this presentation are the particular genetic mechanisms invoked. For example, to simplify exposition I have chosen to discuss heterosis entirely in terms of the additive effects of dominance at many loci. However, there can be no doubt that other mechanisms enter the picture, for example, single-locus heterosis or overdominance. There is abundant evidence that heterozygous gene pairs exist which exceed in value both parental homozygotes. Such heterotic gene combinations could be called $D++$. If such $D++$ combinations exist, it can be argued that $D--$ gene combinations must arise also, and we are faced with the same problem as before. We have to explain why $D++$ combinations are observed rather frequently, and $D--$ combinations seldom, if at all. The preservation of $D++$ combinations in the population has been explained in evolutionary terms already (Mayr, 1963); the elimination of $D--$ combinations must be answered in the same terms. Thus population heterosis remains presumptive evidence for the operation of selection pressures, whatever the underlying genetic mechanisms, and intermediate inheritance of certain traits still suggests their selective neutrality.

IMPLICATIONS

The quantitative characters an experimenter chooses to study are arbitrary abstractions from the infinite number of observable attributes of organisms, and the measures he uses are no less arbitrary. Frequently one measures what is readily measurable in units of measurement which can be conveniently recorded. The data and theoretical considerations presented here suggest that, in spite of this arbitrary choice of characters, it should be possible to sort them into those which increase the fitness of an organism and those which are neutral from an evolutionary point of view. This could be done in breeding experiments of the kind described here. By applying to the results of such experiments the criteria developed above it should be possible to distinguish between traits with and without adaptive value. Certainly, often we will not need to question nature in costly breeding tests since the adaptive value of a trait will be only too obvious. The results of the cholesterol study summarized above, however, should warn us not to be too sure too often. Based on current medical evidence and beliefs, one could have assumed that serum cholesterol level will be lower in hybrids than in inbred animals, but the results of the breeding test would have proved one wrong.

In behavioral research in particular it is often difficult to decide whether a trait has adaptive value or not. Consider, for example, susceptibility to audiogenic seizures (Fuller and Thompson, 1960), preference for alcohol (McClearn and Rodgers, 1961), or emotional defecation in a strange environment (Bruell, 1963a). It would be hard to say whether such traits possibly could have conferred a selective advantage on their bearers, and in case the traits actually were subjected to selection pressures, it would be hard to guess whether heterosis will be positive or negative. By conducting research of the type suggested here, however, and by thus broadening our base for generalization, we may in time discern a pattern: we may learn to spell out better than we can today the characteristics of behavior forms with and without evolutionary significance.

Summary

Over 4,000 mice belonging to 13 inbred strains and 31 groups of F_1 hybrids were studied in two tests of behavior, namely, exploration of a strange environment and spontaneous running in activity wheels. In these test situations the 31 hybrid populations outscored their inbred parents; they explored more and ran more in wheels. Thus they displayed "behavioral heterosis."

Six hundred mice belonging to 5 inbred strains and 20 F_1 groups resulting from the systematic crossing of the inbreds were tested for serum cholesterol and hematocrit percent. In these physiological tests, hybrids did not differ from their parents. Hybrids tended to score midway between their inbred parents. Thus mode of inheritance was intermediate.

Current views regarding intermediate and heterotic inheritance were presented. It was hypothesized (i) that intermediate inheritance is characteristic of "neutral traits," that is, traits which do not confer a selective advantage on their bearers; and (ii) that heterotic inheritance occurs only in traits which had been subjected to selection. The reasoning leading to the formulation of these hypotheses was presented in some detail. In concluding, it was suggested that determination of the mode of inheritance of characters may help one to distinguish between adaptive and selectively neutral traits.

REFERENCES

BRUELL, J. H. Dominance and segregation in the inheritance of quantitative behavior in mice. In E. L. Bliss (Ed.), *Roots of behavior.* New York: Harper & Row, 1962, Ch. 4.

BRUELL, J. H. Emotional defecation in mice, a territory marking response? *Am. Psychol.,* 1963a, **17**, 445.

BRUELL, J. H. Additive inheritance of serum cholesterol in mice. *Science,* 1963b, **142**, 1664–1666.

BRUELL, J. H. Heterotic inheritance of wheel running in mice. *J. comp. physiol. Psychol.,* 1964, **58**, 159–163.

COLD SPRING HARBOR SYMPOSIA ON QUANTITATIVE BIOLOGY Volume 20. Population genetics: The nature and causes of genetic variability in populations. Long Island Biological Association, Cold Spring Harbor, New York: 1955.

COLD SPRING HARBOR SYMPOSIA ON QUANTITATIVE BIOLOGY Volume 24. Genetics and twentieth century Darwinism. Long Island Biological Association, Cold Spring Harbor, New York: 1959.

COLLINS, R. L. Genetics of avoidance conditioning in mice: A diallel study. 1963, Unpublished Ph.D. Thesis, Western Reserve University.

COLLINS, R. L. Genetics of avoidance conditioning in mice: A diallel study. *Science,* 1964, **143**, 1188–1190.

COMMITTEE ON STANDARDIZED GENETIC NOMENCLATURE FOR MICE Standardized nomenclature for inbred strains of mice. Second listing, Cancer Research, 1960, **20**, 145–169.

FALCONER, D. S. *Introduction to quantitative genetics,* 1960, New York: The Ronald Press.

FULLER, J. L., and W. R. THOMPSON *Behavior genetics.* New York: John Wiley and Sons, Inc., 1960.

GOWEN, J. W. (Ed.) *Heterosis.* Iowa: Iowa State College Press, 1952.

LERNER, M. I. *The genetic basis of selection.* New York: John Wiley and Sons, Inc., 1958.

MATHER, K. *Biometrical genetics.* London: Methuen & Co., Ltd., 1949.

MAYR, E. *Animal species and evolution.* Massachusetts: The Belknap Press of Harvard University Press. 1963.

McCLEARN, G. E., and D. A. RODGERS Genetic factors in alcohol preference of laboratory mice. *J. comp. physiol. Psychol.,* 1961, **54**, 116–119.

RUSSELL, E. S., and P. S. GERALD Inherited electrophoretic hemoglobin patterns among 20 inbred strains of mice. *Science,* 1958, **128**, 1569–1570.

T H O M A S   E.   M c G I L L   and
G.   R I C H A R D   T U C K E R

11   Genotype and Sex Drive in Intact and in Castrated Male Mice

The reader will note that the interpretation of the results of this study uses the insights developed in reading 10. If the hypothesis set forth in the discussion of this reading proves to be correct, it will be a further demonstration of the importance of genetic control in behavioral and physiological experimentation.

Reading 16 also concerns the generalization of an "inverse correlation between dependence on gonadal hormones and phylogenetic status."

Reprinted from *Science*, 1964, Vol. 145, pp. 514–515, 31 July 1964, by permission of the American Association for the Advancement of Science. Copyright 1964 by the American Association for the Advancement of Science.

ABSTRACT   Male mice of two inbred strains and one hybrid strain were tested for sexual behavior for 42 consecutive days. Half the males of each strain were then castrated and daily testing was continued until the ejaculatory reflex was lost. Strain differences were found in ejaculatory frequency both before and after castration.

▶ Previous studies have demonstrated that male mice of different inbred strains differ significantly in several aspects of sexual behavior (1, 2). The time required to recover sex drive after an ejaculation is one of the variables which has been shown to be affected by genotype (2). More specifically, males of the inbred strain DBA/2J recovered sex drive (achieved a second ejaculation) in one hour while C57BL/6J males required a median recovery time of four days. Hybrid males resulting from a cross between the two inbred strains resembled DBA/2J males in terms of the time required to recover sex drive after an ejaculation. The previous studies, however, did not show that "fast-recovery" males were in fact capable of more ejaculations over an extended period of testing than were "slow-recovery" males.

One purpose of the present study was to test the above hypothesis; the second purpose was exploratory in nature. One of the accepted generalizations from studies on sexual behavior is that the behavior of animals high on the phylogenetic scale is less dependent on gonadal hormones than is the sexual behavior of animals with a lower phylogenetic status (3). For example, the sexual behavior of experienced, male cats and dogs (4, 5) persists much longer after castration than does the behavior of experienced, castrated rats and guinea pigs (6). The second part of our experiment was designed to determine whether genetic differences *within* a species affect the persistence of sexual behavior after castration.

A total of 72 male mice was used, including 24 C57BL/6J males, 24 DBA/2J males, and 24 B6D2F$_1$ males. The last named strain results from crossing C57BL/6J females with DBA/2J males. Each male was housed with five other males of the same genotype in the intervals between the daily testing sessions.

Two hundred and fifty-two BALB/cJ females were used in the mating tests.

143

Thirty-six of these females were brought into behavioral estrus each day by injections of estrogen and progesterone (7).

All animals were 9 weeks old at the beginning of the experiment. The animals were maintained on a reversed light-dark cycle with the light phase lasting 13 hours. The dark phase began 2 hours before the onset of testing which occurred under normal room illumination between 8:30 a.m. and 2:00 p.m.

Males were placed individually in plastic cylinders 25 cm in diameter and 50 cm in height. In the early stages of the experiment, males were allowed 30 minutes to adapt to the cylinder prior to the introduction of an estrous female. This 30-minute adaptation period became unnecessary as the males gained experience in the test situation. A given male was allowed from 5 to 10 minutes to initiate mating with the estrous female. If the male did not gain intromission during this interval, the female was removed and a second female was presented to the male. When a male "refused" all three females, he was scored as "negative" for that day. In order to achieve a "positive" score, the male was required to mate with one of the three females until ejaculation occurred. Occasionally a male would cease copulating before ejaculation. Such a test was scored as "negative" if 40 minutes elapsed without an intromission.

Daily testing continued for 42 days at which point half the males of each strain were castrated. Castrate groups and noncastrate groups were matched within strains on the basis of number of ejaculations for individual animals. One C57BL/6J male and one DBA/2J male, both of which had previously copulated, died as a result of the operation. Daily testing was resumed 72 hours after castration. Daily tests then continued for each group until at least 14 days had elapsed without the occurrence of the ejaculatory reflex in a castrated male.

The results (Tables 11–1 and 11–2) may be briefly summarized as follows:

(a) DBA/2J males exhibited higher sex drive than C57BL/6J males. This is illustrated in the four measures presented in Table 11–1. All four of the measures revealed statistically significant differences between the two inbred strains (8).

(b) The hybrid males, B6D2F₁, resembled the DBA/2J males in sex drive as defined by the measures presented in Table 11–1. They differed significantly from the C57BL/6J males, but not from the DBA/2J males, on all four measures. This finding agrees with a previous report concerning the "dominance" of the DBA/2J genotype over the C57BL/6J genotype in the determination of sex drive (2).

(c) The data of Table 11–2 illustrate "hybrid vigor" in the persistence of sex drive after castration. The hybrid males re-

TABLE 11-1

Sexual performance of the 24 intact males of each strain
during 42 consecutive days of testing

NO. OF "EJACULATORS" (MALES WHO ACHIEVED EJACULATION)	NO. OF EJACULATIONS PER EJACULATOR MEDIAN RANGE		DAY OF FIRST EJACULATION MEDIAN RANGE		DAYS BETWEEN EJACULATIONS MEDIAN RANGE	
C57BL/6J						
10	2	1–9	17	4–31	6	1–38
DBA/2J						
22	15	4–28	3	1–36	2	1–19
B6D2F₁						
24	15	5–27	2	1–32	2	1–9

TABLE 11-2

Sexual performance after castration

CASTRATES (NO.)	PREOPERATIVE EJACULATORS (NO.)	POSTOPERATIVE EJACULATORS (NO.)	TOTAL "EJACULATIONS" AFTER CASTRATION (NO.)	DAY AFTER CASTRATION ON WHICH LAST "EJACULATION" OCCURRED	
				MEDIAN	RANGE
			C57BL/6J		
11	4	0	—	—	—
			DBA/2J		
11	10	3	3	3	3–8
			B6D2F$_1$		
12	12	9	42	28	3–60

tained the ejaculatory reflex in greater numbers and for a longer time than either inbred parent strain.

This study has shown that genotype has a definite effect on the sex drive of the intact male mouse and that high sex drive seems to be a "dominant" character. The hypothesis, based on a previous study (2), that "fast-recovery" males are capable of more ejaculations over an extended period of testing than are "slow-recovery" males was supported.

Further, the study has demonstrated that the persistence of sex drive after castration varies with genotype *within* a species. Genetic homozygosity was associated with a rapid loss of the ejaculatory reflex in the castrated males; heterozygosity, on the other hand, resulted in a retention of this reflex for a maximum of 60 days after castration. This finding raises a question concerning the accepted generalization of an inverse correlation between dependence on gonadal hormones and phylogenetic status. For example, it may be hypothesized that the differences in decline of sexual behavior between carnivores and rodents is due not to their phylogenetic status, but rather to the amount of heterozygosity in the samples. The carnivores studied have been mongrel cats and dogs, while the rodent groups have been selected from relatively inbred laboratory colonies. Heterozygosity is doubtless greater in the carnivore groups and this may have ac-

counted for the slower decline in sexual behavior. Support for this hypothesis is found in a recent study by Bruell (9) who tested several inbred strains of mice and their hybrids in a running wheel. Hybrid vigor occurred for all crosses, and the degree of hybrid vigor was found to be proportional to the amount of suspected heterozygosity.

Genetic differences may also account for the observation (4, 11) that mongrel cats fall into three different types on the basis of decline of sexual behavior after castration.

There is one previous study regarding the decline of sexual behavior in mice after castration which does not support the foregoing hypothesis. Champlin, Blight, and McGill (10) castrated hybrid males of the CD2F$_1$ strain (BALB/c females × DBA/ 2J males) and found that the ejaculatory reflex was lost within 1 week. The discrepancy between that study and ours may be due to (i) genetic differences (the CD2F$_1$ strain may remain homozygous at critical loci), (ii) maternal effects, or (iii) any of several procedural differences between the two studies.

The hypothesis that heterozygosity determines persistence of sexual behavior is testable. Should experiments support this hypothesis, the search for the underlying physiological differences will be greatly simplified as only one species need be used (12).

parison and the C57BL vs. B6D2F$_1$ comparison were significant (p < 0.0002). DBA males did not differ from B6D2F$_1$ males. The other three measures were analyzed using the Mann-Whitney U test from S. Siegel *Nonparametric Statistics for the Behavioral Sciences* (McGraw-Hill, New York, 1956). The C57BL vs. DBA comparisons and the C57BL vs. B6D2F$_1$ comparisons showed significant differences with p values ranging from 0.02 to 0.002. The comparisons of DBA with B6D2F$_1$ did not reveal significant differences. Two-tailed tests were used in all cases.

REFERENCES

1. McGill, T. E.: *Abstr. Anat. Rec.*, **138**, 367 (1960). T. E. McGill: *Behaviour*, **19**, 341 (1962).
2. McGill, T. E., and W. C. Blight: *J. Comp. Physiol. Psychol.*, **56**, 887 (1963).
3. Beach, F. A.: *Hormones and Behavior* (Hoeber, New York, 1948).
4. Rosenblatt, J. S., and L. R. Aronson: *Behaviour*, **12**, 285 (1958).
5. Beach, F. A.: *Ciba Found. Colloq. Endocrinol.*, **3**, 3 (1952).
6. Beach, F. A.: *J. Expl. Zool.*, **97**, 249 (1944). F. A. Beach and R. S. Pauker: *Endocrinology*, **45**, 211 (1949). J. A. Grunt and W. C. Young: *Endocrinology*, **51**, 237 (1952).
7. The hormone preparations, Progynon B and Proluton, were generously supplied by Dr. R. Richard McCormick, Schering Corporation, Bloomfield, New Jersey.
8. "No. of ejaculators" was tested by "the significance of the difference between two independent proportions" test from G. A. Ferguson, *Statistical Analysis in Psychology and Education* (McGraw-Hill, New York, 1959). The C57BL vs. DBA comparison and the C57BL vs. B6D2F$_1$ comparison were significant (p < 0.0002).
9. Bruell, J. H.: *J. Comp. Physiol. Psychol.*, 1964, **58**, 159–163.
10. Champlin, A. K., W. C. Blight, and T. E. McGill: *Anim. Behaviour*, **11**, 244 (1963).
11. Aronson, L. R.: Chapter 5 of *Comparative Endocrinology*, A. Gorbman (Ed.). (Wiley, New York, 1959.)
12. This research was supported in part by Research Grant 07495 from the Institute of General Medical Sciences, Public Health Service. The second author was a National Science Foundation Research Trainee in the Undergraduate Science Education Program; NSF Grant No. 22864.

section three

NEURAL, HORMONAL, AND CHEMICAL CONTROL

OF BEHAVIOR The readings of the previous section presented many examples of the effects of genotype on behavior. An important question related to the material in that section is *"How* does genotype affect behavior?" The answers to this question are immensely complex and largely unknown. Nevertheless, it is possible to make some general statements about the intermediate steps whereby genes affect behavior. First, it is generally agreed that genes control the production of enzymes and enzyme systems. Enzymes in turn mediate the complex metabolic activities necessary for the growth and differentiation of cells. Tissues and organs are thus formed. The resulting morphology and physiology are the substrates on which behavior ultimately depends. These substrates are, of course, not immutable, and we shall cover many examples of environmental and behavioral effects on physiology and anatomy.

Most important for the study of the physiology of behavior are the nervous system and the endocrine system. Therefore, the readings that follow are concerned primarily with brain function and the influence of hormones on behavior.

Suggestions for Further Reading:

DETHIER, V. G., and E. STELLAR, *Animal Behavior: Its Evolutionary and Neurological Basis.* Englewood Cliffs, N. J.: Prentice-Hall, 1961.

HARLOW, H. W., and C. N. WOOLSEY, Eds., *Biological and Biochemical Bases of Behavior.* Madison, Wis.: University of Wisconsin Press, 1958.

Physiological Mechanisms in Animal Behaviour. London: Cambridge University Press, 1950, Part II.

147

JERRAM L. BROWN and
ROBERT W. HUNSPERGER

12 Neuroethology and the Motivation of Agonistic Behaviour*

Physiological psychology is that branch of psychology concerned with relations between the internal processes of the body and behavior. It thus serves as a bridge between purely physiological and purely behavioral research. Even those behaviorists whose experiments do not directly deal with physiological processes recognize the importance of this discipline. For behavioral theories must not violate physiological principles (just as physiological theories must take into account the facts of biochemistry). When such a violation occurs, the behavioral theory is probably in need of revision. The following reading concerns an example of this problem. See reading 47 for a further discussion of theories of motivation.

Note that "agonistic" is not a synonym for "antagonistic"; agonistic behavior includes fear and escape, as well as threat and aggressiveness. In reading 49, J. P. Scott discusses this term in more detail in his presentation of a classification system for social behavior.

This selection is reprinted from *Animal Behaviour*, 1963, 11, 439–448, by permission of the authors and the publisher: Baillière, Tindall and Cox, Ltd. The experiments described in this reading were carried out at the Physiological Institute of Zürich University.

I. Introduction

The aim of this paper is to bring to the attention of ethologists some findings on the neural bases of agonistic behaviour and to interpret them in relation to some commonly held ethological concepts of motivation. It is hoped that in doing so a better understanding between conventional ethologists and those who experiment directly with the central nervous system will result. Both of these groups depend on each other's findings for the understanding of their own problems; and both share common goals in the study of the mechanisms of behaviour.

The central problems confronting both ethology and the neurological sciences concern the mechanisms by which information coming from outside the nervous system is received and evaluated, and by which responses are selected and programmed to result in co-ordinated and typically adaptive effector performance throughout ontogeny and phylogeny.

The methods of investigating these problems characteristic of ethology and the neurological sciences are fundamentally different. Ethological techniques are generally confined to manipulations and observations external to the organism. In contrast, the neurological sciences investigate directly neural structure and function.

Although ethologists may study such

* Based on a paper presented at the 1961 International Ethological Conference. This investigation was supported in part by a U.S. Public Health Service fellowship (No. MF-11, 884) from the National Institute of Mental Health, P.H.S.

148

internal phenomena as releasing mechanisms and motivation, their method is essentially that of *drawing correlations between externally observable events* and using these correlations to characterize phenomena which are internally mediated.

For example, some ethological studies have concentrated on effector performance and the "internal motivation" of it, such as the study of Baerends, Brouwer & Waterbolk (1955) on the sexual behaviour of the male guppy *(Lebistes reticulatus)*. In this study test females of standardized sizes were presented to the males and the resulting behaviour was correlated with the colour pattern of the male (which reflected its "internal motivation"). Both the colour pattern of the male and his behaviour to the test female may be considered effector responses which were correlated with each other.

A more complex example of concentration on effector performance is the factor analysis of the behaviour of the bitterling *(Rhodeus amarus)* performed by Wiepkema (1961) in which the occurrences of many types of behaviour were correlated with each other and the correlations mathematically attributed to a relatively small number of common factors.

In contrast to the methods used in conventional ethology a common experimental procedure for neuroethology is to make an alteration of some part of the nervous system, for instance, by activating or inactivating a specific part of it, and then to correlate changes in the behaviour with the alteration. The most common means of activation for neuroethology at the present time is the electrical stimulation of circumscribed small areas of the brain. By this means specific neural areas may be implicated in the mechanisms of the behaviour resulting from their stimulation. The neurobehavioural work on the cat will be considered as a specific example of this general approach.

The methods used by the authors are based on the original technique of Hess (1932, 1957), further developed in its electrical part by Wyss (1945, 1950, 1957) and Hunsperger & Wyss (1953).

The term, *agonistic behaviour*, includes all types of behaviour thought to contain elements of *aggressiveness, threat,* or *fear.*

II. Neurobehavioural Investigations of Agonistic Behaviour in the Cat

The programme of research in this laboratory on neural mechanisms in agonistic behaviour of the cat attempts to correlate various aspects of agonistic behaviour with both anatomical and physiological properties of the brain. This paper is based primarily on the findings of Hess & Brügger (1943), Hunsperger (1956), Fernandez de Molina & Hunsperger (1959, 1961), and Brown, Hunsperger & Rosvold (in preparation). The relevant literature including contributions by other workers has been reviewed by Hunsperger (1959).

A. AGONISTIC BEHAVIOUR ELICITABLE BY LOCALIZED STIMULATION

A considerable range of agonistic behaviour patterns may be elicited in the cat by electrical (or chemical; MacLean & Delgado, 1953) stimulation of small areas in the brain. The elicited behaviour depends on the site of stimulation in the brain, the intensity of activation, and the environment. It generally follows one of four patterns. These are (1) threat alone, (2) threat followed by attack, (3) threat followed by escape, (4) escape alone.

Some typical components of threat alone as elicited through brain stimulation are listed below (not in order of appearance, intensity, or other classification).

> Opening of eyes
> Pupillodilatation
> Piloerection
> Folding down of ears
> Folding back of ears
> Crouching
> Forward rotation of whiskers
> Lowering of the head
> Protrusion of claws
> Arching of back

Straightening and stiffening of legs
Faster and deeper respiration
Urination, defaecation
Growling and yowling
Shrieking
Hissing
Standing up
Tail quivering
Tail whipping
Erection of tail base

It is not uncommon to obtain every component in this list from a single brain locus; however, partial coverage of the list is more often obtained.

These components may be fully integrated into a behaviour which cannot be distinguished from the normal behaviour which cats show towards other cats, and sometimes toward other, larger species, such as dogs or humans. A second normal cat placed together with a cat stimulated to show such threat behaviour, reacts to the stimulated cat as it would under normal circumstances.

The behaviour described above is referred to as threat behaviour because it has that general function in social communication.

In the pattern, threat followed by attack, the cat performs threat as described above followed by an attack if a dummy is present or by a short forward rush and an explosive forward extension of the forepaws with claws protruding when no suitable object is present. Attacks on dummies commonly consist of striking the dummy's face with one or both forepaws with sufficient force to knock it over. But in some instances the cat has leaped upon the dummy, bitten it in the nape and ears, and used the hind feet in knocking the dummy over. Thus, the attacks vary in their execution, some appearing more aggressive than others.

In threat followed by escape the cat performs threat as described above followed by jumping off the experimental table, often accompanied by hissing.

In escape alone the cat first looks in all directions and then jumps off the table without any previous growling, hissing, or other actions especially characteristic of threat. The pupils may be dilated and there may be piloerection. When prevented from escaping by enclosure on the table, the cat runs rapidly back and forth looking for an exit.

B. NEUROANATOMICAL LOCALIZATION OF THREAT, ATTACK, AND ESCAPE BEHAVIOUR

No two items in the list of components of threat behaviour above have identical patterns of anatomical localization in the brain, but they all overlap in the general region from which threat behaviour is elicitable. Growling and hissing are generally characteristic of the threat pattern and the areas from which they have been elicited have been plotted in Fig. 1.

Fig. 1 (from Fernandez de Molina & Hunsperger, 1959) represents a parasagittal section of the cat brainstem with, superimposed upon it, some structures of the forebrain lying more laterally, such as the amygdala and hippocampus. It is a diagrammatic summary of many localization experiments and provides an overall view of the agonistic behaviour system in relation to the brain as a whole. In black and cross hatching are shown the areas from which threat behaviour was obtained, using as criteria growling and/or hissing integrated in a reaction involving other threat components. The areas from which escapes were obtained are indicated by vertical lines. Stimulation in other brain areas has not established that any other areas are so intimately concerned with the integration of threat behaviour. These results are in general agreement with those of other authors, such as Nakao (1958; see review by Hunsperger, 1959).

The figure illustrates that anatomically the system for threat behaviour is *not unitary* but *multirepresentational*. It has principal representation at three brain levels: the midbrain, the hypothalamus, and the amygdala.

There is no justification for the argument that the effects are primarily depend-

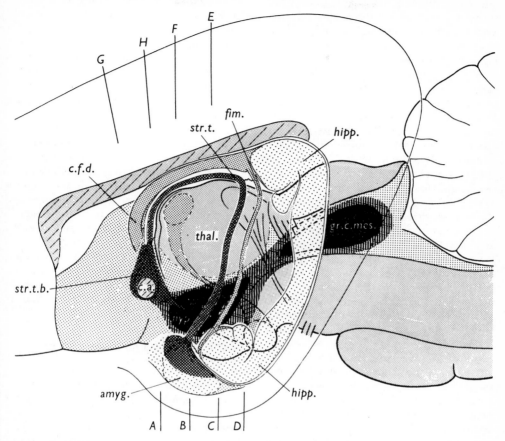

FIG. 1. Sagittal section through the brain stem of the cat with amygdala and other more lateral forebrain structures superimposed illustrating the threat and escape areas of brainstem and forebrain. This schematic representation is based on histological examination of over 800 sites of stimulation (from FERNANDEZ DE MOLINA and HUNSPERGER, 1959.)

  Active field of amygdala, stria terminalis, and stria terminalis bed, continuing into:

  Active field of the hypothalamus and the central gray of the midbrain. Black: inner zone yielding hissing; hatched: outer zone yielding escape.

amyg.	= amygdala.
c.a.	= anterior commissure.
c.f.d.	= descendent column of fornix.
fim.	= fimbria.
gr. c. mes.	= midbrain central gray substance.
hipp.	= hippocampus.
hyp.	= hypothalamus.
str. t. b.	= stria terminalis bed.
thal.	= thalamus.

ent on activation of areas lying outside the threat system. Indeed, the evidence is that activation of the neurons located in these areas is directly responsible for the threat behaviour elicited. Each of these three areas where threat behaviour is elicitable is an area of high cell density, and with the exception of the amygdala, long myelinated fibres are generally absent. The co-ordinated nature of the elicited behaviour, the absence of agonistic responses from stimulations in other brain areas, and the anatomical evidence (including lesion studies; see below) have led to acceptance among neurophysiologists and neuroanatomists of the concept that these areas are integrative in function, concerned with motivation, and depend on the population of neurons located in these areas for their properties.

The threat behaviour patterns elicited from the amygdala, hypothalamus, and midbrain have many elements in common, such as lowering of the head, laying back of the ears, piloerection, pupillodilatation, deepened, more rapid respiration, hunching of the back, hissing, and growling. Differences in the behaviour elicited from these three areas are present, however. The most striking of these is in the vocalizations: from the midbrain hissing is the predominant vocalization; from the amygdala growling predominates although hissing has also been elicited in addition to growling from about half of the points which gave growling. From the hypothalamus the reactions are usually characterized by mixed growling and hissing, thus intermediate behaviourally and anatomically between midbrain and amygdala.

Since growling is correlated more with aggression, and hissing with defence (Leyhausen, 1956), the possibility arises that this difference in behaviour elicitable from anterior and posterior ends of the threat system might reflect an anterior-posterior gradient in aggressiveness of the threat. It would be interesting to know if a similar anterior-posterior gradient in aggressiveness of the elicited threat behaviour occurs in other species.

Another anatomical finding of importance to ethology is that the areas from which escapes may be elicited are located adjacent and overlapping with those for threat. This is consistent with the principle often encountered in neuroanatomy that similar functions are represented close together in the brain. Escape and threat in the cat may both function in self-protection, whether from other cats or other species. In the brainstem escape reactions are elicitable from regions just anterior and posterior to the threat areas in the hypothalamus and midbrain and also to a lesser extent from a thin layer surrounding and interconnecting the threat areas (Hunsperger, 1956). Combinations of threat and escape are often obtained from the border areas. In the amygdala the escape responses are obtained from areas which are also closely related anatomically to those for threat responses (Fernandez de Molina & Hunsperger, 1959; Ursin, 1960).

C. THREAT BEHAVIOUR AS A FUNCTION OF INTENSITY OF ACTIVATION

In addition to being dependent on the *locus* of stimulation the nature of the elicited threat behaviour is also greatly influenced by the *intensity* of stimulation. Raising the intensity of stimulation either through frequency or voltage has the effects of (1) activating the area under direct stimulation more intensely and/or (2) activating a larger area. The more conspicuous effects of increasing the voltage are seen not only in latencies but also in the intensities or rates of expression of the component elements of threat and in the behaviour as a whole. For example, with increasing voltage pupillodilatation and piloerection may become extreme, the ears fully lowered, the rate of growling or hissing may increase, and the loudness and pitch of growling may increase; at near maximum activation the legs are rigidly extended, the tail rigid or whipping, and explosive attacks with the forepaws may be made. The elicited behaviour may also change in character, for example, from growling alone to growling and hissing.

D. MODIFICATION OF CENTRALLY ELICITED BEHAVIOUR BY EXTERNAL ENVIRONMENT

Of the various types of physiological and behavioural changes which can be elicited by central stimulation in the vertebrates ranging from the movement of a finger in man to whole series of natural integrated behaviour patterns in many species it is the latter type which is of special interest in regard to motivation. The neural areas from which natural integrated behaviour may be elicited do not seem to be just motor co-ordination centres, for stimulation of these areas appears to cause real changes in the pre-disposition of the animal. When humans are stimulated in the amygdala, for example, "the strong emotional response is conscious and integrated in the thinking of the patient. . . ." (Heath, Monroe & Mickle, 1955). Similar findings have been reported for the human hypothalamus and midbrain (Sem-Jacobsen & Torkildsen, 1960; Heath & Mickle, 1960).

The basic mood or *motivation, which may be considered as neural activity,* is rather specific to the locus stimulated and appears to be relatively independent of the presence or absence of particular objects in the environment. However, such objects may play a role in the orientation of the behaviour and may bring out some external expression of the elicited motivation which might not otherwise have appeared. Just as the neurosurgeon can characterize the emotions of a patient during stimulation better by talking with him, the neuroethologist can characterize the motivation underlying the elicited behaviour better by varying the external environment through the presence of stuffed or live animals during stimulation and other means.

The independence of the basic motivation elicited during stimulation of areas which elicit threat and escape from various aspects of the external situation is striking. The threat and escape reactions appear in the "neutral" experimental room and re-quire no special factors in the environment. They have appeared in a blind cat and in cats which could not see the experimenters as readily, or more so, as in normal cats in full view of the experimenters.

Sex, age, the individual temperament of the cat (tameness, wildness, submissiveness) and the particular behaviour in which the cat was engaged just before stimulation influence the occurrence of centrally elicited threat and escape relatively little compared to the location of the electrode, in the experience of the authors. The elicited threat and escape behaviour take precedence over apparently all other forms of activity when the appropriate areas of the brain are stimulated. The adaptive value of this attribute of agonistic behaviour is obvious. It also makes agonistic behaviour one of the easier to study of the categories of complex behaviour patterns which may be elicited by brain stimulation.

In many experiments the cat has been stimulated while it was in the presence of a stuffed cat, dog, fox, or pigeon. In order for the dummy to have an effect upon threat behaviour some part of the neural substrate for threat behaviour had apparently to be activated electrically. The dummy had no effect alone. In almost all cases where the presence of the dummy strengthened threat behaviour or brought in an attack it was with electrode placements where stimulation was capable of eliciting elements of threat behaviour even in the absence of any dummies. In a few cases elements of threat and sometimes attacks were brought in by stimulation in the presence of the dummy from loci which elicited escape but did not elicit threat behaviour. In these it seemed likely because of the anatomical location of the electrodes next to the threat zone and the nature of the behaviour which was elicited that part of the threat substrate was being activiated but at subthreshold levels.

The behaviour towards the dummies during stimulation at loci where escape but not elements of threat were elicited consisted primarily of investigative sniffing, especially in the nasal and facial regions (Nasenkontrolle). Unlike the agnostic responses, this sniffing waned rapidly with a few repetitions using the same dummy. The loci lay mostly lateral and posterior to the hypothalamic threat substrate.

Where there was an effect of the dummy on threat behaviour, it consisted of more extreme development of the whole pattern, sometimes with shortened latencies and quickened rates, and in some cases attacks on the dummy with the forepaws.

In order for the elicited threat behaviour to be directed toward the dummy, the species of dummy seems not to be critical. Strong threat reactions with much hissing and growling and apparent fear of the opponent have been given toward the stuffed fox, dog, cat, and pigeon, and also toward a live guinea pig and a live kitten. The motivation elicited by the electrical stimulus, therefore, does not depend in our experience on the species of dummy but primarily on the location of the electrode.

It was at first thought that the strengthening effect was dependent on the cat's perception of the dummy as an enemy. However, in several cases cats directed startling threats and attacks at dummies which they seemed to completely ignore before stimulation. Recent evidence of a preliminary nature indicates that with weak stimulation in the threat zone the perception of the dummy as an enemy (as judged by the cat's behaviour when not stimulated) and the strengthening effect of the dummy on the elicited threat behaviour may wane together. But with strong stimulation in the same area the dummy may acquire new meaning to the cat as a dangerous enemy even when it was ignored beforehand. Thus, the strengthening effect of the dummy may require that the cat regard it as an enemy; but when such regard is absent, it may be generated by the electrical stimulus itself in conjunction with the dummy. Long after-reactions of growling toward the dummy which sometimes occurred are evidence for this view.

In some ways the presence of the dummy had an effect similar to the simultaneous stimulation of a second area eliciting hissing and associated threat elements (see below). This was apparent in the shortened latencies and fuller, more intense development of the threat sequence.

E. INTERRELATIONS

As the nervous system functions on the principle of interdependence of cells and of populations of cells, dynamic aspects of the neural activities mediating the motivation of agonistic behaviour are of primary importance. Unfortunately, however, they are poorly understood. For example, it is largely unknown whether the threat areas, or parts of them, in amygdala, hypothalamus, and midbrain are normally differentially activated according to different motivations and what spatio-temporal patterns of activation occur during different motivations. Also the exact neural paths of input and output to these areas, whether inhibitory or excitatory, are poorly known. Since so little is actually known about these questions only a few aspects can be mentioned.

Some aspects of interdependence have, however, been studied. The work in which a lesion in one area was combined with stimulation of another area (Hunsperger, 1956; Fernandez de Molina & Hunsperger, 1961) illustrates some aspects of the interdependence of the various parts of the threat system. After acute lesions at some levels of the system the threat or escape behaviour elicited from remaining levels was eliminated. The elimination of threat behaviour elicited in one area after lesioning in another area was strikingly dependent on the location of the lesion. Damage to the anterior part of the threat system (amygdala, bilateral) had no effect on the threshold of the threat and escape behaviour elicited more posteriorly; while damage to the posterior parts (midbrain and hypothalamus) eliminated threat behaviour elicited anterior to the lesion immediately after coagulation. Two weeks later it could again be elicited without apparent change in character but at a higher threshold. These studies also indicate that threat behaviour may be elicited from the midbrain area independently from the anterior parts of the system.

Work using the technique of simultaneous stimulation of two brain areas concerned with agonistic behaviour (domestic fowl, von Holst & von Saint Paul, 1958, 1960; cat, Hunsperger & Brown, 1961) has not reached a stage where generalizations concerning the whole threat system can be made. However, studies in this laboratory indicate that within the hypothalamus of the cat are areas which when stimulated strengthen threat and escape reactions elicited and areas which weaken them. Generally when one response may be elicited by each of two electrodes, that response, such as growling, hissing, piloerection, ear-flattening, or escaping, is strengthened by simultaneous stimulation with the two electrodes. Threat behaviour elicited from the hypothalamus is generally strengthened and changed in character by simultaneously elicited escape behaviour, and in these combinations escape behaviour is often delayed.

Since areas for "pure" attack have not been found in the cat brain, it has not been possible to perform the interaction experiment so long desired by ethologists, namely the simultaneous activation of "pure" attack and escape mechanisms. The failure to find these areas is of significance in itself, however, and will be discussed below.

III. Attack-Escape Theory

The neural bases of agonistic behaviour have not been investigated in detail for many species; and until the results of studies in other vertebrate classes are published, the mammals, especially the cat, remain the principle source of information. Knowledge of the neural bases of agonistic behaviour in the cat is only suggestive of the situation in other species; but because of the existence of basic homologies in the anatomy of the brainstem among vertebrate classes it is reasonable to suppose that *some* of the *general* properties of the neural bases of agonistic behaviour will be found to be similar in other species, despite difference in detail. Evidence for basic similarities between bird and mammal in the brainstem organization of certain physiological and behavioural regulatory mechanisms has been given by Åkerman et al., (1961). The more general implications of the works discussed above will be considered as an aid in improving the working hypothesis underlying ethological motivation studies.

Attack-escape theory has apparently never received formal definition in its entirety, nor has it been customarily referred to in print by any name. Rather, it has developed in stages and is best known through the investigations in which it has been applied. The theory became strongly influential on ethological analyses of the motivation of agonistic behaviour through the works of Tinbergen (1952), Hinde (1952), Moynihan (1955) and others. No attempt to assign credit for each development of the theory to individual authors will be made in this paper.

In each of the following four sections we shall attempt briefly to first state the principal conclusions of attack-escape theory, second, mention the types of behavioural observations which have given rise to each conclusion, third, examine the neurological correlations which may be made with these observations, and fourth, compare the neurological experimental results with the conclusions of attack-escape theory.

The principal inferences characterizing attack-escape theory follow:

(a) The motivation of behaviour may be understood through the use of *unitary drive concepts.*

(b) Threat behaviour has *dual* rather than unitary motivation; the two drives being those for *attack* and *escape.*

(c) Threat behaviour is caused to appear by the simultaneous activation and

mutual inhibition of attack and escape drives.

(d) The motivation of different types of threat and other behaviour patterns of a species may be *characterized* by the intensities and relative strengths of attack and escape drives.

(a) Unitary drives. Ethological motivation analyses of agonistic behaviour have been in recent years frequently founded on unitary drive concepts. These allow behaviour to be interpreted in terms of attack, escape, sex, parental, hunger drives, etc. The dangers of unitary drive concepts in ethology have been ably reviewed by Hinde (1959), and the reader is referred to that paper for a detailed discussion. In ethology such concepts have been inferred primarily from the common observation that different behaviour patterns with similar functions (e.g. obtaining of food) frequently occur in close spatio-temporal proximity with each other. This observation has led to the postulating of a common causal mechanism for the behaviour patterns concerned, and this mechanism has in some cases been hypothesized to be a neural "centre". For the central nervous system concepts of unitary centers have a history of inadequacy in the explanation of various physiological and behavioural functions. Fig. 1 reveals that anatomically the concept of central nervous centres for attack and escape has little meaning in the cat. In any case the assumption that unitary mechanisms exist is unnecessary for the investigation of neural mechanisms, and it seems equally unnecessary in purely behavioural investigations.

(b) Dual motivation of threat. That threat behaviour has dual rather than unitary motivation has been concluded from inferences that both attack and escape drives are active during threat. Such inferences concerning the existence of subthreshold activation of attack and escape drives during threat have been made from three types of observation (Tinbergen, 1959). These are:

(1) occurrence of threat in close *tem-poral proximity* with the acts of attack and escape.

(2) occurrence of threat in spatial and temporal *contexts* where attack and escape drives would both be expected to be subthreshold, and

(3) the involvement of acts and *postures* in threatening which are related to or identical with those used in actual attack and escape.

Similar observations can be made in the cat. For example, growling occurs frequently in temporal proximity with attack and hissing with defence and escape (Leyhausen, 1956). Gradations in posture and facial expression between attack behaviour and various kinds of threat behaviour have been shown by Leyhausen (ibid.). Threat and escape behaviour in the cat have in common piloerection and pupillodilatation.

The postulating of unitary attack and escape drives to explain such observations is unnecessary. For such close relationships between threat, attack and escape may be correlated simply with the extensive coincidence of the neural areas where threat and attack may be elicited and the considerable overlap of the neural areas where threat and escape may be elicited.

It has been established that there are in the cat brain definite areas from which threat behaviour may be consistently elicited. This fact appears to contradict the theory that threat behaviour results from simultaneous activation and conflict of neural mechanisms for attack and escape, since *only one area needs to be directly stimulated, not two.* In birds threat can be elicited with one electrode also (von Holst & von Saint Paul, 1958). Furthermore, no anatomical or physiological provisions have been shown in any species for the motivation of threat behaviour by means of antagonistic interaction between neural mechanisms for pure attack and escape. Thus, although the occurrence of threat behaviour may be correlated with simultaneous activation of hypothetical attack and escape drives in some species, it can in the cat and chicken also be correlated with activation of an experimentally demonstratable neural substrate for threat behaviour.

(c) Mutual Inhibition. The inference that both attack and escape drives are active during threat was drawn from the three types of observations discussed above (temporal proximity, spatio-temporal contexts, postures). The failure of attack and escape to appear during threat even though active has been attributed to their mutual inhibition and conflict. The normally observed mutual exclusion of the acts of attack and escape has probably been most responsible for the concept that they are mutually inhibitory or conflicting. For the present we cannot investigate this particular conflict in the cat, if it exists, with neurological methods because it has not been possible to elicit an attack which is not preceded by threat. Stimulation in the threat-attack zone of the hypothalamus often retards escape elicited from the hypothalamus. But stimulation in the escape zone generally strengthens and prolongs simultaneously elicited threat behaviour. In the two cases investigated to date stimulation in the escape zone hastened simultaneously elicited attacks preceded by threats. Present results, therefore, indicate that *mutual* inhibition between threat-attack and escape zones does not occur.

(d) Characterization of Threat Displays. Characterization of the specific threat displays of a species according to the intensities and relative strengths of attack and escape drives has become widespread in recent ethological literature. Such characterizations have been inferred through the three types of observations mentioned above.

For example, from the observations of Leyhausen (1956), on the cat it can be deduced that growling occurs typically and more often than hissing in temporal proximity with attack and that hissing occurs more often than growling in temporal proximity with escape and defence. From these observations the inference could be made according to attack-escape theory that the attack drive was higher during growling than the escape drive and the escape drive higher during hissing than the attack drive.

These observations may also be correlated with experimental findings for the brain: Attacks elicited by brain stimulation are characteristically preceded by growls and hisses. In contrast, escapes elicited from regions of overlap of escape and threat are characteristically preceded by hisses without growls. In addition, growls are characteristically elicited from the amygdala and hypothalamus while hisses are characteristically elicited from the midbrain and hypothalamus. This evidence suggests that the spatial pattern of neural activation within the threat-attack system is different during these two types of threat vocalization. Furthermore, the extensive overlap of the areas where growling and attack may be elicited correlates with the close temporal relationships of growling and attack in normal behaviour. And the overlap of the areas where hissing and escape may be elicited correlates with the close temporal relationships of hissing and escape in normal behaviour. Thus, for the cat different types of threat and their temporal relationships with attack and escape can be correlated with different spatial patterns of central nervous activity.

In summary, when attack-escape theory as discussed above is compared with present knowledge of the structure and function of the nervous system, little direct agreement is found. However, many of the behavioural observations for which attack-escape theory has been invoked may now be correlated directly with the structure and function of the brain.

IV. Terminology

"Pure Attack". Attacks are easily elicited by brain stimulation in the cat, but "pure attacks" are not. According to attack-escape theory "pure attacks" should be

those attacks which have no elements of fear or threat motivation in them. In the cat this might be equivalent to catching a mouse or to attacking in situations where the cat has learned not to be afraid. Such confident attacks do not result from stimulation of the threat-attack zone under the conditions of our experiments. On the contrary, stimulation there has caused cats to threaten in apparent self-defence such harmless objects as a live guinea pig and a small kitten and to attack the guinea pig defensively.

In discussing "pure attack" in the cat Leyhausen (1956) wrote, "Das reine, durch teilweise Ueberlagerung mit anderen Verhaltensweisen nicht gestörte Angriffsverhalten des Katers sieht man nur selten". [Only rarely does one see in the tomcat purely aggressive behaviour that is not partially modified by or combined with other kinds of social behaviour.] However, he also referred to the same behaviour as in "extreme threat position" ("in extremer Drohstellung"). From his own statements, photographs, and descriptions it is clear that this is a threat posture rather than a "pure attack". Moreover, it is not the extreme threat posture obtained by stimulation of the threat zone in the cat brain but a partial development of it. It is similar to some attacks made on dummies during stimulation of the border area between threat-attack and escape zones.

Some clarification of the ontogenesis of "pure attack" may be gained by consideration of established social hierarchies among groups of vertebrates. Under these conditions supplanting attacks are often seen devoid of external signs of fear or threat. The absence of fear evinced in these attacks is specific to the opponent or the location and depends on previous establishment and stabilization of a dominant-subordinate relationship. If the opponent is slow in leaving, a mild threat may occur; and if it stays, strong threat followed by fighting often results. It would appear probable from this relationship that the more hesitant the attack and the more resistance of the opponent, the more activation of a threat system in the attacker.

Conditioning to specific opponents or situations is probably necessary for such attacks, and they could probably also be conditioned in the cat. It is known that mice can be trained to attack or not (Scott, 1958: 18) and rats to be killers of mice or not (Heimstra & Newton, 1961). In 14 of 16 such killer rats bilateral amygdalectomy eliminated the killing response (Karli, 1956) thus implicating a structure known to be part of the threat-attack system in the cat in a learned attack behaviour. In man anger and attack have also been eliminated by ablation of temporal lobe structures including the amygdala (cases reviewed by Ursin, 1960). Work on the cat amygdala in relation to attack is in progress in this laboratory.

Although much has been said about a "threat system" or "threat-attack system", *one should not infer that it is a unitary system* and that all varieties of threat behaviour in the cat are merely the result of quantitatively different levels of activation of a unitary threat system. The term "threat system" has been used in reference to the basic similarities in the behaviour patterns elicited from all parts of it. It should be stressed, however, that important differences also exist in the behaviour elicited from various places in the threat system. Virtually no two component elements of threat behaviour have exactly the same pattern of localization in the brain; and just which combination of elements is elicited appears to vary from place to place within the threat-attack zone.

All factors which affect motivation in the vertebrates, whether external stimuli or internal stimuli and conditions must work through the central nervous system. It follows from this relationship that ethological motivation theories have value primarily through their relevance to actual events in the central nervous system. The terms and concepts employed in such theories are, thus, of critical importance to the understanding of the relationship between the nervous system and behaviour.

Some ethologists may prefer to refrain from making inferences about nervous processes on the basis of their behavioural observations. If so, then to be consistent with neural concepts of motivation the terms "tendency", "drive", and their substitutes would become unnecessary. These terms, which are used interchangeably in this paper, have received two basic types of definition in ethology. One type defines them as reflecting "the state of an animal. . . ." (Tinbergen, 1959: 29); the other type, purposely even less explicit, defines them as "the complex of internal and external factors leading to a given behaviour" (van Iersel & Bol, 1958: 5).

If "tendency" in confined in its meaning to external stimulus factors, then with adequate and accurate description of them the concept of a tendency becomes superfluous and misleading. If "tendency" is defined as including internal factors (both definitions above), then by definition it concerns the state of the central nervous system. If "tendency" is meant to describe explicitly only the behaviour and not to imply anything about the nervous system, then the description would better be made in terms of the units of observation and the correlations between the different measures (these need not be mathematically stated); "tendency" in this case is also superfluous and misleading.

Since confusion is at present inevitable in this subject it would seem advisable either to be explicit in making statements about the theoretical neural state in motivation by using a term such as "neurobehavioural mechanism" (NBM) or not to mention neural states and to restrict the discussion to the units of observation actually used and the correlations between the different observations. In both cases "tendency" and "drive" need not be used at any time and ambiguity would be reduced.

V. Conclusion

Ethologists have been confined primarily to observations of external events. Their form, their quantitative variation, and the correlations between them as analysed by ethologists are some of the phenomena which the neurobehavioural sciences seek ultimately to explain. In the case of agonistic behaviour explanations are sought especially for behavioural relationships concerning (1) temporal proximity and sequence, (2) postural similarities and differences, and (3) general environmental and discrete stimulus contexts. When such phenomena are objectively and clearly described and correlated by ethologists they become more useful to the neurobehavioural sciences. It is hoped that ethologists will provide detailed and quantitative information of these types for the cat, monkey, and other species in common use in the neurobehavioural sciences.

Conversely, ethology may also make use of the contributions of the neurological sciences. Because the motivation and organization of behaviour are mediated through the nervous system, whatever is known about neural mechanisms in behaviour should be utilized by ethologists in the improvement of research hypotheses and theories. The existence in the brain of a multirepresentational system which when activated leads to threat followed sometimes by attack and the existence in close anatomical relationship to it of areas which when activated lead to escape are neurobehavioural facts of direct relevance to ethology.

Summary

1. The methods of ethological investigations are primarily concerned with drawing correlations between externally observable events. Neuroethology concerns additionally direct correlations with activity and structure of the nervous system.

2. Integrated threat behaviour may be

elicited from three different brain areas: in the amygdala, hypothalamus, and midbrain of the cat. The neural substrate for the "motivation" of threat behaviour is, therefore, not unitary but multirepresentational.

3. The neural substrate for "motivation" of threat behaviour in the cat overlaps that for escape. This overlap helps to explain the temporal, postural, and situational similarities of threat to escape behaviour.

4. Attacks may be elicited with high intensity stimulation at some places which at the same and lower intensities of stimulation first yield threat. This functional relationship helps to explain the temporal, postural, and situational similarities of threat to attack behaviour.

5. The basic "mood" elicited by stimulation in these motivation areas is primarily determined by the intensity and locus of stimulation. Dummies and other aspects of the external environment (conversations in the case of man) play a role in the orientation of the behaviour and may bring out some external expressions of the elicited motivation which might not otherwise appear.

6. The attack-escape theory and the terms "drive", "tendency", and "neurobehavioural mechanism" are discussed. Non-neural concepts of drive or tendency are considered to be superfluous and misleading.

Acknowledgments

The authors wish to thank the many people with whom they have discussed these problems and to thank particularly Drs. R. A. Hinde, H. E. Rosvold and N. Tinbergen.

REFERENCES

BAERENDS, G. P., R. BROUWER and H. T. J. WATERBOLK, 1955 Ethological studies on *Lebistes reticulatus* (Peters). I. An analysis of the male courtship pattern. *Behaviour*, **8**, 249–334.

FERNANDEZ DE MOLINA, A., and R. W. HUNSPERGER, 1959 Central representation of affective reactions in forebrain and brain stem: electrical stimulation of amygdala, stria terminalis, and adjacent structures. *J. Physiol.*, **145**, 251–265.

FERNANDEZ DE MOLINA, A., and R. W. HUNSBERGER, 1962 Organization of the subcortical system governing defence and flight reactions in the cat. *J. Physiol.*, **160**, 200-213.

HEATH, R. G., and W. A. MICKLE, 1960 Evaluation of seven years experience with depth electrode studies in human patients. In *Electrical Studies on the Unanesthetized Brain*. New York: Hoeber, Inc., 214–247.

HEATH, R. G., R. R. MONROE, and W. A. MICKLE, 1955 Stimulation the amygdaloid nucleus in a schizophrenic patient. *Amer. J. Psychiat.*, **111**, 862–863.

HEIMSTRA, N. W. and G. NEWTON, 1961 Effects of prior food competition on the rat's killing response to the white mouse. *Behaviour*, **17**, 95–102.

HESS, W. R., 1932 *Beiträge zur Physiologie des Hirnstammes. I. Die Methodik der lokalisierten Reizung und Ausschaltung subkortikaler Hirnabschnitte.* Leipzig: Georg Thieme.

HESS, W. R., 1957 *The Functional Organization of the Diencephalon.* New York, London: Grune and Stratton.

HESS, W. R., and M. BRÜGGER, 1943 Das subkortikale Zentrum der affectiven Abwehrreaktion. *Helv. physiol. Acta*, **1**, 33–52.

HINDE, R. A., 1952 The behaviour of the Great Tit *(Parus major)* and some other related species. *Behaviour, Suppl.*, **2**, x & pp. 201.

HINDE, R. A., 1959 Unitary drives. *Anim. Behav.*, **7**, 130–141.

HUNSPERGER, R. W., 1956 Affektreaktionen auf elektrische Reizung im Hirnstamm der Katze. *Helv. physiol. Acta*, **14**, 70–92.

HUNSPERGER, R. W., 1959 Les représentations centrales des réactions affectives dans le cerveau antérieur et dans le tronc cérébral. *Neuro-Chirurgie*, **5**, 207–233.

HUNSPERGER, R. W. and J. L. BROWN, 1961 Verfahren zur gleichzeitigen elektrischen Reizung verschiedener subcorticaler Areale an der wachen Katze. Abwehr- und Fluchtreaktion. *Pflügers Arch. ges. Physiol.*, **274**, 94.

HUNSPERGER, R. W., and O. A. M. WYSS, 1953   Quantitative Ausschaltung von Nervengewebe durch Hochfrequenzkoagulation. *Helv. physiol. Acta,* 11, 283–304.

HOLST, E. VON, and U. VON SAINT PAUL, 1958   Das Mischen von Trieben (Instinktbewegungen) durch mehrfache Stammhirnreizung beim Huhn. *Naturwissenschaften,* 45, 579.

HOLST, E. VON, and U. VON SAINT PAUL, 1960   Vom Wirkungsgefüge der Triebe. *Naturwissenschaften,* 18, 409–422.

IERSEL, J. J. A. VAN, and A. C. A. BOL, 1958   Preening of two tern species. A study on displacement activities. *Behaviour,* 13, 1–88.

KARLI, P., 1956   The Norway rat's killing response to the white mouse: an experimental analysis. *Behaviour,* 10, 81–103.

LEYHAUSEN, PAUL, 1956   Verhaltensstudien an Katzen. *Z. Tierpsychol.,* Beiheft 2.

MACLEAN, P. D., and J. M. R. DELGADO, 1953   Electrical and chemical stimulation of fronto-temporal portion of limbic system in the waking animal. *Electroenceph. clin. Neurophysiol.,* 5, 91–100.

MOYNIHAN, M., 1955   Some aspects of reproductive behavior in the Black-headed Gull (*Larus ridibundus ridibundus* L.) and related species. *Behaviour, Suppl.* 4, x & pp. 201.

NAKAO, H., 1958   Emotional behavior produced by hypothalamic stimulation. *Amer. J. Physiol.,* 194, 411–418.

OKERMAN, B., B. ANDERSSON, E. FABRICIUS, and L. SVENSSON, 1961   Observations on central regulation of body temperature and of food and water intake in the pigeon (*Columba livia*). *Acta physiol. scand.,* 50, 328–336.

SCOTT, J. P., 1958   *Aggression.* University of Chicago Press.

SEM-JACOBSEN, C. W., and A. TORKILDSEN, 1960   Depth recording and electrical stimulation in the human brain. In *Electrical Studies on the Unanesthetized Brain.* New York: Hoeber, Inc., 275–287.

TINBERGEN, N., 1952   "Derived" activities; their causation, biological significance, origin, and emancipation during evolution. *Quart. Rev. Biol.,* 27, 1–32.

TINBERGEN, N., 1959   Comparative studies of the behaviour of gulls (Laridae): a progress report. *Behaviour,* 15, 1–70.

URSIN, H., 1960   The temporal lobe substrate of fear and anger. *Acta psychiat. neurol. scand.,* 35, 278–396.

WIEPKEMA, P. R., 1961   An ethological analysis of the reproductive behaviour of the Bitterling (*Rhodeus amarus* Bloch). *Arch. néerl. Zool.,* 14, 103–199.

WYSS, O. A. M., 1945   Ein Hochfrequenz-Koagulationsgerät zur reizlosen Ausschaltung. *Helv. physiol. Acta,* 18, 18–24.

WYSS, O. A. M., 1950   Beiträge zur elektrophysiologischen Methodik. II. Ein vereinfachtes Reizgerät für unabhängige Veränderung von Frequenz und Dauer der Impulse. *Helv. physiol. Acta,* 8, 18–24.

WYSS, O. A. M., 1957   Nouveaux appareils électrophysiologiques (VII). *Helv. physiol. Acta,* C49–C50.

J O S E   M.   R.   D E L G A D O

13   Cerebral Heterostimulation in a Monkey Colony

Many of the readings in this volume note that certain animal species form fairly rigid dominance hierarchies within their social groups. These hierarchies usually are maintained, with little actual combat, through systems of ritualized threat on the part of the dominant animal and postures of submission by the subordinate animal. In some cases, however, severe injury or death may result from the attacks of a dominant animal. In the following unique experiment a noted neurophysiologist devises a situation in which a subordinate female monkey may control the behavior of the male "boss" monkey by electrical stimulation of his brain.

Science, Vol. 141, 161–163, 12 July 1963. Copyright 1963 by the American Association for the Advancement of Science. Reprinted with the permission of the author and the American Association for the Advancement of Science. (One figure has been omitted.)

ABSTRACT   In an established colony a subordinate monkey repeatedly pressed a lever which stimulated the caudate nucleus of the boss monkey by radio and inhibited his aggressive behavior. In other experiments, timed stimulations of the posteroventral nucleus of the thalamus of the boss monkey, paired with a tone, increased his aggressiveness and established conditioned escape responses of the whole group. Both types of experiments may be useful in neurophysiological and pharmacological investigations.

▶ Electrical stimulation of some areas of the brain induces positive reinforcement, and rats, cats, and monkeys learn to stimulate themselves by pressing a lever repeatedly for hours or even days (1). This method is very valuable for physiological and pharmacological analysis of the central nervous system. Since animals are capable of self-stimulation, they might stimulate the brain of a cagemate if suitable means were provided.

In a colony of four monkeys (*Macaca mulatta*) the boss, Ali (5.2 kg), was an ill-tempered, powerful male who often expressed his aggressiveness by grimacing and biting his own right hand. Ali had friendly relations with the female, Sarah (4.0 kg), was hostile toward the other female, Elsa (4.6 kg), who ranked No. 3 in the group, and paid less attention to the male, Lou (3.8 kg), who was lowest in social rank, as determined by the peanut test and by offensive-defensive reactions. The colony was housed for several weeks in a cage 7 by 3 by 3 ft. in a soundproof air-conditioned room with constant day and night cycles of 12 hours each. The monkeys were observed through a one-way window from an adjoining room, and their behavior recorded by time-lapse photography (one picture every 2 seconds for 8 hours daily); the data were analyzed with the aid of automation (2). Elsa and Lou were the controls. Multi-lead electrodes were implanted in the head of the caudate nucleus, thalamus, central gray, reticular substance, and other cerebral areas of Ali and Sarah. Two additional subcutaneous leads made connections between any cerebral contact and a small stimulating device strapped to the back of the animal. This device is a modified radio receiver (3) with a sensitivity of 2 to 4 μv, and it is reliable within a range of several hundred feet. Its only function is to close a switch to activate a transistorized stimulator whose output intensity is adjusted before the experiments. In this way cerebral stimulations are reliable and independent of possible variations, such as antenna orientation and changes in radio signals. Further technical details have been published elsewhere (4).

Controls were established first with the monkey lightly restrained in a chair. Each cerebral point was electrically stimulated; voltage and milliamperage were monitored in an oscilloscope, and bipolar recordings of the electrical activity before and immediately after the stimulations were obtained with an eight-channel Grass electroencephalograph. None of the effects described was accompanied by electrical afterdischarges. In all cases stimulations were monopolar, unidirectional, with exponential fall, 0.5 msec of pulse duration, and 100 cy/sec. The electrode resistance was about 50,000 ohms, and intensities up to 4 ma were used.

After stimulation under restraint, Ali and Sarah were both released in the colony, one wearing a radiostimulator and the other a dummy. In both, telestimulation of

FIG. 1. Elsa, pressing the lever, stimulates by radio the caudate nucleus of Ali (on right side of cage), producing behavioral inhibition. Elsa's attitude is significant because her atteniton is directed not to the lever but to Ali. It is unusual for lower-ranking monkeys to look straight at the boss of the colony because this evokes retaliation.

the central gray and of the posteroventral nucleus of the thalamus evoked antisocial behavior with increased chasing, jumping, biting, and fighting which was quantified and analyzed (2). Stimulation of the caudate nucleus induced behavioral inhibition (5) and was selected to test possible heterostimulation. In Ali and Sarah caudate stimulation produced similar effects including slight ipsilateral head turning, loss of interest in food, and inhibition of activities, such as drinking, taking of pellets, walking, picking, self-grooming, and diminution of spontaneous aggressiveness. The latter was more impressive in Ali because of his greater size and ferocity. Caudate stimulation did not modify the behavioral categories of nestling (two monkeys embracing each other), balling (one monkey with head down on knees), lying down, or being groomed by another. During caudate stimulation it was possible to touch the animal with one's bare hands, and in this manner the monkeys were caught repeatedly. The animals were not completely inhibited, and on occasion withdrew a few steps without attempting to retaliate or bite.

After controls were established a lever

was attached to the cage. At any time any monkey could press this bar, which automatically started a tone which was followed 2 seconds later by a 5-second radiostimulation. Tone and stimulation ended simultaneously. In the first series of experiments, the tone was set at 600 cy/sec, and Ali carried the stimulator connected to the caudate nucleus for 4 consecutive days. The lever was located close to a feeding tray, and the first day monkeys exploring the area occasionally touched the lever, starting the tone-stimulation cycle. The second day, Elsa pressed the bar 12 times, while each of the other monkeys, including Ali, touched the lever only 0 to 5 times. On the third and fourth days, Elsa pressed the lever 17 and 25 times, and the other monkeys 0 to 7 times. Figure 1 shows one example of Elsa stimulating Ali (6). After the fourth day, radiostimulation was discontinued, but the tone remained connected for 1 week. The next two recorded lever pressings started the tone and produced some head-turning and behavioral inhibition in Ali, but extinction appeared quickly, and successive tones were not effective. The number of lever pressings by Elsa diminished to 9 the first day and to 1 to 8 per day during the following 6 days. No evidence of increased self-stimulation appeared in those studies. Immediately after these experiments the radio-stimulator was attached to Sarah for three consecutive days, and the tone was changed to 500 cy/sec. For each monkey, including Sarah, 0 to 6 daily lever pressings were recorded with no significant increase in the number for any animal during the 3 days.

Curiosity probably was not the cause of the increase in lever pressing because fewer were recorded on the first than on the fourth experimental day. Correlation with radiostimulation seems more probable because lever pressings during the third and fourth days were more than twice as many as during any of the seven extinction days when only the tone could be activated. The lever was permanently attached to the cage and competed for the monkeys' attention with padlocks and food on the floor, swings, and other parts of the living quarters. This competition may explain the low number of lever pressings, and it makes more significant the increased pressing resulting when Ali was radiostimulated. Observation of the colony and analysis of films showed that several times Ali's threatening attitude was followed by Elsa's lever pressing (6).

The studies continued with the radio-stimulator again strapped on Ali, this time connected to a contact in the posteroventral nucleus of the thalamus, and with the tone set at 900 cy/sec. Previous radiostimulations of this area had increased Ali's aggressiveness. When the lever was attached to the cage, it was triggered only seven times during three consecutive days. Then the lever was removed and was actuated by a timer once every minute for half an hour. After the fourth trial, signs of conditioning were evident. At the onset of the tone, Ali showed increased aggressiveness, and the other three monkeys grimaced and climbed to the cage ceiling. On several occasions this escape reaction to the tone started before Ali initiated any

threat. Later the stimulation was discontinued, and during 30 trials the tone continued to sound once every minute and induced a reaction 25 times in Elsa, 11 times in Ali, and 7 times in both Sarah and Lou. This experiment was duplicated on three different days with results showing similar characteristics and indicates that conditioning may be established through association of the tone with aggressive behavior evoked in Ali. In another series of investigations, there was no individual or social conditioning when motor areas were stimulated in Ali and in Sarah by radio-timed control.

Performance of instrumental responses may be induced by cerebral stimulation and may be conditioned to auditory or visual cues (7). The fact that "spontaneous-like" behavior evoked by brain excitation may also be conditioned to an indifferent stimulus is a relatively new finding. These results have been confirmed in further experiments (8). Behavioral conditioning has also been established on a time basis by programmed stimulations of the superior vestibular nucleus of the thalamus without giving the monkey any cue other than fixed interval of 1 minute between stimulations (9).

Social conditioning may help in the analysis of cerebral stimulation because each member of the colony is an interpreter of the reactions of the stimulated animal. Heterostimulation presents obvious questions about hierarchical control, reciprocal punishment, instrumental self-defense, and other problems related to human behavior (10).

REFERENCES AND NOTES

1. BRADY, J. V.: In *Reticular Formation of the Brain*, H. H. Jasper *et al.*, Eds. (Little, Brown, Boston, 1958), p. 689; B. BURSTEN and J. M. R. DELGADO: *J. Comp. Physiol. Psychol.* **51**, 6 (1958); J. OLDS and P. MILNER: *Ibid.* **47**, 419 (1954); J. OLDS: *Ibid.* **51**, 675 (1958); M. SIDMAN, J. V. BRADY, J. J. BOREN, D. G. CONRAD, and A. SCHULMAN: *Science* **122**, 830 (1955).

2. DELGADO, J. M. R.: In *Pharmacological Analysis of Central Nervous Action,* W. D. M. Paton, Ed. (Pergamon, Oxford, 1962), vol. 8, p. 265; J. M. R. DELGADO and R. RODRIGUEZ DELGADO: *Phil. Sci.* **29,** 253 (1962).

3. "Venus" frequency-modulated radio receiver modified with miniature coils (Lafayette Radio MS-828) and miniature relays (Elgin National Watch Co. type NMIC-50).

4. DELGADO, J. M. R.: In *Bio-Telemetry,* L. Slater, Ed. (Pergamon, New York, 1963), p. 231.

5. BUCHWALD, N. A., E. J. WYERS, C. W. LAUPRECHT, and G. HEUSER: *Electroencephalog. Clin. Neurophysiol.* **13,** 531 (1961); J. M. R. DELGADO: *Federation Proc.* **16,** 29 (1957); R. G. HEATH and R. HODES: *Trans. Am. Neurol. Assoc.* **77,** 204 (1952); B. W. ROBINSON and M. MISHKIN: *Proc. Intern. Union Physiol. Sci.* **2,** 362 (1962); E. H. RUBINSTEIN and J. M. R. DELGADO: *Ibid.* **2,** 366 (1962); J. R. STEVENS, C. KIM, P. D. MacLEAN: *A.M.A. Arch. Neurol.* **4,** 47 (1961).

6. Two months later Elsa and Ali were part of a new colony with three other monkeys. The radiostimulator was then strapped to Ali and connected to his caudate nucleus. Heterostimulation of Ali by Elsa was recorded 22 times in 1 day, and during the bar pressing Elsa's attention was usually directed toward Ali, in a way similar to that shown in Fig. 1. Reproducibility of the phenomenon of heterostimulation was thus demonstrated.

7. DELGADO, J. M. R., W. W. ROBERTS, and N. E. MILLER: *Am. J. Physiol.* **179,** 587 (1954); J. M. R. DELGADO, H. E. ROSVOLD, and E. LOONEY: *J. Comp. Physiol. Psychol.* **49,** 373 (1956); D. E. SHEER: Ed., *Electrical Stimulation of the Brain* (Univ. of Texas Press, Austin, 1961).

8. DELGADO, J. M. R.: In Symposium on *Pharmacology of Conditioning, Learning and Retention,* 2nd Intern. Congr. Pharmacol., Prague, August 1963.

9. DELGADO, J. M. R.: In *Electroencephalog. Clin. Neurophysiol.* Suppl. 24, in press.

10. Supported by grants from the U. S. Public Health Service (M2004-06) and the Office of Naval Research (ONR 609-08).

V. G. DETHIER and
DIETRICH BODENSTEIN

14   Hunger in the Blowfly*

One of the purposes of publishing an experiment is to provide detailed descriptions of procedures used. These descriptions make possible independent replications of the experiment by other scientists. In this way, the self-correcting characteristics of science are maintained. The "Materials and Methods" section of the following reading typifies a well-written procedural description, notwithstanding the delicacy and unusualness of the operations described.

Reference: *Zeitschrift für Tierpsychologie,* 1958, **15,** 129–140. Reprinted with the permission of the authors and the publisher: Paul Parey, Berlin and Hamburg. (Figure 2 has been omitted.)

Introduction

Although psychologists and ethologists have directed a great deal of attention to the study of motivation and drive in vertebrates and are now seeking a physiological basis for these concepts, no penetrating studies of the problem have been undertaken with the invertebrates. Because of the earlier position which the invertebrates

* This work was aided by a grant from The National Science Foundation.

occupy on the evolutionary scale and their relatively simpler behavioral organization it would seem that an investigation of drive and motivation in these animals should prove rewarding.

The two kinds of behavior which have lent themselves most readily to analyses of drive and motivation in the vertebrates have been feeding and sexual activity. Since the physiology of feeding is understood better in insects than in other invertebrates, and better than the physiology of sex, feeding is the activity of choice in the study contemplated. Most adult insects are periodic feeders; they eat for a while, then stop and remain trophically inactive for varying periods of time. Some knowledge of the identity of the physiological factors which start and stop feeding, and the conditions under which they are operative, is available. The question of what constitutes hunger and satiety remains unanswered. An analysis of these two states would appear to be a logical initial step toward the larger problem of drive. That is the purpose of this communication.

One of the earliest observed correlates of food deprivation in insects was change in threshold of response to such acceptable substances as sugars. As early as 1922 Minnich had shown that the concentration of sucrose which was acceptable to the red admiral butterfly, *Pyrameis atalanta* L., and elicited extension of the coiled proboscis, was low if the butterfly had been deprived of food for some time but was elevated as a consequence of feeding. Kunze (1927) and von Frisch (1927) obtained results of a similar nature when they experimented with honey bees. Such changes in the response thresholds for taste substances, coincidental with changes in the duration of time since the last feeding, have since been reported by a great number of investigators for a variety of insects (cf., e.g., Haslinger 1935). A striking feature of the change is its magnitude. In the blowfly *Phormia regina* Meigen a ten-million-fold increase in the acceptance threshold for sucrose has been demonstrated to occur (Dethier and

Rhoades 1954). Changes of the order of one-hundred-thousand-fold have been reported for other species (Anderson 1932), and ten-thousand-fold changes are quite usual (cf, e.g., Minnich 1929).

Another characteristic of the change in threshold is the dependence of the rate of change upon the nature of the food previously ingested. Evans and Dethier (1957) have shown, for example, that the fall in glucose threshold of the blowfly after a meal of 1 M fucose is very rapid, requiring only twenty-five hours to regain its basal level; while after 1 M mannose feeding a period of one hundred hours is required. Although after the feeding of any particular sugar there may be variations in the rate of decline depending upon which set of receptors (i.e., oral or tarsal) is tested (Minnich, 1922a, 1922b; Haslinger 1935), the comparative rates with different sugars ingested bear a constant relation to one another. This fact plus the fact that the rate of threshold change depends upon the identity of the sugar ingested and not upon which sugar is employed as a test stimulus suggests that threshold change is causally related to feeding rather than to events occurring in the peripheral sensory system.

All of these changes in behavioral threshold to acceptable taste substances bear a predictable relation to food deprivation and satiety; consequently, it was reasonable to assume that an analysis of the regulation of threshold would yield information relative to the problems of hunger and feeding. It had been shown that feeding by a hungry fly was initiated by adequate sensory input from mouth or leg receptors and that it continued only as long as the sensory input continued effectively (Dethier 1955). When receptors became adapted, feeding ceased temporarily until disadaptation occurred (Dethier, Evans, and Rhoades 1956; Evans and Dethier 1957). However, the ultimate cessation of feeding for any given meal could not be ascribed to sensory adaptation. Prolonged elevation of threshold and prolonged feeding inactivity had to be attributed to some other factor. The following were eliminated as regulatory factors: blood-sugar levels, stored glycogen depletion, and crop contents (Evans and Dethier 1957, Hudson 1958). It was concluded that some region of the gut other than the crop was the critical part for threshold regulation. The experiments reported here were designed to reveal the mechanisms of threshold regulation and its bearing on hunger, satiation, and feeding activity.

Materials and Methods

The black blowfly, *Phormia regina* Meigen, was the animal employed in all experiments. All the animals were operated upon without anaesthesia. In order to fix them in the desired position for the various operations, they were held on the operating table by small strips of plasticene. The table consisted of a black wax plate into which depressions of different shapes were cut to aid in bedding and holding the animals in the desired position. The operations were performed under a dissecting microscope. Sometimes, as in the case of the cutting of the recurrent nerve, a rather high magnification (50×) was necessary. Watchmaker's forceps, sharpened to a fine point, and iridectomy scissors in which the blades had been thinned, narrowed, and finely pointed by appropriate grinding were satisfactory instruments.

SEVERING OF THE RECURRENT NERVE

The procedure for cutting the recurrent nerve, perhaps the most difficult operation performed, was as follows: a shallow depression in the shape of the fly's body (thorax and abdomen) was cut into the wax. The depth of the depression was about two-thirds of the dorsal-ventral width of the thorax. In front of this depression a second smaller one was made to hold the fly's head. Thus a narrow wax bridge separated the two depressions. The fly was placed dorsal side up into the large depression and held in place by a strip of plasticene laid across the anterior portion of the thorax. The head of the fly was then carefully manipulated into the second small depression so that the neck stretched across the wax bridge. The head was held down by a plasticene strip. In this manner the dorsal neck skin was brought into clear view. A drop of physiological solution was placed on the neck; it covered part of the thorax and the head. This drop not only kept moist the tissues that were to be exposed, but also acted as a lens and thus aided considerably in the performance of the next steps. With the drop in place, the skin of the neck was cut along the midline with an iridectomy scissors. The cut had to extend posteriorly to the point where the neck meets the thorax. The wound was then widened by pulling the cut skin apart with two pairs of forceps. This exposed the longitudinal neck muscles that extend dorsally close below the skin. Some of these were severed but care had to be taken not to destroy too many of the lateral neck muscles. With some of the uppermost dorsal neck muscles cut, the foregut and the two large lateral tracheal trunks come into clear view. Near the prothorax one can also see the anterior border of the proventriculus (Figure 1E). Somewhat left and slightly in front of the proventriculus, the allatum-cardiacum complex is located; it is rather easy to distinguish from other tissues by the light bluish sheen of the cardiacum. The recurrent nerve which passes from the anterior part of the cardiacum forward, is as yet not visible. The cardiacum adheres laterally to the left tracheal trunk. With the fine tip of the forceps, this adhesion was broken. As soon as this is done, the recurrent nerve becomes visible. By holding the nerve close to the cardiacum with forceps, it can be lifted up slightly and then cut. This finished the operation. The wound border was now pressed together with forceps, the physiological solution removed and the fly freed. After a successful operation, the freed animal behaves normally and if given food, it feeds almost immediately.

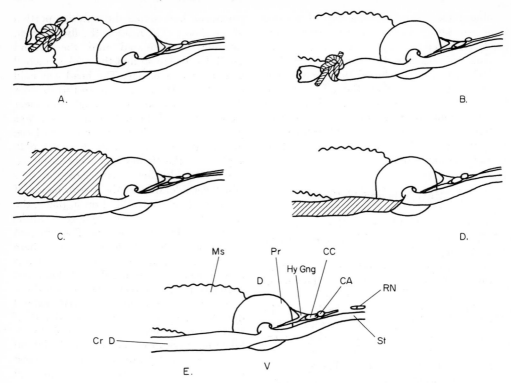

FIG. 1. Diagrams of the region of the foregut of *Phormia regina*. A. Point at which midgut was ligated. B. Point at which crop duct was ligated. C. Most anterior advance of fluid injected into the midgut via the anus. D. Most anterior advance of fluid in crop duct when crop valve is closed. E. Point at which recurrent nerve was cut. Ms = mesenteron (midgut), Pr = proventriculus, CrD = crop duct, St = stomodaeum (foregut), HyGng = hypocerebral ganglion, CC = corpus cardiacium, CA = corpus allatum, RN = recurrent nerve, D = dorsal, V = ventral.

OPERATIONS ON THE INTESTINAL TRACT

In order to ligate the midgut (Fig. 1, A) behind the proventriculus, the fly was placed dorsal side up into a depression of the wax plate and held in position by two plasticene strips—one across the abdomen and the other across the head. With iridectomy scissors, a small wedge of muscle tissue was removed from the prothorax. The cut extended anteriorly almost to the neck, but left intact a small chitin ridge close to the neck. Posteriorly, the cut extended to about one-half of the length of the thorax. The broadest part of the tissue wedge to be removed was the dorsal surface of the thorax. The sloped cuts on each side met in the midline, just above the gut.

Removal of this cut wedge exposes the anterior portion of the midgut and shows clearly the junction of the midgut and the proventriculus. A drop of physiological solution was placed in the wound. The cut-out tissue wedge was also placed in a drop of physiological solution to keep it from drying. With forceps, the midgut could now be lifted up and cut. If ligation was desired, the gut was lifted up with one pair of forceps, while at the same time a fine silk thread, held with the second pair of forceps, was pushed below the gut from one side to the other. The diameter of the silk thread used corresponded roughly to that of a human hair. Silk has however the advantage of being more flexible than hair.

The two ends of the thread were then manipulated into a sling which was tightened just behind the proventriculus. After the knot was tight, the ends of the thread were cut. If it was desired to cut the midgut, a second ligature had to be applied. The gut was then cut between the two ligatures. Now, the cut-out tissue wedge was replaced and the wound thus closed. Any excess of blood and physiological solution that was pressed from the wound by the replacement of the cut-out piece was carefully soaked up by filter paper. The fly was now ready for the test. Animals thus operated upon are, of course, unable to fly because the various incisions have severed the flight muscles.

To ligate or remove the crop, the fly was held on the operating table, ventral side up, by two plasticene strips, one crossing the mid-thorax, and the other the posterior end of the abdomen. The crop lies somewhat to the right side, close to the midline, on the border of thorax and abdomen. At this site, a small incision was made into the skin of the abdomen and the crop carefully pulled out. A silk loop was slipped over the exposed crop and its duct tied off at its entrance into the crop (Fig. 1 B). The crop was then pushed back through the wound into the abdomen and the animal released. If the crop was to be removed, a second ligature was tied around the duct and the duct cut between the two constrictions.

The action of the stomach valves and the route ingested food takes were observed in the living fly. For this, the fly was placed on the operating table ventral side up and held by sealing its wings to the wax table by a heated needle. As much of the ventral half of the thorax as was necessary to uncover the intestinal tract was then removed and physiological solution dropped into the gaping opening. Flies prepared in this manner live for several hours and take in food which is offered them. By offering a sugar solution containing a dye (carmine or fuchsin), one can follow the course of the ingested food visually with ease.

INJECTION EXPERIMENTS

All injection experiments were performed with an injection apparatus used for *Drosophila* work (Bodenstein 1950). In the transfer of blood from fed to unfed individuals, physiological solution was injected first into the abdominal cavity of fed flies. The injected solution was allowed to mix with the blood of the host for several minutes. It was then withdrawn, and the mixture of physiological solution and blood thus obtained was injected into unfed individuals.

For certain experiments it was necessary to inject sugar solution via the anus into the gut. To this end, the fly was sealed by its wings to the wax table, ventral side up, and then injected. This injection procedure proved to be rather difficult. The wall of the hindgut, close to the anus, is very thin and the needle often pierced the gut wall; this resulted in forcing the injected fluid into the abdominal cavity instead of into the gut. The success of the injection was therefore carefully checked in each case by opening the animal after testing its threshold responses. Since a colored solution was used for the injection, it could easily be determined whether or not the injected fluid was in the gut or in the abdomen. In successful cases, the hind and midgut were filled with the colored fluid (Fig. 1 C). The proventricular valve blocked the solution from passing into the proventriculus. Only such positive cases were used in the evaluation of the experiments.

In some instances sugar solution was also injected directly into the midgut through a prepared opening in the thorax, as was used for the midgut ligation experiments.

THRESHOLD DETERMINATION

Measurements of the lowest concentration of sucrose which would elicit extension of the proboscis by the fly were made by stimulating the chemoreceptors of the tarsi with doubled concentrations of sucrose beginning with 0.001 M and presented consecutively. For this purpose all flies were affixed by the wings to paraffin-tipped applicator sticks and permitted to drink water ad libitum so that there would be no proboscis extension to water.

Results

BLOOD TRANSFUSION

As Evans and Dethier (1957) had demonstrated, changes in the levels of the normal blood sugar, trehalose, and of various sugars which entered the blood by way of the midgut or by direct injection had no measurable effect on the threshold of response to sugars. The possibility still remained, however, that feeding caused liberation into the blood of a humoral agent which effected threshold change. To test this possibility blood was transfused from flies which had been fed two hours previously to eighty-one flies which had been starved for twenty-four hours. When the thresholds of transfused flies were measured immediately after transfusion and at intervals over a subsequent two hour period, eighty per cent of the flies had a threshold which did not differ from the previously measured starvation level. There is a possibility that the quantity of blood injected or the effect of dilution with saline might have obscured the action of a hormone, but barring this it can be concluded that feeding did not cause the liberation into the blood of any humoral substances contributing to a rise in threshold. This conclusion is strengthened by the observation that an isolated head, removed from a fully fed fly with a high threshold, will feed.

MIDGUT INVOLVEMENT

Earlier work had eliminated the crop as the regulatory region of the alimentary canal but had not provided direct proof of the role of any other region. The two types of complementary experiments which were conducted to supply the missing information consisted of elimination of the midgut and hindgut and of loading the mid- and hindgut.

Five unfed flies, which exhibited low acceptance thresholds, received ligatures immediately behind the proventriculus (Fig. 1). A post-operative check of threshold immediately after ligation indicated that the operation had had no untoward effect on behavior. The flies were then fed to satiation on 1 M sucrose. Threshold was now measured periodically over a four-hour period. Up to three hours after feeding the threshold remained high and only then began to fall. Identical results were obtained if the flies were fed 1 M sucrose prior to ligation. Furthermore, no differences were observed between the effects of ligation alone and ligation plus complete section of the midgut. From these experiments it was concluded that the presence of sugar in the mid- and hindgut was not necessary to maintain threshold elevation for a period longer than that accounted for by sensory adaptation.

The complementary experiments consisted of loading the mid- and hindgut. Of sixty-four starved flies which were given enemas of 1 M glucose, thirty-one were shown on subsequent post-mortem examination to have had the gut completely loaded from the rectum forward to the cardiac valve. While the flies were still living, periodic tests of threshold over a four-hour period revealed no change in the initial low pre-operative value. In other words, loading the gut by enema did not result in a rise in threshold.

In a comparable series of experiments 2 M glucose was injected through the wall of the midgut of twenty-five starved flies, and water was similarly injected in eight flies. Again in eighty per cent of the cases there was no rise in threshold over that of the starved condition. In a sham operation the threshold remained the same in seventy-six per cent of the cases. The results of these experiments are in agreement with the results obtained with ligation and sectioning in showing that the presence of sugar in the mid- and hindgut does not cause a rise in threshold.

FOREGUT INVOLVEMENT

If the gut was indeed involved in threshold regulation, the only portion remaining for consideration was the small area of foregut extending from the head to and including the proventriculus (Fig. 1). With one exception, attempts to inject sugar into this delicate region without damaging nerve tissue were unsuccessful. In the single successful case there was a thirty-fold rise in threshold. While little reliance can be placed on a single case, the reult was suggestive. Accordingly, an attempt was made to approach the problem by denervating this particular region of the foregut.

RECURRENT NERVE SECTION

An examination of Fig. 1 will show that the gut is innervated by the recurrent nerve, which with its branches and ganglia constitutes the stomatogastric system, the analogue of the vertebrate autonomic system. The recurrent nerve passes from the frontal ganglion posteriorly along the dorsal wall of the oesophagus to the vicinity of the junction of the crop duct. Here it is connected with the hypocerebral ganglion, gives off nerves to the endocrine glands, and sends fibers to the crop and proventriculus. Experiments in which the crop had been removed had demonstrated that section of this branch of the recurrent nerve was without effect as far as threshold regulation was concerned (Evans and Dethier 1957). The experiments involving removal of the midgut as reported above demonstrated that section of the proventricular branch of the recurrent nerve at a point posterior to the proventriculus was also without effect. There remained only to section the recurrent nerve anterior to the hypocerebral ganglion in the hope thereby of removing any innervation of the foregut. This difficult operation was performed successfully on twenty-five starved flies (Fig. 1 E, RN).

The results were decisive and spectacular. Section of the nerve trunk produced a complete hyperphagia. Flies began to feed in the normal fashion and ceased, as was to be expected, when the oral receptors became adapted; however, as soon as disadaptation occurred vigorous feeding was resumed. Tests revealed that the normal prolonged rise in threshold failed to appear. If a hyperphagic fly was fed on 1 M sucrose and disadaptation of the receptors allowed to occur, the fly then showed a threshold of response to 0.1 M sucrose. As a consequence of the absence of threshold rise the operated flies fed continuously as long as they lived and became enormously bloated. Death finally ensued probably as a result of starvation, because in the absence of stomatogastric innervation the valves regulating the passage of food in the midgut failed to operate properly, and food never left the swollen crop.

Discussion

The picture which emerges of the feeding activity of the fly is as follows. When an unfed fly encounters food (e.g., sugar), contact chemoreceptors on the tarsi are stimulated. This sensory input results in extension of the proboscis. Extension brings the chemosensory hairs on the aboral surface of the labellum into contact with the sugar. In response to this stimulation the labellar lobes open, thus bringing the receptors (interpseudotracheal papillae) on the oral surface into contact with the sugar. Stimulation of these receptors, as well as of the labellar hairs, initiates sucking. Feeding is thus initiated and driven by input from oral receptors (cf. Dethier 1955). At the beginning of feeding the threshold of response (assuming a starved fly) is at its lowest level and, while there is as yet no direct evidence that this level equals the absolute threshold of the receptors themselves—as Minnich (1929) and von Frisch (1935) postulated—, it seems reasonably certain that it represents the minimal amount of *summed* sensory input that can activate the motor system under any circumstances.

As imbibition continues, its rate is determined by the intensity of sensory input

(Evans and Dethier 1957). The greater the intensity, that is, the concentration of the stimulus, the more rapidly the muscles of the cibarial pump contract. The duration of imbibition depends upon the time required for a high level of adaptation of the oral receptors (loc. cit.), and varies, of course, with the concentration of the stimulus. For example, duration varies from 90 sec. at 2 M sucrose to 36 sec. at 0.25 M sucrose. When adaptation attains a sufficiently high level, feeding ceases. There is now no effective sensory input, and the threshold of response is high.

The sugar solution which is imbibed goes initially to both the midgut and crop. When the midgut is filled, the cardiac valve closes, and the continued influx of sugar is directed into the crop. Waves of peristalsis passing posteriorly in the crop duct constantly press the fluid back into the crop itself. When feeding has ceased, the crop duct closes. The region of the foregut now contains sugar residue from more anterior regions of the oesophagus and preoral cavity.

When the sugar in the midgut is utilized, the crop valve opens momentarily, peristalsis in the duct is reversed so that a slug of fluid is driven energetically into the foregut region, the crop valve closes, a wave of peristalsis in the foregut drives the fluid toward the proventriculus where the cardiac valve opens briefly to permit passage to the midgut.

Although disadaptation of the oral receptors has by this time set in, the threshold of response remains elevated, and feeding is blocked. Threshold elevation can only be due to impulses passing up the recurrent nerve and inhibiting sensory input from the mouth. This inhibition, as manifest by high threshold, continues as long as there is sugar in the foregut.

When the recurrent nerve is cut, feeding resumes every time disadaptation sets in so that a fly feeds almost continuously in an intermittent fashion. In these hyperphagic flies the crop valve remains open and the cardiac valve closed, except in occa-

sional cases where extreme hydrostatic pressure apparently forces some liquid through into the midgut. The enormous distension characteristic of hyperphagic flies is reminiscent of the honey ants (*Myrmecocystus horti-deorum*) which under normal circumstances are hyperphagic. It would be interesting to speculate upon the evolutionary development of these castes in terms of possible functional changes in the stomatogastric nervous system.

The fine synchronization of valves and peristalsis of the normal fly is disrupted in the hyperphagic fly. It would appear that emptying of the midgut somehow signals the crop to deliver food to the foregut and that the cardiac valve then opens in response to some neural message which is not relayed when the recurrent nerve is cut. The complete sequence of events in this interesting region of the gut invites further investigation.

It would appear that hunger in the fly can be equated with absence of stimulating fluid in the foregut, in other words, absence of inhibition. As early as 1929 Minnich has postulated that starvation could be conceived of as eliminating inhibition in the central nervous system. This is now proved to be the case. At the moment there is no conclusive evidence of hunger "drive" in the sense of positive input from external receptors, internal receptors, or endogenous centers within the central nervous system. As long as there is sensory input from oral or leg receptors and no recurrent inhibition, the fly feeds. If the head is removed from a fly which has fed to repletion and possesses a high acceptance threshold, the isolated head will show a low threshold and will feed until sensory adaptation occurs. This experiment confirms the conclusion that high threshold and satiety occur as a result of neural information received directly from regions posterior to the head, and that no humoral factor in the blood is necessary for this purpose.

On the other hand, low threshold alone is not sufficient to insure feeding. The fly must encounter food. Naturally its chances are enhanced if it increases its activity. Experiments being conducted in this laboratory by Evans and Barton Browne do indeed show that as the period of food deprivation increases a fly becomes increasingly active. The increase in activity is correlated with a drop in threshold. Further experiments are in progress to ascertain whether or not the regulation of threshold and of activity are under unitary control.

It is of considerable interest that the consummation of feeding is brought about, neither by the fulfillment of a metabolic need nor by the fulfillment of any motor pattern. If a fly is fed the non-metabolizable sugar fucose to repletion, its acceptance threshold remains elevated and feeding is terminated. Such a fly is "metabolically hungry" but "behaviorally satiated." It will eventually starve to death through failure to feed even in the presence of enough glucose to keep it alive.

The fulfillment of a motor pattern (e.g., swallowing) is not in itself a consummatory act. It cannot terminate feeding as seen from the fact that flies with recurrent nerve sections indulge in prolonged sucking and swallowing without a cessation of feeding ensuing. Consummation is brought about by inhibition originating somewhere in the foregut region. In other words, feeding is controlled by a sensory feedback mechanism. As soon as internal receptors are stimulated, they block at some internuncial level the flow of information from external receptors which drive feeding. The exact nature of this feedback mechanism is not yet completely understood. The receptors have not yet been identified. It is not known whether the adequate stimulus is chemical, osmotic, or mechanical.

The exact mode of operation of the feedback requires clarification. It has been shown, for example, that threshold does not remain maximally elevated as long as there is the least bit of sugar in the crop. Instead, it falls off gradually in a manner characteristic of the specific sugar imbibed (Evans and Dethier 1957). It is known, moreover, that the concentration of the crop contents remains unaltered from beginning to end. How then is the message from the recurrent nerve graded in such a way as to inhibit less and less effectively as the crop progressively empties? One possibility which remains open for investigation is that the frequency of crop delivery to the midgut varies with time after feeding and that the degree of recurrent inhibition is a function of frequency.

It was pointed out earlier that the characteristic slope of threshold decline with increasing deprivation depended upon the nature of the food which had been ingested. This fact can be explained in terms of rate of utilization of the specific food. If different carbohydrates are absorbed from the midgut at different rates, then these rates would determine the frequency of demand upon the crop, hence, the rate of crop delivery to the foregut region. If the hypothesis that frequency of stimulation in the foregut determines the effectiveness of inhibition is correct, the differences in rate of threshold decline after feeding on different sugars are understandable.

In comparison with the rat the fly apparently possesses a much simpler mechanism for the regulation of feeding although more work with the fly may reveal that this simplicity is an illusion. In the rat there are two neural centers known to regulate feeding. It has been shown (see Brobeck 1946 for summary) that a bilateral lesion in the region of the ventromedial nuclei of the hypothalamus causes a pronounced increase in food consumption. Lesions in the lateral hypothalamus, on the other hand, produce hypophagia or aphagia (Anand and Brobeck 1951: Teitelbaum and Stellar 1954). Thus there appears to be in the rat a "feeding" center and a "satiety" center. Anliker and Mayer (1957) have presented evidence in support of the contention that the latter receives information from the bloodstream via glucoreceptors. Destruction of the satiety center acts to release the feeding center from the inhibitory influence of the satiety center with resulting hyperphagia. There is yet no evidence of a feeding center in the fly if by feeding center one means a center whose endogenous activity initiates feeding. If by feeding center one means a region of internuncials which processes information received from peripheral sense organs, then the fly does possess one. On the other hand, no way has been found so far to produce experimental hypophagia or aphagia.

In the rat it seems possible to separate experimentally factors controlling food intake and those controlling hunger considered as a drive, or in other words, to separate the control of satiation from hunger drive reduction. Miller, Bailey, and Stevenson (1950) were able to show that when rats were trained to press a bar to obtain food, the normals would work harder than rats (hyperphagics) with lesions in the ventral hypothalamus. Yet normally the hyperphagics ate more. Accordingly, it appears that the lesions had different effects than hunger and that the mechanism of hunger and that governing food consumption may be different.

Furthermore, Miller and Kessen (1956) have shown that the volume of food taken with increased deprivation increased to a maximum by six hours after which there was no further increase, that stomach contractions paralleled the intake curve, but that work performed and the amount of quinine which would be tolerated in the food continued to increase. Thus it was clear that intake leveled off but that hunger increased (up to 54 hours).

In the fly the evidence presently available suggests that the factors governing intake (satiation) and possible factors responsible for that which Miller terms "hunger drive" are one and the same. Our experiments to date indicate that hunger is merely the absence of satiation. The usual simpler types of experiments employed to separate the factors of satiation and hunger cannot be applied successfully to the fly. For example, an increase in the viscosity of a solution makes it more difficult for a fly to imbibe, and the rate of sucking decreases (Evans and Dethier 1957). One might ask whether flies will work harder, that is, longer, to imbibe a viscous solution as they become hungrier. However, since feeding is driven by input from oral receptors and ceases when they adapt, the amount of solution taken in will not be a function of the degree of hunger but rather of the rate of sensory adaptation (which controls satiation).

Similarly, although both the fly and the rat will tolerate greater quantities of an adulterant (e.g., quinine or salt) as they become hungrier, the mechanisms probably are different. In the rat the amount of quinine tolerated seems to be a measure of hunger (Miller 1957). In the fly the amount tolerated actually reflects a change in the behavioral threshold to sugar, which has been shown to be a function of recurrent nerve inhibition, that is, the mechanism controlling satiation. The observation that insects will tolerate greater concentrations of unacceptable compounds mixed with sugar as the period of deprivation lengthens does not really indicate that rejection threshold increases with starvation. Rejection threshold is the lowest concentration of a substance which will prevent acceptance of the material (sugar) with which it is mixed. As the concentration (hence stimulating effectiveness) of sugar is increased, the amount of adulterant required to prevent response must likewise be increased (Dethier 1955). As an insect is starved its sensitivity to sugar increases; therefore, more salt is required to prevent the response. Haslinger (1935) measured the rejection threshold of the fly *Calliphora* for HCl during starvation by presenting HCl in fructose the concentration of which was varied so as to be just three times the threshold for fructose on each day of testing. Under these conditions no real change in rejection threshold for HCl was found, nor for salts, sugar alcohols, or quinine. For the honey bee von Frisch (1934) found no change in salt threshold but an increase for HCl and quinine. Thus, although the relation of rejection to food deprivation is somewhat conflicting and closer scrutiny of the phenomenon is required, the data of Haslinger strongly suggest that changes in rejection really mean changes in acceptance threshold and are, therefore, associated with the mechanism controlling satiety.

In the rat, according to Miller (1957), there are three possible sources of drive reduction: the performance of the consummatory response, the taste of the food, the presence of food in the stomach. Miller and Kessen (1952) showed that the first two are certainly not the sole factors. Clearly in the fly the performance of the consummatory response is not a factor. The "taste" is, and the foregut (= gastric factor?) is only insofar as it inhibits "taste."

Changes in behavior associated with starvation must be considered as resulting from the usual stimuli which impinge upon the external receptors having a different effect in the central nervous system due to modifying influences from internal receptors, chemical or osmotic changes in the internal milieu, or endogenous activity within the central nervous system. There seems to be little point in talking about "drive" and "motivation" unless one is referring to behavior resulting from one or more of the mechanisms referred to above. And it is manifestly more informative to talk in terms of mechanisms. It is certainly true in the fly that changes in the threshold of response are attributable to the modifying (in this case, inhibitory) effect which internal stimuli ultimately produce upon peripheral sensory input to the brain. Hunger, aside from being a synonym for food deprivation, is the absence of this inhibition.

Presumably the question of the presence of spontaneous activity in the central nervous system which activates the fly to seek food and to feed may be approached further by studying feeding as a function of some deterring action which does not operate through the chemosensory system. But until the nature of the relation between threshold and general activity is clarified, no function of activity can be used as a tool to separate the sensory factors which regulate feeding from possible internal factors.

Summary

When an unfed fly encounters food, contact chemoreceptors on the tarsi are stimulated. As a result of this sensory input the proboscis is extended. Extension brings chemosensory hairs on the labellum into contact with the food. In response to this stimulation the labellar lobes open, thus bringing the receptors on the oral surface into contact with the food. Stimulation of either set of receptors on the proboscis initiates sucking.

As feeding continues its rate is determined by the intensity of oral sensory input. The duration of feeding depends upon the time required for a high level of adaptation of oral receptors to occur, and it varies with the concentration of the stimulus. When adaptation attains a sufficiently high level feeding ceases.

At the beginning of feeding the threshold of response is at its lowest level. At the cessation of feeding the threshold is very high. Even after disadaptation has set in the threshold remains elevated for many hours. The duration of threshold elevation varies with the kind of food eaten. None of the following factors are involved in threshold regulation: blood sugar level, stored glycogen depletion, crop content, midgut content, humoral agents in the blood. Threshold is regulated by information originating in the foregut and passing by way of the recurrent nerve to the brain where it inhibits the effect of sensory input from oral receptors. When the recurrent nerve is cut, inhibition no longer occurs, and feeding is continuous until the fly dies. In these hyperphagic flies the threshold of response to sugar is never elevated.

Hunger can be equated with absence of stimulating fluid in the foregut, i.e., absence of inhibitory impulses carried by the recurrent nerve. At the moment there is no conclusive evidence of hunger "drive" in the sense of positive input from external or internal receptors or from endogenous centers within the central nervous system.

Consummation of feeding is brought about neither by the fulfillment of a metabolic need nor of a motor pattern. If a fly is fed the nonmetabolizable sugar fucose, its threshold of response is elevated and feeding is terminated. Such a fly is "metabolically hungry" but "behaviorally satiated." Flies with recurrent nerve sections suck and swallow indefinitely; hence, the motor pattern itself is not a consummatory act.

In the fly there is no evidence of a "feeding center" if by feeding center is meant a higher center whose endogenous activity drives feeding.

REFERENCES

ANAND, B. K., and J. R. BROBECK, 1951 Localization of a "feeding center" in the hypothalamus of the rat. *Proc. Soc. Exp. Biol. and Med.*, 77, 323–324.

ANDERSON, A. L., 1932 The sensitivity of the legs of common butterflies to sugars. *J. exp. Zool.*, 63, 235–259.

ANLIKER, J., and J. MAYER, 1957 The regulation of food intake. Some experiments relating behavioral, metabolic and morphologic aspects. In: *Symposium on Nutrition and Behavior. Nutrition Symposium Series* No. 14, 46–51, The National Vitamin Foundation, Inc., N. Y.

BODENSTEIN, D. 1950 The postembryonic development of *Drosophila*. In *Biology of Drosophila*, pp. 275–367 (ed. M. Demerec). John Wiley and Son, N. Y.

BROBECK, J. R., 1946 Mechanism of the development of obesity in animals with hypothalamic lesions. *Physiol. Revs.*, 26, 541–559.

DETHIER, V. G., 1955 The physiology and histology of the contract chemoreceptors of the blowfly. *Quart. Rev. Biol.*, 30, 348–371.

DETHIER, V. G., and M. V. RHOADES, 1954 Sugar preference aversion functions for the blowfly. *J. exper. Zool.* 126, 177–204.

DETHIER, V. G., D. R. EVANS, and M. V. RHOADES, 1956 Some factors controlling the ingestions of carbohydrates by the blowfly. *Biol. Bull.* Woods Hole, 111, 204–222.

EVANS, D. R., and V. G. DETHIER, 1957 The regulation of taste thresholds for sugars in the blowfly. *J. Insect Physiol.*, 1, 3–17.

VON FRISCH, K., 1927 Versuche über den Geschmackssinn der Bienen. *Naturwiss.*, 15, 321–327; 1935: Über den Geschmackssinn der Biene. *Z. vgl. Phys.* 21, 1–156.

HASLINGER, F., 1935 Über den Geschmackssinn von *Calliphora erythrocephala* Meigen und über die Verwertung von Zuckern und Zuckeralkoholen durch diese Fliege. *Z. vgl. Phys.*, 22, 614–639.

HUDSON, A., 1958 The effect of flight on the taste threshold and carbohydrate utilization of *Phormia regina* Meigen. *J. Insect Physiol.*

KUNZE, G., 1927 Einige Versuche über den Geschmackssinn der Honigbiene *Zool. Jb. Abt. Allg. Zool. u. Physiol.*, 44, 287–314.

MILLER, N. E., 1957 Experiments on motivation. *Science*, 126, 1271–1278.

MILLER, N. E., C. J. BAILEY, and J. A. F. STEVENSON, 1950 Decreased "hunger" but increased food intake resulting from hypothalamic lesions. *Science*, 112, 256–259.

MILLER, N. E., and G. L. KESSEN, 1952 Reward effects of food via stomach fistula compared with those of food via mouth. *J. Comp. Physiol. Psychol.*, 45, 555–564.

MINNICH, D. E., 1922a The chemical sensitivity of the tarsi of the red admiral butterfly, *Pyrameis atalanta* L. *J. exp. Zool.*, 35, 57–81; 1922b: A quantitative study of tarsal sensitivity to solutions of saccharose, in the red admiral butterfly, *Pyrameis atalanta* L. *J. exp. Zool.*, 36, 445–457; 1929: The chemical sensitivity of the legs of the blowfly, *Calliphora vomitoria* L., to various sugars. *Z. vgl. Phys.* 11, 1–55.

TEITELBAUM, P., and E. STELLAR, 1954 Recovery from the failure to eat produced by hypothalamic lesions. *Science*, 120, 894–895.

CHARLES H. PHOENIX,
ROBERT W. GOY,
ARNOLD A. GERALL, and
WILLIAM C. YOUNG

15

Organizing Action of Prenatally Administered Testosterone Propionate on the Tissues Mediating Mating Behavior in the Female Guinea Pig*

Aided by a succession of able students and colleagues, W. C. Young for many years has been a leading researcher in the area of hormone-behavior interactions. In this reading, Young and his coauthors note an interesting parallel in the action of hormones on (1) genital structure and (2) behavior. The fact that prenatal and postnatal hormones play different roles in the determination of behavior is a finding of great significance.

For a discussion of the effects of exogenous hormones on the development of the Müllerian and Wolffian embryonic duct systems, see Burns, R. K., "Role of Hormones in the Differentiation of Sex," Chapter 2, Volume I of W. C. Young, ed., *Sex and Internal Secretions* (3d ed.). Baltimore: Williams and Wilkins, 1961.

Reprinted from *Endocrinology*, 1959, **65**, 369–382, with the permission of the authors, the publisher, and the editor: F. G. Hofmann.

ABSTRACT   The sexual behavior of male and female guinea pigs from mothers receiving testosterone propionate during most of pregnancy was studied after the attainment of adulthood. As a part of the investigation, the responsiveness of the females to estradiol benzoate and progesterone and to testosterone propionate was determined.

The larger quantities of testosterone propionate produced hermaphrodites having external genitalia indistinguishable macroscopically from those of newborn males. Gondadectomized animals of this type were used for tests of their responsiveness to estradiol benzoate and progesterone and to testosterone propionate. The capacity to display lordosis following administration of estrogen and progesterone was

greatly reduced. Male-like mounting behavior, on the other hand, was displayed by many of these animals even when lordosis could not be elicited. Suppression of the capacity for displaying lordosis was achieved with a quantity of androgen less than that required for masculinization of the external genitalia.

The hermaphrodites receiving testosterone propionate as adults displayed an amount of mounting behavior which approached that displayed by the castrated injected males receiving the same hormone.

The data are uniform in demonstrating that an androgen administered prenatally has an organizing action on the tissues mediating mating behavior in the sense of producing a responsiveness to exogenous hormones which differs from that of normal adult females.

No structural abnormalities were apparent in the male siblings and their behavior was essentially normal.

* This investigation was supported by research grant M-504 (C6) from the National Institute of Mental Health, Public Health Service.

The results are believed to justify the conclusion that the prenatal period is a time when fetal morphogenic substances have an organizing or "differentiating" action on the neural tissues mediating mating behavior. During adulthood the hormones are activational.

Attention is directed to the parallel nature of the relationship, on the one hand, between androgens and the differentiation of the genital tracts, and on the other, between androgens and the organization of the neural tissues destined to mediate mating behavior in the adult.

▶ Investigators interested in reproductive behavior have demonstrated that one role of the gonadal hormones in adult male and female mammals is to bring to expression the patterns of behavior previously organized or determined by genetical and experiential factors (1, 2, 3, 4, 5). The hypothesis that these hormones have an organizing action in the sense of patterning the responses an individual gives to such substances has long been rejected (6, 7, 8, 9, 10). As far as the adult is concerned, this conclusion seems well founded. Female hormone, instead of feminizing castrated male rats as Kun (11) claimed, increased their activity as males (6). Male and female guinea pigs gonadectomized the day of birth, and a female rat with a congenital absence of the ovaries, displayed normal patterns of behavior when injected with the appropriate hormones as adults (3, 9, 12).

Unexplored since the studies of Dantchakoff (13, 14, 15), Raynaud (16) and Wilson, Young and Hamilton (17), is the possibility that androgens or estrogens reaching animals during the prenatal period might have an organizing action that would be reflected by the character of adult sexual behavior. If the existence of such an action were revealed, it would 1) extend our knowledge of the role of the gonadal hormones in the regulation of sexual behavior by providing information bearing on the action of these hormones or related substances during the prenatal period, 2) be suggestive evidence that the relationship between the neural tissues

mediating mating behavior and the morphogenic fetal hormones parallels that between the genital tissues and the same hormones, and 3) direct attention to a possible origin of behavioral differences between the sexes which is *ipso facto* important for psychologic and psychiatric theory (18). Although comprehensive experiments have not yet been performed, initial investigations with an androgen have yielded effects which are so much more in line with current thought in the area of gonadal hormones and sexual differentiation (19, 20, 21, 22) than the earlier experiments on behavior, that the results are summarized here.

Materials and Methods (the production of hermaphrodites)

Most of the experimental animals were born to mothers which had received intramuscular injections of testosterone propionate†,‡ during much of gestation. One group was composed of females in which there were no visible abnormalities of the external genitalia. These are referred to as the *unmodified females*. Their mothers were given an initial injection of 1 mg. of testosterone propionate some time between day 10 and day 27 after conception and 1 mg. every third or fourth day thereafter until the end of pregnancy.

The larger group was composed of females in which the external genitalia at the time of birth were indistinguishable macroscopically from those of their male siblings and untreated males. These animals are designated *hermaphrodites*. Laparotomy

† Testosterone propionate (Perandren propionate) was supplied by Ciba Pharmaceutical Products, Inc.

‡ The injections were made by Mr. Myron D. Tedford, a Public Health Service Predoctoral Fellow, who is using these and other animals treated similarly for a study of the structural changes in the gonads, genital tracts, and external genitalia, and the course of gestation. We are indebted to him for supplying us with the animals whose behavior was investigated.

was necessary in order to distinguish these genetical females from males; it was performed within the first week after birth. Their mothers received an initial injection of 5 mg. of testosterone propionate on day 10, 15, 18, or 24 of the gestation period and 1 mg. daily thereafter until day 68.

Control animals were females and males from untreated mothers from the same stock as the experimental animals.

All these animals, i.e., the unmodified females, the hermaphrodites, their male siblings, and the control females and males, were used in four experiments designed to test the effects of testosterone propionate received prenatally on the responsiveness of the animals as adults to male and female hormones.

Experimental

Experiment I. *The behavior of gonadectomized adult unmodified females and hermaphrodites injected with estradiol benzoate and progesterone.*

SUBJECTS

Fourteen females from untreated mothers.

Fourteen unmodified females.

Nine hermaphrodites.

Eight males from untreated mothers.

Except for four unmodified females gonadectomized when they were 45 days old, all the unmodified females and hermaphrodites were gonadectomized at 80 to 150 days of age. No data from the laboratory indicate that the response to exogenously administered sex hormones is influenced by age at the time of gonadectomy. The eight males were castrated before they were 21 days old.

TESTS

After gonadectomy, when the animals were 90 to 160 days old, tests were made of the responsiveness to 1.66, 3.32, and 6.64 μg, of subcutaneously injected estradiol benzoate followed 36 hours later by

0.2 mg. of progesterone.§ Observations were continuous for 12 hours, beginning immediately after the injection of progesterone. Following the procedure of Goy and Young (4) hourly checks were made for the occurrence of the lordosis reflex in response to fingering. Individual records were kept of this measure of behavior and of the frequency of male-like mounting.

In three tests the control females, hermaphrodites, and males were observed for the occurrence of mounting in the absence of exogenous hormone. The unmodified females were given one such test.

The means and medians of the measures of behavior for which data were obtained were calculated from the individual averages and they are based on the data from the animals which responded to the hormones. For purposes of statistical analysis, maximum values (12 hours) for latency and 0 values for all other measures were arbitrarily assigned to the individuals failing to respond.

RESULTS

The data bearing on all the measures of the estrous response except mounting are summarized in Table 15–1. The lower values for the per cent of tests positive for estrus, the mean duration of heat, and the median duration of the maximum lordosis were conspicuous effects of the treatment given prenatally and the differences among the groups are highly significant (P <.001). Among the two groups of experimental females and the castrated males, the low gutteral growl which is so characteristically a part of the pattern of lordosis in normal females, was commonly, and in some individuals always, lacking. Had the estimation of the duration of maximum lordosis been based only on complete responses, the differences among the groups would have been even greater.

Variations in medians for the duration

§ Estradiol benzoate (Progynon-B) and progesterone (Proluton) were supplied by the Schering Corporation.

TABLE 15-1

Duration of heat and lordosis in gonadectomized guinea pigs given different amounts of estradiol and 0.2 mg. of progesterone

SUBJECTS	TESTS[a] N	PER CENT OF TESTS POSITIVE FOR ESTRUS	MEAN LATENCY IN HOURS	MEAN DURATION OF HEAT IN HOURS	MEDIAN DURATION OF MAX. LORD. IN SECONDS
		1.66 µg.			
Control females	19	89	5.7	5.7	11.5
Unmodified females	20	65	6.5	2.8	8.5
Hermaphrodites	9	22	8.5	2.5	2.0
Castrated males	8	38	6.0	1.2	2.0
		3.32 µg.			
Control females	33	94	4.4	7.3	12.3
Unmodified females	38	68	5.6	2.8	5.1
Hermaphrodites	18	22	8.0	2.0	3.0
Castrated males	16	31	4.5	3.2	2.7
		6.64 µg.			
Control females	28	96	3.7	7.2	9.3
Unmodified females	22	77	5.8	3.3	6.0
Hermaphrodites	18	22	9.2	2.0	2.0
Castrated males	16	0	——	——	——

a All the animals were given one or more tests at each level of hormone.

of maximum lordosis were not systematically related to quantity of estradiol given prior to the tests. The analysis, therefore, was based on the medians of individual averages over all dosages. These medians were 11.3, 6.5, 2.3, and 2.5 seconds for control females, unmodified females, hermaphrodites, and castrated males, respectively. The median of the unmodified females, which most closely resembles that of the control females, is significantly different ($U = 22$, $P < .002$) from that of the controls.

Other differences also are indicative of the changes that were induced. Per cent response and duration of heat tended to increase in the control groups as the quantity of injected estradiol was increased. Latency which is related inversely to the duration of heat (4) decreased. Among the experimental groups (unmodified females, hermaphrodites, and castrated males), similar relationships were seen only in the unmodified females.

In general the suppression of the capac-ity to display lordosis was proportional to the quantity of androgen injected prenatally. Amounts insufficient to alter external genital structures resulted in disturbances in the lordosis in only 50% of the animals, but the larger amounts that produced the hermaphrodites affected the lordosis in all. Within each group the effect on lordosis was not related to the quantity of androgen received prenatally. Among unmodified females, even siblings differed, one showing complete suppression of the lordosis and the other responding normally. The findings demonstrate that suppression of the capacity for displaying lordosis does not depend on masculinization of the external genitalia; clearly less androgen was required for the former than for the latter.

Additional evidence for the masculinizing effect of the prenatally administered androgen is provided by the data on the male-like mounting displayed by each group (Table 15–2). When estradiol and progesterone were injected all groups displayed mounting, and the differences

TABLE 15-2

The quantity of mounting with and without estradiol and progesterone

SUBJECTS	WITHOUT HORMONE	WITH HORMONE[a]
	MEAN NUMBER OF MOUNTS	MEAN NUMBER OF MOUNTS
Control females	0	10.7
Unmodified females	0	8.8
Hermaphrodites	4.4	5.6
Castrated males	11.8	16.7

[a] Variation in the amount of mounting was not related to the quantity of estradiol. The means therefore are based on the averages for each individual whether the dosage was 1.66, 3.32, or 6.64 μg. of the hormone.

among the groups are not statistically significant. In contrast, on tests when no hormones were given, the hermaphrodites and castrated males were the only animals that mounted.

The interval from the beginning of the test to the display of mounting differed among the groups. Of the males which mounted, all did so at least once during the first hour. Of the 7 hermaphrodites which mounted, 5 or 71% mounted at least once during the first hour, but only 1 normal female (7%) and 1 unmodified female (7%) mounted this early in the test. The modal time for the onset of mounting was the 1st hour for the castrated males and hermaphrodites and the 6th and 7th hours for the control females and unmodified females, respectively. In this respect the hermaphrodites closely resembled the castrated males and seem to have been masculinized. The latency of mounting in the unmodified females was not different from that in the control females.

In one way the mounting performance of the unmodified females did differ from that of the controls. More unmodified than control females displayed mounting on tests after injections when the lordosis reflex could not be obtained. Of 8 unmodified females which failed to show lordosis, 6 or 75% mounted. Because of the small number of control females which failed to display lordosis after injection, older data on normal females from the same genetical

stock are used for comparison. These data combined with those from the present study reveal that of 38 normal females failing to display lordosis after injection with comparable amounts of estradiol and progesterone only 4 or 10.5% mounted. The difference between the proportions of control females and unmodified females displaying mounting in the absence of lordosis is significant (C.R.=4.02, P<.001). Inasmuch as mounting was displayed spontaneously by the hermaphrodites, it was not possible with the animals available to determine the extent to which this behavior was being shown in response to the estradiol and progesterone.

CONCLUSIONS

1. Prenatally administered testosterone propionate suppressed the capacity for displaying lordosis following gonadectomy and the injection of estradiol and progesterone. The effect was manifested either by an absence of lordosis or by a marked abnormality in its character when it was displayed.

2. Suppression of the capacity for displaying lordosis was achieved with a smaller quantity of the androgen than was necessary for the gross modification of the external genitalia.

3. The capacity to display male-like mounting was not suppressed.

4. Quantities of testosterone propionate sufficient to suppress lordosis and mas-

culinize the genitalia also reduced the interval before mounting behavior was displayed.

Experiment II. *Permanence of the effects of prenatally administered androgen.*

SUBJECTS

Group 1. Three hermaphrodites used in the previous experiment.

Group 2. Seven unmodified females used in the previous experiment.

Group 3. Eight control females used in the previous experiment.

Group 4. Six hermaphrodites injected with 500 μg. of testosterone propionate per 100 gm. body weight per day from birth to 80 days of age.

Group 5. Six normal females injected with the same amount of testosterone propionate from birth to 80 days of age.

Group 6. Five mothers of hermaphrodites injected with testosterone propionate during pregnancy as described in Materials and Methods.

Group 7. Eight untreated females comparable in age with those injected with testosterone propionate during pregnancy.

The animals in Groups 1 through 5 were gonadectomized when they were 80 to 150 days of age, those in Groups 6 and 7 when they were 1.5 to 3 years old. The operations on the animals in Group 6 were performed approximately 10 months after the last injection of testosterone propionate.

TESTS

All the animals received 3.32 μg. of estradiol benzoate followed 36 hours later with 0.2 mg. of progesterone. The tests were similar to those given the hermaphrodites, unmodified females, and controls in Experiment I. The number, however, differed for each group and is shown in the description of the results. The values reported in the tables and the statistical treatment of the data were determined by the methods described in Experiment I.

RESULTS

The behavior of the 3 hermaphrodites, the 7 unmodified females, and the 8 control

TABLE 15-3

Behavioral responses to 3.32 μg. of estradiol and 0.2 mg. of progesterone

		TESTS AT 6–9 MONTHS OF AGE	TESTS AT 11–12 MONTHS OF AGE
Hermaphrodites (Group 1)	Per cent response	33.0	0
	Latency to heat in hours	7.5	——
	Duration of heat in hours	2.5	——
	Median maximum lordosis in seconds	2.0	——
	Mean number of mounts	3.0	45.2
Unmodified females (Group 2)	Per cent response	55.0	71.0
	Latency to heat in hours	6.3	7.5
	Duration of heat in hours	2.2	2.3
	Median maximum lordosis in seconds	4.0	5.8
	Mean number of mounts	8.7	17.5
Normal females (Group 3)	Per cent response	95.0	94.0
	Latency to heat in hours	4.4	6.1
	Duration of heat in hours	7.2	4.5
	Median maximum lordosis in seconds	10.0	10.2
	Mean number of mounts	9.9	9.6

TABLE 15-4

Per cent response, duration of heat, and maximum lordosis after cessation of treatment with testosterone propionate from birth to 80 days of age

| | | APPROXIMATE AGE IN DAYS AT TIME OF TEST | | | |
		90	140	160	175
Hermaphrodites (Group 4)	Per cent response	0	0	0	0
	Mean duration of heat in hours	——	——	——	——
	Median maximum lordosis in seconds	——	——	——	——
Females (Group 5)	Per cent response	0	84	66	66
	Mean duration of heat in hours	0	4.6	1.7	3.7
	Median maximum lordosis in seconds	0	9.0	5.5	9.5

TABLE 15-5

Behavior of normal females treated with testosterone propionate for 50 days during pregnancy and tested 10 months later

	PER CENT RESPONSE	LATENCY OF HEAT IN HOURS	DURATION OF HEAT IN HOURS	MEAN NO. OF MOUNTS
Treated females (Group 6)	84	6.7	4.2	17.8
Untreated females (Group 7)	62	7.6	3.2	8.1

females is summarized in Table 15–3 and compared with that displayed during the earlier tests when the animals were 6 months old. The results reported in Table 15–3 are based on at least 2 tests of each individual at each age level. No significant change occurred in the hermaphrodites and unmodified females for per cent response, latency to heat, duration of heat, and the duration of maximum lordosis. The normal females, however, showed a significant decrease in the duration of heat (T=0, P=.01), reflecting perhaps a decrease in responsiveness to the hormones as the animals aged. The increase in mounting is significant for the unmodified females (T=0, P=.02). The 3 hermaphrodites displayed increased mounting behavior, but the increase could not be evaluated statistically. Of the normal females, 3 showed increases, 3 a decrease, and 2 remained the same.

The contrast between the effects of prenatal and postnatal treatment is revealed by the results obtained from the animals treated neonatally (Groups 4 and 5) and from those treated during pregnancy (Group 6). During the period after withdrawal of the testosterone propionate, 5 of the 6 normal females which had been injected for 80 days after birth regained the ability to display lordosis, whereas the hermaphrodites did not (Table 15–4). The effects of the postnatally administered androgen on the mounting behavior displayed by the animals in the two groups were complex and their presentation is being postponed until a further discussion can be given. The females treated with testosterone propionate while pregnant (Group 6) did not, like their "daughters," lose the capacity to display lordosis. Comparison of their behavior in response to estradiol and progesterone in five tests with that of untreated females of the same age (Group 7) (Table 15–5), revealed that the differences between the groups are not significant for latency, duration of heat, and mounting.

CONCLUSIONS

1. The suppression of the capacity for displaying the feminine components of the sexual behavior pattern which followed the administration of testosterone propionate prenatally appears to have been permanent.

2. Amounts of testosterone propionate which were effective prenatally had no conspicuous lasting effects when administered postnatally.

Experiment III. *The behavior of gonadectomized hermaphrodites in response to testosterone propionate.*

SUBJECTS

Five hermaphrodites gonadectomized between 86 and 112 days of age.

Five normal females gonadectomized between 80 and 106 days of age.

Eight normal males castrated before 21 days of age.

When the animals were approximately 180 days old all received 2.5 mg. of testosterone propionate daily for 16 consecutive days.

TESTS

A sexual behavior test was given the day before the first injection. Additional tests were given on days 1 and 2 of the injection period, and every other day thereafter until each animal had received 9 tests. The ninth test was given the day of the sixteenth injection.

RESULTS

The median value for mounting by the hermaphrodites and females in the single test prior to the injection of testosterone propionate was 0. For the males the median was 5.5.

The remaining data are summarized in Table 15–6. They demonstrate the masculinizing effect of prenatally administered testosterone propionate on the female. Castrated males and hermaphrodites obtained the highest sexual behavior scores, the control females the lowest. The overall difference in scores was significant ($P \sim .02$). The differences between the castrated males and hermaphrodites were not significant, whereas both groups differed significantly from the control females ($P = .05$). The overall difference in the number of tests to the first display of mounting was significant ($P < .01$). As with the sexual behavior scores, the difference between males and hermaphrodites was not significant, but both groups differed significantly from the control females ($P = .02$). There was a significant overall difference ($P < .01$) in the amount of testosterone propionate required before the first appearance of mounting. Again, the hermaphrodites resembled the castrated males in that there was no significant difference

TABLE 15–6

Masculine behavior in gonadectomized adult animals injected with testosterone propionate

GROUP	MEAN SEXUAL BEHAVIOR SCORE	MEAN MOUNTS PER TEST	MEDIAN NUMBER OF TESTS TO THE FIRST DISPLAY OF MOUNTING	MEDIAN MG. OF T.P. PRIOR TO THE DISPLAY OF MOUNTING
Spayed untreated females	2.1	5.8	7.0	30.0
Spayed hermaphrodites	3.6	15.4	3.0	10.0
Males castrated prepuberally	5.0	20.5	1.5	3.8

TABLE 15-7

Mean sexual behavior scores obtained by the three groups of adult males

GROUPS[a]	TESTS				
	I	II	III	IV	V
Untreated	6.9	6.6	9.2	7.2	10.4
Testosterone propionate prenatally	10.4	9.3	9.1	9.3	12.2
Testosterone propionate prenatally and postnatally	10.9	11.2	7.3	11.1	9.4

a Difference among the groups not significant; $F = 1.30$; $df = 2, 12$.

between these two groups, but both groups displayed mounting with significantly less hormone ($P=.02$) than the control females.

CONCLUSIONS

1. Adult hermaphrodites gonadectomized and injected with testosterone propionate were more responsive to this hormone than gonadectomized normal females.

2. The earlier appearance and greater strength of masculine behavior by the hermaphrodites given testosterone propionate are believed to be effects of the prenatally administered testosterone propionate on the tissues mediating masculine behavior and therefore to be expressions of its organizing action.

Experiment IV. *The behavior of adult male siblings of the hermaphrodites.*

SUBJECTS

Five males from untreated mothers.

Five males born to mothers receiving testosterone propionate during pregnancy. No hormone was administered after birth.

Five males born to mothers receiving testosterone propionate during pregnancy. These animals received 500 μg. of the hormone per 100 gm. body weight daily beginning 1 to 3 days after birth and continuing 80 to 90 days.

TESTS

Five tests were given when the animals were 11 months old. In a test the subject was placed with a receptive female of approximately the same size, and the frequency of the display of selected measures of behavior was recorded for a maximum of 10 minutes. These measures included sniffing and nibbling, nuzzling, abortive mounting, mounting, intromissions, and ejaculation. A description of the measures and the method for computing scores are given by Valenstein, Riss and Young (23).

RESULTS

The mean scores are summarized in Table 15-7. It is clear that any effect of the exogenous testosterone propionate was slight. There was no evidence of suppression of the capacity to display masculine behavior, if anything, the animals receiving the hormone prenatally achieved higher scores than the controls.

CONCLUSION

The sexual behavior of adult males which had received testosterone propionate prenatally was not significantly different from that of untreated controls.

Discussion

The data from the four experiments summarized in the preceding sections support the hypothesis that androgenic substances received prenatally have an organizing action on the tissues mediating mating behavior in the sense of altering permanently the responses females normally give as adults. This possibility was suggested by the work of Dantchakoff (13, 14, 15), Raynaud (16), and Wilson, Young and Hamilton (17). Probably, however, because interest in the role of gonadal hormones in the regulation of mating behavior was concentrated so largely on the neonatal individual and adult, the suggestion was never incorporated in our theories of hormonal action. This step may now be taken, but when what has been learned from the present investigation is related to what has long been known with respect to the action of androgens on the genital tracts, a concept much broader than that suggested by the older studies is revealed.

The embryonic and fetal periods, when the genital tracts are exposed to the influence of as yet unidentified morphogenic substances (19, 20, 21, 22, 24), are periods of differentiation. The adult period, when the genital tracts are target organs of the gonadal hormones, is a period of functional response as measured by cyclic growth, secretion, and motility. The response depends on whether Müllerian or Wolffian duct derivatives have developed, and although generally specific for hormones of the corresponding sex, it is not completely specific (25). For the neural tissues mediating mating behavior, corresponding relationships seem to exist. The embryonic and fetal periods are periods of organization or "differentiation" in the direction of masculinization or feminization. Adulthood, when gonadal hormones are being secreted, is a period of activation; neural tissues are the target organs and mating behavior is brought to expression. Like the genital tracts, the neural tissues mediating mating behavior respond to androgens or to estrogens depending on the sex of the individual, but again the specificity is not complete (26, 27).

An extension of this analogy is suggested by the work done on the embryonic differentiation of the genital tracts, particularly that by Burns and Jost and summarized in their reviews (20, 21, 22). It will be recalled from the data reported in the present study that testosterone propionate administered prenatally affected the behavior of the male but slightly, whereas the effects on the female were profound. Not only was there a heightened responsiveness to the male hormone as revealed by the stronger masculine behavior displayed when testosterone propionate was given, but there was a suppression of the capacity to display the feminine components in response to treatment with an estrogen and progesterone. In studies of the genital tracts there were no effects on the male except for a slight acceleration in the development of the prostate and seminal vesicle and an increase in the size of the penis (28). Within the female, the Wolffian duct system was stimulated (13, 14, 15, 28, 29), and locally, when a fetal testis was implanted into a female fetus (20, 21), there was an interruption of the Müllerian duct on that side. What has not been seen when an exogenous androgen was administered, except by Greene and Ivy (30) in some of their rats, is a suppression or inhibition of the Müllerian duct system corresponding to the suppression of the capacity for displaying the feminine component of behavior.

The failure to detect a corresponding suppressing action on the Müllerian duct does not exclude the possibilities 1) that such an effect will be found, and 2) that the suppressing action is in the nature of a reduction in the responsiveness of the genital tract to estrogens rather than in the inhibition of its development. Such an effect was encountered in rats given testosterone propionate prenatally (17) when it was found that uterine as well as behavioral responses to estrogen and progesterone were suppressed.

A final suggestion with respect to the analogy we have postulated arises from a comparison of our results with those reported by Dantchakoff and Raynaud. These investigators stressed the increased responsiveness of their masculinized guinea pigs and mice to exogenous androgens, and seemed to regard the change as the expression of an inherent bisexuality. The possibility that there might have been a suppression of the capacity to respond as females and therefore an inequality of potential does not seem to have been considered. Like Dantchakoff (13, 14, 15), Raynaud (16), and many others (9, 31, 32, 33, 34, 35), the existence of a bisexuality is assumed. We suggest, however, that in the adult this bisexuality is unequal in the neural tissues as it is in the case of the genital tissues. The capacity exists for giving behavioral responses of the opposite sex, but it is variable and, in most mammals that have been studied and in many lower vertebrates as well, it is elicited only with difficulty (27). Structurally, the situation is similar. Vestiges of the genital tracts of the opposite sex persist and are responsive to gonadal hormones (36, 37), but except perhaps in rare instances, equivalence of organs and responses in a single individual is not seen (36, 37, 38, 39).

The concept of a correspondence between the action of gonadal hormones on genital tissues and neural tissues contains much that is new and its full scope is not yet clear. The possibility must be considered that the masculinity or femininity of an animal's behavior beyond that which is purely sexual has developed in response to certain hormonal substances within the embryo and fetus.

Thus far the permanence of the effect achieved when testosterone propionate was received prenatally has not been achieved when the same hormones were administered to adults or to newborn individuals. The dependence of this "permanence" on the action of the hormone during a possible critical period must be ascertained.

The nature of the modifications produced by prenatally administered testosterone propionate on the tissues mediating mating behavior and on the genital tract is challenging. Embryologists interested in the latter have looked for a structural retardation of the Müllerian duct derivatives culminating in their absence, except perhaps for vestigial structures found in any normal male. Neurologists or psychologists interested in the effects of the androgen on neural tissues would hardly think of alterations so drastic. Instead, a more subtle change reflected in function rather than in visible structure would be presumed.

Involved in this suggestion is the view that behavior may be treated as a dependent variable and therefore that we may speak of shaping the behavior by hormone administration just as the psychologist speaks of shaping behavior by manipulating the external environment. An assumption seldom made explicit is that modification of behavior follows an alteration in the structure or function of the neural correlates of the behavior. We are assuming that testosterone or some metabolite acts on those central nervous tissues in which patterns of sexual behavior are organized. We are not prepared to suggest whether the site of action is general or localized.

REFERENCES

1. BEACH, F. A.: *J. Genet. Psychol.* 60: 121. 1942.
2. ZIMBARDO, P. G.: *J. Comp. & Physiol. Psychol.* 51: 764. 1958.
3. VALENSTEIN, E. S., W. RISS, and W. C. YOUNG: *J. Comp. & Physiol. Psychol.* 48: 397. 1955.
4. GOY, R. W., and W. C. YOUNG, *Psychosom. Med.* 19: 144. 1957.
5. ROSENBLATT, J. S., and L. R. ARONSON: *Animal Behav.* 6: 171. 1958.
6. BALL, J.: *J. Comp. Psychol.* 24: 135. 1937.
7. BALL, J.: *J. Comp. Psychol.* 28: 273. 1939.
8. BEACH, F. A.: *Endocrinology* 29: 409. 1941.
9. BEACH, F. A.: *Anat. Rec.* 92: 289. 1945.
10. RISS, W., E. S. VALENSTEIN, J. SINKS, and W. C. YOUNG: *Endocrinology* 57: 139. 1955.
11. KUN, H.: *Endokrinologie* 13: 311. 1934.

12. WILSON, J. G., and W. C. YOUNG: *Endocrinology* 29: 779. 1941.
13. DANTCHAKOFF, V.: *Compt. rend. Acad. sci.* 206: 945. 1938.
14. DANTCHAKOFF, V.: *Compt. rend. soc. Biol.* 127: 1255. 1938.
15. DANTCHAKOFF, V.: *Compt. rend. soc. Biol.* 127: 1259. 1938.
16. RAYNAUD, A.: *Bull. Biol. France et Belgique* 72: 297. 1938.
17. WILSON, J. G., W. C. YOUNG, and J. B. HAMILTON: *Yale J. Biol. & Med.* 13: 189. 1940.
18. HAMPSON, J. L., and J. G. HAMPSON: Allen's Sex and Internal Secretions, ed. by W. C. Young, Baltimore, Williams & Wilkins. 1961.
19. JOST, A.: *Arch. Anat. micro. et Morph. exper.* 36: 271. 1947.
20. JOST, A.: *Rec. Prog. Hormone Res.* 8: 379. 1953.
21. JOST, A.: Gestation. Transactions of the Third Conference, ed. by C. A. Villee, New York, Josiah Macy, Jr. Foundation, 129. 1957.
22. BURNS, R. K.: Allen's Sex and Internal Secretions, ed. by W. C. Young, Baltimore, Williams & Wilkins. 1961.
23. VALENTINE, E. S., W. RISS, and W. C. YOUNG: *J. Comp. & Physiol. Psychol.* 47: 162. 1954.
24. HOLYOKE, E. A., and B. A. BEBER: *Science* 128: 1082. 1958.
25. BURROWS, H.: Biological Actions of Sex Hormones, Cambridge, Cambridge University Press. 1949.
26. ANTLIFF, H. R., and W. C. YOUNG: *Endocrinology* 59: 74. 1956.
27. YOUNG, W. C.: Allen's Sex and Internal Secretions, ed. by W. C. Young, Baltimore, Williams & Wilkins. 1961.
28. GREENE, R. R.: *Biol. Symposia* 9: 105. 1942.
29. TURNER, C. D.: *J. Morphol.* 65: 353. 1939.
30. GREENE, R. R., and A. C. IVY: *Science* 86: 200. 1937.
31. STEINACH, E.: *Zentrabl. Physiol.* 27: 717, 1913.
32. STEINACH, E.: *Arch. f. Entwcklngsmechn. d. Organ.* 42: 307. 1916.
33. LIPSCHÜTZ, A.: The Internal Secretions of the Sex Glands, Baltimore, Williams & Wilkins, 1924.
34. BEACH, F. A.: *J. Comp. Psychol.* 36: 169. 1942.
35. BEACH, F. A.: *Physiol. Zool.* 18: 390. 1945.
36. MAHONEY, J. J.: *J. Exper. Zool.* 90: 413. 1942.
37. PRICE, D.: *Anat. Rec.* 82: 93. 1942.
38. BURNS, R. K.: *Contr. Embryology,* Carnegie Institution of Washington, 31: 147. 1945.
39. BURNS, R. K.: *Am. J. Anat.,* 98: 35. 1956.

LESTER A. ARONSON

16   Hormones and Reproductive Behavior: Some Phylogenetic Considerations*

As reading 11 pointed out, one of the accepted generalizations concerning sexual behavior is that an inverse correlation exists between dependence on gonadal hormones and the phylogenetic status of the animal. In the following reading, L. R. Aronson of the American Museum of Natural History's Department of Animal Behavior examines some of the evidence adduced to support this generalization and concludes that "distinct phylogenetic trends are not discernible."

* The researches of the author and collaborators cited in this article were supported in part by grants from the Committee for Research in Problems of Sex, National Academy of Sciences, National Research Council.

For a recent review of the effects of endocrine secretions on sexual behavior, see Young, W. C., "The Hormones and Mating Behavior," Chapter 19, Volume II, of W. C. Young: ed., *Sex and Internal Secretions* (3d edition). Baltimore: Williams and Wilkins, 1961.

This article originally appeared in Aubrey Gorbman, ed., *Comparative Endocrinology.* New York: John Wiley, 1959, 98–120. Reprinted by permission of the author and publisher.

Problems in evolution have constituted a major line of research and advanced thought at the American Museum of Natural History since its inception. It is not surprising, therefore, that a Museum scientist and student of behavior, F. A. Beach (1942), was first to devote serious attention to the phylogenetic relationships of reproductive behavior. By 1947 Beach had formulated his evolutionary hypotheses concerning the relationships between the central nervous system, gonadal hormones and sexual behavior. These hypotheses will be reviewed in part, and discussed in the light of recent advancements in this field.

The Theoretical Picture

Central to Beach's (1947, 1948) theory are the concepts of sexual arousal and the sexual arousal mechanism which he later (Beach, 1956) labeled the S.A.M. In male mammals the S.A.M. functions to increase sexual excitement to the point where the copulatory threshold is attained. Approach to the receptive female, mounts, intromissions, and ejaculations follow more or less in this order, though specific copulatory patterns may differ. The stimuli which activate the arousal mechanism are multisensory. They may include olfactory, auditory, visual, chemical, tactile, pressure, and genital sensations (Beach, 1942a, 1951). These are integrated in the central nervous system to the extent that a deficit in one stimulus modality can be overcome by a higher level in others.

The motor functions of sexual behavior are mediated by central neural structures below the forebrain, while the cerebral neocortex serves to integrate the sexual stimuli of the S.A.M. The cortex, in turn, facilitates or activates the motor mechanisms.

Gonadal hormones are believed to sensitize the S.A.M., thus lowering the copulatory threshold. Moreover, endocrine deficits can be compensated for, up to a certain point, by increased sensory stimulation (Beach, 1942b). Likewise, cortical deficits can be compensated for, in part, by high levels of androgen (Beach, 1942b). The regular order in which the major elements of the mating pattern in male rodents disappear following castration (first ejaculation, then intromission, and finally mounting) reflects differences in the arousal thresholds of the neural mechanisms mediating these patterns.

In the evolution of vertebrates, the forebrain attains an increasingly dominant position. This change is commonly referred to as encephalization. The term refers especially to the development of the cerebral cortex in mammals, and to the progressively greater role of the neocortex in the sensory and motor functions of higher mammals. According to Beach (1947) this increase in the functional position of the forebrain includes greater control over the sexual responses. In mammals, lower neural mechanisms mediating the various elements of the sexual pattern become more and more dependent upon activation by the neocortex. In considering the phylogenetic progression (Beach, 1948) from the lower mammals (rodents and lagomorphs), through an intermediate group (especially carnivores and ungulates) to primates and man, (1) the variety of external stimuli which evoke the sexual responses increases, (2) the sexual responses become more variable, and (3) the direct importance of gonadal hormones to sexual behavior tends to decrease. It is this last generalization that particularly concerns us here.

The major lines of evidence which Beach used to develop this hypothesis are as follows: (1) In adult male rodents and lagomorphs, sexual behavior drops off rapidly after castration, whereas in primates and man the complete sexual pattern may last for months or even years. (2) In female mammals other than primates, estrous behavior is closely associated with the cyclical activity of the ovaries, and can no longer be elicited when the ovaries are removed. In monkeys, apes, and man, on the other hand, receptivity of the female is largely independent of the condition of the ovaries and may continue after ovariotomy. (3) Extra-sexual stimuli, previous sexual experiences, and social situations are much more important factors in initiating sexual activity in primates than in other mammals. (4) Infantile sex play is much more frequent and complete in primates than in nonprimates. (5) Sexual behavior in both male and female prepuberally castrated primates is much more pronounced than in lower mammals.

If, with encephalization of the forebrain, and with elaboration of the neocortex, direct participation of the gonadal hormones in the elicitation of sexual behavior decreases, it follows that in the lower vertebrates, with little or no cortical representation, we should expect a very direct action of gonadal hormones in mediating sexual behavior. Beach has not offered an answer to this question, presumably because of the limited available evidence. However, since this problem is basic to our understanding of hormone-behavior relationships, I will attempt an evaluation with this point in mind.

Fishes

Among the Elasmobranchs, Cyclostomes and other primitive vertebrates I have found no information bearing upon this question. In teleosts, much of the evidence has been derived from the castration of adult individuals. A few investigators have claimed a rapid decline in sexual behavior when the gonads are removed. Thus Bock (1928), Ikeda (1933), and Baggerman (1957) report nearly complete cessation of nest-building behavior following castration in the three-spined stickleback, *Gasterosteus aculeatus*. Likewise, a castrated male *Salmo salar* "showed no interest in females," but surgically sterilized control males exhibited normal spawning activity (Jones and King, 1952). Among females, spayed jewel fish, *Hemichromis bimaculatus,* and Siamese fighting fish, *Betta splendens* exhibited no sexual activities when placed with ripe males (Noble and Kumpf, 1936), and I have obtained similar negative results with spayed females of the West African mouthbreeding cichlid, *Tilapia macrocephala.*

On the other hand, considerable sexual activity has been observed after gonadectomy in other species or under other conditions. Thus Noble and Kumpf (1936) reported typical courtship, fertilization movements, and brooding behavior in male jewel fish for as long as 202 days after castration. Likewise, spayed swordtails, *Xiphophorus helleri,* remained "sexually attractive to males." Unfortunately, this study was published only in abstract, and there is no indication in this brief report whether the gonadectomized individuals were ever examined for completeness of the operation. This is an item of paramount importance in studies of gonadal relationships in fishes, since testicular and ovarian remnants can be overlooked easily during the operation, and these remnants may induce a variable amount of gonadal regeneration. Moreover, small gonadal fragments, in fact as little as two percent of the whole gonad, are sufficient to maintain normal secondary sex characters (reviewed by Forselius, 1957: 523).

A male or female *Tilapia macrocephala,* separated by a glass partition from a spawning female, may build his or her own nest. In a group of 15 males so kept opposite females, nests were found on the male side 17 per cent of the times that the female spawned. When castrated males or intact females were placed opposite spawning females, nests were found in an equivalent percentage of spawnings, but spayed females placed opposite intact females only occasionally built nests (Aronson, 1951). In this experiment nests were found built up to 14 months after castration.

In *Tilapia,* courtship, spawning and parental patterns of males and females are qualitatively alike, but there are decided differences in the frequency with which various elements of the pattern are displayed (Aronson, 1949). When two females are paired, they frequently spawn. Under such circumstances the female that does not deposit eggs will perform all of the elements of the mating pattern at a rate close to that of males. When a spayed female was paired with a normal female, the operated fish exhibited a level of nest-building and nest-cleaning activity within the range of variability of intact males. However, several other elements of courtship appeared infrequently or not at all.

When males of the gobiid fish *Bathygobius soporator* were isolated in small aquaria they promptly attacked any other introduced male of the species. On the other hand, the resident male courted gravid and nongravid females that were introduced, but responses to the latter were shorter in duration. Following castration, the resident males became nondiscriminatory and courted introduced males, gravid and nongravid females in like manner. The vigorous fanning movements of courtship became spasmodic in the castrates, but characteristic gasping and snapping movements were more frequent than in the intact controls. In castrated males, behavior patterns associated with spawning (e.g., darkening, nest-rubbing, erection of genital papilla, and fertilization movements) were similar to those of intact fish. In this experiment Tavolga (1955) interpreted the failure of the castrated males to make the usual discriminations as due to changes in perceptual capacities.

Most recently we have studied the behavior of another cichlid fish, the blue acara, *Aquidens latifrons.* Observations have been made of eight spawnings of three males, and these records (Table 16–1) have been compared with observations of four postcastrational spawnings by the same three males. Up to 1½ months after operation all elements in the mating pattern were still present, most of these showing little change in frequency of occurrence or duration from their own preoperative levels. There was, however, a decided increase among the castrates in frequency of nest-passing behavior (rubbing genital papilla over nest), as well as increases in several other items of behavior, particularly during the observation periods one day after spawning. On the other hand, there was a noticeable decline after operation in nest-building behavior (scooping up gravel with mouth).

Thus far we have been considering oviparous species in which the sexual acts are intimately associated with deposition of eggs by the female. In viviparous forms such as the platyfish, *Xiphophorous maculatus,* the sequence of reproductive events is much more akin to that of mammals. Here during copulation, the transfer of sperm is accomplished by contact of the gonopodium (modified anal fin) with the genital aperture of the female (Clark, Aronson and Gordon, 1954). The frequency of occurrence of the major items in the mating pattern was studied before and after castration in 24 males (Table 16–2). Copulations (i.e., prolonged gonopodial contact with the female usually resulting in insemination), thrusts (i.e., momentary gonopodial contact with the female), swings (i.e., undirected lateral and forward movement of gonopodium), and sidling (i.e., movement of male alongside of female) dropped in frequency or duration in tests after operation. In the remaining items of behavior no changes could be ascertained. A further analysis of the data is presented in Table 16–3 for three of the above patterns, namely, thrusting, swinging, and sidling.

TABLE 16–1

Average behavior of three male blue Acaras before and after castration

		TOTAL NO. OF SPAWN-INGS	NEST PASSING		NEST BUILDING		BODY QUIVERING		MOUTHING		SLATE CLEANING		NEST CLEANING		FANNING			GUARDING		
			♂/♀ [a]	NO. MIN.	♂/♀	NO. MIN.	♂/♀	NO. MIN.	♂/♀	NO. MIN.	♂/♀	NO. MIN.	♂/♀	NO. MIN.	♂/♀	NO. MIN.	DUR. MIN.	♂/♀	NO. MIN.	DUR. MIN.
½ hr. Pre.[b]	Intact	3	0.2	0.2	2.0	0.2	0.3	1.0	0.2	0.3	0.5	2.0	0.7	0.4						
	Castrated	7	1.0	0.5	0.6	0.2	0.3	1.0	0.2	0.3	0.5	1.0	0.2	0.2						
Spawning	Intact	4	0.4	0.9	6.0	0.1	1.0	0.1	4.0	0.3	0.3	0.04	1.0	0.1						
	Castrated	8	0.7	2.0	1.0	0.03	3.0	0.3	5.0	0.6	0.4	0.1	5.0	0.4						
½ hr. Post.[c]	Intact	4	0.3	0.2	1.0	0.3	2.0	0.2	0.2	0.1	0.4	0.04	2.0	0.6	0	0	0	0.5	2.0	6.0
	Castrated	8	0.3	0.7	0.5	0.1	0.6	0.05	2.0	4.0	0	0	2.0	0.3	0.2	0.02	0.08	1.0	0.3	5.0
1 day Post.[d]	Intact	3			3.0	0.6	0.3	0.04	1.0	0.3	0.1	1.0	3.0	0.3	0.4	0.2	0.3	3.0	0.9	12.0
	Castrated	6			2.0	0.5	2.0	0.2	13.0	0.7	1.0	0.2	2.0	2.0	0.2	0.1	2.0	2.0	0.5	10.0

a Frequency.
b ½ hour record before first egg appeared.
c ½ hour record after first fanning.
d A 20-minute record 1 day later.

TABLE 16-2

Sexual behavior of male Platyfish before and after castration[a]

BEHAVIOR[b]	NO. OF FISH SHOWING PATTERN		MC NEMAR TEST FOR SIGNIF.	AVERAGE NO. OR DURATION OF ACTIVITY PER TEST		WILCOXON TEST FOR SIGNIF.	
	PREOP.	POSTOP.		PREOP.	POSTOP.		
Copulations (No.)	6	2	N.S.[c]	0.11	0.004	T < 0.025 > 0.01	S.
Thrusts (No.)	23	14	S.[d]	4.5	1.3	T < 0.01	S.
Swings (No.)	24	12	S.	8.1	2.2	T < 0.01	S.
Swings (duration)				1.24 sec.	1.1 sec.	T > 0.025	N.S.
Sidles (duration)	24	20	N.S.	66.9 sec.	27.6 sec.	T < 0.01	S.
Pecks (No.)	24	23	N.S.	22.9	14.2	T > 0.025	N.S.
Backs (No.)	24	22	N.S.	2.8	3.9	T > 0.025	N.S.
Approaches[e]				89.5 sec.	118.6 sec.	T > 0.025	N.S.

a Unpublished data of Chizinsky and Aronson.

b Based on 24 fish, with 10 preoperative tests for each one, and with an average of 10 postoperative tests for each one.

c Not significant }
d Significant } at .05 level.

e Time from beginning of test to first approach.

These acts persisted in some individuals up to nine months after castration, a time which represents the main part of the test period. The data in Table 16–3 also show that the duration of persistence after castration is highly variable among individuals, and that within any group the patterns drop out in different sequences (Chizinsky and Aronson, unpublished).

The variable effects of castration on sexual behavior as outlined in this section may, perhaps, be due in part to species differences. In addition, variable technical procedures used, for example in looking for gonadal remnants, and differences in testing arrangement may also be responsible. Despite these uncertainties, the evidence as it accumulates seems to support increasingly the following conclusions: (1) Removal of testes or ovaries causes an eventual decline in some or all elements of sexual behavior. (2) In all species studied, the decline is more pronounced in the female than in the male. (3) Among various species certain elements of the pattern are affected more rapidly and more drastically than others. (4) In males of some species, parts of the sexual pattern may persist for long periods after the gonads have been removed and after the androgen level has presumably dropped. Thus, it seems likely that in fishes, sexual behavior of experienced male adults is relatively independent of the direct action of testicular hormones.

In many species of fish it is easy to observe that sexual behavior makes its first appearance when the gonads are maturing and the secondary sex characteristics are developing. Also, male behavior has been induced in immature male and female platyfish and guppies with androgenic compounds (Eversole, 1941; Cohen, 1946; Tavolga, 1949). From such observations and experiments one may conclude that the development or organization of the mating pattern is directly contingent upon the presence of increasing levels of gonadal hormone. Until more adequate tests are performed, however, as for example by studying prepuberal castrates, this must remain an open question.

Pickford (1952, 1954) reported that

TABLE 16-3

Persistence of thrusting, swinging and sidling after castration of adult male Platyfish[a]

MALE NO.	WEEKS[b] TESTED	THRUSTING (WEEKS)	SWINGING (WEEKS)	SIDLING (WEEKS)
2	22	10	19	22
5	28	28	28	28
17	40	36	40	40[c]
30	22	22	0	22
32	15	5	2	5
35	8	7	7	7[c]
38	41	35	19	33
40	41	7	2	22[c]
52	8	4	0	7
56	10	0	10	1
61	10	10	10	10
78	8	0	0	0
Sham Operates[d]				
47	10	9	10	10
48	10	10	10	10
71	8	8	8	8
95	9	8	9	9
36[e]	28	19	19	28[c]

a Unpublished data of Chizinsky and Aronson.
b No. of weeks after castration that males were tested. Approximately one test every other week.
c Fish checked histologically for gonadal remnants.
d Similar abdominal incision.
e Partial castrate—gonadal remnants found.

sexual responses in male *Fundulus* may be controlled directly by pituitary action, and Wilhelmi, Pickford and Sawyer (1955) have identified the responsible agents as oxytocin and vasopressin from the neurohypophysis. Additional evidence suggesting a direct action of pituitary hormones on sexual behavior has been reviewed by Aronson (1957) and by Pickford and Atz (1957). One should not overlook the possibility that direct actions such as these may represent a primitive condition in vertebrates. On the other hand, the same concept was also suggested a number of years ago for mammals (Smith, 1930), but it has never received additional support.

The effects of castration as reviewed above might be taken as evidence opposing the evolutionary theory of sexual behavior stated previously. Yet, it is important to consider that the forebrain of teleosts has evolved in a unique fashion, as a specialized offshoot from the main line of vertebrate evolution. In some teleostean families the forebrain is a small relatively simple structure. At the opposite end of this evolutionary progression we find families in which the forebrain is a complex and highly differentiated body which in some species includes cortex-like arrangements (Papez, 1929; Meader, 1939; Aronson, 1957). Those species cited above in which sexual behavior seems relatively independent of gonadal secretion are at least intermediate in this evolutionary progression of the teleostean forebrain. In other words, we must also recognize the possibility that, incorporated within the complex teleostean forebrain, there may be a mechanism equivalent to that indicated in higher mammals, whereby some elements of the reproductive pattern have been released from the functional control of the gonadal hormones.

Amphibians and Reptiles

The amphibians and reptiles will be treated more briefly, since rather little has been added to this topic since the reviews by Beach (1948, 1951). Several investigators (Nussbaum, 1905; Noble and Greenberg, 1941; Reynolds, 1943) have observed that following gonadectomy, mating behavior is eliminated in male frogs and in lizards of both sexes. Noble and Aronson (1942) tied recently castrated male *Rana pipiens* to the backs of ovulating females. The latter oviposited in normal fashion but the action of the female did not elicit ejaculatory movements by the operated males. The clasp reflex will not develop in frogs if castration is performed well before the breeding season (Schrader, 1887; Steinach, 1910; Baglioni, 1911). When castration is performed during the breeding season the clasp reflex persists for a considerable time (Golz, 1869; Tarcharnoff, 1887; Busquet, 1910).

Castration of the male toad *Bufo arenarum* caused a gradual regression of the clasp reflex, which was nearly complete by 60 days. Croaking behavior, however, was unaffected by the operation (Burgos, 1950; Houssay, 1954).

As in fishes, the development of the sexual pattern may be directly dependent on gonadal hormones, since treatment of immature male frogs and lizards with androgens will induce mating responses (Noble and Greenberg, 1940, 1941; Blair, 1946). Similarly, estrous behavior can be induced in female *Anolis* with estrogen treatment (Greenberg and Noble, 1944).

Concerning the clasp reflex, it may be said that once the pattern becomes organized, it is less dependent upon gonadal hormones for its continued performance, at least for the remainder of the spawning season. Also, as in fishes, the possibility of a direct pituitary action is suggested by the experiments of Rey (1948) and Burgos (1950), who found that the simultaneous action of testosterone and hypophyseal hormones is necessary to restore the clasp reflex in intact and castrated *Bufo vulgaris* and *Bufo arenarum* males.

Birds

It is evident from the work of many investigators that castration in birds reduces the frequency of crowing, courtship, and copulatory behavior (Lipschütz and Withelm, 1929; Scott and Payne, 1934; Van Oordt and Jung, 1936). The effects are particularly pronounced when castrations are performed at an early age (Goodale, 1913; Guhl, 1949). However, as Collias (1950) notes, it is not always easy to evaluate studies on castration in birds because of difficulties in achieving complete removal of the gonads and in detecting small gonadal remnants at autopsy.

Although sexual activity is reduced by removal of the testes, it is not eliminated in all individuals, for some males continued mating (Goodale, 1918) even when complete gonadectomy seemed certain (Benoit, 1929). In this respect, Carpenter's work (1933, 1933a) is most important, since he used large numbers of experimental animals, quantitative techniques for recording behavior, and regular monthly observations up to nine months in one group. When the experiments were terminated he examined histologically all tissues suspected of containing testicular nodules. Seven out of fourteen completely castrated birds copulated after operation, but a gradual reduction in sexual activity took place, so that only four were still copulating when the last observations were made at eight months after the testes were removed. Eleven of these castrates continued billing after the operation and in some cases even a pronounced increase in billing was observed in later tests.

In contrast with the events in males, ovariotomy apparently eliminates all sexual activity shortly after operation (Goodale, 1913; Noble and Wurm, 1940; Allee and Collias, 1940; Davis and Domm, 1943).

As in lower vertebrates, sexual precocity can be induced in young males by treatment with testosterone propionate (Noble and Zitrin, 1942; Hamilton and Golden, 1939) and in young females by treatment with alpha-estradiol benzoate (Noble and Zitrin, 1942).

Davis (1957) reported that male starlings maintained "fighting and song" for a month after castration and had a clear social rank which was not affected by adequate doses of testosterone. He suggests as a possible explanation a direct action of gonadotrophic hormones on behavior.

These data, although limited in scope, make it evident that birds also conform to a general vertebrate pattern which is becoming better defined. Thus, we note the following: (1) Removal of the gonads depresses sexual behavior in females more rapidly and effectively than in males. (2) The gonadal hormones seem to be more important in males for the organization of the sexual pattern than for its continued performance. (3) Some elements of the pattern are affected by removal of the gonads, to a greater extent than others, but in this there is considerable individual variation. (4) Some elements of the mating pattern increase in frequency of performance after castration. (5) Some elements may be directly influenced by hormones of hypophyseal origin.

Mammals

In reference to mammals, I shall confine my remarks mainly to recent experi-

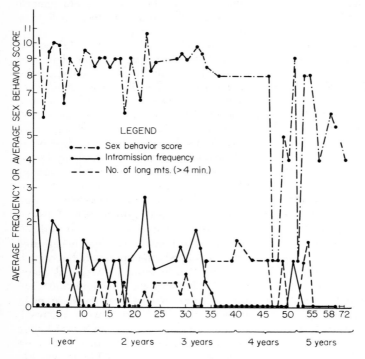

FIG. 1. Condensed sex behavior record of castrated male cat Spike. Ordinate graphed on logarithmic scale. [From ROSENBLATT and ARONSON (1958).] The sex score represents a comprehensive index of sexual behavior. For details of this scoring method, see p. 302 of the above reference.

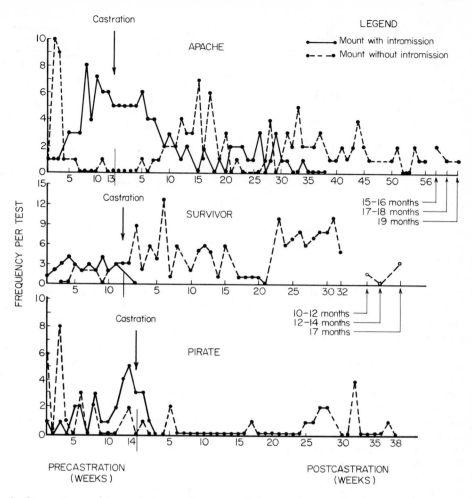

FIG. 2. Comparisons of intromissions and mounts of three male cats, Apache, Survivor, and Pirate, typifying the three modes of decline of sexual behavior after castration. [From ROSENBLATT and ARONSON (1958).]

ments in our laboratory, particularly to some aspects of the studies on male cats by Rosenblatt and Aronson (1958, 1958a). We discovered early in our experiments that castration of sexually experienced male cats produces highly variable behavioral effects. On the one hand, an experimental male, Spike, continued to copulate in tests over 3½ years, and to mount the female in tests over 4½ years (Fig. 1). White, at the other extreme, never achieved intromission after castration, while his mounting was sporadic

and soon ceased altogether. Further study of many other animals showed that we could divide them into three groups with respect to the retention and eventual decline in sexual responses. In type A animals (Fig. 2), intromissions lasted for many months or even years, whereas the capacity for mounting continued almost indefinitely. In type B males, capacity for intromissions lasted for about two months, but mounts without intromission increased in frequency and continued for a year or more. Many of

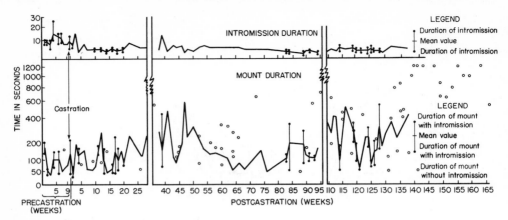

FIG. 3. Details of a part of Spike's record of sexual behavior before castration and for three years after castration. Ordinate graphed on logarithmic scale. [From ROSENBLATT and ARONSON (1958).]

the tests were also characterized by a large number of very brief mounts. In type C animals, intromissions dropped out rapidly, whereas mounting was weak and sporadic and rapidly disappeared. It is apparent that the extreme effects of castration described recently by Green, Clemente, and de Groot (1957) refer to type C animals.

The long persisting type A animals are particularly interesting in that the changes occurring after castration can be traced through and analyzed. Thus we recognized four postoperative periods with specific behavioral characteristics. In Spike (Fig. 3) the first period of 5 weeks was characterized by no obvious changes from his preoperative performance. Period 2 extended from the 5th to the 110th week, during which time there occurred a gradual increase in mounting time, a marked decrease in duration of intromission, and an increase in the number of long mounts not terminating in intromission. In the third period, from the 110th to the 138th week, prolonged mounts not terminating in intromissions were frequent, and in some tests intromission did not take place. In the final period intromissions dropped out, but prolonged mounts were common, and often lasted the full 20 minutes of the testing period.

In prepuberally castrated males brought into sexual behavior by treatment with testosterone propionate, these same three types of decline were observed (Fig. 4) when the hormone treatment was withdrawn (Rosenblatt and Aronson, 1958a).

Several questions and ideas are suggested by the above observations. In mammals there need be no concern about the completeness of castrations. However, the explanation has often been advanced that in cases like our long persisting type A animals, androgens of sufficiently high level to facilitate the mating responses are being secreted by the adrenal cortex. Recent studies in hamsters (Warren and Aronson, 1952, 1956, 1957), in cats (Cooper and Aronson, 1958), and in dogs (Schwartz and Beach, 1954) militate strongly against such an explanation.

Are the three types of decline unique for cats? We think not. We have examined comparable data for rats (Stone, 1927; Beach and Holz, 1946) and hamsters (Beach and Pauker, 1949, with additional data furnished by Pauker) and find striking evidence of several types of reproductive decline (Rosenblatt and Aronson, 1958). The clinical literature on castrations as reviewed by Beach (1947, 1947a, 1948) suggests a similar situation in man. The data

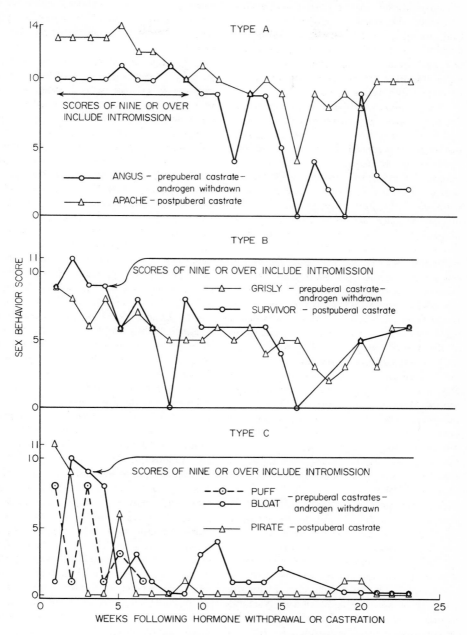

FIG. 4. Decline in sexual behavior of androgen-treated prepuberally castrated male cats, compared with the decline of males after postpuberal castration. These graphs illustrate the three types of decline. [From ROSENBLATT and ARONSON (1959).]

for the lower vertebrates, although admittedly limited, also point to a comparable situation. We must recognize, of course, that among species with very varied reproductive structures and patterns, the number and detailed characteristics of such types are likely to be very different from corresponding types in cats.

The analysis of behavior by types underlines some important concepts which can easily be overlooked when only group trends are considered. Thus, in our cats the increase in frequency and duration of mounts following the cessation of intromission in type A and B males, and the characteristic behavioral changes in period 2 of type A males, are attributable to special physiological conditions stemming from the depletion of androgen and resulting in weakness or loss of erection. However, other parts of the total pattern are mostly unaffected. As another example, the repetitive short mounts which occur frequently in the later stages of type B males indicate on the one hand that the sensory aspects of the female perceived at a distance remain unchanged, and on the other hand that stimulation resulting from contact with the female is insufficient to sustain the mount. Here it would seem that the sensory receptive mechanism, particularly on the ventral surfaces of the male's body may be altered in these males by lack of testicular hormone. In type C animals, the rapid decline of interest in the female suggests changes in the distance sensory receptors and in the perceptive mechanism, to the extent that the female can no longer elicit positive responses from the male.

The conclusions of Soulairac (1952, 1952a) are in accord with this concept of the relative independence of the different components of sexual behavior. From this research, as summarized by Larsson (1956), Soulairac attempts to show that sexual behavior in the rat is controlled by nervous and endocrine processes. The behavior is described in terms of distinct reflexes and temporal relationships, which are regulated by three specific physiological mechanisms:

"(1) the ejaculatory reflex by the endocrine balance; (2) the copulatory reflex by the cerebral cortex; and (3) the refractory period by enzymatic processes in the nervous tissue."

Although alterations in the level of gonadal hormones undoubtedly cause changes in central nervous processes, and may account for decreases or increases in the copulatory thresholds, peripheral changes and changes in systems other than the central nervous system must not be overlooked. Castration not only causes marked effects on genital structures, as for example changes on the surface and structure of the penis (Retterer and Lelievre, 1912, 1913; Pezard, 1949; Beach and Levinson, 1950), but many other morphological characteristics and physiological processes are also affected which may be directly or only indirectly related to the reproductive processes. These include cutaneous changes (Hartley, Grad, and Leblond, 1951), changes in olfactory thresholds (Le Magnen, 1952) and in the composition and strength of certain muscles (Wainman and Shipounoff, 1941). These widespread influences of the gonadal hormones seem to be characteristic of all vertebrates and their relevance to the functioning of the sexual pattern has been recognized by Beach (1951), Grunt and Young (1953) and Schneirla (1956). In addition, as shown by Valenstein and Young (1955) and Rosenblatt and Aronson (1958, 1958a), sexual experiences gained prior to castration will markedly affect the course of events after operation, and represent important factors both in the organization and retention of sexual behavior. If the retention or decline in sexual behavior after castration is the resultant of changes in a great many structures and processes, it is not surprising that the timing and sequence of events is as variable at it appears to be in many vertebrates.

We can define puberty in the male cat as starting at 3 to 4 months of age, for it is then that the hormone sensitive spines on the glans penis begin to develop (Aron-

TABLE 16-4

Sexual performance of prepuberally castrated male cats during ten tests in adulthood (332-503 days) [a]

ANIMAL	NO. OF MOUNTS	NO. OF DORSAL NECKGRIPS	NO. OF VENTRAL OR LATERAL NECKGRIPS	NO. OF "APPROACHES"
Angus	14	9	7	17
Grisly	0	4	15	9
Charlie III	0	0	1	0
Charlie II	0	0	2	1
Bloat	0	0	1	3
Sleepy	0	0	6	10
Spotty	0	0	0	2
Fighter	0	0	4	1
Snowy	0	0	4	2
Puff	0	0	1	2
Charlie IV	0	0	7	3
Rusty	0	0	0	0
Charlie I	0	0	0	0

[a] Data from Rosenblatt and Aronson (1958a).

son and Cooper, unpublished). Animals castrated at this age and tested for sex behavior in adulthood were surprisingly unresponsive (Table 16–4). There were no intromissions; only 1 out of 13 males mounted, and the animal that mounted did not show typical stepping or thrusting movements. One additional male obtained occasional neck grips (Levy, Aronson and Rosenblatt, 1956; Rosenblatt and Aronson, 1958a). Although it is difficult to compare levels of sexual behavior in different species, we feel that this record for prepuberally castrated cats is distinctly inferior to results obtained for comparable groups of rats (Beach, 1942; Beach and Holz, 1946), guinea pigs (Sollenger and Hamilton, 1939), and hamsters (Warren and Aronson, 1957). The experiments of Rosenblatt and Aronson (1958a) also show that androgens and sexual experience are indispensable for the organization of the mating pattern at puberty. But this behavior, once organized, becomes partially independent of the hormone.

In considering the phylogenetic relationship of testicular hormone to mating behavior in primates, considerable weight has been given to the performance of one prepuberally castrated chimpanzee, Don, who showed a high level of sexual behavior (Clark, 1945). However, Rosenblatt and Aronson (1958a) recently reviewed the published protocols and find no entry indicating that Don ever copulated *before* testosterone therapy began. Thus, in regard to prepuberal castrates, we feel that much more evidence is needed before a phylogenetic trend can be recognized.

Concluding Remarks

There is no question that the relations of the gonadal hormones to sexual behavior vary as we compare one species with another. These differences are particularly pronounced if we compare postpuberally castrated or spayed rodents with primates. However, the evidence does not reveal any clear-cut steps between these two mammalian orders, and below mammals an evolutionary progression is even less obvious.

In the past we depended extensively on the use of a single criterion, such as "sex drive," "hyper- or hyposexual behavior," "sex score" as used by Young and his collaborators in sex studies in guinea pigs (Young and Grunt, 1951), and "sexual arousal" as used by Beach. I fully concur in the concept that the forebrain contains an excitatory apparatus, even in lower vertebrates (Aronson, 1945, 1948), and that the gonadal hormones are likely to affect this mechanism, but evidence is accumulating that this is only one part, and possibly not even the most significant part, of the total organization of sexual behavior.

If we are going to discover phylogenetic trends in the relations of hormones to behavior, which evidently exist and certainly should be sought, it will be necessary to pay more attention to processes and structures controlling individual elements of the sexual acts. Investigations stemming from hypotheses searching out the direct and indirect action of the hormones on elements of the pattern seem more likely to reveal evolutionary trends than does research based on the conceptions of sexual behavior affected only as a unitary whole.

Summary

In teleosts, amphibians, reptiles, birds, and mammals, experiments involving prepuberal and postpuberal castrations and the treatment of immature individuals with gonadal hormones reveal the following characteristics which seem to be common to all classes of vertebrates: (1) Removal of the gonads tends to depress sexual behavior but more so in females than in the males. (2) The gonadal hormones are more important for the organization of sexual behavior than for its continued performance. (3) Some elements of the sexual pattern are affected to a greater extent than others by the removal of hormonal stimulation, but considerable individual variability is recognized. (4) Some elements of the mating pattern may increase in frequency of performance at least for a time after castration. (5) Some elements of the mating pattern may be directly influenced by hormones of hypophyseal origin. This last matter needs considerably more investigation.

Experiments on mammals, and particularly on male cats, show that sexual behavior comprises several relatively independent processes which respond differentially to hormonal action or depletion. This accounts for the pronounced individual variation in response to changes in hormonal level. For this reason it seems more appropriate to analyze sexual behavior in terms of the several mechanisms comprising the total pattern rather than in terms of a single criterion, such as "sex drive," or "level of sexual arousal."

Although there are differences among species in the relations of gonadal hormone to sexual behavior, particularly noticeable when rodents and primates are compared, distinct phylogenetic trends are not discernible. It is suggested that the evolution of the endocrine mechanisms controlling reproductive behavior can be approached more effectively by the analysis of individual components of the pattern than by the consideration of sexual behavior as a single, well-circumscribed entity.

REFERENCES

ALLEE, W. C., and N. COLLIAS, 1940 The influence of estradiol on the social organization of flocks of hens, *Endocrinology*, **27**: 87–94.

ARONSON, L. R., 1948 Problems in the behavior and physiology of a species of African mouthbreeding fish, *Trans. New York Acad. Sci.*, Ser. II, **2**: 33–42.

ARONSON, L. R., 1949 An analysis of reproductive behavior in the mouthbreeding cichlid fish, *Tilapia macrocephala* (Bleeker), *Zoologica*, **34**: Pt. 3, 133–158.

ARONSON, L. R., 1951 Factors influencing the spawning frequency in the female cichlid fish, *Tilapia macrocephala*, *Amer. Mus. Novit.* (1484) 1–26.

ARONSON, L. R., 1957 Reproductive and parental behavior, in *The Physiology of Fishes*, edited by M. E. Brown, Chap. III, Part 3, 271–304.

ARONSON, L. R., and G. K. NOBLE, 1945 The

sexual behavior of Anura. 2. Neural mechanisms controlling mating in the male leopard frog, Rana pipiens, Bull. Amer. Mus. Nat. Hist., 86: 87–139.

BAGGERMAN, B., 1957 An experimental study of the timing of breeding and migration in the three-spined stickleback, Arch. Néerl. Zool., 12: 1–213.

BAGLIONI, S., 1911 Zur Kenntnis der Zentrentätigkeit bei der sexuellen unklammerung der Amphibien, Zeentralbl. f. Physiol., 25: 233–238.

BEACH, F. A., 1942 Central nervous mechanisms involved in the reproductive behavior of vertebrates, Psychol. Bull., 39: 4: 200–226.

BEACH, F. A., 1942(a) Analysis of the stimuli adequate to elicit mating behavior in the sexually-inexperienced male rat, Jour. Comp. Psychol., 33: 163–207.

BEACH, F. A., 1942(b) Analysis of factors involved in the arousal, maintenance and manifestation of sexual excitement in male animals, Psychosom. Med., 4: 173–198.

BEACH, F. A., 1947 A review of physiological and psychological studies of sexual behavior in mammals, Physiol. Rev., 27: 2: 240–307.

BEACH, F. A., 1947(a) Hormones and mating behavior in vertebrates, in Recent Progress in Hormone Research, edited by G. Pincus, pp. 27–63.

BEACH, F. A., 1948 Hormones and Behavior, New York: Harper & Brothers, 368 pp.

BEACH, F. A., 1951 Instinctive behavior: reproductive activities, in Handbook of Experimental Psychology, edited by S. S. Stevens, pp. 387–434.

BEACH, F. A., 1956 Characteristics of masculine "sex drive," in Nebraska Symposium on Motivation, edited by M. R. Jones, pp. 1–32.

BEACH, F. A., and M. HOLZ, 1946 Mating behavior in male rats castrated at various ages and injected with androgen, Jour. Exp. Zool., 101: 91–142.

BEACH, F. A., and G. LEVINSON, 1950 Effects of androgen on the glans penis and mating behavior of castrated male rats, Jour. Exper. Zool., 114: 159–171.

BEACH, F. A., and R. S. PAUKER, 1949 Effects of castration and subsequent androgen administration upon mating behavior in the male hamster (Cricetus auratus), Endocrinology, 45: 211–221.

BENOIT, J., 1929 Le déterminisme des caractères sexuels secondaires du coq domestique, Arch. Zool. Expér. Gen., 49: 217–499.

BLAIR, A. P., 1946 The effects of various hormones on primary and secondary sex characters of juvenile Bufo fowleri, Jour. Exper. Zool., 103: 365–400.

BOCK, F., 1928 Kastration und sekundäre Geschlechtsmerkmale bei Teleostiern, Z. wiss. Zool., 130: 455.

BURGOS, M. H., 1950 Regulación hormonal de los caracteres sexuales secundarios en el sapo macho, Rev. Soc. Argent. Biol., 26: 359.

BUSQUET, H., 1910 Existence chez la grenoille male d'un centre médullaire permanent présidant à la copulation, Compt. rend. soc. de biol., 62: 880–881.

CARPENTER, C. R., 1933 Psychobiological studies of social behavior in Aves. I. The effect of complete and incomplete gonadectomy on the primary sexual activity of the male pigeon, Jour. Comp. Psychol., 16: 25–57.

CARPENTER, C. R., 1933(a) Psychobiological studies of social behavior in Aves. II. The effect of complete and incomplete gonadectomy on secondary sexual activity, with histological studies, Jour. Comp. Psychol., 16: 59–96.

CLARK, G., 1945 Prepuberal castration in the male chimpanzee, with some effects of replacement therapy, Growth, 9: 327–339.

CLARK, E., L. R. ARONSON, and M. GORDON, 1954 Mating behavior patterns in two sympatric species of xiphophorin fishes: their inheritance and significance in sexual isolation, Bull. Amer. Mus. Nat. Hist., 103: art. 2: 135–226.

COHEN, H., 1946 Effects of sex hormones on the development of the platyfish Platypoecilus maculatus, Zoologica, 31: 121.

COLLIAS, N. E., 1950 Hormones and behavior with special reference to birds and the mechanisms of hormone action, in Steroid Hormones, edited by E. S. Gordon, 277–329.

COOPER, M., and L. R. ARONSON, 1958 The effect of adrenalectomy on the sexual behavior of castrated male cats, Anat. Rec., 131: 3: 544.

DAVIS, D. E., 1957 Aggressive behavior in castrated starlings, Anat. Rec. 128: 537.

DAVIS, D. E., and L. V. DOMM, 1943 The

influence of hormones on the sexual behavior of domestic fowl, in *Essays in Biology*, California, U. Calif. Press, 171–181.

EVERSOLE, W. J., 1941   The effects of pregneninolone and related steroids on sexual development of the fish *(Libestes reticulatus), Endocrinology,* **28**: 603.

FORSELIUS, S., 1957   Studies of anabantid fishes. III. *Zool. Bidrag Fran Uppsala,* **32**: 379–597.

GOLTZ, F., 1869   *Beitrage zur Lehre von den Functionen der Nervencentren des Frosches,* Berlin, Hirschwald.

GOODALE, H. D., 1913   Castration in relation to the secondary sexual characters in brown leghorns, *Am. Nat.,* **47**: 159–169.

GOODALE, H. D., 1918   Feminized male birds, *Genetics,* **3**: 276–299.

GREEN, J. D., C. D. CLEMENTE, and J. DE GROOT, 1957   Rhinencephalic lesions and behavior in cats, *Jour. Comp. Neurol.,* **108**: 505–536.

GREENBERG, B., and G. K. NOBLE, 1944   Social behavior in the American chameleon *(Anolis carolinensis* Voigt), *Physiol. Zoöl.,* **17**: 392–439.

GRUNT, J. A., and W. C. YOUNG, 1953   Consistency of sexual behavior patterns in individual male guinea pigs following castration and androgen therapy, *Jour. Comp. Physiol. Psychol.,* **46**: 138–144.

GUHL, A. M., 1949   Heterosexual dominance and mating behavior in chickens. *Behaviour,* **2**: 106–120.

HAMILTON, J. P., and W. R. C. GOLDEN, 1939   Responses of the female to male hormone substances with notes on the behavior of hens and newly-hatched chicks, *Endocrinology,* **25**: 737–748.

HOUSSAY, B., 1954   Hormonal regulation of the sexual function of the male toad. *Acta Physiol. Latino-Amer.,* **4**: 2–41.

IKEDA, K., 1933   Effect of castration on the secondary sexual characters of anadromous three-spined stickleback, *Gasterosteus aculeatus. Japan. Jour. Zool.,* **5**: 135.

JONES, J. W., and G. M. KING, 1952   The spawning of the male salmon parr (*Salmo salar* Linn. juv.), *Proc. Zool. Soc. London,* **122**: 615.

LARSSON, K., 1956   Conditioning and sexual behavior in the male albino rat, *Acta Psych. Gotheburgensia,* I: 1–269.

LEVY, M., L. R. ARONSON, and J. ROSENBLATT, 1956   Effects of prepuberal adrenalectomy

on the development of sexual behavior in male cats maintained on DCA—a comparison with intact and prepuberally castrated males, *Anat. Rec.* **125**: 587.

LIPSCHÜTZ, A., and O. WITHELM, 1929   Castration chez pigeon, *Jour. Physiol. et Path. Gen.,* **27**: 46–54.

MEADER, R. G., 1939   The forebrain of bony fishes, *Proc. Koninkl. Ned. Akad. Wetenschap.,* **42**: 3.

NOBLE, G. K., and L. R. ARONSON, 1942   The sexual behavior of Anura. I. The normal mating pattern of *Rana pipiens, Bull. Am. Mus. Nat. Hist.,* **80**: 127–142.

NOBLE, G. K., and B. GREENBERG, 1940   Testosterone propionate, a bisexual hormone in the American chameleon, *Proc. Soc. Exper. Biol. & Med.,* **44**: 460–462.

NOBLE, G. K., and B. GREENBERG, 1941   Induction of female behavior in male *Anolis carolinensis* with testosterone propionate, *ibid.,* **47**: 32–37.

NOBLE, G. K., and K. F. KUMPF, 1936   The sexual behavior and secondary sexual characters of gonadectomized fish. *Anat. Record,* **67** (suppl.): 113.

NOBLE, G. K., and M. WURM, 1940   The effect of testosterone propionate on the black-crowned night heron, *Endocrinology,* **26**: 837–850.

NOBLE, G. K., and A. ZITRIN, 1942   Induction of mating behavior in male and female chicks following injections of sex hormones, *Endocrinology,* **30**: 327–334.

NUSSBAUM, N., 1905   Innere Sekretion und Nervenienfluss, *Ergeb. Anat. u. Entwicklungsgeschichte,* **15**: 39–89.

OORDT VAN, G. J., and G. C. A. JUNG, 1936   Die hormonal Wirkung der Gonaden auf Sommer—und Prachtkleid. III. Der Einfluss der Kastration auf männliche Kampfläufes *(Philomachus pugnax), Arch. Entwicklungsmech. Organ.,* **134**: 112–121.

PAPEZ, J. W., 1929   *Comparative Neurology,* New York, Crowell, 378 pp.

PAUKER-WARREN, R., and L. R. ARONSON, 1952   The relation of the adrenal cortex to mating behavior in the golden hamster, *Anat. Rec.,* **113**: 4: 546–547.

PICKFORD, G. E., 1952   Induction of a spawning reflex in hypophysectomized killifish, *Nature,* **170**: 807.

PICKFORD, G. E., 1954   The response of hypophysectomized male killifish to purified fish growth hormone, as compared with the response to purified beef growth hormone, *Endocrinology*, **55**: 274.

PICKFORD, G. E., and J. W. ATZ, 1957 *The Physiology of the Pituitary Gland of Fishes*, New York Zoological Society, New York.

REY, P., 1948 Sur le déterminisme hormonal du réflexe d'embrassement chez les males de Batraciens anoures, *Jour. Physiol.* (Paris), **40**: I, 292A–293A.

REYNOLDS, A. E., 1943 The normal seasonal reproductive cycle in the male *Eumeces fasciatus* together with some observations on the effects of castration and hormone administration, *Jour. Morphol.*, **32**: 331–371.

ROSENBLATT, J., and L. R. ARONSON, 1958 The decline of sexual behavior in male cats after castration with special reference to the role of prior sexual experience, *Behaviour*, **12**: 4: 285–338.

ROSENBLATT, J., and L. R. ARONSON, 1958a The influence of experience on the behavioral effects of androgen in prepuberally castrated male cats, *Jour. Animal Behaviour*, **6**: 3, 4: 171–182.

SCHRADER, M. E. G., 1887 Zur Physiologie des Froschgehirns, *Pflüger's Arch.*, **41**: 75–90.

SCHWARTZ, M., and F. A. BEACH, 1954 Effects of adrenalectomy upon mating behavior in castrated male dogs, *Am. Psychol.*, **9**: 467–468.

SCOTT, H. M., and L. F. PAYNE, 1934 The effect of gonadectomy on the secondary sexual characters of the bronze turkey (*M. gallaparo*), *Jour. Exp. Zoöl.*, **69**: 123–136.

SMITH, P. E., 1930 Hypophysectomy and a replacement therapy in the rat, *Am. Jour. Anat.*, **45**: 205.

SOLLENBERGER, R. T., and J. M. HAMILTON, 1939 The effect of testosterone propionate upon the sexual behavior of castrated male guinea pigs, *Jour. Comp. Psychol.*, **28**: 81–92.

SOULAIRAC, A., 1952 La signification physiologique de la période réfractaire dans le comportement sexuel du rat mâle, *Jour. Physiol.*, **44**: 99–113.

SOULAIRAC, A., 1952(a) Analyse expérimentale des actions hormonales sur le comportement sexuel du rat mâle normal, *Jour. Physiol.*, **44**: 327–330.

STEINACH, E., 1910 Geschlechtstrieb und echt sekundare Geschlechtsmerkmale als Folge der innersekretorischen Funktion der Keimdrusen. II. Über die Entstehung des Umklammerungsreflexes bei Froschen, *Zentralbl. Physiol.*, **24**: 551.

STONE, C. P., 1927 The retention of copulatory ability in male rats following castration, *Jour. Comp. Psychol.*, **7**: 369–387.

TARCHANOFF, J. R., 1887 Zur Physiologie des Geschlechtsapparates des Frosches. *Arch. ges. Physiol. Pflüger's*, **40**: 330–351.

TAVOLGA, M. C., 1949 Differential effects of estradiol, estradiol benzoate and pregneninolone on *Platypoecilus maculatus*, *Zoologica*, **34**: 215.

TAVOLGA, W. N., 1955 The effects of gonadectomy and hypophysectomy on the prespawning behavior in males of the gobiid fish *Bathygobius soporator*, *Zoologica*, **28**: 218.

WARREN, R. P., and L. R. ARONSON, 1956 Sexual behavior in castrated-adrenalectomized hamsters maintained on DCA, *Endocrinology*, **58**: 3: 293–304.

WARREN, R. P., and L. R. ARONSON, 1957 Sexual behavior in adult male hamsters castrated-adrenalectomized prior to puberty, *Jour. Comp. and Physiol. Psychol.*, **50**: 5: 475–480.

WILHELMI, A., G. E. PICKFORD, and W. SAWYER, 1955 Initiation of the spawning reflex response in *Fundulus* by the administration of fish and mammalian neuro-hypophyseal preparations and synthetic oxytocin, *Endocrinology*, **57**: 243.

YOUNG, W. C., and J. A. GRUNT, 1951 The pattern and measurement of sexual behavior in the male guinea pig, *Jour. Comp. Physiol. Psychol.*, **44**: 492–500.

DANIEL S. LEHRMAN, PHILIP N. BRODY,
and ROCHELLE P. WORTIS†

17 The Presence of the Mate and of Nesting Material as Stimuli for the Development of Incubation Behavior and for Gonadotropin Secretion in the Ring Dove *(Streptopelia risoria)* *

It has long been known that hormones affect behavior. What is not so obvious is the fact that feedback from behavior to the endocrines occurs and, further, that external stimuli (including those emanating from another animal) affect hormone secretion. Daniel S. Lehrman has spent the past few years investigating these complex interactions in birds. The following reading is a good example of Lehrman's work; for a more complete review of the field, see Lehrman, D. S., "Hormonal Responses to External Stimuli in Birds," *Ibis*, 1959, **101**, 478–496.

Reprinted from *Endocrinology*, 1961, **68**, 507–516, by permission of the authors, the publisher, and the editor: F. G. Hofmann.

ABSTRACT We have studied the effects of stimuli provided by the presence of a bird of opposite sex, and by the presence of a nest-bowl and nesting material, on the development of readiness to incubate eggs in male and in female ring doves, and on gonadotropin secretion in females. All subjects had previous breeding experience. The results show that the presence of a male in the cage causes the gradual development, over an 8-day period, of readiness to sit on eggs, and that the additional presence of a nest-bowl and nesting material augments this effect, starting on about the 6th day. The presence of the female, and of nesting material, have similar effects on the incubation behavior of the male, except that the effect of nesting material may be seen earlier (about the 4th day) in the male than in the female. Gonadotropin ac-

tivity in the female, as indicated by oviduct growth and by incidence of ovulation, is stimulated by the presence of a male, and augmented by the presence of nesting material. The occurrence of incubation behavior in females is closely associated with that of ovulation, and a number of lines of evidence suggest that a progestin is implicated in the instigation of this behavior.

* Supported by a research grant (M-2271) from the National Institute of Mental Health, United States Public Health Service.

† National Science Foundation Cooperative Graduate Fellow.

▶ When a pair of ring doves which have had previous breeding experience is placed in a breeding cage containing a nest and eggs, they do not sit on the eggs until after several days, during which they exhibit the progression of courtship and nest-building behavior which normally precedes the laying and incubation of their own eggs (10). Both sexes participate in incubation. It has been shown that association with the mate, and the presence of a nest-bowl and nesting material, facilitate the successive development of the pair's readiness to build a nest and to sit on eggs, although our previous work has not distinguished between the role of the male and that of the female. Nest-building can be induced by exogenous estrogens, and incubation behavior by exogenous progesterone (11, 23).

These findings suggest that the onset of incubation behavior may be associated with the presence of gonadal hormones, and that the secretion of these hormones may be elicited or facilitated by stimuli coming from the mate and from the nesting situation. The purpose of the present experiment is to examine: a) the effect of the presence of the mate and of a nesting situation (nest-bowl and nesting material) on the devolment of readiness to incubate in male and in female ring doves; b) the effect of these stimuli on gonadotropin secretion in the female ring dove, as indicated by ovarian activity; and c) the relationship between ovarian activity and readiness to incubate.

Material and Methods

Animals. The subjects were ring doves *(Streptopelia risoria)* procured from Mr. J. W. Steinbeck of Concord, California, or the first-generation offspring of animals from this source.

Cages and Maintenance. Experimental cages were of wood, each 32″ wide, 18″ deep, and 14″ high, with wire-mesh front doors. They were provided with dispensers for water, food and a grit-and-mineral mixture, and (when required) a glass bowl 4¼″ in diameter, in which the birds build their nests. These cages were illuminated by strips of fluorescent lights mounted on a wall 5′ 6″ in front of the doors.

Stock cages were 35″ cubical cages built with wooden frames and wire-mesh sides.

Isolation cages were metal rat cages 16½″ wide, 9½″ deep, and 7″ high, mounted in racks.

Water, food and grit were continuously available in all cages. Nesting material consisted of pine needles or hay placed on the floor in a corner of the breeding cage.

Breeding cages, stock cages and isolation cages were kept in separate rooms. Lights in all rooms were clock-controlled, being turned on at 6:00 A.M. and off at 8:00 P.M., EST. Temperature in all rooms was 72°–74°F., except for brief and irregularly-distributed periods of malfunctioning of the temperature-control apparatus.

Experience prior to testing. The laboratory-reared birds were hatched in experimental cages. All birds were kept in stock cages after being separated from their parents at the age of 21 days, or after being received from the supplier. The sex and degree of maturity were determined by an exploratory laparotomy, and the birds placed in pairs in experimental cages. They were allowed to breed once, their young being removed when 21 days of age. At the same time, the subjects were removed to individual isolation cages. They were kept in isolation for 3–5 weeks, and then placed in the experimental cages for testing. During the tests, subjects were never paired with birds with which they had previously been mated.

In summary, all subjects were birds with previous breeding experience consisting of one successful breeding cycle, and had been in isolation for from 3 to 5 weeks prior to testing.

Experimental procedure. The general procedure was to place birds, singly or in pairs, in experimental cages for a variable number of days, after which they were tested to determine whether they would sit on eggs, and the females were autopsied to determine oviduct weights, and whether they had ovulated.

Three groups were arranged. *Control:* females were placed alone in breeding cages without nest bowl or nesting material; *Mate:* subjects were placed in the breeding cages in male-female pairs, without nest bowl or nesting material; *Mate+ Nesting material:* birds were placed in pairs in the cages, with a nest bowl and a supply of nesting material in each cage.

The birds were taken from the isolation cages and placed in an experimental cage

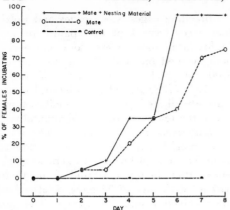

FIG. 1. Effects of association with a mate or with a mate + nesting material on the development of incubation behavior in female ring doves.

Each point is derived from tests of 20 birds. No individual bird is represented in more than one point.

The abscissa represents the duration of the subject's association with a mate or with a mate + nesting material, or (for the control group) the time spent alone in the test cage, just prior to being tested for response to eggs. "Day 0" means that the bird was tested immediately upon being placed in the cage.

between 9:00 A.M. and 10:00 A.M. (on day 0). Between 0 and 8 days later, at the same hour, a nest bowl containing a nest and two eggs, taken from a breeding pair in the colony, was placed in the cage, the original nest bowl, if any, being removed. The cage was then visited every 30 min. to determine whether either of the birds was sitting on the eggs. If neither bird had sat by the end of 3 hours, both birds were removed. If either bird sat during the 3-hour period, it was removed, and the other bird allowed to remain in the cage until it sat, or until 3 additional hours had passed. All females were killed for autopsy as soon as they were observed sitting, or at the end of the observation period.‡

In summary, birds kept in test cages for varying periods of time (0 to 8 days),

‡ The authors are indebted to Mr. Willis Butler for assistance with the autopsies.

either alone, with a mate, or with a mate and nesting material, were tested for incubation response to eggs, and then killed for autopsy.

Twenty pairs of birds were used for each treatment and each time interval in the experimental groups, and 20 females for each time interval in the control group, a total of 340 males and 400 females.

Results

INCUBATION BEHAVIOR

Females left alone in test cages for varying periods of time, up to 7 days, and then tested by being presented with nests and eggs, do not sit on the eggs (Fig. 1, "control"). Previous work has shown that birds of either sex, kept singly in cages with nests and eggs, and with nesting material, do not sit on them during test periods of up to 6 weeks (10).

By contrast, when birds are placed *in pairs* in the cages, and then presented with nests and eggs after periods of up to 8 days, incubation behavior is induced, the number of birds sitting on the eggs gradually increasing from day to day, both in females (Fig. 1, "mate") and in males (Fig. 2, "mate").

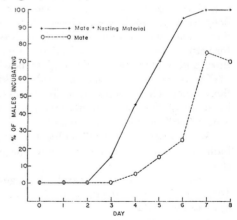

FIG. 2. Effect of association with a mate or with a mate + nesting material on the development of incubation behavior in male ring doves. See caption, Fig. 1.

TABLE 17-1

**P-values for differences in incidence of incubation behavior between "mate"
and "mate + nesting material" groups[a]**

| SEX | NUMBER OF DAYS ASSOCIATION WITH MATE (OR WITH MATE + NESTING MATERIAL) | | | | | | | | |
	0	1	2	3	4	5	6	7	8
Female	n.d.[b]	n.d.	n.d.	.5[c]	$> .3$[d]	n.d.	$< .001$	.05	.08
Male	n.d.	n.d.	n.d.	.12	$< .02$	$< .01$	$< .001$	.02	.01

a Incidences taken from Fig. 1 (females) and Fig. 2 (males).

b No difference between frequencies of occurrence of incubation behavior with and without nesting material.

c P-values in ordinary type are calculated by Fisher's exact method. Conditions for the use of x^2 not met (25).

d P-values in italics are based on x^2.

The presence of a nest bowl and nesting material in the cage during the period before the introduction of the nest and eggs further stimulates the development of incubation behavior, as shown by the greater numbers of birds of both sexes (Figs. 1, 2, "mate+nesting material") which sit on the eggs under these conditions, compared with birds stimulated only by the presence of the mate.

It may be noted that the two sexes do not respond in quite the same way to the presence of nesting material. P–values for the differences between the incidence of incubation behavior in the two stimulus situations are shown for the various days, separately for males and for females, in Table 17–1, where it will be seen that the presence of nesting material induces a higher incidence of such behavior (compared with that occurring in birds kept with a mate alone) starting on the 4th day in the males, but not until the 6th day in the females, a difference which is also apparent on visual comparison of Figures 1 and 2. Possible reasons for this difference between the sexes will be discussed below.

OVARIAN ACTIVITY AND THE RELATION BETWEEN OVARIAN ACTIVITY AND INCUBATION BEHAVIOR

Figure 3 shows the incidence of ovulation in females autopsied on the same day

as that on which they were tested for incubation behavior. The absence of ovulations in the control group (kept alone in cages), and the sharply rising frequencies of ovulation in the two groups kept with mates and nesting material, indicate that ovulation is induced by stimuli associated with the presence of the mate, augmented by those associated with the presence of the nest bowl and nesting material.

The close similarity between the curves describing the incidence of incubation behavior (Fig. 1) and of ovulation (Fig. 3) in the females of the various groups sug-

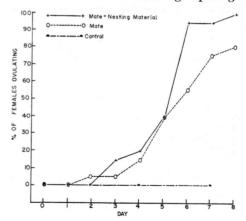

FIG. 3. Effect of association with a mate or with a mate+nesting material on the occurrence of ovulation in female ring doves. See caption, Fig. 1.

TABLE 17-2

Coincidence of incubation behavior and of precurrent or concurrent ovulation in female ring doves

OVARIAN ACTIVITY	BEHAVIOR	
	INCUBATED	DID NOT INCUBATE
Ovulated	111	18
Did not ovulate	14	177

$X^2 = 200.4$.

gests that the physiological conditions associated with ovulation are the same as those associated with readiness to incubate eggs. Table 17–2 shows the relationship between the readiness to incubate on the test day and the occurrence of ovulation prior to the test (i.e. up to the time of autopsy), for all females in the groups in which incubation behavior and ovulations occurred. The chi-square value of 200.4 indicates a very high degree of association between the occurrence of ovulation and of incubation behavior. The same strong association is shown when the "mate+nesting material" group ($X^2=111.95$) and the "mate" group ($X^2=86.51$) are examined separately.

Oviduct weights, summarized in Figure 4, show a similar pattern: no increase

in oviduct weight occurs while the female dove is alone in the cage; duct weight increases as a result of the presence of a male; and this increase is augmented by the presence of nesting material. The inversion of the oviduct weight curves for the "mate+nesting material" and the "mate" groups between the 6th and 7th day is due to the fact that most birds of the "mate+nesting material" group ovulated earlier than those of the "mate" group, giving up oviduct weight in the form of albumen secretion (21). In each of the two groups, the oviduct weights on day 2 are significantly higher than on day 0 (Mann-Whitney U Test, P<.05) (25), indicating that increases in oviduct weights can be detected within 48 hours after the beginning of association with a male.

Discussion

Most species of birds breed seasonally, the timing of the breeding season being influenced by a variety of environmental variables, such as daily light period, weather, availability of nesting sites, presence of other birds, etc. (12, 13). It has long been apparent from naturalists' observations that one of the functions of the courtship singing and posturing of male birds is to stimulate the development of sexual receptivity in the female (8), and F. H. A. Marshall, in his classic papers on sexual cycles (15, 16), suggested that this stimulation occurs *via* the elicitation of the secretion of gonad-stimulating hormones by the female's hypophysis.

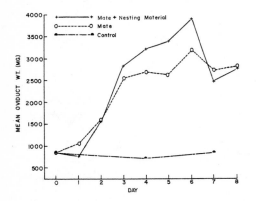

FIG. 4. Effect of association with a mate or with a mate+nesting material on oviduct growth in female ring doves. See caption, Fig. 1.

Harper (6), Craig (2), and Matthews (17) have shown that in female pigeons and doves, egg-laying may be stimulated by the presence of a male. It has further been demonstrated in English sparrows (19) and in starlings (1) that the ovary-stimulating effects of additional illumination in the non-breeding season may be augmented by the presence of males. In our laboratory, adult females kept in isolation from other birds do not lay eggs, and the present study shows that the presence of the male is necessary to stimulate the secretion of gonadotropins sufficient to elicit ovulation.

This experiment does not demonstrate that *no* gonadotropin secretion occurs in the absence of the male. The oviducts of our control animals are considerably heavier (700–800 mg.) than those of doves taken just before the onset of gonadotropin secretion at sexual maturity (400–500 mg.) (12a). Further, all these experiments were carried out at a constant day length of 14 hours light, 10 hours dark. Unpublished experiments from our laboratory indicate that, if the birds are placed without mates in a shorter day-length (9 hours) the ovaries and oviducts regress considerably below the level found in our control birds. The effect of stimulation from the male on gonadotropin secretion in our birds is, therefore, co-active with stimulation from other sources, and this interaction is now under study here.

Naturalists' observations also suggest that the presence of an appropriate nesting site and of nesting material is a factor in the conditions stimulating normal gonadotropin secretion during the breeding season in birds. A number of field observers have noted that breeding may be delayed by the absence of nesting material during the normal season (9), and Hinde and Warren (7) found that depriving female domestic canaries of nest material and of a nest site delayed the laying of eggs in the spring. Some dry-country tropical birds breed irregularly, always following rainfall, and Marshall and Disney (14) demonstrated experimentally in the case of the African red-billed weaver, *Quelea quelea,* that the presence of green grass, used for nesting material, is the principal stimulus for the beginning of breeding. In the present study it is clearly indicated that the presence of nesting material augments the effect of the male in stimulating gonadotropin secretion in the female.

It is apparent that the onset of the readiness of female doves to incubate is related to ovarian activity. This is indicated in the present study by the close similarity between the incidences of incubation behavior and of ovulation. Further, incubation behavior can reliably be induced in doves by the administration of progesterone (11), which probably appears endogenously at about the time of ovulation (4).

In female doves, it thus appears that the secretion of gonadotropins is in part stimulated by the mate and by the nesting situation (nest bowl and nesting material), and that the ovarian secretory activity thus induced contributes to the occurrence of incubation behavior at about the time of ovulation. The situation in the male is more obscure. We have not yet been able to demonstrate any histological differences between those males which do, and those which do not, sit on eggs; nor between males which have, and males which have not, been placed with females and with nesting material. Nevertheless males, like females, develop incubation behavior as a result of being associated with a mate, and this development is augmented by the presence of nesting material. We are continuing this study, and it is of course possible that we will detect changes in the testes or hypophysis (or elsewhere) associated with the onset of incubation behavior. Another possibility, also now under study, is that the endocrine condition of the male does not change as a result of association with a female, but that his behavior changes in response to the changes in *her* behavior, consequent on the endocrine changes induced in her by association with the male. We cannot at present decide the point. It may be noted, however, that the consensus of data in the literature of sexual photoperiodicity is that males of most wild bird species can be brought to full spermatogenesis by increased light-period alone, while ovum growth brought about solely by this stimulus never achieves ovulation (3).

The fact that the presence of nesting material appears to influence the incidence of incubation behavior in males by the 4th day, while it does not do so in females until the 6th day (Table 17–1) requires some explanation. In ring doves, as in other species of pigeons and doves (5) the male does most of the gathering of nesting material, which he carries to the nest, where the female does most of the building. It may be that the presence of nesting material alters the reproductive condition of the female partly by altering the behavior of the male toward her.

What of the role of prolactin in initiating incubation behavior in doves? This hormone is traditionally stated to form the principal physiological background of such behavior in chickens (22) and is sometimes assumed to be involved in all types of parental behavior in birds and other animals as well (20). The results reported here suggest that, in doves, ovarian hormones are the principal instigators of incubation behavior. Further, injected progesterone induces incubation behavior in doves, without any evidence of crop growth, and crop growth does not normally begin until after the beginning of incubation (11). There is evidence that participation in incubation induces prolactin secretion (18), and that prolactin so induced maintains incubation behavior (24), but it may be questioned whether the *initiation* of this behavior depends upon this hormone. Unpublished experiments in our laboratory indicate that prolactin does not induce incubation behavior in doves as reliably as does progesterone, even in doses large enough to cause full crop development, and that it does not do so at all when the dosage is small enough so that no appreciable crop growth occurs.

REFERENCES

1. BURGER, J. W.: *Anat. Rec.* **84**: 518. 1942.
2. CRAIG, W.: *J. Morph.* **22**: 299. 1911.
3. FARNER, D.: *Recent Studies in Avian Biology*, A. Wolfson, Ed.: 198. Univ. of Ill. Press, Urbana, 1955.
4. FRAPS, R. M.: *Mem. Soc. Endocrin.* **4**: 205. 1955.
5. GOODWIN, D.: *Avicult. Mag.* **1955**: 54. 1955.
6. HARPER, E. H.: *Amer. J. Anat.* **3**: 349. 1904.
7. HINDE, R. A., and R. P. WARREN: *Anim. Behav.* **7**: 35. 1959.
8. HOWARD, H. E.: *Territory in Bird Life.* Chatto and Windus, London, 1920.
9. LACK, D.: *Proc. zool. Soc. Lond.* **1933**: 231. 1933.
10. LEHRMAN, D. S.: *J. comp. physiol. Psychol.* **51**: 32. 1958.
11. LEHRMAN, D. S.: *J. comp. physiol. Psychol.* **51**: 142. 1958.
12. LEHRMAN, D. S.: *Ibis* **101**: 478. 1959.
12a. LEHRMAN, D. S., and P. BRODY: *Proc. Soc. exp. Biol.*, N. Y., **95**: 373. 1957.
13. MARSHALL, A. J.: *Ibis* **101**: 456. 1959.
14. MARSHALL, A. J., and H. J. DE S. DISNEY: *Nature* **180**: 647. 1957.
15. MARSHALL, F. H. A.: *Phil. Trans.* **226B**: 423. 1936.
16. MARSHALL, F. H. A.: *Biol. Rev.* **17**: 68. 1942.
17. MATTHEWS, L. H.: *Proc. roy. Soc.* **126B**: 557. 1939.
18. PATEL, M. D.: *Physiol. Zoöl.* **9**: 129. 1936.
19. POLIKARPOVA, E.: *C. R. Acad. Sci. U.R.S.S.* **26**: 91. 1940.
20. RIDDLE, O.: *Proc. Amer. phil. Soc.* **75**: 521. 1935.
21. RIDDLE, O.: *Endocrinology* **31**: 498. 1942.
22. RIDDLE, O., R. W. BATES and E. L. LAHR: *Amer. J. Physiol.* **111**: 352. 1935.
23. RIDDLE, O., and E. L. LAHR: *Endocrinology* **35**: 255. 1944.
24. SAEKI, Y., and Y. TANABE: *Poult. Sci.* **34**: 909. 1955.
25. SIEGEL, S.: *Nonparametric Statistics.* McGraw-Hill, New York, 1956.

DAVID KRECH, MARK R. ROSENZWEIG, and EDWARD L. BENNETT

18 Relations between Brain Chemistry and Problem-Solving among Rats Raised in Enriched and Impoverished Environments*

For the past few years David Krech and Mark R. Rosenzweig, two University of California psychologists, have been working in collaboration with Edward L. Bennett, a biochemist, on the relations between brain chemistry and behavior. They are primarily concerned with two substances that occur in the brain. The first, acetylcholine (ACh), is a synaptic-transmitter substance. As a nerve impulse reaches the end of certain presynaptic neurons, a minute amount of ACh is released. The ACh then fires the postsynaptic neuron and the synapse has been crossed. However, if the concentration of ACh becomes too great, transmission across the synapse will cease. An enzyme, cholinesterase (ChE), is known to hydrolize ACh and thus maintain the conditions necessary for synaptic transmission. There is some evidence that ACh and ChE function in the central nervous system, and this led the experimenters to hypothesize that varying concentrations of these substances might be correlated with variations in learning ability. A series of experiments from their laboratory has been concerned with ACh and ChE as both dependent and independent variables (see the introduction to Section II for definitions of these terms). In the following reading, genotype and age (both of which are known to affect brain chemistry) are controlled; environmental complexity is the independent variable, and ChE concentration and problem-solving ability are the dependent variables.

The S_1 strain of rats used in this experiment is descended from Tryon's maze-bright group (see reading 6).

This article is from the *Journal of Comparative and Physiological Psychology*, 1962, **55**, 801–807. It is reprinted here with the permission of the authors and the American Psychological Association.

We have recently reported on a series of experiments which investigated the effects of varying the rat's environment upon changes in the biochemistry and morphology of the brain. In the first report of this series (Krech, Rosenzweig, and Bennett, 1960) it was shown for six strains of rats that, with an increase in the animal's environmental complexity and training (ECT), there was a *drop* in specific cholinesterase (ChE) activity of the sensory cortex and an *increase* in the specific ChE activity of the subcortex. (Specific ChE activity was measured in terms of moles of

* This investigation was supported in part by Grant M-1292 from the National Institute of Mental Health, United States Public Health Service. It also received support from the United States Atomic Energy Commission. The first two authors are members of the Department of Psychology, and E. L. Bennett is a Research Biochemist in the Lawrence Radiation Laboratory.

We wish to thank Hiromi Morimoto, Marie Hebert, and Felice Movich for their skilled assistance in the chemical procedures, Michael G. Saslow and James F. Zolman for their capable help in the behavioral phases of the experiment, and Carol Saslow for her conscientious aid in the statistical analyses.

213

acetylcholine, ACh, hydrolyzed per minute per milligram of tissue.) The clearest effect of ECT, therefore, was to decrease the cortical-subcortical (CS) ratio of specific ChE activity.

A later finding, reported in the second article in this series (Rosenzweig, Krech, Bennett, and Diamond, 1962), helped to explain, in part, the puzzle of the drop in the specific ChE of the cortex. We found that *total* ChE of the cortex (total ChE activity taken without regard to the weight of the tissue) actually increased somewhat in the ECT animals as compared with their littermates, but that the *weight* of the cortex increased to a greater degree. Thus *specific* ChE (ChE per unit weight) had decreased even though *total* ChE had increased.

The present experiment was designed to measure the learning ability of young animals immediately after 1 mo. of exposure to our complex environmental situation—an exposure period which Zolman and Morimoto (1962) had shown was sufficient to lower the CS ratio of ChE. The ECT conditions were originally adopted in our program because many studies from other laboratories (e.g., Bingham and Griffiths, 1952; Forgays and Forgays, 1952; Hymovitch, 1952) had shown that training and opportunities for experience can produce changes in learning capacity. But, as we stated at the 1958 Pittsburgh Symposium, ". . . the mechanism of these effects has not been explained. In this connection we will want to consider whether effects of training can be detected in changes in brain chemistry" (Rosenzweig, Krech, and Bennett, 1961, p. 90). Having now established that our enriched environmental conditions can induce cerebral changes, it is still necessary to demonstrate that these environmental conditions can enhance learning capacity. The necessity for this is underscored by the fact that the interpretation of the evidence from other laboratories on the enhancing effects of enriched environment is now being challenged. Thus Woods, Fiske, and Ruckels-

haus concluded that the characteristically poor maze-solving performance of the animals brought up in a restricted environment ". . . is not due to a deficiency in intelligence or maze-solving ability, but more likely due to a heightened exploratory drive" (1961, p. 169). Furthermore, a number of experiments claiming to have demonstrated the beneficial effects of early experience have neglected certain important precautions, thus rendering the results equivocal.

Our experimental design, detailed in Method, was intended to overcome three major difficulties which have made the interpretation of other experiments ambiguous: *(a)* The prejudicing of the results by the unwitting bias of E who, when testing the learning capacity of the animal, is fully aware which animal comes from the enriched environment, which from the impoverished; *(b)* the possibility of confusing increased learning ability with effects of specific positive transfer to handling, due to the experimental animal's being handled by the same E during the "enriched environment" phase and the learning-testing phase; and *(c)* the confounding of exploratory behavior with error scores. Because we wanted a problem-solving test which would make a "heavy" demand on the animal's capacity for adaptive behavior, we chose a visual reversal discrimination test.

Method

SUBJECTS

Male rats of the S_1 strain were weaned at 21 to 28 days of age and placed in the experimental conditions. This strain had shown marked effects of enriched environment on brain chemistry and morphology in our previous work. Fifteen pairs of littermates were used, each pair taken from a different litter. Three subgroups were run in succession, 6 pairs in the first group, 4 in the second, and 5 in the third. One animal of each pair, chosen at random, was assigned to the Environmental Complexity (EC) conditions, and its littermate was assigned to the Isolated Control (IC) conditions.

EC AND IC CONDITIONS

In the EC condition, the animals lived 10 to a large cage. (Extra rats of the same strain, age, and sex were added to each subgroup to bring the number up to 10.) The cage contained a small maze, and each day two wooden "toys" from a set of seven were placed in the cage. For 30 min. daily, the rats explored the Hebb-Williams apparatus with the pattern of barriers changed daily. Unlike our previous experiments, no formal training was given, so this condition is called EC rather than ECT as in our previous experiments.

The IC animals lived in individual cages where they could not see or touch another rat. Both the IC and EC animals had food and water ad lib. Both conditions lasted for 30 days. During this period the IC animals were handled only six times, for weighing.

At the end of the 30-day period, the E in charge of this first phase recaged the rats, three to a usual colony cage, so that some cages contained one EC and two IC rats, while the others contained two EC and one IC rat. The extra rats living in the EC conditions were caged separately and retained as weight controls for the EC and IC animals. The rats, identified only by code numbers that did not reveal their group, were then turned over to a second E for the second phase of the experiment.

REVERSAL DISCRIMINATION

In the second phase the animals were run for food reward on a reversal discrimination schedule in the Krech Hypothesis Apparatus—which consists, essentially, of four successive units of two-choice discrimination boxes (see Fig. 1, Krech, Rosenzweig, and Bennett, 1956). A 10-day pretraining period accustomed the animals to the 24-hr. deprivation schedule, trained them in a pretraining apparatus to leave the start box, run through doorways, and enter the goal box, and gave the previously re-

stricted animals a period of social and environmental exploration before the start of testing. A daily session during the testing period of 18 days consisted of 10 trials, comprising 40 choices.

The reversal discrimination schedule followed that used by Krechevsky (1932). The animals were first trained on a light-correct problem. Criterion was not more than 1 error in 5 successive trials, i.e., 19 correct choices out of 20. As soon as an animal reached criterion, it was started on the first *reversal* problem, dark-correct. Training on dark-correct was continued until the same criterion was reached, whereupon the problem was switched to light-correct, etc. At the end of the 18-day testing period, animals were run for 2 control days, with the doors open in the same daily sequence as before but with both alleys lighted at each choice point.

It was hoped that exploratory behavior was restricted both by the design of the apparatus and by the motivating conditions. Over the 18 days of testing, the animal divides its 720 choices among the same 8 alleys. Furthermore, the 24-hr. deprivation schedule produces strong motivation in young animals, and this should compete successfully with the exploratory drive.

CONTROL OF WEIGHT

While the EC and IC rats were receiving training and testing, the weight-control rats continued to receive food and water ad lib. and gained about 40% during this 30-day period. The weights of the EC and IC rats were stabilized during testing at about 88% of that of the weight-control group. The EC and IC rats ended the 30-day period about 16% heavier than they had begun. They always ran well and never appeared to be seriously undernourished.

Careful control of food deprivation was essential both to treat EC and IC animals similarly and to preclude retardation of growth of the brain in young animals. As we have shown elsewhere (Rosenzweig et al., 1961), underfeeding may produce significant loss of brain weight and may result in striking changes in labile constituents of the brain.

CHEMICAL ANALYSIS

Within 3 days after the end of the testing period, the animals, now aged from 84 to 90 days, were sacrificed for chemical analysis of their brains. The brain of each animal was dissected into five parts: (*a*) a sample from the visual cortex of both hemispheres (V) weighing on the average 52 g.; (*b*) a sample from the somesthetic cortex of both hemispheres, weighing about 45 g. (S); (*c*) the remaining dorsal cortex; (*d*) the ventral cortex and contiguous tissue, and (*e*) the rest of the brain, including the cerebellum. This last sample will be referred to as "subcortex II." The V and S samples, taken together, will be referred to as "sensory cortex." These tissue samples have been defined more fully and their location shown by diagrams in a previous report (Rosenzweig et al., 1962).

Littermates were sacrificed and analyzed consecutively, with the sequence randomized as between the EC and IC member of each pair. The analysts did not know to which group any animal belonged. For each tissue sample, three measures were obtained: (*a*) wet weight, determined to 0.1 g., (*b*) total ChE activity. This is expressed in terms of moles acetylcholine (ACh) $\times 10^8$ hydrolyzed per minute. (*c*) Specific ChE activity, which is total ChE activity divided by the weight of the tissue sample. Specific ChE activity is expressed in terms of moles ACh $\times 10^{10}$ hydrolyzed per minute per milligram of tissue. The analytical procedures, using an automatic titrator, have been reported previously (Rosenzweig, Krech, and Bennett, 1958).

Results

COMPARISON OF PERFORMANCE
OF EC AND IC GROUPS

The main results of the behavioral testing are shown in Figure 1. The initial light-correct problem was relatively simple, and

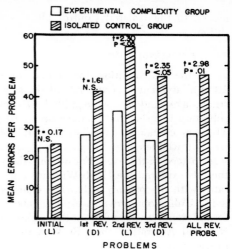

FIG. 1. Mean errors per problem made by rats of the EC and IC groups.

there was practically no difference in the mean numbers of errors made by the EC and IC groups. The first *reversal* problem, dark-correct, was slightly more difficult for the EC animals but was considerably more difficult for the IC animals; the 51% difference between groups was not, however, statistically significant. The second reversal problem was still more difficult than the preceding problem, and one IC animal failed to master it by the end of the 18-day experimental period; the computations are therefore based on 14 littermate pairs, eliminating the unsuccessful IC rat and its littermate. The difference between the EC and IC groups (54%) is significant for this second reversal problem at the .05 level. For the third reversal problem, the difference between groups (now 79%) is significant at the .05 level. Two IC rats failed on this problem, so they and their littermates had to be dropped from these calculations. The elimination of the unsuccessful IC animals from the second and third reversal problems minimized the differences between groups, since these animals were slow learners and made many errors. The EC littermates of these two IC animals showed scores very close to the mean of the other EC animals.

The mean number of reversal problems solved by the EC animals was 6.1 and by the IC group, 4.5, a difference short of significance ($p < .10$). The last set of bars in Figure 1 shows the mean number of errors per problem for *all* reversal problems attempted by each animal. For this measure, the difference between groups (68%) reaches the .01 level of significance.

It is clear that the animals exposed to a complex environment for 30 days performed better on the reversal discrimination problems than did their littermates kept in isolation for 30 days.

During the 18 days the animals had confronted the same sequence of 40 right and left opened alleys—no matter whether they were working on a light-correct or a dark-correct problem. The possibility remains therefore that the animals had been gradually learning this spatial sequence rather than solving visual reversal discrimination problems. One check of this possibility comes from the data from Days 19 and 20. During these control days, the animals were run in the apparatus with the doors open in the same daily sequence as before, but with both alleys lighted at each choice point. If the animals had by this time learned the spatial sequence, then under these control conditions they should have been able to do better than chance in choosing the open alley. Since each animal was given a total of 80 choices in this con-

trol situation, the score to be expected by chance alone was 40. The results of this control test are unequivocal. The mean number of choices of the open alley was 39.7 for the EC group, and 40.5 for the IC group. It would appear, then, that at the end of the 18-day period the animals were still attacking the problem in terms of the visual discriminanda.

BRAIN WEIGHT AND ChE

The brains of the EC and IC groups were compared for all the biochemical and morphological indices which, on the basis of previous work (Krech et al., 1960; Rosenzweig et al., 1962), have significantly differentiated animals reared for 80 days under our ECT and IC conditions. The results of this comparison are presented in Table 18–1.

The total ChE activity of the EC group exceeds that of the IC group by 3% in the sensory cortex and by 4% in the total cortex. There is practically no difference between the groups in subcortex II. In weight, the EC group exceeds the IC group by 2% in the sensory cortex and by 3% in total cortex, with almost no difference in the subcortex. While these differences in ChE activity and cortical weight are consistent with our previous findings between ECT and IC animals, none of them is statistically significant.

The other comparisons yield results

TABLE 18–1

Mean values of cerebral cholinesterase and weight for EC and IC animals

MEASURE	GROUP	SENSORY CORTEX[a]	TOTAL CORTEX[b]	SUBCORTEX II[c]
Total ChE	EC	67.5	613.6	1827.1
	IC	65.7	588.3	1820.1
Weight (in mg.)	EC	97.8	647.4	919.4
	IC	95.6	630.6	916.9
Specific ChE	EC	69.7	94.8	198.8
	IC	69.2	93.3	198.5

a Sensory cortex is composed of the samples from the visual and somesthetic areas of cerebral cortex.

b Total cortex comprises sensory cortex, remaining dorsal cortex, and ventral cortex.

c Subcortex II is what remains of the brain after total cortex has been removed.

which differ from that of our other work. Thus, the increase of weight of the cortex (EC over that of IC) is no greater than the increase of total ChE activity of the cortex, where in our previous work cortical weight consistently showed the greater increase. In consequence, specific ChE (total ChE divided by tissue weight) does not differentiate between EC and IC groups for the cortex, nor does it for the subcortex. This again differs from our findings with our ECT and IC groups where the specific ChE was lower for the ECT group in the sensory cortex and higher in the subcortex. As a final consequence of this, the CS ratio of specific ChE—the index which best differentiates between ECT and IC groups in all of our previous experiments—here does not discriminate at all between the EC and IC groups: The EC group shows a ratio of .381 and the IC, of .380.

The cortical-subcortical weight ratio does, however, show much the same differentiation between our present EC and IC groups as it has between our former ECT and IC groups (Rosenzweig et al., 1962). Weight of the total cortex divided by weight of subcortex II shows the EC group greater by 2.5% than the IC group, but this difference is short of significance ($p = .10$, two-tailed t test).

CORRELATIONS OF PERFORMANCE AND CEREBRAL MEASURES

It remains to be determined whether the individual differences in problem solving are related to individual differences in brain measures.

The behavioral index employed was the mean number of errors per reversal problem attempted by the animal. This ratio reflects the two basic performance measures: the total errors made on reversal problems and the total number of successive reversal problems the animal tackled during the training period. It will be recalled that by this ratio, the EC group was significantly superior to the IC group (see Fig. 1).

On the physiological side we also used

ratios—the CS ratios of specific ChE and of weight discussed previously. These ratios were used because, as has been indicated, each of these had been shown in our previous work to differentiate between animals brought up under enriched environments and animals brought up under impoverished environments.

The 15 littermate pairs, it will be remembered, were run in three subgroups of 6, 4, and 5 pairs, separated widely in time. Since small variations in the processes of enzymic assay render somewhat questionable the comparison of absolute biochemical values obtained weeks or even months apart, we therefore determined the correlations between performance and cerebral measures separately for the three successive subgroups. The three correlations were then combined, using Fisher's r to z transformation, after statistical tests indicated that such combinations were legitimate.

The correlation of the CS weight ratio against the performance measure was $-.77$ for the EC group (significant at better than the .01 level of confidence), and for the IC group it was $-.15$ (nonsignificant). The sign of the correlations is what should have been expected from theory: Since the performance measure is an error measure, and the effect of enriched experience is to *increase* the cortical weight in relation to the subcortical weight, the error score should decrease as the CS weight ratio increases.

For the CS ratio of specific ChE activity, the correlations with performance records were surprisingly high. For the EC group the correlation was .81 (significant at better than the .01 level of confidence), and for the IC group it was .53 (significant at better than the .05 level). Here, the correlations are positive since the CS ratio of specific ChE has always been found to *decrease* with enriched experience, and therefore the lower the ratio, the fewer the errors. Figure 2, the scatterplot for the EC data, illustrates the stable and reproducible nature of these correlations. It can be seen from Figure 2 that each subgroup had

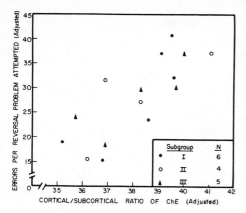

FIG. 2. Scatterplot of cortical-subcortical ratio of specific ChE versus mean errors per reversal problem. (For both variables, the values were adjusted so that the means of each subgroup equalled the overall mean.)

a high positive correlation. The same was true of the EC correlations involving the weight ratio.

It is clear from this correlational analysis that for animals raised in an enriched environment during infancy there is a substantial and stable relation between performance measures on the reversal discrimination problem and those morphological and biochemical measures of the rat's brain which are most affected by the enriched environment. For the rats raised in an impoverished environment during infancy, correlations of the same sign are also present, but of a lower magnitude.

Discussion

Our data seem to support three major conclusions and pose one major paradox:

We have shown that exposure of 1 mo. to enriched or impoverished environment for weanling rats is sufficient to bring about significant differences in their ability to cope with a series of reversals of discrimination. The use of two different E for the two phases of the experiment precluded the possibility of E's biasing the results and of benefitting the frequently handled EC

rats through specific positive transfer to the E's handling from one experimental phase to the other. It would also seem difficult to attribute the inferior performance of our IC group to "a heightened exploratory drive," as Woods, Fiske, and Ruckelshaus (1961) have done in the case of their restricted-environment group. The two groups did equally well on the initial discrimination problem and began to grow apart in performance only during the succeeding days as the difficulty of the problem increased — by which time the same eight alleys of the apparatus had already been traversed hundreds of times.

We have found substantial and significant correlations between two indices of brain morphology and biochemistry and the animal's problem-solving ability. The two physiological indices (CS ratios of ChE activity and of weight) are the ones which have most consistently differentiated between rats reared in an enriched environment and rats reared in an impoverished environment. The problem-solving measure against which these indices have been correlated (errors per reversal problem) is also the measure which most clearly and most significantly differentiates our EC rats from our IC rats. And in each case, the records of the EC rats yielded higher correlations than did those of the IC.

The biochemical and morphological differences between the EC and the IC rats were highly attenuated in comparison with all of our previous findings on the effect of environment on brain physiology. For one of these measures—the CS ratio of brain weight—the difference was slight and significant at only the .10 level of confidence. For the other measure—CS ratio of specific ChE—there was almost no difference at all.

The paradox derives from a consideration of the three findings taken together: The EC rats are clearly superior problem-solvers to the IC rats, and the problem-solving performance of all the animals is correlated with those morphological and biochemical indices which normally differentiate "enriched" and "impoverished" animals, *but these very indices* do not clearly differentiate the EC from the IC rats!

In order to resolve this paradox, let us first consider some of our results in relation to some of those of Zolman and Morimoto (1962). They assigned one littermate of each of 15 pairs of S_1 weanlings to the ECT condition and the other to the IC condition. At the end of 30 days the ECT littermate was found in 14 of 15 pairs to have the lower CS ratio of specific ChE activity (as in our previous experiments). The mean values of the CS ratios for these ECT and IC groups are shown by the two points to the left in Figure 3 (55 days). Their ECT

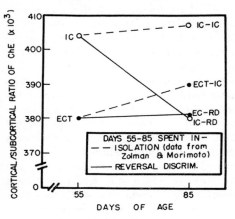

FIG. 3. Mean cortical-subcortical ratios of specific ChE ($\times 10^3$) for groups of S_1 rats exposed to different experimental conditions.

condition differed from our EC condition only in including one trial a day in the Lashley III maze during the last 8 days. At the age of 55 days, our rats in the present experiment presumably had CS ratios very close to those of the corresponding groups of Zolman and Morimoto, since the animals were alike in strain, age, and sex, and since the IC conditions of the two experiments were identical while the EC and ECT conditions were very similar.

In another part of their experiment, Zolman and Morimoto ran 15 littermate pairs in ECT or IC conditions for 30 days and then kept both groups in isolation for

another 30 days before sacrificing them at 85 days of age. It will be seen that an additional 30 days of isolation had little effect on the group that had been isolated since weaning—the line across the top of the figure from IC to IC-IC is almost flat. The isolation had more effect on the CS ratio of the group originally exposed to the ECT condition, as is shown by the upward slope of the line from ECT to ECT-IC.

Now consider the results of the present experiment in the light of the others: At the lower right of Figure 3 are shown the mean CS ratios of the group given EC and then tested on reversal discrimination (EC-RD) and of the group first isolated and then tested on reversal discrimination (IC-RD). The mean value of the EC group is almost identical to that of the corresponding IC group. For the group exposed from weaning to a complex environment, the effect of presenting the animals with a complex task was only to keep the CS ratio at about the level that it had at the end of the first phase—the line across the bottom of the graph from ECT to EC-RD is almost horizontal. For the group started in the IC condition, however, the switch to the reversal discrimination situation caused a relatively large drop in the CS ratio (IC to IC-RD).

Both analyses suggest that CS ratios of specific ChE and weight are not immutably fixed after a 30-day enriched or impoverished environment. To some degree, the changes induced by an enriched environment can be lost if the animal is placed in an impoverished environment, and to a much greater extent, the originally impoverished animal's brain can be brought to the status of the enriched animal through intensive training on complex problems.

Now we are in a position to understand how the CS ratio could correlate with behavior of the animals within a group (and especially strongly within the EC group) and yet not differentiate between the EC and IC groups. The CS ratio of the EC group, as we have seen in Figure 3, presumably remained rather stable throughout the learning phase; therefore, the value obtained at the end was representative of the level existing throughout the behavioral testing, and a high correlation with the behavioral scores was possible. The CS ratio values for the IC animals, on the other hand, must have been changing during the learning phase, and the values determined at the end of the experiment could not so adequately represent this varying course, hence no very high correlation with the behavioral measure could be anticipated.

Summary and Conclusions

Fifteen littermate pairs of male rats of the S_1 strain were used, one member of each pair being assigned at weaning to the environmental complexity (EC) situation and the littermate to the isolated control (IC) situation. The EC or IC experience lasted for 30 days, and then during a second period of 30 days the animals of both groups were pretrained and tested on reversal discrimination problems under condition of food deprivation. The EC group was significantly superior to the IC group on this test. Within the EC group, high and significant correlations were found between the behavioral scores and the cortical-subcortical ratios of cholinesterase and between the behavioral scores and the cortical-subcortical ratios of brain weight. Within the IC group the corresponding correlations were lower, and only the first of them was significant. Differences between the EC and IC groups on brain measures were small and insignificant. Presumably the EC and IC groups differed in brain measures at the end of the phase of differential environmental treatment, as found in related experiments. Partially as a consequence of these cerebral differences, the EC animals had an initial advantage in problem-solving ability over the IC animals. As training progressed, the brain values of the IC group approached those of the EC group. Since analyses of the brains could be done only at the end of the experiment, these end-point values showed little or no differ-

ences between the two groups. Furthermore, such end-point determinations presumably reflected rather accurately the relatively stable cerebral values of the EC group during the problem-solving phase and less accurately the changing values of the IC group, thus permitting higher correlations of brain measures with behavior for the EC than for the IC group.

REFERENCES

BINGHAM, W. E., and W. J. GRIFFITHS The effect of differential environments during infancy on adult behavior in the rat. *J. comp. physiol. Psychol.*, 1952, **45**, 307–312.

FORGAYS, D. G., and J. W. FORGAYS The nature of the effects of free-environmental experience on the rat. *J. comp. physiol. Psychol.*, 1952, **45**, 322–328.

HYMOVITCH, B. The effects of experimental variations on problem-solving in the rat. *J. comp. physiol. Psychol.*, 1952, **45**, 313–321.

KRECH, D., M. R. ROSENZWEIG and E. L. BENNETT Dimensions of discrimination and level of cholinesterase activity in the cerebral cortex of the rat. *J. comp. physiol. Psychol.*, 1956, **49**, 261–266.

KRECH, D., M. R. ROSENZWEIG and E. L. BENNETT Effects of environmental complexity and training on brain chemistry. *J. comp. physiol. Psychol.*, 1960, **53**, 509–519.

KRECHEVSKY, I. Antagonistic visual discrimination habits in the white rat. *J. comp. Psychol.*, 1932, **14**, 263–277.

ROSENZWEIG, M. R., D. KRECH and E. L. BENNETT Brain enzymes and adaptive behaviour. In, *Ciba Foundation: Symposium on neurological basis of behaviour.* London, England: Churchill, 1958. Pp. 337–355.

ROSENZWEIG, M. R., D. KRECH and E. L. BENNETT Heredity, environment, brain biochemistry, and learning. In, *Current trends in psychological theory.* Pittsburgh: Univer. Pittsburgh Press, 1961. Pp. 37–110.

ROSENZWEIG, M. R., D. KRECH, E. L. BENNETT and M. C. DIAMOND Effects of environmental complexity and training on brain chemistry and anatomy: A replication and extension. *J. comp. physiol. Psychol.*, 1962, **55**, 429–437.

WOODS, P. J., A. S. FISKE and S. I. RUCKELSHAUS The effects of drives conflicting with exploration on the problem-solving behavior of rats reared in free and restricted environments. *J. comp. physiol. Psychol.,* 1961, **54**, 167–169.

ZOLMAN, J. F., and H. MORIMOTO Effects of age of training on cholinesterase activity in the brains of maze-bright rats. *J. comp. physiol. Psychol.,* 1962, **55**, 794–800.

JOHN D. DAVIS and NEAL E. MILLER*

19   Fear and Pain: Their Effect on Self-Injection of Amobarbital Sodium in Rats

The field of psychopharmacology, the study of the effects of drugs on behavior, is an important and rapidly growing discipline that has already made significant contributions to our knowledge of the physiology of behavior. The following reading describes a promising technique enabling an animal to control his own injection schedule.

Science, Vol. 141, pp. 1286–1287, 27 September 1963. Copyright 1963 by the American Association for the Advancement of Science. Reprinted with the permission of the authors and the American Association for the Advancement of Science.

ABSTRACT.   Rats receiving occasional brief electric shocks pressed a bar, which caused them to be injected with amobarbital sodium, more frequently than the control rats to which they were yoked and which were injected when their partners pressed but whose own bar activated only a recorder. This differential effect was not shown by pairs run without shocks.

▶ A variety of experimental studies summarized by Miller (1) support the hypothesis that one of the effects of amobarbital sodium is to reduce fear. Experimental evidence shows that the rapid reduction of fear reinforces the response immediately preceding this reduction (2). Therefore, if amobarbital does reduce fear, rats maintained in a fear-evoking environment should learn a response which is immediately followed by a painless, quick-acting dose of amobarbital. Such learning would

be a new type of evidence for the hypothesis that this drug reduces fear and also would be relevant to the problem of drug addiction.

Twenty-eight male albino rats weighing approximately 330 g were prepared, each with a cannula, inserted permanently in the jugular vein, which terminated either at the tricuspid valve or in the auricle of the heart (see 3). In this way the drug was administered painlessly and gave immediate effects.

The rats were run in yoked pairs in adjoining Skinner boxes, one rat in each pair serving as a control for the random (operant) level of responding, as well as for the exciting or depressing effects of the drug or of the shocks to be administered. The bar in one box was active so that each time it was pressed an injection of 0.012 ml of a 40 mg/ml solution of amobarbital (equivalent to approximately 1.5 mg/kg) was injected at a rate of 0.144 ml/min simultaneously into both rats. The bar in the second box, containing the yoked control rat, was

* This work was supported by research grant MY 2949 to one of us (N. E. M.) from the National Institute of Mental Health, U. S. Public Health Service.

connected only to a counter. Thus the injections of the rat in the first box were contingent on its pressing its bar; for the rat in the second box the injections were not contingent on its pressing its bar. Since the pair of rats was treated alike in all other respects, any reliable differences in the number of times they pressed the bars must be due to the fact that receiving the drug was contingent on bar pressing in the one case, but not in the other.

Each pair of rats was run for 1 hour each day. One group of eight pairs was subjected to fear and pain by being given unavoidable electric shocks of approximately 0.1-second duration and 1-ma strength every 60 seconds during the hour. The other group of six pairs was run without shocks. The total number of times each rat pressed its bar was recorded at the end of each hour.

The effect of receiving the drug immediately after pressing the bar is indicated by the difference between the scores of the contingent and noncontingent members of each pair. In the pairs not receiving shock, there was no appreciable difference

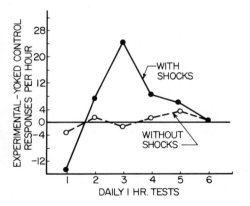

FIG. 1. The reinforcing effect of amobarbital sodium on rats receiving occasional electric shocks and those not receiving shocks. The effect is measured as the difference in rate of bar presses by rats whose responses produce injections of the drug, and of the controls that are yoked to them, who are injected when their partners respond, irrespective of their own responses.

throughout the six days of the experiment; hence the lower curve fluctuating around zero, shown in Fig. 1. As is typical of rats introduced to a new situation without any reinforcement for bar pressing, both groups showed a daily response rate that declined progressively from approximately 17 presses per hour on the first day, to approximately 5 presses per hour on the fifth day, after which the rate remained relatively constant.

In the group receiving shock, the control (noncontingent) rats showed a curve indistinguishable from that of the two groups which did not receive shock. But the experimental (contingent) rats, which happened by chance to start below the rate of their partners and hence yielded an initially negative difference score, increased their responses progressively until the third day, and thereafter showed a decrease in the number of responses, as shown by the upper curve in Fig. 1.

Analysis of variance performed on these data yielded a significant interaction between shock conditions and days ($p < .025$) showing that the obvious difference between the two curves in Fig. 1 is, indeed, statistically reliable. Since inspection showed that this difference was due to the performance of the shocked animals, an analysis of trend was performed on their data. It indicated that the quadratic component, representing the up-and-down aspect of the upper curve, was highly significant ($p < .005$), accounting for approximately 70 percent of the variance.

From these data, one can conclude that for the shocked rats, the injections of amobarbital sodium immediately following bar pressing had a reinforcing effect which caused learning through the third day. This effect could either be due to a reduction in fear as postulated, or to a reduction in pain.

Under the conditions of this experiment, amobarbital did not appear to have any appreciable reinforcing effect for animals run without shock. If the rats had been made physically dependent on the drug so that they showed severe withdrawal symptoms, it is conceivable that this drug would have had a reinforcing effect even in the group not receiving shock. Preliminary results of experiments still in progress suggest that both psychological stress and withdrawal symptoms are involved in determining the rate at which rats will work to inject themselves with morphine.

Fig. 1 shows that after the third day the superiority of the contingent animals in the shocked group gradually disappeared, indicating that the drug was losing its reinforcing effect. This result shows a similarity to the clinical picture in which a drug prescribed to relieve fear and tension may be quite effective at first, but becomes less so with repeated use.

REFERENCES

1. MILLER, N. E.: *Am. J. Psychol.* **16**, 12 (1961); in *Animal Behaviour and Drug Action*, H. Steinberg, Ed. (Churchill, London), in press.
2. MILLER, N. E.: In *Handbook of Experimental Psychology*, S. S. Stevens, Ed. (Wiley, New York, 1951), pp. 435–472.
3. WEEKS, J. R., and J. D. DAVIS: In preparation.

section four

THE DEVELOPMENT OF BEHAVIOR, CRITICAL PERIODS, AND IMPRINTING

The preceding section covered material that might be described as part of the "biological background" of animal behavior. Although we are by no means finished with this topic, the emphasis in the present section is on early experiential factors that affect later behavior. This important area of research has been under intensive investigation in recent years. The findings of these investigations, in combination with those of behavior genetics and behavioral physiology, foretell the development of major insights into the determinants of behavior. The next major breakthrough in science may well be concerned with the interactions of genotype, physiology, and experience in determining behavior.

The first three readings of this section emphasize the inherent complexity, and the need for strict control, in research on the development of behavior. Readings 23–26 deal with the important and controversial concept of "critical periods" in development. These are followed by selections illustrating the effects of early social deprivation on later behavior. The final reading concerns the ethological concept of imprinting.

225

S E Y M O U R   L E V I N E
and P. L. B R O A D H U R S T

20 Genetic and Ontogenetic Determinants of Adult Behavior in the Rat*

Seymour Levine, an American psychologist, is known for his work on the effects of early experience on later emotional behavior. P. L. Broadhurst, an English behavior-geneticist, has conducted experiments on the inheritance of emotionality in the rat. The collaboration of two such well-qualified scientists on an analysis of factors affecting emotional behavior is a fortunate event. The results of this study indicate the great complexity of the genotype-experience interactions and the difficulty of arriving at generalizations about them.

Reprinted from the *Journal of Comparative and Physiological Psychology*, 1963, **56**, 423–428, by permission of the authors and the American Psychological Association.

ABSTRACT. 80 rats from the Maudsley Reactive and Nonreactive Strains, selected for emotional defecation, were subjected to controlled infantile stimulation. When adult, they were tested for open-field emotionality and escape-avoidance conditioning in a factorial design, which included strain, treatment, sex, and test-order variables. Both heredity and environment had significant effects, and also display interaction. The scores from the open-field showed that infantile stimulation caused a significant decrease in emotionality indexes which is attributed to a change in the capacity to respond to stress. The reactive strain was significantly poorer in escape-avoidance conditioning.

▶ The past decade has seen an accumulation of literature relating to genetic and ontogenetic determinants of behavior. Much of the research has been concerned with behavior patterns related to the concept of emotionality, and the importance of hereditary factors in the emotional reactivity of the rat has been amply demonstrated (Broadhurst, 1960). The evidence concerning differences due to environmental factors during infancy has been more recent and is still controversial (Bovard, 1958; King, 1958). There is, however, considerable evidence that stimulation during infancy is implicated in adult emotionality, and a general finding (Levine, 1962a, 1962b) has been that organisms stimulated in a variety of ways as infants (by manipulating, shocking, stroking, etc.) are significantly less emotional than non-stimulated controls. Recent reports suggest that the extent and duration of the effects of such ontogenetic factors on subsequent emotionality are partly dependent upon genetical constitution. Thus King and Eleftheriou (1959) showed that avoidance behavior in two subspecies of deermice was differentially affected by infantile manipulation. In one subspecies (*gracilis*) avoidance learning was significantly improved, whereas in the other subspecies (*bairdii*) the infantile treatment resulted

* A preliminary report of this experiment was made to a meeting of the British Psychological Society (Levine and Broadhurst, 1961). We are indebted to Sylvia B. Parsons and K. B. Wright for testing and computational help, to P. Slater for statistical advice, and to V. Denenberg, J. A. King, and G. Lindzey for their comments on a draft of this paper.

in an impairment. Ginsburg (1960) has reported a similar interaction between genetic and ontogenetic determinants of behavior. Infantile manipulation caused either an increase or a decrease in the exploration by adult mice on an elevated runway, the direction depending upon the strain.

The present experiment was designed to study the interaction of genetical differences and infantile stimulation in two strains of laboratory rat, bidirectionally selected for high and low emotional defecation in a standardized and revised version of Hall's open-field test. They also show a correlated genetical response to selection in characteristics other than defecation (Broadhurst, 1960, p. 53), most important among which, for our present purpose, is the change in ambulation (exploratory activity) in the open field. Animals from the high defecating strain typically have low ambulation scores, and vice versa.

The effects of infantile manipulation on both open-field test behavior and conditioned avoidance learning were studied. It was hypothesized that if the effects of infantile experience upon emotionality are dependent upon the genetical constitution of the organism, then it was likely that they would be more profound in the emotionally reactive strain; that is, that infantile manipulation would decrease defecation, increase ambulation in the open field, and improve escape-avoidance conditioning based on electric shock.

Method

SUBJECTS

The Maudsley Reactive and Nonreactive Strains, No. 163f and 163g, respectively, in the (British Laboratory Animal Centre) *Catalogue of Uniform Strains* (1958) were used. A total of 120 rats (60 males and 60 females) were drawn from the two inbred albino strains at the fourteenth generation of selection (S_{14}; Broadhurst, 1960) which was augmented for the purpose of

the present study by rebreeding fertile parents already selected from the previous generation by the usual selection criteria. The details of these criteria, of the husbandry, and environmental controls routinely employed will be found elsewhere (Broadhurst, 1960, pp. 41-43). The independent environmental variable (infantile manipulation) used in the present study can be regarded as a departure from these conditions in the directions of increased, or reduced, infantile stimulation. Eighty Ss were used for these two conditions. The 40 remaining Ss of both sexes randomly chosen from the strains of the S_{14} generation were reared under routine laboratory procedures. These Ss were given only the open-field test at 100 days. The differences between the routine procedure and that used for our non-manipulated Ss are that in the former, firstly, all Ss are weighed at the day of birth and thus receive some manipulation and, secondly, on Day 12 of life their nesting material is removed from the cage although at this time the Ss are not handled. This difference thus permits an evaluation of the effect of a single day's manipulative treatment, immediately after birth, on subsequent open-field behavior.

PROCEDURE

Five replications of a 2^4 factorial design were used, employing 80 Ss. The variables investigated were strain, sex, presence or absence of infantile manipulation, and order effects in adult testing. Assignment to the subgroups was made randomly within the limitation of insuring an equal distribution of sexes within strains. However, complete orthogonality with respect to the order of testing variable was not maintained. As a consequence its interactions with all the other variables are included in the error variance, giving it 71 *df*.

These Ss were derived from 17 litters. Alternate Ss from each strain were assigned at birth to a control or to a manipulated group. The control group comprised 5 litters from the reactive strain and 4 from the nonreactive, and the manipulated group 4 reactives and 4 nonreactives. All the litters used contained between 4 to 9 pups each with an average litter size of 7.1 for the manipulated Ss and 7.0 for the nonmanipulated Ss.

The manipulated litters were subjected to treatment starting on the day of birth and ending at weaning at 21 days, which involved removing the complete litter once daily from the mother, placing it in a cardboard container for 3 min., and then returning the pups to the nest. The nonmanipulated controls received no experimental intervention until the time of weaning. In this respect the treatment differed from that accorded routinely reared animals in the selection program since they are handled at birth for sexing and weighing. The purposes of this study necessitated the avoidance of any handling of our control group whatsoever. After weaning, and until the time of testing, all the animals were treated identically.

Testing of these 80 Ss started at 106.2 ± (SD) 6.1 days of age, and continued for 5 consecutive days, 4 of which were devoted to the open-field test and 1 to escape-avoidance conditioning. The order of testing was determined by the group to which the S had been assigned. Thus, half the Ss were first given the standardized open-field test described in detail elsewhere (Broadhurst, 1960, pp. 32-33). Briefly, it consists of exposing each S for 2 min. per day on 4 successive days to uniform sound and light fields within a circular arena. The number of fecal boluses deposited during each trial constitutes the defecation score, and the number of compartments marked on the floor, and roughly equal in size, through which the rat passes, provides the basis for the ambulation scores converted into meters run per day. These Ss were then tested in a shuttle box apparatus for the acquisition of a conditioned avoidance response (Levine and England, 1960). The CS, a buzzer, was presented for 8 sec. followed by the US, an electric shock of 0.25 ma. The escape response terminated both buzzer and shock; an avoidance response ter-

minated the buzzer. The intertrial interval averaged 50 sec. with a range of 33 to 67 sec., randomly presented. Each S was run for 90 consecutive trials in a single session, and the number of avoidance responses was recorded together with the CS and US latencies for each trial. The second half of the Ss were tested initially for avoidance conditioning and then in the open field. All Ss were weighed at 21 days, 50 days, and the day following the last experimental session.

Results

OPEN-FIELD TEST

Figure 1 presents the defecation and ambulation scores on each of the four daily trials in the open-field test. It should be noted that the defecation scores shown are those of the reactive strain *only* because, by S_{14}, almost all the nonreactive Ss yield zero defecation scores regardless of treatment. This absence of distribution of values within the nonreactive strain necessarily limits the analysis of variance of defecation scores to the reactive strain. Within this strain a significant effect of infantile manipulation ($F = 7.58$, $df = 1/35$, $p < .01$) was detected with the infantile treatment resulting in a significant overall reduction of defecation, the mean for the manipulated Ss being 3.1±1.8 fecal boluses per trial and for the nonmanipulated controls, 4.4±1.3. No other main effects or interactions were significant in this analysis, which was carried out on repeated measures to permit any between-trials (days) effects to emerge.

The analysis of variance of ambulation scores, also carried out on repeated measures showed the main effects of sex, strain, and infantile treatment to be significant beyond the .001 level (Fs of 33.9, 33.6, and 31.4, respectively; $df = 1/71$ in each case). The relevant means are: for strain, reactive 7.8 ± 2.6 m. run per day, nonreactives 10.3 ± 2.5; for sex, males 7.8 ± 2.5, females 10.3 ± 2.7; and for treat-

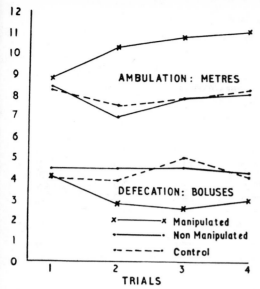

FIG. 1. Changes in open-field test scores on successive daily trials (abscissa). (The common ordinate shows the ambulation score—upper curves—and the defecation score—lower curves—for the reactive strain only.)

ment, manipulated 10.3 ± 2.5, nonmanipulated 7.8 ± 2.7. There were no significant interactions within days, but the Treatment × Days interaction reached significance at the .05 level ($F = 3.4$, $df = 3/216$). The nature of this interaction may be seen from Figure 1, and analysis of the daily scores by two-tailed t tests shows that on the first day of open-field testing the two groups did not differ significantly whereas on each subsequent trial differences significant beyond the .01 level were found in favor of the manipulated group.

The analysis of the data obtained from the routine laboratory-reared Ss (control in Figure 1) revealed no significant differences between the scores of these Ss and the nonmanipulated Ss in either total defecation or ambulation scores. In each case, however, these Ss did differ significantly from the manipulated Ss in showing higher defecation scores (reactive strain only) and lower ambulation scores (both strains). The order of testing did not prove signifi-

cant for either score derived from the open-field test.

AVOIDANCE LEARNING

The raw data for the avoidance learning scores showed a highly significant heterogeneity of variance which was not lessened by either a square-root or a log transformation. The main source of this heterogeneity is apparent from the means and standard deviations given in Table 20–1 (upper part), variability being much greater among the reactive strain. An analysis of variance was nevertheless performed which showed the strain difference to be highly significant (.001 level), with the nonreactive strain making the greater number of avoidance responses. This finding was checked by use of the two-tailed t test, which is relatively insensitive to inhomogeneity of variance. Thus the nonreactive strain learned the avoidance response extremely rapidly and gave a mean value of 87% of the total (of 90 trials) as avoidance responses. In contrast, 66% avoidance responses were made by the Ss from the reactive strain. This clear-cut difference appeared to justify the separation of the data for the two strains in the subsequent analyses. Within the reactive strain, the analysis of variance of the number of avoidance responses yielded sex, infantile treatment, and order effects significant at the .05 level. ($Fs = 4.3, 4.1,$ and 5.1, respectively, all with $df = 1/35$.) The female Ss made significantly more avoidance responses that the male Ss, the nonmanipulated Ss were higher than the manipulated Ss (see Table 20–1 for details), and the Ss trained in the order avoidance-open field made more avoidance responses (65.1 ± 10.7) than those trained in the reverse order, open field-avoidance (53.7 ± 21.7). The variances of the reactive strain avoidance scores were homogeneous.

However, in the analysis of the nonreactive strain data the requirement of homogeneity of variance again could not be met. The heterogeneity is due to the differences

TABLE 20–1

Results

| GROUP | SEX | STRAIN | | | |
| | | REACTIVE | | NONREACTIVE | |
		M	SD	M	SD
Total Number of Avoidance Responses					
Manipulated	Males	51.3	21.0	79.7	3.9
	Females	57.2	14.6	76.0	9.9
Nonmanipulated	Males	57.0	18.1	79.8	2.4
	Females	72.0	5.9	76.8	7.1
Percentage Weight Gain Between 50 and 111 Days of Age					
Manipulated	Males	113.6	15.0	83.9	17.0
	Females	60.9	7.1	75.3	9.7
Nonmanipulated	Males	98.3	12.8	61.7	16.6
	Females	59.1	4.2	54.0	9.3

in variance between the sexes within this strain (see Table 20–1) and was not improved by the standard transformation. However, the analysis was performed and yielded no significant differences attributable to any of the variables. Since lack of homogeneity of variance would in general tend to magnify any differences (Cochran and Cox, 1950, p. 83), we are confident that such differences do not exist within the nonreactive strain.

The analysis of variance of the data for latency of avoidance responses was also performed on each strain independently, again because of the difficulty in finding a transformation to eliminate the significant inhomogeneity of variance. A log transformation reduced it to around the .01 level, and a preliminary analysis of these data indicated a significant ($p < .001$) strain difference in the latencies, with the nonreactive strain showing significantly shorter shock-avoidance responses to the buzzer (1.6 ± 0.3 log sec.) as opposed to 2.4 ± 0.5 for the reactives. In the separate analyses performed on the untransformed data, the only effect that proved to be significant was the order effect for the reactive

strain. ($F = 4.4$, $df = 1/35$, $p < .05$), the Ss given the tests in the order avoidance-open field making shorter avoidance responses to the buzzer (5.9 ± 1.8 sec.) than those tested in the order open field-avoidance (7.4 ± 2.8). The analysis of the nonreactive strain data revealed no significant differences.

GROWTH

Differences between the body weights of the two strains have been a feature of the response to selection for high and low defecation (Broadhurst, 1960, pp. 61-64) and have been in the direction of a heavier reactive strain, especially among males. Thus in order to evaluate the differences in body weight as a function of the variables under investigation, the weight data were expressed as a percentage increase in weight. Since the Ss were weighed three times during the course of the experiment, at weaning, at 50 days of age, and at the end of the experiment at 111 days, data are available for the percentage increase from weaning to 50 days, and for percentage increase from 50 days to 111 days.

The analysis of variance for the increase from weaning to 50 days, performed after the inhomogeneity of variance had been shown not to exceed the .05 level, revealed only a highly significant sex difference ($F = 93.5$, $df = 1/71$, $p < .001$), males gaining more than females, 299.3 ± 32.7% as opposed to 231.3 ± 28.2. None of the other main effects approached significance, nor were there any significant interactions. But analysis of variance for the percentage increase from 50 days to the end of the experiment indicated significant differences for sex ($F = 144.0$, $p < .001$), infantile treatment ($F = 8.6$, $p < .001$), and order ($F = 5.3$, $p < .051$), and in addition there was a significant Sex × Strain interaction ($F = 19.0$, $p < .001$): $df = 1/71$ in each case. Thus male Ss again gained significantly more weight than females, 92.6 ± 20.2% and 58.9 ± 10.8, respectively; the reactive strain gained more than the nonreactive strain Ss, 83.0 ± 25.9 and 68.6 ± 17.8, respectively; Ss subjected to infantile manipulation gained more than nonmanipulated Ss, 79.9 ± 25.0 and 71.7 ± 19.7, respectively; and Ss tested in the order open field-avoidance showed a significantly greater gain that the Ss tested in the reverse order, avoidance-open field, 79.0 ± 24.53 and 72.5 ± 21.7, respectively. The Sex × Strain interaction is attributable to the fact that the females did not differ significantly between strains in contrast with the males, which did. The means and standard deviations for the various subgroups are shown in the lower part of Table 20–1.

Discussion

The results presented above once again demonstrate the efforts of infantile stimulation in the rat and the importance of genetic differences in emotional defecation. Another striking difference between the strains was in avoidance conditioning, with the nonreactives showing superior learning. This parallels a previous finding (Owen, in press). The implications of this

finding and a subsequent confirmation of it are discussed elsewhere (Broadhurst and Levine, in press).

The evidence for the interaction of these environmental and hereditary variables is somewhat more tenuous. Thus, infantile manipulation had little effect upon defecation and avoidance learning of the nonreactive strain, whereas the reactives showed differences in both measures in response to manipulation. The effect of test order on avoidance latency is also limited to the reactive strain. Conversely, ambulation scores and body growth display no such strain-limited effect.

The present study provides only a first approximation to an analysis of this interaction, since it does not permit the evaluation of the respective components of variation of each. A refined design would involve the crossing of inbred strains in a way suitable for a genetical analysis and rearing offspring, as well as parents only, in different environmental conditions. Broadhurst and Jinks (1961, p. 358) discuss a similar problem relating to environmental stimuli operating during learning tasks.

But the effects of infantile manipulation as observed here are unclear in implication, for, while it reduced emotional reactivity in the open field (lowered defecation and increased ambulation), it also retarded the avoidance learning. It has been reported that infantile manipulation can result in an impairment of avoidance learning (Denenberg and Karas, 1961; King and Eleftheriou, 1959). Denenberg and Karas report that manipulation from 1 to 20 days of age decreases avoidance learning, whereas, in contrast, 1 to 10 days of manipulation produces the reverse effect. Consequently, they postulated that a curvilinear relationship exists as a function of duration of manipulation. Thus, nonmanipulated Ss show poorer avoidance learning as a function of being highly emotional, whereas the poorer avoidance learning in their 1 to 20-day manipulated Ss is a function of insufficient motivation. This hypothesis, however, cannot account for the present data. Although the strain difference in avoidance learning could fit Denenberg's hypothesis (1959), this hypothesis would also predict that infantile manipulation should have decreased emotionality, and in the reactive strain such a decrease in emotionality should have resulted in an increase in avoidance performance since they are less emotional than the reactive controls but still more emotional than the nonreactive Ss. The fact that a further decrease in avoidance learning occurs as a function of infantile manipulation in the reactive strain does not fit any currently held concept of the effects of infantile manipulation on adult avoidance learning.

Infantile stimulation also influenced the pattern of differences in the open-field scores. On the first day of testing none of the groups differed significantly, whereas on the subsequent three daily trials the differences due to manipulation were highly significant. In early work on infantile treatment, it was hypothesized that one of its major effects was to reduce the Ss behavioral and physiological response to stress. But in some of the subsequent experiments, the manipulation caused a marked increase in the response to stress (Levine, 1962a, 1962b; Levine, Alpert and Lewis, 1958). The present study, in conjunction with the results of other experiments (Denenberg, Morton, Kline, and Grota, 1962), suggests that it is the capacity to adapt to stressful conditions which changes with infantile manipulation, as may be seen in the decrease in defecation and increase in ambulation. The concept of adaptation must always be defined in situational terms, but the fact that our manipulated Ss adapted more quickly is further evidence that the adaptation process differs with infantile manipulation.

The order effects detected suggest a greater responsiveness to shock among rats which experienced avoidance conditioning before the less stressful open-field test. Thus, these Ss showed shorter escape latencies and a smaller weight gain, i.e., a probable loss of weight, than Ss which had the previous test experience. The postulated weight loss may also have occurred in the test sophisticates but failed to be detected, not being fully in evidence when these animals were weighed at the end of the experiment, i.e., on the day after their avoidance conditioning.

REFERENCES

BOVARD, E. W.   The effects of early handling on viability of the albino rat. *Psychol. Rev.,* 1958, **65,** 257–271.

BROADHURST, P. L.   Experiments in psychogenetics: Applications of biometrical genetics to the inheritance of behaviour. In H. J. Eysenck (Ed.), *Experiments in personality.* Vol. 1. *Psychogenetics and psychopharmacology.* London, England: Routledge & Kegan Paul, 1960. Pp. 1–102.

BROADHURST, P. L., and J. L. JINKS   Biometrical genetics and behavior: Reanalysis of published data. *Psychol. Bull.,* 1961, **58,** 337–362.

BROADHURST, P. L., and S. LEVINE   Behavioral consistency in strains of rats selectively bred for emotional elimination. *Brit. J. Psychol.,* 1963, **54,** 121–125.

COCHRAN, W. G., and G. M. COX   *Experimental designs.* New York: Wiley, 1950.

DENENBERG, V. H.   Interactive effects of infantile and adult shock levels upon learning. *Psychol. Rep.,* 1959, **5,** 357–364.

DENENBERG, V. H., and G. G. KARAS   Interactive effects of infantile and adult experiences upon weight gain and mortality in the rat. *J. comp. physiol. Psychol.,* 1961, **54,** 585–589.

DENENBERG, V. H., J. R. C. MORTON, M. J. KLINE and L. J. GROTA   Effects of duration of infantile stimulation upon emotionality. *Canad. J. Psychol.,* 1962, **16,** 72–76.

GINSBURG, B. E.   Genetic control of the ontogeny of stress behavior. Paper read at the annual meeting American Psychological Association, Chicago, September 1960.

KING, J. A.   Parameters relevant to determining the effect of early experience upon the adult behavior of animals. *Psychol. Bull.,* 1958, **55,** 46–58.

KING, J. A., and B. E. ELEFTHERIOU   Effects of early handling upon adult behavior in two subspecies of deermice, *Peromyscus* maniculatus. *J. comp. physiol. Psychol.*, 1959, **52**, 82–88.

LABORATORY ANIMALS CENTRE   *Catalogue of uniform strains of animals maintained in Great Britain.* (2nd ed.) Carshalton, Surrey: LAC, 1958.

LEVINE, S.   Plasma-free corticosteroid response to electric shock in rats stimulated in infancy. *Science,* 1962, **135**, 795–796. (a)

LEVINE, S.   The psychophysiological effects of infantile stimulation. In E. Bliss (Ed.), *Roots of behavior.* New York: Hoeber, 1962. Pp. 246–253. (b)

LEVINE, S., M. ALPERT and G. W. LEWIS   Differential maturation of an adrenal response to cold stress in rats manipulated in infancy. *J. comp. physiol. Psychol.,* 1958, **51**, 774–777.

LEVINE, S., and S. J. ENGLAND   Temporal factors in avoidance learning. *J. comp. physiol. Psychol.,* 1960, **53**, 282–283.

OWEN, S.   The effect on avoidance response extinction in rats of CS continuation and emotional constitution. *J. genet. Psychol.,* 1963, **103**, 147–151.

WILLIAM   R.   THOMPSON

21   Influence of Prenatal Maternal Anxiety on Emotionality in Young Rats

In this experiment William R. Thompson illustrates the importance of strict control in behavioral experimentation. The experiment shows that environmental factors affecting later behavior begin to operate before the birth of the organism. Note the careful control of possible postnatal maternal effects through the use of cross-fostering. William R. Thompson is coauthor, with John L. Fuller, of *Behavior Genetics.* (New York: Wiley, 1960).

Reprinted from *Science,* Vol. 125, pp. 698–699, 12 April 1957, by permission of the author and the American Association for the Advancement of Science.

The purpose of the observations reported in this article [*] was to test the hypothesis that emotional trauma undergone by female rats during pregnancy can affect the emotional characteristics of the offspring. By now, a good deal of evidence favoring this possibility has accumulated from diverse sources, including teratology (1), pediatrics (2), experimental psychology (3), and population biology (4). While none of the studies done has directly confirmed this

[*] This research was done at Queens University, Kingston, Ontario, and supported by grants from the Queens Science Research Council and the National Science Foundation. Grateful acknowledgment is made to C. H. Hockman for his invaluable aid in helping to build the apparatus and to test the animals.

hypothesis, many of them indicate that such hormones as cortisone, adrenalin, and adrenocorticotropic hormone, injected into the mother during pregnancy, have drastic effects on the fetus via the maternal-fetal blood exchange. Since strong emotion may release such substances into the mother's blood stream, there are grounds for supposing that it may have an important influence on fetal behavioral development. This experiment was the first in a projected series designed to examine this question in detail.

The rationale of the procedure was to create a situation which would predictably arouse strong anxiety in female rats, and to provide them with a standard means of reducing this anxiety; then to expose them to the anxiety-arousing situation during pregnancy, but block the accustomed means of escaping it. The assumption was that strong, free-floating anxiety would be generated in the pregnant females, and that any endocrine changes resulting would be transmitted through the maternal-fetal blood exchange to the fetus. The experiment was done by training five randomly chosen female hooded rats in a double compartment shuttlebox, first to expect strong shock at the sound of a buzzer, and then to avoid the shock by opening a door between the compartments and running through to the safe side. When the rats had learned this, the five experimentals, together with five control females, were mated to five randomly chosen males in a large cage. As soon as the experimentals were found to be pregnant (by vaginal smears), they were exposed to the buzzer three times every day in the shock side of the shuttlebox, but with the shock turned off and the door to the safe side locked. This procedure was terminated by the birth of a litter. The controls were placed in breeding cages during the same time.

Possible postnatal influences were con-trolled by crossfostering in such a way as to yield a design with six cells, each containing ten offspring with two main variables—namely, prenatal and postnatal treatment. The data obtained from tests given to the young were examined by means of analysis of variance. In all tests of significance, three error estimates were used: the within-cell variance, the within-plus-interaction variances, and the within-plus-interaction plus between-postnatal-treatment variances. Thus, as shown in Table 21–1, all tests of significance reported involve three F values.

The emotional characteristics of the 30 control and 30 experimental offspring were compared by two tests given at 30 to 40 and 130 to 140 days of age. In test A, measures of amount and latency of activity in an open field were taken in three daily sessions of 10 minutes each. In test B, emotionality was measured by latency of leaving the home cage, and latency of reaching food at the end of an alley way leading out from the cage after 24 hours' food deprivation. In the second test, the maximum time allowed an animal to reach food was 30 minutes. In the measures used, low activity

TABLE 21-1

Comparison of experimental and control animals on two tests of emotionality

ITEM	TEST A		TEST B	
	AMOUNT OF ACTIVITY (DISTANCE)	LATENCY OF ACTIVITY (SECONDS)	LATENCY TO LEAVE CAGE (MINUTES)	LATENCY TO FOOD (MINUTES)
Tests given at age 30 to 40 days				
Experimentals	86.0	146.3	14.9	23.7
Controls	134.5	56.8	5.2	11.8
F values	(15.79, 14.21, 13.57)	(8.51, 7.91, 8.07)	(16.13, 16.46, 15.62)	(31.73, 25.66, 25.87)
p	< .001	< .01	< .001	< .001
Tests given at age 130 to 140 days				
Experimentals	114.5	71.5	4.8	11.6
Controls	162.3	26.8	2.1	6.2
F values	(9.77, 9.12, 8.76)	(4.95, 4.79, 4.57)	(2.39)	(4.48)
p	< .01	< .05	> .05	< .05

and high latency were taken as indices of high emotionality.

The results are summarized in Table 20–1. On test A, striking differences between experimentals and controls were obtained in amount of activity, both at 30 to 40 days and at 130 to 140 days. On the first testing, a significant interaction was obtained which probably represents genetic variation. On the second measure, experimental animals showed a much higher latency of activity than controls at both ages of testing. In neither of these activity measures were there any significant differences due to postnatal treatment or interaction besides the one mentioned.

In test B, experimental animals were slower to leave the home cage than controls at the first age of testing. There was no significant difference between groups in this measure, however, at 130 to 140 days of age. Similarly, experimentals showed a much higher latency than controls in getting to food at the end of the alley way at the first age of testing. The difference was less at the later age of testing. At both ages, significant interaction variances were found. As before, both may well be due to genetic variation. On neither of the measures used in test B were any significant differences found between methods of postnatal treatment.

It is clear from this analysis that the experimental and control animals differ strikingly on the measures of emotionality used, and that these differences persist to a great extent into adulthood. While there is no question about the reliability of these differences, there is some ambiguity regarding their cause. Thus, we do not know exactly how the stress used had effects. It is possible that the buzzer was strong enough to act on the fetuses directly rather than indirectly by causing release of hormones in the mother. Only a more careful

repetition of the experiment will throw light on this problem.

A more serious objection than this is that, besides the main factor of prenatal stress, genetic variation could also have been responsible for the offspring differences if there had been inadverent selection of nonemotional mothers for the control group and emotional mothers for the experimental group. However, several points argue against this possibility. Choice of female animals for the two groups was carried out randomly, and at least some of the genetic variance was included in the error estimates used to test the main effects. Further, an examination of scores within and between individual litters indicates that interlitter variances tend to be smaller than intralitter differences. This means that, in the population used, genetic variation was relatively slight compared with environmental variation. Consequently, it is improbable that even if accidental selection had occurred it could have resulted in an experimental group genetically very different from the control group.

Accordingly, we may state that there are some grounds for supposing that prenatal maternal anxiety does actually increase the emotionality of offspring. This conclusion is offered tentatively until further experimentation has been completed.

REFERENCES

1. FRASER, F. C., and T. D. FAINSTAT: *Am. J. Diseases Children*, **82**, 593 (1951).
2. SONTAG, L. W.: *Am. J. Obstet. Gynecol.* **42**, 996 (1941).
3. THOMPSON, W. D., and L. W. SONTAG: *J. Comp. and Physiol. Psychol.* **49**, 454 (1956).
4. CHITTY, D.: "Adverse effects of population density upon the viability of later generations," in *The Numbers of Man and Animals* (Oliver and Boyd, London, 1955).

J O H N   A .   K I N G †

22

Parameters Relevant to Determining the Effect of Early Experience upon the Adult Behavior of Animals*

In this excellent review zoologist John A. King catalogs the various operational definitions of "early experience" and "adult behavior." He also makes specific suggestions for future experimentation in this field.

Reprinted from the *Psychological Bulletin*, 1958, **55**, 46–58, with the permission of the author and the American Psychological Association.

The hypothesis that some experiences early in the life of an organism profoundly and persistently affect the behavior of the adult has recently been subjected to a large number of experimental tests with animal subjects. Some investigators (15, 19, 42) have approached this general hypothesis from the viewpoint of Freudian theory, which suggests that the development of an infant is arrested or fixated at an early age (11). Other investigators (8, 9, 20) have oriented their experiments in terms of Hebbian theory, which stresses the importance of early perceptual experiences on later performance in a learning situation (16). The approach of other investigators (24, 43) has been to test for a critical period in which a given experience has a greater effect on adult behavior than the same experience at a later age (41). Regardless of the approach, all of the experiments re-

* This review was originally presented at the 1956 annual meeting of the American Psychological Association in the symposium entitled "Heredity and the Development of Behavior." Its preparation was supported by Grant M-123 from the National Institute of Mental Health, U. S. Public Health Service.

† Acknowledgment for the critical reading of the manuscript is given to J. P. Scott, J. L. Fuller, S. Levine, V. Denenberg, and W. C. Stanley.

viewed here have attempted to test whether some early experiences have a profound and lasting effect on later behavior.

Since the test of this hypothesis ultimately depends upon the adequacy of the methods used, it is desirable to examine these methods. The isolation of variables in any "longitudinal approach to the study of animal life is obviously more beset with methodological problems than studies concerned with only one portion of the life span" (2, p. 259). Although all the variables affecting development cannot be isolated and, perhaps, recognized, it is the purpose of this paper to analyze the recognizable parameters in the study of the effects of early experience on later behavior. This analysis deals chiefly with methodology, rather than results and conclusions. Most of the material is drawn from experimental studies on nonhuman mammals, particularly the rat and mouse, which show comparable rates of maturation.

Seven recognizable variables are of particular significance to the experiments under examination. They are: (a) the age of the animal when the experience is given, (b) age at the time of the test, (c) the duration or quantity of the experience, (d) the type or quality of the experience, (e) the type of the performance task required of the adult animal, (f) the method for testing persistence of the effects, and (*g*) the relation of the experience to the genetic background of the animal.

Age at the Time of the Experience

In considering the effect of time in relation to the commonly accepted theory that the past experience of an animal determines in part his present behavior, it is possible to make three alternate assumptions: (*a*) that the same experience at any time of life will have the same effect, (*b*) that the same experience will have a greater effect early in development and in proportion to the youth of the subject, and (*c*) that there are certain critical periods in development (some of which may occur early in life), during which the same experience may have a much more profound effect than at other times.

This quotation from Scott and Marston (41, p. 26) is followed by a refutation of the first two possibilities and a confirmation of the last, drawn largely from embryological and observational evidence. If the critical period hypothesis is to be adequately tested, the age of the animal at the time it is given the experience becomes particularly important. A test of the hypothesis demands answers to the questions: when do these critical periods occur; and, if they occur early in life, what is early? For purposes of age comparisons, a number of investigations on the rat and mouse are illustrated in Fig. 1. The age when the mouse or rat has been exposed to a given "early" experience varies from birth until over 100 days of age. Certainly, in view of this range, "early" does not mean the same thing to all investigators. Upon examination of Fig. 1, three age patterns appear in reference to the maturational processes of the rat or mouse.

First, there are *infantile* studies in

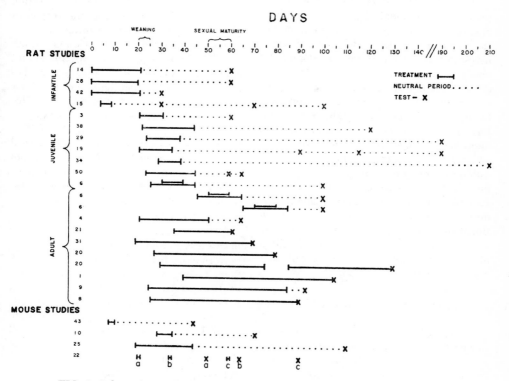

FIG. 1. Subjects' ages at treatment and test in selected experimental studies.

which the experimental treatment is administered during the period from birth until weaning in the rat. Some investigators have treated their subjects over the entire 20- or 25-day period (14, 26, 28, 42), while others have selected a shorter interval during this period (15, 43). The second age period can be called the *juvenile* period, extending from weaning to sexual maturity—a period of approximately 40 days in the rat or mouse. Again, the entire period may be used for treating the rat (4, 50) or shorter periods of 10 to 15 days (19, 29). The third period of treatment begins sometime before *sexual maturity* and continues into the adulthood of the rat (1, 8, 9, 20).

This classification of developmental periods of the rat into infantile, juvenile, and adult utilizes only the conspicuous changes induced by birth, weaning, and sexual maturity. These convenient landmarks are quite arbitrarily chosen, for subtle neurological or physiological modifications may actually be more important to the hypothesis under examination. However, in many investigations even these developmental changes of weaning and sexual maturity are not distinguished in administrating the treatment. Although this general approach to the study of the age variable is acceptable in the absence of physiological and neurological correlates to behavioral development, systematic examination of the different age periods is necessary. In experiments not designed to study the age variable, the treatment period should terminate before maturity, while most maturational processes are active. This procedure will distinguish experiments on the effects of early experience from those not directly concerned with maturation.

Age at the Time of the Test

The age variable must be controlled during the testing period as well as during the treatment period. The crosses in Fig. 1 illustrate the age when the pretest or test period began in the experiments represented. Most experimenters began the testing procedures after the rats were full-grown. The exceptions to this practice have been studies in which weight (3, 32, 42, 50, 51), temperatures (50), or behavioral changes (37, 41) were taken during the treatment period and those experiments in which the tests began before or shortly after the rats reached sexual maturity (14, 15, 21, 26, 28, 42, 50). Those experiments, in which the animals are tested at intervals during the treatment, aid in the interpretation of adult behavior but are essentially descriptions of the maturational process.

The interval between the end of the treatment period and the beginning of the test period also varies considerably throughout the experiments. Some test periods began immediately after the treatment (8, 20, 21, 31) and, therefore, test for the *immediate* effects of the experience rather than *later* effects. Many treatments, of course, necessitate the immediate testing for effects in order to show the responses of an animal when first permitted to see or when first released from restriction (5, 36, 44, 45). Another group of experiments includes an interval of varying length between the early treatment and the later tests (4, 6, 9, 10, 14, 26, 28, 29). This interval has been as short as 5 days (9) and as long as 150 days (29). During this interval, both experimental and control groups are usually treated alike. This period of "neutral" experience for experimental and control animals is essential for testing the effect of early experiences upon adult behavior.

The duration of the testing period is necessarily varied according to the type of performance task required of the animal. Some testing procedures have lasted almost as long as two years (42) while others have terminated after one week (21). Although the longer periods may contribute to our knowledge of persistence, which will be discussed later, they may also increase the danger of confusing the experiences gained early in life with those gained during the testing procedures. In general, the length of the testing period should be as short as possible in order to reduce practice effects. The minimum length which will give reliable results is probably the optimum.

Duration or Quantity of Early Experience

The hypotheses concerning the duration or quantity of the early experience propose that the experience may be anywhere from a brief period of exposure, such as a traumatic experience (12) or imprinting (30), to a relatively long accumulation of minor perceptual cues, such as learning to perceive (16). Most investigators have given their subjects relatively long periods of treatments, perhaps less because of a theoretical orientation than because they were eager to include a significant developmental period within the treatment span. The shortest treatment periods have been 1 day (10, 22) and 4 days (15, 43). Long treatment periods have lasted for as many as 65 days (1, 8). The short treatment periods provide a valid method for testing the effect of trauma and for discovering critical periods. While long treatment periods will do little to establish critical periods, they are useful for studying the effects of a particular kind of treatment on a particular performance task.

The most successful method for locating critical periods in the life span of an animal is to vary the age at treatment and vary the duration of the treatment. Hymovitch (20) has adequately demonstrated the technique of this procedure, and Eingold (6) has systematized it in a recent doctoral thesis. In the latter's study six experimental groups of rats were exposed to a free-environment treatment in a factorial design with two different lengths of exposure in each of three age classes. This procedure permitted Eingold to draw conclusions concerning the effects of the treatment with different durations of exposure as well as the effects at different ages. With a different procedure, King (24) found a

25-day treatment given to mice immediately after they were weaned had an effect on adult behavior. By reducing the duration of the treatment to 10 days and then to 5 days in subsequent groups, he was able to discover the minimum amount (duration) of treatment necessary to produce the effect on the adult mice. This amount of treatment was then given to another group of mice at adulthood. Fredericson (10) used a similar technique, by reducing the treatment from 7 days to 1 day; however, he did not give the treatment to mice at different ages.

If the age-location and duration of a critical period can be established, physiological and anatomical changes during this period can be correlated with the effects of the experiences. Physiological correlations with behavior may not enable the isolation of the effective variable because physiological and anatomical stages in maturation "cannot usually be controlled independently of each other" (2, p. 257). However, correlations comparing several strains or species may eventually reduce the importance now given to age per se by permitting, for example, experimental manipulation at the period of myelinization, or at a given period of sensory sensitivity, or after a certain proportion of cholinesterase in the brain has been attained.

Type or Quality of Experience

The types of experiences given to the developing subjects cover such a wide array that any enumeration without some classification is meaningless. On the other hand, no single classification adequately eliminates overlapping. Most experiments on this subject were stimulated by the theories of either Freud or Hebb (2). "The impact of Freudian theory, which led to various studies, such as those which limited food supply and feeding responses in young animals" (2, p. 239) are usually attempts to arrest psychosexual development of the subjects (11) or to measure later development of food directed motivation (18, 19, 29, 33, 34, 42). Experiments involving stress, whether shock (14, 28, 38, 43), temperature extremes, rotation, or intense auditory stimulation (14, 15) are usually designed to provide a traumatic experience to the developing organism (12). A second group of treatments which reduce stress through handling (3, 26, 28, 34, 38) or gentling (50, 51) may be placed in the same category. Experiments derived essentially from Hebbian concepts usually modify the environment of the subject. This modification may be either to increase the environmental complexity (4, 6, 9, 31) or to restrict the environment of the subject (4, 7, 20, 44, 45) beyond that of the usual conditions under which the animal is raised. The third group of treatments may fit either of the two theories, but probably deserves a separate category because the social environment is manipulated. This manipulation may be in the form of isolation (25, 48) or exposure of the young subject to an aggressive (22) or sexual (21) situation.

Within each category the variety of treatments that has been used is extensive (Fig. 2). Electric shock, for example, may include different intensities, durations, and frequencies in each experiment. A restricted environment may be stovepipes (20), squeeze boxes (4), or small cages (7, 44). Visual experience has been manipulated by blinding (20), raising animals in darkness (36), covering eyes with opaque or prismatic lenses (17), or enclosing the subject in a transparent cage (9). Social treatments include attacks by an adult (22), fighting over food (10), exposure to the opposite sex (21), or living together in a group (25).

This variety of early treatments has been necessary in order to investigate the scope of treatments which have an effect upon adult behavior and to test the hypotheses of the different theories. Further contributions to the effect of early experiences on adult behavior will probably depend less on devising new types of treatments than upon examining the more "important theoretical issue . . . of the relationship between the quality of the early experience and the nature of the task to be solved" (9, p. 220).

Types of Performance Task

After the animal has been given any of the preceding experiences, it is subjected to some test in order to learn the effect of the experience. Although many different tests are used, they are not as heterogeneous as the treatments (Fig. 2). For the most part, the tests fall into four categories: emotion, learning, consummatory responses, and social. Emotional tests are most frequently activity and defecation scores in an open field (15, 51). Occasionally the field is electrified (38) or an intense auditory stimulus is applied (4, 14, 42) to increase emotional responses. Learning tests are usually either mazes (4, 9, 14, 20) or avoidance conditioning (26, 28, 43). The Lashley jumping tests (4, 14), a discrimination box (3), and operant conditioning (29) have also been used. Consummatory responses are chiefly those of hoarding (18, 19, 33, 42), food consumption (34, 42), and water consumption (27). The social tests are principally those developed for sex (21, 49) or aggression (10, 22, 25).

The number of tests given to any single group of subjects varies from 1 to 10 (42). Although most investigators administered only 1 test, the mean for 16 of the experiments reviewed here is 2.4 tests. This does not include training or extinction measures as separate tests, although both have been reported as separate indices in the results. In experiments including more than one test, the tests usually follow each other instead of being given in a random order or such a systematic order as provided by a latin square. This multiple testing procedure raises the question of what effect prior tests have upon subsequent ones. If one test affects the performance of the subject in another test, the direct effect of the early experience becomes lost in the complexity of interactions. One treatment and one kind of test, with a number of measures, is the

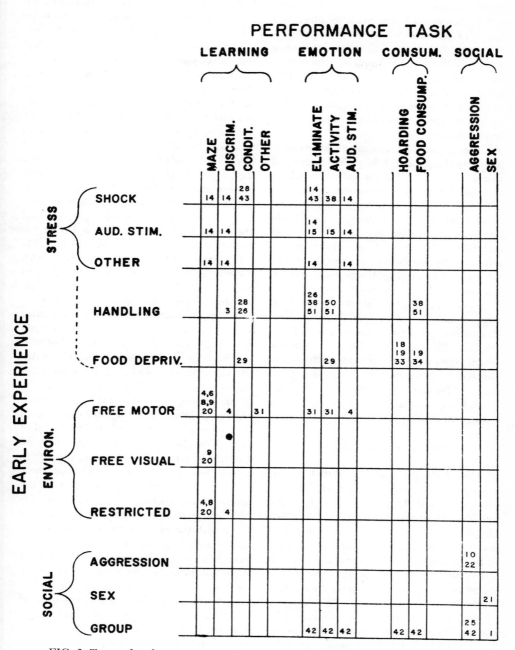

FIG. 2. Types of early experience and performance task of subjects in experiments.

most satisfactory method unless the investigator is specifically searching for interactions. Some animals, such as dogs and monkeys, are so expensive to rear that it is too costly to offer the grown subject only one test. With these animals, which may be particularly affected by preceding tests, every procedure should include a schematic or random order of testing and/or an examination of interactions among the tests and treatment.

The results of experiments incorporating more than one test may yield important information regarding the extent to which a certain type of early experience may generalize into different patterns of behavior. Does a complex environment early in life affect adult emotionality as well as adult learning? Although it is preferable to answer this question with two separate groups which have been given the same treatment, one group of mice showed that early experience apparently affected both their adult aggressive and sexual behavior, but these adult behavior patterns were not correlated (23). Such results may indicate which types of adult behavior patterns are affected by a single type of early experience. Additional factors related to the number of tests a subject receives are considered in the next section.

Persistence of Effects

One concept explicitly stated in the hypothesis concerning the effects of early experience is that the effects last throughout life (2) or are even irreversible (30). Despite the significance of these hypotheses, there have been few experimental tests of the persistence of the effects. Three different methods have been used by the investigators who have attempted to measure persistence.

The first method can be illustrated by Hall's (15) experiment. After subjecting 4- to 7-day-old mice to an intense sound, he counted the frequency of their elimination at 30 to 40 days in an open-field washtub and then he repeated the same test when the mice were 100 to 110 days old. The first and second tests were *interrupted* by a period of 60 days, during which the mice were kept in a neutral environment. This procedure runs the risk of having the first test affect the performance of the animal during the second test. The second procedure has been to make a *continuous* series of observations after the initiation of a single test (27). For example, Levine (27) measured water consumption in a control and experimental group 4 consecutive days after 18 hours of water deprivation each day. The initial differences in the two groups disappeared by the fourth day. Other investigators have left the animals in a test situation for extended periods and then they have made additional observations from time to time (7, 39). Fisher (7), for example, put young dogs back with their litter mates after they were raised in isolation. He found that the dogs raised in isolation were first highly responsive to their group-raised litter mates, but later tended to withdraw and remain isolated from the litter mates over a period of several months. It is possible that the withdrawal of the isolated dogs from the litter mates was enhanced in this situation by compounding the effects of the early experience of isolation with the later experiences derived while living together with the other dogs. The third procedure, which may be considered a test of persistence, consists in giving two groups of animals the same treatment at different ages (6, 20). If the group which received an early treatment is different from the group receiving a later treatment, the effect of the early treatment can be said to persist through the later period, because the later period of treatment does not produce the same effect. Since only one test is given to each group of animals in this procedure, a real measure of persistence is lacking. A single test only defines the type of behavior elicited. A second test given to the same group of animals at a later age will reveal whether the behavior defined in the first test persists until the second test. A fourth possible procedure, which has not been used, would be to give the same treatment to several groups of animals at the same age and test them at different adult ages. Such an experiment should be designed to isolate and evaluate all interactive effects.

Certainly further studies on persistence of the effects of an early experience are needed. Most procedures run the risk of confounding the variables of early and late experiences, because the later experiences may enhance or inhibit the effect of the early experience. However, mammalian subjects cannot be kept in a vacuum, and it is likely that canalization may occur (35). Procedures designed to interpret this type of interaction between the later experiences and the early experiences of the subject may ultimately contribute more to the understanding of how adult behavior patterns are formed than procedures which prevent any interaction from occurring by keeping subjects in a "neutral" environment for different periods of time before testing them. Until such procedures are developed, the most reliable experiments will include a neutral period.

Genetics and Early Experience

The seventh and last variable considered here is the effect which different genetic backgrounds have upon subjects undergoing the same early experience. Genetic effects may be illustrated either by comparison of different species of animals or by the study of breeds or strains within one species. Species comparisons make possible an evaluation of the generalizations made from one species to another. Breed and strain comparisons indicate the effectiveness of a particular experience operating upon different genotypes.

The effect of early experience on later behavior has been studied in only a few common laboratory mammals. No single study has made direct species comparisons using similar techniques for more than one species. As indicated earlier, most work has been done on the laboratory rat. A few

studies have been done on inbred mice (10, 15, 22, 25, 43). Valenstein and co-workers (13, 46, 47, 48, 49) have undertaken an investigation of guinea pigs, including the effects of early experience upon adult sexual behavior. Published investigations on carnivores are limited to dogs (5, 7, 44, 45), although some work has been done on cats at the American Museum of Natural History. Experimental studies on primates include Riesen's (36) investigation of rearing chimpanzees in the dark and work currently being undertaken at the University of Wisconsin on rhesus monkeys.

Species comparisons provide a basis for generalizations from one species to another, but they fail to indicate the relation of early experience to different genotypes because of the wide variation in sensory-motor capacities and rates of maturation among different species. The effect of early experience on animals of different genetic backgrounds is best studied in closely related animals, such as breeds or strains. In such studies, animals of different genotypes are given the same treatment and the same tests which offer comparative data for assessing the importance of genetic factors. Similar early experiences have been shown to have different effects on the adult behavior of two inbred strains of guinea pigs (47, 48), two inbred strains of mice (24), and several breeds of dogs (7). The demonstration of strain or breed differences is only the first step in a genetic analysis, but it is an important first step because it answers the question: do organisms of different genetic backgrounds respond alike to the same early experience?

Summary and Conclusions

This review has attempted to examine some of the variables involved in the experiments dealing with the effects of early experience on later behavior. In order to accomplish this analysis, the methods used in the experiments on this subject were examined in relation to seven variables. The experiments as a whole reveal a lack of attention to variables other than the one being manipulated. Other variables were controlled as they suited a particular experimental design rather than as a possible important contribution to the effects of early experience. This is particularly obvious upon inspection of Fig. 1, where the age variables are illustrated. The age of the animal at the time of treatment, for example, has included practically any age prior to the time the later test was given. Consequently, we are unable to make any definitive statement concerning which ages are most affected by a given experience. One of the most effective procedures for studying this age variable is that employed by Eingold (6), who gave the same experience to several groups of rats at different ages during their development.

The age at the time of testing also requires further exploration, both in respect to the absolute age at which the animals are tested and in relation to the age of the early experience. No experiment has attempted to test animals at different ages, with the possible exception of experiments repeating a test on the same group of animals. Until this variable is adequately examined experimentally, it is possible to conclude only that the early experience affects an animal at *some* later age.

In the examination of the duration or quantity of experience given to the animal, we again encounter too much diversity to permit us to conclude how long the animal must endure its early treatment. The model for future experiments in testing this variable is again best demonstrated by Eingold, who varied the duration of treatment from 10 to 20 days in three groups of rats at different ages (Fig. 1). This method has the advantage of keeping the age variable separate from duration. More refinement in this procedure could be made by including other groups of different durations at each age and by controlling the length of the neutral period. The intensity of the experience also deserves attention and may be easily controlled with some types of stimuli, such as shock. Since the quantity of the early experience is important from the clinical point of view, it deserves much more attention than it has received in most experiments.

The type or quality of experience has been explored more thoroughly than the other variables. Most experiments have included at least two types of treatment (control and experimental) in the experimental design while the other variables are controlled. Because most investigators have used type of experience as their independent variable and because a number of them have controlled the age of treatment in nearly the same fashion, some generalizations are warranted. At the present time there is no adequate theoretical review of this material beyond the few introductory remarks preceding the report of each experiment.

The types of performance tasks, or the dependent variable, used to test the later behavior, are sufficiently varied to enable an assessment of the best measures of the effect of the treatment, except that the same animals are usually given a number of different tests at different ages. This procedure confounds the type of performance task with the age at time of testing and exposes the subjects to the effect of one test upon the other tests. The obvious solution here is to use different groups of animals for each test and to hold the age at testing constant. Although this procedure may require many more subjects, the refinement of the performance task is important to any conclusions regarding how one type of early experience may generalize to different types of behavior.

Persistence of the effects is probably the most difficult variable to examine because of the possibility that prior tests may affect later tests. This review described three procedures which have been used and suggested a fourth untried procedure. The particular virture of the fourth procedure is that it would permit evaluation of the interactive effects resulting from successive testing. Perhaps in this indirect manner we can provide sufficient evidence to permit some conclusions regarding the persistence of behavior.

The last variable—that of genetics—has been held constant, at least to the species level, in all experiments. However, only the experiment of Valenstein et al. (48) has attempted to manipulate this variable in a single experiment. Further experiments using slightly different genetic strains (preferably inbred strains) will probably reveal more about the effect of this variable than species comparisons. Ultimately it will be desirable to make species comparisons, particularly if equivalent treatments and tests can be developed. At the present time any extrapolations beyond the species studied will be hazardous.

Until the effects of the seven variables discussed in this review are analyzed further, it is possible to accept only the general hypothesis that some early experiences affect later behavior. Once each variable is isolated and we can accurately predict its effect upon later behavior, we will be in a position to study interactions and ultimately arrive at a comprehensive theory to account for many patterns of adult behavior on the basis of the experiences of the developing subject.

REFERENCES

1. Beach, F. A.: Comparison of copulatory behavior of male rats raised in isolation, cohabitation, and segregation. *J. genet. Psychol.*, 1942, **60**, 121–136.
2. Beach, F. A., and J. Jaynes: Effects of early experience upon the behavior of animals. *Psychol. Bull.*, 1954, **51**, 239–263.
3. Bernstein, L.: A note on Christie's: "experimental naïveté and experiential naïveté." *Psychol. Bull.*, 1952, **49**, 38–40.
4. Bingham, W. E., and W. J. Griffiths: The effect of different environments during infancy on adult behavior in the rat. *J. comp. physiol. Psychol.*, 1952, **45**, 307–312.
5. Clarke, R. S., W. Heron, M. L. Fetherstonhaugh, D. G. Forgays, and D. O. Hebb: Individual differences in dogs: preliminary report on the effects of early experience. *Canad. J. Psychol.*, 1951, **5**, 150–156.
6. Eingold, B.: Problem-solving by mature rats as conditioned by the length, and age at imposition, of earlier free-environment experience. Unpublished doctor's dissertation, Univer. of Florida, 1956.
7. Fisher, A. E.: The effects of differential early treatment on the social and exploratory behavior of puppies. Unpublished doctor's dissertation, Pennsylvania State Univer., 1955.
8. Forgays, D. G., and J. W. Forgays: The nature of the effect of free-environmental experience in the rat. *J. comp. physiol. Psychol.*, 1952, **45**, 322–328.
9. Forgus, R. H.: Early visual and motor experience as determiners of complex maze-learning ability under rich and reduced stimulation. *J. comp. physiol. Psychol.*, 1955, **48**, 215–220.
10. Fredericson, E.: Competition: The effects of infantile experience upon adult behavior. *J. abnorm. soc. Psychol.*, 1951, **46**, 406–409.
11. Freud, S.: Three essays on the theory of sexuality. In *The basic writings of . . .* New York: Modern Library, 1938.
12. Freud, S.: The aetiology of hysteria. In *Collected papers*. London: Hogarth Press, 1950. Vol. 1.
13. Goy, R. W., and W. C. Young: The importance of genetic and experimental factors for organization of sexual behavior patterns in the female guinea pig. *Anat. Rec.*, 1956, **124**, 296. (Abstract.)
14. Griffiths, W. J., and W. F. Stringer: The effects of intense stimulation experienced during infancy on adult behavior in the rat. *J. comp. physiol. Psychol.*, 1952, **45**, 301–306.
15. Hall, C. S., and P. H. Whiteman: The effects of infantile stimulation upon later emotional stability in the mouse. *J. comp. physiol. Psychol.*, 1951, **44**, 61–66.
16. Hebb, D. O.: *The organization of behavior.* New York: Wiley, 1949.
17. Hess, E. H.: Maturation and learning in the development of pecking accuracy in chicks. *Amer. Psychologist*, 1953, **8**, 367. (Abstract.)
18. Hunt, J. McV.: The effects of infant feeding-frustration upon adult hoarding in the albino rat. *J. abnorm. soc. Psychol.*, 1941, **36**, 338–360.

19. HUNT, J. McV., H. SCHLOSBERG, R. L. SOLOMON, and E. STELLAR: Studies of the effects of infantile experience on adult behavior in rats. I. Effects of infantile feeding frustration on adult hoarding. *J. comp. physiol. Psychol.*, 1947, **40**, 291–304.

20. HYMOVITCH, B.: The effects of experimental variations on problem solving in rats. *J. comp. physiol. Psychol.*, 1952, **45**, 313–320.

21. KAGAN, J., and F. A. BEACH: Effects of early experience on mating behavior in male rats. *J. comp. physiol. Psychol.*, 1953, **46**, 204–208.

22. KAHN, M. W.: The effect of severe defeat at various age levels on the aggressive behavior of mice. *J. genet. Psychol.*, 1951, **79**, 117–130.

23. KING, J. A.: Sexual behavior of C57BL/10 mice and its relation to early social experience. *J. genet. Psychol.*, 1956, **88**, 223–229.

24. KING, J. A.: Relationships between early social experience and adult aggressive behavior in inbred mice. *J. genet. Psychol.*, 1957, **90**, 151–166.

25. KING, J. A., and N. L. GURNEY: Effect of early social experience on adult aggressive behavior in C57BL/10 mice. *J. comp. physiol. Psychol.*, 1954, **47**, 326–330.

26. LEVINE, S.: A further study of infantile handling and adult avoidance learning. *J. Pers.*, 1956, **25**, 70–80.

27. LEVINE, S.: The effect of shock and handling in infancy on consummatory response in adulthood. *Amer. Psychologist,* 1956, **11**, 397. (Abstract.)

28. LEVINE, S., J. A. CHEVALIER, and S. J. KORCHIN: The effects of early shock and handling on later avoidance learning. *J. Pers.*, 1956, **24**, 475–493.

29. LITTMAN, R. A.: Infantile experience and adult behavior in the white rat. *J. genet. Psychol.*, 1956, **88**, 11–24.

30. LORENZ, K.: Der Kumpan in der Umwelt des Vogels. *J. Orn., Lpz.,* 1935, **83**, 137–213; 289–413.

31. LUCHINS, A. S., and R. H. FORGUS: The effect of differential post-weaning environment on the rigidity of an animal's behavior. *J. genet. Psychol.*, 1955, **86**, 51–58.

32. McCLELLAND, W. J.: Differential handling and weight gain in the albino rat. *Canad. J. Psychol.*, 1956, **10**, 19–22.

33. McKELVEY, R. K., and M. H. MARX: Effects of infantile food and water deprivation on adult hoarding in the rat. *J. comp. physiol. Psychol.*, 1951, **44**, 423–430.

34. MARX, M. H.: Infantile deprivation and adult behavior in the rat: retention of increased rate of eating. *J. comp. physiol. Psychol.*, 1952, **45**, 43–49.

35. MURPHY, G.: *Personality.* New York: Harper, 1947.

36. RIESEN, A. H.: The development of visual perception in man and chimpanzee. *Science,* 1949, **106**, 107–108.

37. ROSS, S.: Sucking frustration in neonate puppies. *J. abnorm. soc. Psychol.,* 1951, **46**, 142–149.

38. SCOTT, J. H.: Some effects at maturity of gentling, ignoring or shocking rats during infancy. *J. abnorm. soc. Psychol.,* 1955, **51**, 412–414.

39. SCOTT, J. P.: Social behavior, organization and leadership in a small flock of domestic sheep. *Comp. Psychol. Monogr.,* 1945, **18**, No. 4.

40. SCOTT, J. P., E. FREDERICSON, and J. L. FULLER: Experimental exploration of the critical period hypothesis. *Personality,* 1951, **1**, 162–183.

41. SCOTT, J. P., and M. V. MARSTON: Critical periods affecting the development of normal and mal-adjustive social behavior of puppies. *J. genet. Psychol.,* 1950, **77**, 25–60.

42. SEITZ, P.: The effects of infantile experience upon adult behavior in animal subjects: I. Effects of litter size during infancy upon adult behavior in the rat. *Amer. J. Psychiat.,* 1954, **110**, 916–927.

43. STANLEY, W. C., and J. A. MONKMAN: A test for specific and general behavioral effects of infantile stimulation with shock in the mouse. *J. abnorm. soc. Psychol.,* 1956, **53**, 19–22.

44. THOMPSON, W. R., and W. HERON: The effects of early restriction on activity in dogs. *J. comp. physiol. Psychol.,* 1954, **47**, 77–82.

45. THOMPSON, W. R., and W. HERON: The effects of restricting early experience on the problem-solving capacity of dogs. *Canad. J. Psychol.,* 1954, **8**, 17–31.

46. VALENSTEIN, E. S.: The role of learning and androgen in the organization and display of sexual behavior in the male guinea pig. *Amer. Psychologist,* 1954, **9**, 486. (Abstract.)

47. VALENSTEIN, E. S., W. RISS, and W. C.
YOUNG: Sex drive in genetically heterogeneous and highly inbred strains of male
guinea pigs. *J. comp. physiol. Psychol.*,
1954, 47, 162–165.
48. VALENSTEIN, E. S., W. RISS, and W. C.
YOUNG: Experiential and genetic factors
in the organization of sexual behavior in
male guinea pigs. *J. comp. physiol. Psychol.*, 1955, 48, 397–403.
49. VALENSTEIN, E. S., and W. C. YOUNG: An
experiential factor influencing the effec-

tiveness of testosterone propionate in eliciting sexual behavior in male guinea pigs.
Endocrinology, 1955, 56, 173–177.
50. WEININGER, O.: Physiological damage
under emotional stress as a function of
early experience. *Science*, 1954, 119, 285–
286.
51. WEININGER, O.: The effects of early experience on behavior and growth characteristics. *J. comp. physiol. Psychol.*, 1956, 49,
1–9.

T. C. SCHNEIRLA and JAY S. ROSENBLATT

23   Behavioral Organization and Genesis of
the Social Bond in Insects and Mammals

T. C. Schneirla has made outstanding contributions to the study of animal
behavior for over thirty years. His *Principles of Animal Behavior* (McGraw-Hill,
1935), written with N. R. F. Maier, is frequently consulted and cited by contemporary workers in the field. His pioneering studies on army ants are models of
careful observation, experimentation, and analysis. Findings from these studies
are reviewed in the first part of the following reading. Then, a series of experiments on socialization in the neonatal kitten is reviewed, followed by a comparison of these two very different animal groups.
The student should note carefully Schneirla and Rosenblatt's views on the
concept of critical periods.

This article originally appeared in *The American Journal of Orthopsychiatry*,
1961, 31, 223–253. Copyright, the American Orthopsychiatric Association, Inc.
Reproduced by permission of the authors and the publisher.

Our discussion centers on the topic of instinctive behavior, which may be defined
operationally as species-typical behavior
studied from the standpoint of development. Insects and mammals both commonly exhibit group and parental behavior distinctive of the species and typical of their
developmental patterns. Certain basic similarities are discernible in the different
group-behavior phenomena of insects and
mammals, and yet striking differences appear, in that the former may be characterized as *biosocial*, the latter as *psychosocial*
(Schneirla, 10). Two such patterns, that of
the army ants and that of domestic cats,

may be compared on the basis of evidence
from our departmental research program.

Properties of the Army-Ant Functional System

Evidence bearing on the incorporation
of the individual insect into its colony and
on the maintenance of a species-standard
pattern of relationships between individual
and group is organized most effectively in
terms of a doctrine of reciprocal-stimulative processes (Schneirla, 7, 9).

The tropical American army ants of
Eciton species, as investigated both in field

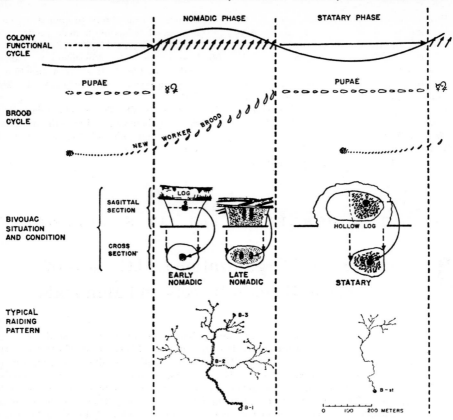

FIG. 1. Schema of the functional cycle of the army-ant species *Eciton hamatum*. From the top: 1) the two phases in the cycle indicated by a sine curve; arrows indicate large daily raids and nightly emigrations in the nomadic phase;—2) typical correspondence between phases in the colony cycle and developmental stages of successive broods;—3) types of bivouac in each of the two activity phases, indicating placement of brood in each;—4) type of raiding system prevalent in each of the principal activity phases (*B-1, 2, 3,* successive bivouac sites; *B-st:* statary bivouac site). (From *Proc. Amer. Philos. Soc.,* **101**: 1957 [SCHNEIRLA, 13].)

and laboratory (Schneirla, 7, 13), are characterized by frequent predatory raids and by a nomadic life involving frequent emigrations. Their daily raids involve immense numbers and are well organized, constituting in fact the most intricate unitary social operation carried out regularly away from the home site by any animal except man. Their periodic emigrations, also highly organized in typical ways, are found closely related to the predatory expeditions from which they arise. Investigation discloses regular fluctuations in the

occurrence and intensity of these activities which, studied analytically, throw significant light on the nature of the group functional pattern and of group unity.

The functional pattern of one army-ant species, *Eciton hamatum*, schematized in Figure 1, is typified by nomadic phases and statary phases of predictable duration which alternate in regular cycles throughout the year. Functional conditions in the two phases are very different, as the figure indicates. Throughout each nomadic phase, the daily raids are large, and emigration occurs nightly; throughout each statary phase daily raids are small or absent and no emigrations occur.

BROOD-STIMULATION PROCESSES
BASIC TO COLONY UNITY

The figure also represents the striking and prevalent fact that the phase of the functional cycle existing at any time in a colony corresponds directly to the developmental stage of the brood. Regularly, as indicated, in the statary phase a brood in the pupal condition is present and a new brood in the egg stage is produced, whereas in the nomadic phase a brood developing through the larval stage is present. This correspondence of conditions, as much evidence shows, is based upon the fact that colony function in these ants is grounded in an intimate adult responsiveness to the brood. Through its metabolic condition and activities, the brood furnishes to the workers a variety of attractive and excitatory tactual and chemical stimulation. The all-worker broods appear in regular succession at intervals of about 36 days in Eciton, are very large (about 80,000 in *hamatum* and 200,-000 in *burchelli*) and exert a major stimulative effect on the colony population. In the nomadic phase, when active, feeding larvae are present, great daily raids and nightly emigrations occur; but when these larvae reach maturity and spin their cocoons the general level of excitation falls to a low ebb and a statary phase is entered. That statary phase ends when this pupal brood matures and, emerging as excitable callow workers, stimulates the worker population once again to a high level at which a new nomadic phase is entered by the colony.

This evidence supports a brood-excitation theory (7) by which the brood is held the decisive agency in the Eciton cycle, entering into diverse relationships of reciprocal stimulation with the worker population which at a high level maintain nomadism, at a low level maintain the statary condition. This view of a reciprocal relationship involving diverse types of stimuli goes considerably beyond Wheeler's concept (17) of "trophallaxis" (or "food exchange") to contend that stimuli from many organic sources, summating through a regular behavioral interplay among the members of a colony, are basic to the unity and the functional condition of that colony. In other words, the communicative relationships—i.e., behavior and the products of behavior influencing function in other individuals—determine not only the functional pattern of the colony and its excitatory level, but also the very existence of the colony.

This fact is shown clearly by a test in which most of the young brood (eggs; microlarvae) is removed from a colony near the end of a statary phase. Emergence of the pupal brood from cocoons excites the colony greatly and initiates a nomadic phase in the typical way; but within a few days, when the stimulative effect from the callows has waned, daily raids lessen and emigration begins to fail through the absence of the major stimulative factor normally maintaining nomadic function. Comparibly, when a colony loses its queen through death or removal, it maintains a fairly normal cyclic function only so long as the broods she has produced are still in development; thereafter the colony enters a statary condition in which it will eventually perish unless fusion occurs with another colony of that species.

FACTORS IN THE SPECIES RAIDING PATTERN

Analytical investigations show that the characteristic organization of the colony behavior pattern in these ants is not determined by any one type of individual but, as evidence schematized in Figure 2 suggests, is a composite result of factors contributed by all types of individuals—queen, brood, workers and males—interacting in the colony situation. Let us consider the species raiding pattern. In *Eciton hamatum*, as Figure 1 indicates, this pattern is one of branching columns; in the closely related species *Eciton burchelli*, on the other hand, the raid is headed by a large unitary

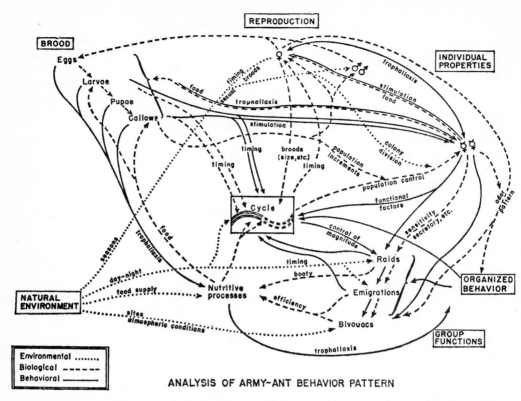

ANALYSIS OF ARMY-ANT BEHAVIOR PATTERN

FIG. 2. Schema of factors underlying the behavior pattern of terrestrial army-ant species. Major sources of factors are indicated marginally (e.g., individual properties); principal relationships demonstrated (e.g., trophallaxis = reciprocal stimulation) are indicated by appropriate arrows; arrows also indicate relevance to functional cycle, represented in center. (From *Proc. Amer. Philos. Soc.*, **101**: 1957 [SCHNEIRLA, 13].)

swarm, with branching columns a secondary feature. Field and laboratory results point to certain characteristics of the adult workers as basic to these species differences. Identifiable among these are properties of glandular equipment (accounting for a heavier, more diffuse trail-chemical in *burchelli* than in *hamatum*), of olfactory threshold (accounting for a less precise discrimination and, with secretory factors, for a much more facile massing of individuals in *burchelli* than in *hamatum*) and of individual excitability (which can rise to a significantly higher level in *burchelli* than in *hamatum*).

Eciton workers make and follow their raiding trails in highly stereotyped ways, essentially dependent upon tactual and olfactory sensitivity, as their minute eyes and degenerate visual equipment normally play little part in their orientation. For this, however, hypotheses of "blind instinct" or of innate patterns offer little and are misleading, for the functioning of individuals in colony adjustments has many variable aspects dependent upon the developmental situation. Species-specific organic factors such as olfactory thresholds and glandular properties are clearly basic in this complex. We must, however, also consider the fact that the worker, on emerging from her cocoon, does not attain adult function directly, but instead requires a few days in which she first circulates within the temporary nest of the colony, then gradually extends the scope and efficiency of operations outside the nest on the raiding trails. Callow workers artificially removed from their cocoons and held apart from the colony for several days cannot follow the trails efficiently as young workers of corresponding ages normally do, but instead blunder about ineptly. Although organic maturation may account partially for the improvement shown in trail-following within the first few days, we must also postulate a factor of simple habituation learning, through which disturbance reactions are inhibited and general responses of approach and turning-to become conditioned by experience with a pervasive stimulus aspect. Despite evidence that this indicated gain from experience represents an exceedingly low-level type of learning, it is doubtful that the army-ant adaptive pattern could be maintained without it.

The problem of distinctive colony reactions or "nest-mate recognition" in ants is not simple but has numerous variable aspects. One of these is suggested by the fact that although the workers of *Eciton burchelli* and *hamatum* normally attack each other when brought together, a certain modification may be effected by the procedure of juxtaposing representative groups of workers of these two species for a few days, separating them only by a cheesecloth partition through which air circulates. Each thereby evidently acquires some of the other species' odor, as is shown by what happens when they are then introduced through tubes into a common chamber. Instead of attacking at once, as do new control groups, these test groups first mingle in a single circular column in which dark *burchelli* workers and lighter *hamatum* workers follow one another in a regular manner indicating strong individual responses to a common tactuo-chemical field of stimulation. After several minutes, however, when variations in circling have introduced sufficient interruptions in the

running, reactions to odor differences appear to summate, and general combat sets in.

THE BIVOUAC AND COLONY UNITY

Another aspect of the army-ant pattern, the temporary nest or bivouac, as indicated in Figure 1 also presents a striking difference in the two phases of the functional cycle. This unique structure, constructed of the clustered bodies of the workers, hanging from a natural ceiling such as the underside of a log, affords the colony both a temporary shelter and a center of operations for its predatory raids, as well as serving as an efficient incubator for the great broods always present in operative colonies. Figure 1 represents the striking fact that in the nomadic phase of the cycle these nesting clusters are formed largely in the open, whereas in the statary phase they are formed in enclosed places as in the hollows of logs or trees. Observational data and the results of tests suggest that the principal factor underlying these striking differences is that the Eciton worker population, when in a high state of tension as at the end of the nomadic phase, is strongly reactive to air currents and thus can form its clusters selectively in places where air currents are much reduced. Evidence for this hypothesis has been obtained with worker groups representing colonies at different stages in the cycle, tested in the laboratory in their resistance in clusters to controlled air-current stimulation. Those from colonies in the late nomadic stage, which in the forest would then be entering enclosed bivouac sites, are the first to break and to recluster where the air is quiet. The level of individual excitation, which normally varies significantly in any colony through the functional cycle, represents an important factor in the army-ant pattern.

One important specific factor contributing to the army-ant clustering reaction is a structural characteristic, the strong recurved double hooks on the last tarsal segment of each leg. Clustering, a vital component in the army-ant adaptive system, is not to be considered simple. Among other factors indicated as significant by tests we find a susceptibility to become quiescent when the general stimulative level is low, under conditions of gentle contact, under the prevalence of colony odor, and when stretching (as through the hooking-on of other workers) induces a reaction of tonic immobility. The workers thus serve as the basic fabric of their own colony nest, may form bridges or smooth the road in raiding, or may cluster about their queen when she is halted in the nocturnal emigration.

Colony odor, a chief factor contributing to army-ant clustering, involves another important set of relationships. When various local clusters are forming in the nocturnal emigration, as is typical, the one with the best chance of becoming the colony bivouac is that entered by the queen. Army-ant workers cluster in the presence of queen-odor alone, as is shown by the formation of persistent clusters in laboratory arenas in places where the colony queen has rested only for a few minutes. Under natural conditions, a colony deprived of its queen exhibits a clearly decreasing capacity for establishing a concentrated bivouac cluster, but instead on successive nights forms increasingly diffuse gatherings which finally became carpetlike masses spread out on the ground.

SPECIES-TYPICAL DEVELOPMENT
A MOSAIC PROCESS

The army-ant functional pattern is thereby seen as a mosaic, to which numerous factors from numerous sources contribute. As indicated, one factor contributed by the queen is her distinctive odor, strongly unifying to the colony. The queen-odor, in fact, represents the most critical component of the general colony odor. This hypothesis is well supported by evidence that although workers of colonies with queens, belonging to the same species, normally never mix when their raids meet in the forest, a marked exception occurs when one of two colliding colonies lacks a queen. If this colony has been without its queen

for as little as 12 to 20 hours, the workers intermingle readily with those of a colony of the same species when its columns are encountered, instead of becoming disturbed and remaining apart as normally occurs. The usual outcome is that the entire population of the queenless colony becomes absorbed in that of the queenright colony. To account for such results, we may postulate three factors: 1) a normally effective habituation of workers to the colony queen-odor that becomes sufficiently weakened in the queenless colony to permit most of the workers to meet the different queen-odor of another colony without disturbance, although 2) through the continuous presence of the colony queen this specific odor-habituation is normally maintained in all workers of a colony, and that 3) workers in a queenless colony lose (by virtue of volatilization) their individual coats of queen-odor within a few hours, sufficiently to permit their being received by the workers of a queen-right colony and adopted in this colony without much disturbance. It is also of interest to note that after the queenless population has entered a queenright colony with its brood, this brood is cannibalized in the course of time, whereas the brood of the queenright colony survives. Normally, therefore, the odor of the colony queen diffusing through the bivouac to the brood seems to be an important factor in the treatment of that brood by the workers, who lick, carry it about and tend it, rather than consuming it along with the prey.

The army-ant functional pattern, as Figure 2 indicates, is the product of many factors coexisting in the functional situation, introduced into that situation by conditions in the natural environment, the worker population, the broods and the queen. The interaction of these various factors is emphasized strikingly by evidence that each further operation of brood-production by the queen is initiated and completed through the effect of extrinsic conditions in the colony situation governing the amount of food and of worker-induced stimulation received by the queen. Thus, near the end of each nomadic phase, the nearly mature larval brood, by virtue of conditions in its current metamorphosis, excites the workers increasingly although at the same time it consumes less and less food. The result is an aroused colony with surplus food in which the workers now greatly increase their stimulative attentions to the queen and feed her abundantly. The queen's abdomen then increases rapidly in size as she accelerates in maturing a great brood of eggs which is laid some days later, midway in the statary phase. This is only one link, although a very critical one, in the complex army-ant functional cycle.

The recurrence of each change in the cycle thus is the product of reciprocal relationships between brood, worker and queen functions, and not of a special timing mechanism or "biological clock" endogenous to the queen (13). The cyclic pattern of army ants therefore is based upon numerous structural, physiological, behavioral and environmental factors capable of interacting under the conditions normal to the forest environment. The organization of this pattern is not determined through the heredity of any one type of individual —queen, workers or brood—nor is it additive from factors of organic maturation alone. "The organic factors basic to the species pattern have evolved in close relationship to the general environment, which therefore supplies key factors essential for their contemporary integration into a functional system" (Schneirla, 12, p. 401).

Analysis of Socialization in a Mammal

THEORETICAL CONSIDERATIONS

From birth, in neonate mammals, behavior is typified by reciprocal stimulative relationships between parent and young. The neonate attracts the female stimulatively; the female presents to the newborn a variety of tactual, thermal and other stimuli, typically of low intensity and

therefore primarily approach-provoking (Schneirla, 14). On this basis the process of socialization begins. Behavioral development, because it centers on and depends upon reciprocal stimulative processes between female and young, is essentially social from the start.

Mammalian behavioral development is best conceived as a unitary system of processes changing progressively under the influence of an intimate interrelationship of factors of maturation and of experience— with *maturation* defined as the developmental contributions of tissue growth and differentiation and their secondary processes, *experience* as the effects of stimulation and its organic traces on behavior (12). There is no implication here that these two factoral complexes are sharply distinguishable in their contributions to behavioral development; our position, rather, is that such a distinction, although a theoretical convenience, constitutes a gratuitous assumption not well supported by evidence. This view of the matter is supported by the results of investigations discussed here on the behavioral development of one mammal, the domestic cat, considered in particular from the standpoint of its social behavior.[*]

Social behavior is a broad term, and one of highly variable meaning in dependence upon the age and previous developmental experience of the animal. There have been very different approaches to studying the phenomena of socialization in animals, and the results frequently have been canalized by the experimenter's point of view as dictating hypotheses and method. One recent didactic appraisal of mammalian socialization is that of Scott (15), who borrowed the term "critical period" from embryology to express his idea that

[*] The research on mammalian behavioral development discussed in the following section of this paper was supported by grants from the National Science Foundation and from the Rockefeller Foundation. The results are to be reported in papers now in manuscript or in preparation, cited with the references.

there is a period in the ontogeny of puppies, coming at about 18 days, which is crucial for social development by virtue of maturative processes then occurring. Apparent support for this view was derived from the finding of Fuller et al. (3) that a conditioned leg withdrawal to a buzzer paired with leg-shock cannot be established in puppies until about the 18th neonatal day. Scott took these results to mean that the indicated time marks for the puppy ". . . the beginning of the period of socialization, in which its primary social relationships are formed." The main assumption here seems to be that certain processes of maturation taken alone are crucial for the described behavioral advances and hence for a turning point in social behavior, or actually for the basis of social behavior. This conclusion we are unable to accept.

It is clear that comprehensive analytical investigations of behavioral development are needed for the solution of major problems such as that of turning points, qualitative progress from one stage to the next, and the like. An investigation of this type, to be reported in the remainder of this paper, was derived by us from the theoretical standpoint that 1) processes of mammalian socialization begin at parturition or even before, and 2) that mammalian social ontogeny involves a complex progressive organization depending upon intervening variables of maturation and of experience in the individual, in the perceptual development of the female, and in reciprocal stimulative relationships between female and young (10, 11).

METHOD

The general method in the studies to be discussed here involved both qualitative and quantitative procedures for observing and recording the course of events in the developmental phenomena investigated in replication, and special procedures designed for an intensive analysis of these phenomena under conditions modified in ways found significant in pilot work. To

FIG. 3. Two Aronson keyboards (below), the microswitches of which control movements of corresponding pens on one of the Esterline-Angus process recorders (above) for quantitative records of behavioral items.

obtain quantitative records of these occurrences at all stages, behavorial items identified as significant in pilot studies were represented on the respective keys of the Aronson keyboard (Clark et al., 1), represented in Figure 3, which controlled the corresponding pens of an Esterline-Angus process recorder. Tracings representing the frequency, duration and concurrences of these items were thus obtained for analysis.

SOCIAL PROCESSES BEGINNING AT PARTURITION

Studies in our laboratory by Tobach et al. (16) tested hypotheses derived from a mosaic-developmental theory of instinctive behavior in their bearing on parturition in the cat. The results, summarized below, indicated in detail that the behavioral bond between female and offspring, and therefore socialization of the young, begins with the initial stages of delivery.

We are led to characterize the event, for cats, as an interplay or even competition between the stimulative effects of endogenous events (e.g., uterine contractions; emergence of fetus) and the external results of such events (e.g., fluids, neonate).

These stimulative by-products of organic processes tend to intrude themselves upon the female's attention in a somewhat variable order, timing and duration. Each one, as it arises, demands a specific perceptual and behavioral adjustment on her part. The parturitive phenomenon here is not a regular, patterned flow of events, but a series of rather sporadic organic and behavioral episodes, together with variable activities not specifically parturitive in themselves. Thus the female exhibits, in a not very predictable order, the predictable items of self-licking, licking newborn or floor, eating after-birth, general movement and sitting or lying. Intervals of intense activity indicating a high level of excitement, *a condition facilitating delivery operations,* are interspersed with intervals of exhaustion and rest, *facilitating initiation* of nursing and other stimulative relations of mother and newborn.

In these mammals, parturitive behavior is indicated as a loose assemblage of functions centering on the stimulative consequences of organic events. A sequence of hormonally-induced endogenous changes sets a loose temporal order for behavioral adjustment, dependent in sequence and timing upon the female's variable attention to competing organic and environmental stimuli. Persistently in evidence is an orientation to the posterior body and particularly to the vaginal area, a perceptual set which enormously aids normal parturitive operations. This factor, presumably based upon self-stimulative experience in youth, is very possibly indispensable for an adaptive outcome and survival of the young (Schneirla, 12, p. 421).

In other words, we conclude that the events of parturition, in which the neonate kitten participates rather passively and incidentally at first, provide a broad foundation for a social bond between female and young which persists and develops thereafter. The female-neonate bond, grounded particularly in processes such as licking, involves the elaboration of numerous stimulus-response processes which in time become increasingly bilateral and reciprocal. We believe that the extent and adequacy to which the conditions of pregnancy and parturition (including the female's pre-parturitive organic and behavioral preparation) admit a functional basis for reciprocal relationships, with the properties of the developmental situation prevalent during the litter period, govern the general trend of maternal-young relations and of socialization. This conclusion is supported by the results of further research with cats, recently completed in our laboratory, involving both detailed analytical investigations of the processes of group behavior and special research on aspects of individual development.

ONTOGENESIS OF ORIENTATION

Studies on the development of individual orientation, by Rosenblatt, Turkewitz and Schneirla (4, 5), show clearly that the origin point of social behavior is the home site, the home corner in our experimental cage, usually established and saturated chemically by the female in parturition or earlier in pregnancy. We find that the neonate's first adjustment to this locus occurs promptly after parturition and leads into a progressive process of orientation farther afield. In the first stage, from birth to about ten days, this process develops on a tactuo-chemical, nonvisual basis. From early hours, presence of the female quiets the neonates, as does also the presence of odor-cues on the saturated substratum of this site. If the regular floor unit is replaced by a fresh one, the tested kitten is strongly disturbed, as quantitative records of its movements and vocalization show clearly; also, in periodic orientation tests, kittens do not then re-enter the home corner readily, as they do under normal conditions.

By such testing procedures we have traced out an advancing process of orientation based on tactual and olfactory cues. Through these developments, which doubtless involve learning as a necessary factor, the kitten at 8-10 days of age, for example, can make test returns to the home

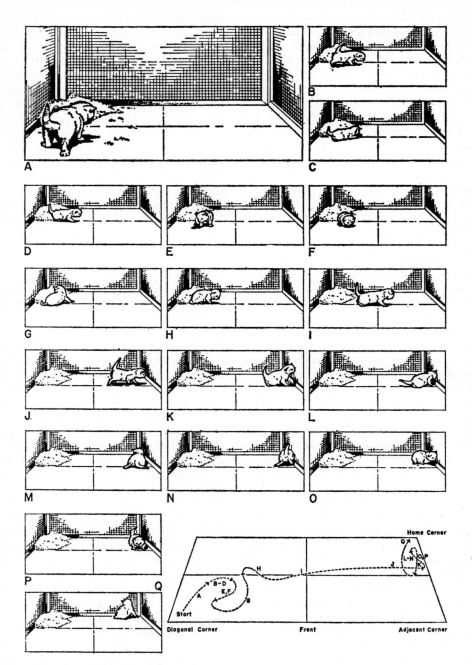

FIG. 4. A 20-day-old kitten, set down in the diagonal corner in an orientation test, takes a course through the open field in reaching the home corner. Drawings show successive positions at 5-second intervals; diagram gives a tracing of the path.

corner from the corner diagonally opposite, moving with reference to the wall although only occasionally touching the wall, and passing through the intervening adjacent corner. By 12-15 days, some days after the kitten's eyes have opened, a transitional process is evident whereby the kitten now begins to make its way diagonally across the cage in the open and by the 20th day (Fig. 4), a direct diagonal path can be taken. These progressive adjustments in spatial orientation advance concurrently with what we find are closely related changes in the kitten's adjustment to the female.

DEVELOPMENT OF SPECIALIZATION
IN FEEDING

In their feeding adjustments to the female, as our findings (Rosenblatt, Wodinsky, et al., 6) show, the neonates progress from the first trials. At first the newborn kittens reach the female only through a slow, variable process, always with much circuitous nuzzling and fumbling in attaining the female's mammary surface and attaching to a nipple. The quantitative results show, however, that the adjustments of individual kittens to the mammary surface begin to take on an increasingly characteristic specificity, even within the first two hours after birth. The typical result is that in the first one or two neonatal days most of the kittens in the litter are already able to take individually specific nipple positions with appreciable consistency. That is, with further approaches to the female and further attachments, certain neonates in a litter acquire an early specificity to a particular nipple or mammary region (posterior, anterior or intermediate), others suckle alternately from either of a pair of nipples, and still others are variable, suckling from any available nipple. Our conclusions, therefore, based on results from studies of 25 litters ranging in size from one to six kittens,† differ from Ewer's report (2) of a prevalent suckling-specificity from observations of 4 litters.

Our results on early feeding show, as do those on cage orientation, that these events undergo a steady change promoting increasing efficiency from shortly after birth, suggesting that discriminative and perceptual-motor processes basic to them progress steadily in organization and scope. The learning process postulated is an elementary pattern of conditioning, involving proximal stimuli effective through tactual, olfactory and thermal experience with the female and nest situation, with approach and suckling as basic responses. Feeding processes have an obvious central significance in social development; hence our research has centered on feeding.

NORMAL PROGRESS IN KITTEN-FEMALE
RELATIONSHIPS

Suckling often appears in the first-born before parturition is completed; thereafter, in the litter period, it recurs as a response that changes significantly in its organization and social relationships. At length normally, as weaning begins in the fifth week, suckling declines and is gradually replaced by self-feeding, which generally is specific by the eighth week. In the remainder of this paper, results of investigations by Rosenblatt, Wodinsky et al. (6) are reported, analyzing the development of feeding adjustments in some detail both for kittens developing in the regular litter situation and for others subjected to a technique of isolation.

Our results for the development of feeding in the normal litter situation reveal not just one suckling pattern, but variable suckling adjustments which after the described neonatal beginnings progress steadily in ways reflecting progress in perceptual, motor and motivational organization. We find that from birth there is a sequence of interrelated changes in the suckling and orientative behavior of the neonates and

† J. Wodinsky, J. S. Rosenblatt, G. Turkewitz, and T. C. Schneirla, "The Development of Individual Nursing Position Habits in Newborn Kittens." Paper presented at 1955 annual meeting, Eastern Psychol. Assn., New York City.

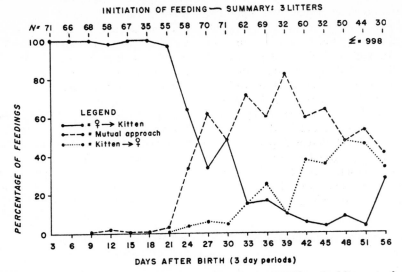

FIG. 5. Three principal stages in the initiation of suckling in normally-raised litters in the domestic cat (data from three litters). Points on graphs show stages of responses of each type summarized for the daily observations of each three-day interval. (*N* = number of feedings observed in each interval.)

in the nursing and related behavior of the female. These changes are the product of complex reciprocal stimulative processes that lead, on the one hand, to weaning and independent functioning of the young and, on the other, to the gradual decline of the female's maternal behavior associated with this litter.

By means of procedures yielding both qualitative and quantitative evidence, we have traced the development of what may be called the normal suckling and nursing pattern of several litters from birth to the end of the eighth week. The general results, graphed in Figure 5 for a representative litter, may be summarized in the following terms.

In stage 1, from birth to about the twentieth day, essentially all of the feedings are initiated by the female. She approaches the kittens where they are huddled (in the home corner, as a rule), lies down with her mammary surface against them, and arches her body around them in what we call the *functional-U*. The kittens, responding to tactual and other stimuli from the female, and variously influenced

by her licking operations, soon stir about and begin variable movements that, in the course of time, lead into nipple localization and to nipple-attachment and suckling. As this first stage progresses, although the female continues to initiate the procedure, the kittens become increasingly involved in the organization of feeding situations. This fact is emphasized by their rapid progress in localizing nipples, to the extent that by the fourth neonatal day most of them have established individually distinctive types of adjustment to the female.

In stage 2, which may be described as typical from about the 20th to shortly after the 30th day, the initiation of feeding involves active approaches on the part of both female and kittens. Initiation of feeding approaches by kittens to the female first becomes evident under particular conditions, as for example when she is resting somewhere outside the home area, or when she is crouched over the food dish. Although either the female or the kittens may be the more active according to circumstances, the initiation of feeding remains a distinctively bilateral process throughout this period. To the approaches of the kittens, increasingly vigorous and versatile, the female nearly always responds appropriately. According to conditions, she soon assumes her nursing posture or, if already lying down, she facilitates the nipple-localization adjustments of the kittens by stretching out or at least by remaining in place. For the kittens, perceptual developments underlying improved efficiency in feeding are indicated by the results of tests demonstrating an increased facility and scope of orientation in the cage, as well as an increasing resourcefulness in transferring their reactivity from a specific cage locality to the female as the focus of action.

We interpret these changes as marking a steady improvement in the perceptual-motor abilities of the kittens, a developmental process for which an increasingly comprehensive motivational basis for responding to the female and other kittens is indicated. Relevant to this interpretation is the increase in the frequency and variety of casual joint activities ("play") among the kittens and of nonfeeding responses to the female such as toying with her tail. These results support the view that feeding provides a functional center for the socialization of the kittens, as feeding itself, considered at any stage, is a reciprocal activity and is inherently social.

In stage 3, which generally begins shortly after the 30th day, the initation of suckling depends more and more and finally almost altogether upon the kittens. They now follow the female about the cage with greater frequency and increasing persistence, remaining at the place of her disappearance when she leaps to the wall shelf. When she happens to be accessible to them, they persist with vigor in attempts to nuzzle which at times result in attachment and suckling, but with increasing frequency, as through prompt counteraction by the female, may end in little more than a brief social exchange. In various ways, consequently, the kittens forcibly influence the female's behavior more and more. Her changing attitude toward the kittens is in-dicated clearly by the increasing frequency and duration of her stays on the shelf, at least until the kittens themselves can reach the shelf. From the time the kittens can get to the shelf, at about the 45th day, the female avoids it increasingly. In the third stage, therefore, the intimacy of the social bond between female and young has decreased with their changing behavioral relationships—i.e., as their social distance has increased.

This evidence, indicating a predictable series of changes in the formation and later in the waning and disappearance of the described reciprocal feeding relationships, is interpreted by us as centering on progressive changes in the organization and qualitative nature of these relationships and in social processes relating to them. In many ways these changes show that the development of socialization centers on feeding relationships and is essentially one of reciprocal stimulation throughout. In the processes of individual development involved, no sharp distinction can be drawn between nutritive and social adjustments, as both of these aspects are indicated in progressively diversified and indirect ways in the bilateral relationships characteristic of the litter situation.

ISOLATION EXPERIMENTS

A principal part of this program involved research on the suckling behavior and maternal adjustments of kittens reared normally in the litter situation, in comparison with the responses of kittens returned to female and litter after isolation periods introduced experimentally at different times in the first two months of life. The aim was to analyze the normal socialization processes by determining the effects of social deprivation introduced at different times on the feeding behavior and other behavioral adjustments of kittens.

1. General treatment and behavior of isolated kittens. The experimental kittens were isolated in a special incubator, a cubical enclosure in which a brooder or "artificial mother" (Fig. 6) was placed on

the floor near one wall.‡ This brooder, constructed in a functional-U form and covered with soft toweling, was designed to constitute a model that would be attractive to the kitten by virtue of its thermal, tactual and spatial properties, and that would also present a nipple from which the isolate kitten could draw through its own efforts in suckling a synthetic formula available at a controlled temperature. The

FIG. 6. Week-old isolate kitten in position and suckling at the nipple in the brooder or "artificial mother." Rear-guard panel and milk supply are indicated.

brooder was made in the functional-U form to duplicate the effect of sensory canalization normally contributed by the female lying on one side with her body arched and legs extended at right angles to her abdomen. The brooder therefore served as a crude, partial substitute for the lactating female, to the extent that it obviated the need for forced feeding by hand and other special attentions that might have been equivalent in a more comprehensive sense to the normal properties of

‡ This piece of equipment was developed in a prototype form in 1949 in connection with studies on parturition in the cat, was modified by Dr. Alan Frank, Fellow of the National Institute of Mental Health in our laboratory during 1950–1951, and was further improved in pilot work for the present investigation.

the female. One other procedure carried out in this situation as a limited substitute for the female's normal activities was a brief daily manipulation of the isolate kitten during the first two neonatal weeks, to effect the routine stimulative operations essential to facilitate onset of defecation and urination.

By routine, each isolate kitten was first introduced manually to the nipple in the brooder, so that the process of independent feeding might be started equivalently in different subjects without any undue delays. The neonates were all able to acquire within their first three days the ability to crawl up into the brooder, locate the nipple and attach independently. From that time, self-initiated suckling occurred at regular intervals in all of the isolated subjects. In the course of time, a gradual change appeared in how each isolate approached the nipple from in front of the brooder. The earliest trend was to follow a more or less canalized path along one or the other arm of the brooder, in close contact with the soft surface. Then, after a few days, a variable approach was made through the open central area of the brooder, between the arms; also, the amount of preliminary nuzzling near the nipple decreased steadily. Finally, kittens held in isolation to the fourth week became versatile in their manner of approaching the nipple, and could reach it directly across the arms or through the central area, attaching efficiently with a minimum of nuzzling.

After their isolation periods in the incubator, kittens detained there for scheduled intervals were returned individually to their respective females and litters for observations of individual reactions in the following days, with emphasis on suckling responses, on general cage orientation and on social reactions to female and littermates.

2. Appearance of suckling after isolation. Effective suckling responses appeared, although in different ways and in different timing, on the test returns to the female and litter situation of *all* of the kit-

TABLE 23-1

**Records for suckling responses in isolate kittens on test returns to female
and litter from the incubator**

AGE AND DURATION OF ISOLATION (DAYS)	N	AVERAGE DAYS ISOLATED	% SUCKLING ON RETURN TO FEMALE
A. Kittens suckled from brooder during isolation:			
0–7	3	7	100
6–23	5	18	100
18–33	2	16	100
23–44	4	22	25
2–44	4	43	00
B. Kittens in isolation that did not suckle from the brooder:			
34–49	4	16	100
47–54	3	7	100

tens isolated from birth to the 7th day, from the 6th to the 23d day, and from the 18th to the 33d day. The results for the cage-return tests of these kittens are reported in Table 23–1.

On the other hand, suckling from the female was not accomplished in corresponding tests by any except one of the kittens isolated from the 23d to the 44th day, or by any of the kittens isolated from the 2d to the 44th day. These last kittens failed to suckle although, like the others, they remained continuously with their females from the time their tests began.

Insufficient hunger was not responsible for the failure of certain of the isolate kittens to suckle on return to the female. A strong, mounting hunger was indicated by their increasingly restless activities on return to the litter situation, and independent tests showed that they would have fed readily had they been returned to the brooder. The difficulty was in feeding from the female. In a special test, two of the brooder-kittens that had not suckled were placed with their females and left for two days without food. The female was fed on schedule outside the cage, and each time she returned two mother-reared kittens also present suckled promptly. As for the isolates, no signs of suckling appeared even after they had been without food for two

days. Other isolates, however, returned to the female and cage at the 49th or 54th day, after periods in the brooder in which they had fed from dishes with no opportunity to suckle, all suckled from the female (Table 23–1, B). The failure of certain of the experimental subjects to suckle cannot therefore be attributed either to the absence of hunger or to any "natural decline" in suckling, although the latter might seem possible from the fact that suckling normally has declined by the 44th day in litter-reared kittens.

Our findings show that suckling may arise in isolated kittens returned to the litter situation, whether or not these subjects had developed a suckling reaction to the female prior to their period in the brooder. Of three kittens isolated from birth, all suckled in the course of time after having been placed in the litter situation for testing, but of eight kittens whose isolation began after an appreciable amount of suckling experience, only one accomplished this response on its return to the litter situation. Of these eight kittens, four had suckled during 23 days in the litter situation prior to isolation, yet three of them did not suckle after their return to female and litter at 34 days after an intervening isolation period.

Failure of the feeding adjustment to

TABLE 23-2

Contact latencies and suckling latencies in kittens returned to female and litter after different periods of isolation

AGE AND DURATION OF ISOLATION (DAYS)	N	INDIVIDUAL CONTACT-LATENCIES	GROUP AV. CONTACT-LATENCIES	INDIVIDUAL SUCKLING LATENCIES	GROUP AV. SUCKLING LATENCIES
0–7	3	04 min. 10 min. 2 hr., 18 min.	51 min.	1 hr., 25 min. 5 hr., 35 min. 4 hr., 33 min.	3 hr., 11 min.
6–23	5	22 min. 35 min. 48 min. 1 hr., 04 min. 2 hr., 23 min.	1 hr., 02 min.	45 min. 5 hr., 17 min. 25 hr., 14 min. 29 hr., 15 min. 38 hr., 00 min.	19 hr., 42 min.
18–33	2	45 min. 47 min.	46 min.	7 hr., 05 min. 23 hr., 15 min.	15 hr., 10 min.
23–44	4	19 hr., 07 min. 29 hr., 00 min. 71 hr., 28 min. 72 hr., 00 min.	47 hr., 56 min.	72 hr., 25 min. No suckling in the three others	
2–44	4	1 hr., 00 min. 24 hr., 40 min. 44 hr., 47 min. 70 hr., 00 min.	35 hr., 07 min.	No suckling	
34–49	4	16 min. 48 min. 1 hr., 49 min. 93 hr., 35 min.	24 hr., 07 min.	24 hr., 40 min. 26 hr., 05 min. 50 hr., 35 min. 93 hr., 35 min.	29 hr., 24 min.
47–54	3	1 min. 6 min. 31 min.	13 min.	1 min. 33 min. 5 hr., 56 min.	2 hr., 10 min.

the female in certain cases could not have been due to any inability to execute the action of suckling, as efficient suckling was observed in the brooder in all of the test isolates not long before they were removed for the cage tests. Furthermore, when in control tests several of the kittens that had not suckled during three days in the litter-situation tests were returned to the incubator, all of them promptly suckled from the brooder nipple. It is clear that the interference with the suckling adjustment in the litter situation was centered specifically on the female, on the litter situation itself, or on both of these.

3. Latency in female-contact and in suckling. The appraisal of our results for cage-return tests with respect to the relative delay of suckling, when that response appeared, provided one valuable clue as to the effects of isolation. Table 23–2 gives the latencies for suckling in each of the five groups of isolates in which this response appeared in the tests. It is seen that latencies were relatively short in both the kittens isolated from birth to 7 days and in those isolated from the 47th to the 54th day. Values for suckling latency were higher in kittens isolated from the 6th to the 23d day, and in those isolated from the 18th to the 33d day, as for these groups the average latencies were 15–20 hours

and the longest delays as high as 38 hours. The maximal latencies were obtained in the group isolated from the 34th to the 49th day, for which the average was 48 hours and the longest delay 93 hours.

Analysis of the behavioral facts shows that the delay in suckling on return to the litter situation is dependent upon two different adjustments to the female by the isolate. The first of these is an initial general adjustment, called "contact latency" and recorded by us as ending when the kitten's first sustained contact with the female was achieved; the second was the subsequent interval, called by us the "suckling delay," elapsing before suckling began. In Table 23–2 these two measures, given for each group of isolates, are seen to be very different. The reasons for these differences become clear when the characteristic responses of litter-reared kittens to the female are compared with those of isolate kittens.

4. Reactions to the female of litter-reared and of isolate kittens. A study of the data in the five isolate groups in which suckling appeared indicates that in nearly all of the cases the main difficulty lay in either the initiation of the suckling act or in the performance of this act, rather than in achieving a preliminary adaptation to the female. Table 23–2 shows that in most cases, as in kittens isolated from the 6th to the 23d day and in others isolated from the 34th to the 49th day, the first sustained contact with the female was arrived at relatively soon, after which the accomplishment of suckling required a rather long interval. In the two groups of isolates that did not suckle (days 2–44; days 23–44) the behavior protocols indicated the existence of an additional and special difficulty in effecting a sustained contact with the female, marked by an evident tension and a heightened excitement in her vicinity, so intense and lasting that any attainment of suckling seemed out of the question.

Signs of intense disturbance, including in most cases piloerection of fur on tail and body, ear-retraction, back-arching and overt withdrawal, were observed in three of the four 23d–44th day isolates and in all of the 2nd–44th day isolates. It is also of interest that the 34th–49th day isolates, the one other group in which such disturbance signs appeared (hissing and other disturbance signs in 40%; overt withdrawal in 60%), were the group with the longest suckling delays of those subjects accomplishing the suckling adjustment to the female. The facts suggest that although in the last group the tendency for disturbance in the presence of the female had decreased sufficiently within two hours to admit a suckling adjustment to her, these reactions differed only in degree from those in the two nonsuckling groups. Had the kittens of these three isolate groups been free to run from the cage, all would doubtless have done so, thereby eliminating any chance that a suckling relationship might develop.

5. Reactions to the female of litter-reared and of isolate kittens. Clearly, suckling marks the accomplishment of a complex adaptive relationship between female and young for which many of the isolate kittens were not prepared under the conditions of their tests. From our results, the kitten's attainment of a sustained contact with the female, although difficult, is only a preliminary and a partial adjustment, and delays in effecting a suckling response are attributable to behavioral interferences beyond those involved in this limited relationship of female and young. We have noted the fact that in certain of the isolate groups not only the initial phase of the suckling act but also the further progress of this act was affected. To understand the difficulty in these cases, we must examine the circumstances of the isolate's adjustment both to the litter situation and to the female.

In tests of cage-orientation carried out regularly with isolates after their return, kittens in the group isolated from birth to seven days were found seriously deficient, as compared with litter-raised kittens, in their ability to orient spatially and return to the home corner even when started close by. Subject to serious shortcomings in their orientative adjustments, these isolates could not regain the home corner, and all of them spent considerable intervals of time alone away from this locale. As a result, their first contacts with the female had to occur largely by chance. When one of these isolates chanced to brush the female, the first contact was followed by a reaction of turning toward her and pushing against her body, then nuzzling into her fur. In such responses these isolates were somewhat more efficient than were neonate kittens, a fact attributable not only to greater strength, motility and other gains of maturation, but also to a certain amount of stimulus equivalence between the brooder and female in their tactual and thermal properties, as well as in spatial properties such as the functional-U. But on the other hand the returned isolates, both in their cruder orientative responses to the female and in their less efficient nipple-localizing actions as compared with normal subjects, revealed the handicap of having been deprived of certain benefits of experience with the female.

The disadvantages of isolation may be illustrated in a comparison of isolates returned at one week with litter-raised controls of the same age with respect to the important action of nuzzling. Most of the time, female-reared kittens at this age are in or near the home corner where they can soon reach the female when she is nearby. As a rule they generally locate an area of the female's abdomen soon after reaching her, and thereafter they are likely to nuzzle about only briefly before finding and attaching to a nipple, with the nuzzling usually restricted to the immediate vicinity of the nipple. In such behavior, littermates are never nuzzled, although they may be touched frequently in the orientative processes. The seven-day isolates, in contrast, after having been set down in the test, got to the female only by reaching the home corner accidentally in wandering about, or perhaps through being retrieved by the female. Their local responses differed strikingly from those of normal kittens, once the female was reached. When, for example, an isolate strayed close to the female while she was lying down, nursing the litter, she would generally respond by licking it. Typically, this action influenced the kitten's orientation, causing the kitten to turn toward the female and push, as described, against whatever part of her body happened to be touched. In such cases, isolates would commonly nuzzle over the female's entire furry surface, including paws, neck and back, although somewhat more frequently around her genital region than elsewhere. The isolate's proximal orientation to the female thus was at first very generalized and not significantly more efficient than that of a neonate. The female and the brooder evidently were equivalent to the extent that both furnished attractive low-intensity stimulation and optimal thermal stimulation, but localizing a nipple clearly was a different problem in the two situations.

These isolate kittens nevertheless operate on a different behavioral basis than do neonates, as they have had one week of physical maturation and of experience in the brooder. These differences somehow account for a handicap in adjusting to the litter situation, as we find the week-old isolates requiring definitely more time to achieve their first suckling adjustments to the female than neonates require. Analysis of the protocols shows that the difference is based on both the female's behavior and on certain aspects of the isolate's behavior. The female's nursing behavior, as we have noted, undergoes progressive changes in the first week, in relation to changes in the suckling pattern and the general behavior of the kittens that have been with her since parturition. Because these kittens as a group are now particularly attractive to the female, drawing her visually to the home corner, and because they begin suckling promptly when she arches her body around them there, they often hold her to this spot for some time. These prevalent circumstances reduce the chances that female and isolate will come together as the isolate wanders afield in the cage. The week-old isolates therefore, through their superior motility and their greater freedom as solitary individuals, are handicapped as compared with both neonates and week-old litter-reared kittens with respect to current factors in female behavior promoting the suckling relationship.

From our results, kittens isolated from the 6th to the 23d day also were clearly inferior to normally raised littermates in the initiation and early performance of suckling. Although these isolates were able to achieve their first contacts with the female early in their test periods, as for example through being attracted visually to her, their first suckling reactions had a much greater latency than those of the first-week isolates. At the same time the littermate controls were suckling once or twice each hour, each of the 6th–23d day isolates in its test continued for nearly 20 hours in an orientation to the female's face and anterior body rather than to her mammary region. Like the first-week isolates, these kittens all were generalized in their nuzzling, spending long intervals going over the bodies of other kittens and the furry nonmammary surfaces of the female, before localization of a nipple and attachment occurred. These isolates did not seem to gain any particular advantage from having been visually attracted to the female. Neither, in localizing a nipple, were they helped reliably by their early suckling experience in the litter situation prior to isolation. We conclude that their difficulties in suckling centered on the fact that the period in the brooder deprived them of specific litter experiences essential for dealing with the female at the stage of their return.

Difficulties were also great but were somewhat different in the test adjustments of kittens isolated from the 18th to the 33d day. Although these subjects, like the 6th–23d day isolates, were slow in localizing the female's mammary region, they had less difficulty in localizing nipples. Their difficulties, rather than involving this specific act, concerned adjusting to the female as an object from which to suckle.

An even longer time was required by kittens isolated later in the litter period, from the 34th to the 49th day, to make their first suckling adjustments to the female in the test returns. There is evidence that the difficulties were somewhat different in these groups of isolates; as indicated, in all of them the principal handicap seemed to be in achieving an appropriate general suckling orientation to the female rather than in the specific operations of localizing a nipple and suckling.

In the results for suckling latency, a sharp difference appeared between kittens in the groups isolated for periods starting at different times between the 6th and the 34th day, and the group isolated from the 47th to the 54th day. Although these last kittens were held in the brooder for one week from the time weaning normally begins in the litter situation, they all accomplished suckling adjustments in the return tests. Furthermore, their suckling delays were the shortest of those in all isolation groups, despite the fact that they had to accomplish their nipple localizations and attachments while the female was moving about the cage. One of these kittens had begun to suckle within one minute after the test began, and a second required less than an hour, in contrast to delays of many hours common for kittens isolated at times after the first week and before weaning time.

6. *Suckling readjustments to the female and to the brooder.* In what ways may the acts of suckling at the female and at the brooder facilitate each other or interfere with each other? In order to compare the recall or reinstatement of these two acts, readjustment to the brooder was tested in kittens that had suckled from the female for several weeks, and readjustment to the female was tested in kittens returned to the litter after a period of isolation and feeding at the brooder nipple. All of these kittens had suckled neonatally in the litter situation, but isolation in the brooder began for two of them at the 6th day, for one at the

TABLE 23-3

**Suckling reactions of representative subjects tested with the female after earlier periods
with female and in the incubator, and of others in subsequent tests
with brooder or with female**

INI-TIAL PERIOD WITH FEMALE (DAYS)	FOLLOW-ING PERIOD IN INCU-BATOR (DAYS)	TEST WITH FEMALE		SUBSE-QUENT PERIOD WITH FEMALE (DAYS)	NEXT SUCKLING TEST WITH BROODER OR FEMALE			
					BROODER		FEMALE	
		DAY	SUCKLING LATENCY		DAY	SUCKLING LATENCY	DAY	SUCKLING LATENCY
1–6	7–24	25th	12 hr., 15 min.	25–47	48th	12 min.		
1–6	7–25	26th	19 hr., 40 min.	26–47	48th	25 min.		
1–17	18–32	33rd	23 hr., 15 min.	33–46	47th	10 min.		
1–24	25–40	———	—	—			41st	72 hr., 25 min.
1–24	25–38	———	—	—			39th	No suckling
1–24	25–41	———	—	—			42nd	No suckling

18th day, and for the last three at 24 days, and retesting with female or with brooder came at correspondingly later times.

As the results in Table 23–3 show, readjustment to the female was very difficult for the three kittens tested after having been isolated in the incubator following long initial periods in the litter situation. In their terminal tests with the female, one of these kittens had a suckling latency of more than three days and the other two did not suckle at all. On the other hand, all of the three kittens retested with the brooder made efficient suckling adjustments after relatively short latencies. These last three kittens, however, on their subsequent test returns to the litter situation from the brooder between the 25th and 35th days, at times earlier than other comparable subjects, reinstated the suckling adjustment only after latencies of from 12 to 24 hours.

Let us review the results for test returns with respect to the effects of differences in the duration of the intervening period, as concerns the nature of the suckling adjustment operative in that period. When returned to the female after intervals in the incubator ranging from 8 to 17 days, 11 kittens averaged 31 hours in their suckling latencies. In test returns to the brooder, however, after intervals with the female

ranging from 10 to 36 days, 8 kittens scored a minimal suckling latency of only 12 minutes. In female tests following brooder isolation the shortest suckling latency was 33 minutes (after an isolation period of 8 days), the longest was 93 hours, and one kitten did not suckle at all in the female test after 16 days in the brooder. In brooder tests after intervening periods with the female, the shortest latency was 3 minutes after 17 days with the female, the longest was just 25 minutes after 24 days with the female, but one kitten suckled promptly in the brooder test after having been away from the brooder for 36 days. It is definite that the brooder-suckling pattern was far more readily reinstated than was the female-suckling pattern.

Summary and Discussion

Our evidence from analytical research on behavioral development in army ants and in domestic cats favors for each of these a distinctive theory of the mosaic or developmental-integration type rather than a common theory using postulations of innate organization. There is no demonstrated single formula for instinctive behavior throughout the animal series. Also, there are strong arguments against strictly nativistic hypotheses of genically determined, intraneurally controlled behavior patterns in any species (Schneirla, 10). Each type of species-standard behavioral system requires investigation as a distinctive problem in development, with all hypotheses as to its nature and derivation subject to experimental test.

The army-ant species-typical pattern constitutes a functional system formed through the working together of very different processes contributed by very different types of individuals and sources in the characteristic developmental situation. Figure 1, representing the species mosaic, emphasizes the fact that the essential pattern is not inherited by any type of individual. The queen's ovulation rhythm, for example, is not innate to her as a timing process controlling the cycle, but is governed by a set of convergent biological factors which, in the colony situation with its conditions such as those related to brood-development rate, produce a species-typical reproductive schedule. The cyclic patterns of army-ant species and their chief turning points actually arise through the influence of many different contributive factors in the colony situation.

The insect and mammalian patterns we have studied represent very different functional integrative levels. There is a certain similarity between these levels in the nature of the organic factors involved—stimulative secretory processes, reproductive processes, processes of stage-conditioned sensitivity, and others. The general similarity extends further in that, in the typical functional situation, these factors contribute to the organization of a species-characteristic system or mosaic. In this system, in the case of the ants, larval cuticular secretions function in a way roughly similar to the parturitive fluids in cats, facilitating the formation of a social bond, although in the two cases the physiological details are very different. Behaviorally, such factors enter into social processes of reciprocal stimulation in both cases, essential to the formation of social bonds.

The manner in which the social bonds develop is strikingly different, however, in the insects and mammals. On the insect level, a *biosocial* organization is achieved, directly dominated throughout in its behavioral manifestations by sensory, secretory and other organic processes, and changing specifically under their impress. The recurrent cyclic shifts so characteristic of the army-ant pattern illustrate this point strikingly. On the mammalian level, although organic factors such as uterine contractions, birth fluids and others are basic to the forming of a social bond, their effects constitute intervening variables leading indirectly to a *psychosocial* system in the development of which the intimate cooperation of factors of maturation, experience and learning is paramount at all stages.

Our results substantiate the principle (10, 12) that processes of reciprocal stimulation are basic to all levels of social integration, however different their developmental history and behavioral expressions may be. Even in the army-ant system, experience plays a part, although its role here seems limited to a simple process of habituation, directly tied to organic factors as in approach-fixation to colony odors. But in the kittens, as our longitudinal studies of orientation show, factors of experience and learning play a complex and progressive role. A striking example is the expanding significance of tactual and odor cues in the kitten's early nonvisual stage of orientation; in the same neonatal period, progress in related perceptual developments involving cues from the female is indicated in our results for individual specialization in suckling. In both types of adjustment, a shift to visually dominated perceptual patterns, arising from and modifying the nonvisual system, occurs within a few days after eye-opening. The psychosocial aspect of these developmental changes in altricial mammalian young lacks a real counterpart on the insect level.

Our research has been based on the theory (Schneirla, 8, 14) that, since low-intensity stimulative effects such as contact and odor are basically approach-evocative in animal development, relationships of reciprocal-stimulation involving such stimuli play an appreciable role in socialization. We also recognize that relationships of feeding normally play a major role in social development, furnishing a center of organization for all of the reciprocal-stimulative processes involved in maintaining social bonds. Because our investigations of behavioral ontogeny in cats have been aimed at understanding species-standard patterns, our experimental situations all combine opportunities for both low-intensity stimulation and feeding.

We hold that experimental studies, as by the method of isolation, cannot be validly interpreted *except* in close reference to searching longitudinal investigation of the normal or species-standard developmental pattern. For normal behavioral development, in which the formation of a perceptual bond with and adjustment to the female as feeding object progresses without a break from the time of birth, we have described three successive, overlapping stages, of 1) female-initiation, 2) mutual initiation, and 3) kitten-initiation of the feeding adjustment and related social processes. Because feeding processes clearly reveal the nature of the social bond, and are found central to socialization, we have explored feeding adjustments comparatively as they develop in the normal litter situation and in kittens variously isolated and deprived of intervals of social experience.

Although our brooder presents attractive low-intensity stimulation and opportunities to acquire a routine feeding adjustment, it lacks motility, behavioral reactivity and individual capacities for modifying behavior, and thus constitutes a very limited substitute for the lactating female available to normally raised young. The approach-fixation that develops in isolated kittens is a perceptually limited one, very stereotyped in comparison with that developing normally. Kittens isolated from birth, along with others isolated later in the nonvisual stage, exhibit their ineptitude for normal maternal adjustments particularly in the nature of their nuzzling. In these early isolates, nuzzling is generalized to kittens and is an over-all response to the female, in distinct contrast to the versatile orientative abilities and local discriminations of normal subjects at the corresponding ages. The brooder experience is a minimal one, routine and relatively static in perceptual cues and motor processes of approach and feeding; hence the feeding reaction to it can be readily reinstated at a later time. The adjustment to the female, in contrast, is found after different isolation intervals to be out of keeping with the situation and inadequate in significant respects. Our results show that although isolation from the brooder did not significantly impair a subsequent reinstatement of the feeding response there, isolation from the situation of female and litter interfered very substantially with subsequent adjustment under those conditions.

These differences are understandable in terms of a review of results from our studies of normal events in the litter situation. A contrast of the pattern of relationships prevalent between female and young at the time the kitten was removed for isolation and that prevalent at the time of return and test discloses that the female-young relationship is always a complex and changing one in which the roles of the participants vary progressively. Because the relationships of the partners in the feeding act normally progress through three very different stages of perceptual-motor adjustments, each returned isolate is confronted by a psychological situation materially different from that prevalent at the time of removal. The differences center notably on the condition of the female, her behavior and her responses to (or attitude toward) the young.

The returned isolate must meet new conditions, and perhaps radically new conditions at certain times, without having participated in the genesis of the changed conditions. In general this presents an increasingly difficult task to kittens returned at later stages, as with time the necessary social and nutritive adjustments become more complex and more divergent from the individual's pre-isolation responses to the litter situation. In contrast, return to the brooder presents the kitten with a situation that has changed very little in its functional relevance, in ways dependent on the kitten itself. Results show that adjustment to the brooder involves a relatively simple pattern, evidently of the approach-conditioning type, substantially unimpaired by intervening litter-situation experiences and therefore reinstated readily on the kitten's return to the brooder.

Our findings consequently emphasize the necessity of a continued behavioral and functional interchange with female and littermates if the kitten is to develop an adequate suckling adjustment typical of its age group. Psychological processes concerning perceptual and behavioral organization are required in which organic factors underlying reciprocal stimulation play a basic, inextricable role. The contrast with the specific, dominant role of analogous organic processes in insects is striking, as to the resultant adaptive organization. Although in mammalian development the feeding pattern is central to the standard socialization process, it is not a simple routine mode of feeding by suckling, as in the brooder, but a perceptual adjustment adapted to the current pattern of the female and the prevalent social situation.

These considerations favor a very different view of the concept of "critical periods" from the one now held by many writers. In the social development of the cat, we are led to the idea that striking changes in the essential progression are grounded not only in the growth-dependent processes of maturation but also, at the same time, in opportunities for experience and learning arising in the standard female-litter situation. This conception of social ontogeny encourages stressing not just one or a few chronologically marked changes in the behavior pattern, but rather indi-

cates that normally each age-period is crucial for the development of particular aspects in a complex progressive pattern of adjustment. Furthermore, the principles of development may be somewhat different for the diagnosis of different periods according to their duration, their character or their time of occurrence, and research is essential to clarify what factors at any one stage may become critical for specific or restricted as against inclusive and widely organized adjustments of the same or of later stages.

Because factors depending on experience in the normal developmental situation are crucial for progress in social adjustment, the result is that isolation at any time from the normal situation so deprives a kitten of advantages typically available in that period that on its return after isolation the subject shows characteristic defects in social adjustment. We conclude therefore that critical periods in social development are not matters of maturation per se. Rather, time-conditioned factors depending on experience in the normal situation, in close conjunction with growth-dependent factors, are necessary for both the turning points and the intervening progress in social adjustment.

Diagnosing shortcomings in social adjustment thus depends on our knowledge about disadvantageous combinations of conditions affecting factors of experience and maturation together, rather than on either of these alone. How the subject can readjust to the normal social situation after an absence in isolation is found so conditioned by a complex of factors concerning age, the duration and conditions of isolation, and the type of social situation re-encountered, that specific research seems essential to clarify what factors may be critical for any one developmental period as compared with others. The effects of atypical conditions such as those of isolation must be studied in close comparison with those holding under species-standard developmental conditions, for an adequate judgment of ontogeny in either case. Mammalian social development is thus seen as advancing from birth in ways that, for the species-characteristic outcome, continuously require not only the standard conditions of organic maturation but also the presence of the standard developmental setting with its progressively changing behavioral properties.

REFERENCES

1. CLARK, EUGENIE, L. R. ARONSON, and M. GORDON: *Mating Behavior Patterns in Two Sympatric Species of Xiphophorin Fishes: Their Inheritance and Significance in Sexual Isolation.* Bull. Am. Mus. Nat. Hist., **103**: 139–335, 1954.

2. EWER, R. F.: *Suckling Behaviour in Kittens.* Behaviour, **15**: 146–162, 1959.

3. FULLER, J. L., C. A. EASLER, and E. M. BANKS: *Formation of Conditioned Avoidance Responses in Young Puppies.* Am. J. Physiol., **3**: 462, 1950.

4. ROSENBLATT, J. S., G. TURKEWITZ, and T. C. SCHNEIRLA: *Analytical Studies on Maternal Behavior in Relation to Litter Adjustment and Socialization in the Domestic Cat. III. Development of Orientation.* (In ms.)

5. ROSENBLATT, J. S., G. TURKEWITZ, and T. C. SCHNEIRLA: "The Development of Suckling and Related Behavior in Neonate Kittens—A Résumé," in *The Roots of Behavior* (E. Bliss, Ed.), New York: Harper & Row, 1962.

6. ROSENBLATT, J. S., J. WODINSKY, G. TURKEWITZ, and T. C. SCHNEIRLA: *Analytical Studies on Maternal Behavior in Relation to Litter Adjustment and Socialization in the Domestic Cat. II. Maternal-Young Relations from Birth to Weaning.* (In prep.)

7. SCHNEIRLA, T. C.: *A Theory of Army-Ant Behavior Based upon the Analysis of Ac-tivities in a Representative Species.* J. Comp. Psychol., **25**: 51–90, 1938.

8. SCHNEIRLA, T. C.: *A Theoretical Consideration of the Basis for Approach-Withdrawal Adjustments in Behavior.* Psychol. Bull., **37**: 501–502, 1939.

9. SCHNEIRLA, T. C.: *Social Organization in Insects, as Related to Individual Function.* Psychol. Rev., **48**: 465–486, 1941.

10. SCHNEIRLA, T. C.: *Problems in the Biopsychology of Social Organization.* J. Abnorm. Soc. Psychol., **41**: 385–402, 1946.

11. SCHNEIRLA, T. C.: "A Consideration of Some Problems in the Ontogeny of Family Life and Social Adjustments in Various Infrahuman Animals," in *Problems of Infancy and Childhood: Transactions of the Fourth (1950) Conference* (M. J. E. Senn, Ed.), pp. 81–124. New York: Josiah Macy, Jr. Foundation, 1951.

12. SCHNEIRLA, T. C.: "Interrelationships of the 'Innate' and the 'Acquired' in Instinctive Behavior," in *L'Instinct dans le Comportement des Animaux et de l'Homme,* pp. 387–452. Paris: Masson & Cie, 1956.

13. SCHNEIRLA, T. C.: *Theoretical Consideration of Cyclic Processes in Doryline Ants.* Proc. Am. Philos. Soc., **101**: 106–133, 1957.

14. SCHNEIRLA, T. C.: "An Evolutionary and Developmental Theory of Biphasic Processes Underlying Approach and Withdrawal," in *Nebraska Symposium on Motivation, 1959* (M. R. Jones, Ed.), pp. 1–42. Lincoln: Univ. of Nebraska Press, 1959.

15. SCOTT, J. P.: *Critical Periods in the Development of Social Behavior in Puppies.* Psychosom. Med., **20**: 42–54, 1958.

16. TOBACH, E., M. L. FAILLA, R. COHN, and T. C. SCHNEIRLA: *Analytical Studies on Maternal Behavior in Relation to Litter Adjustment and Socialization in the Domestic Cat. I. Parturition.* (In ms.)

17. WHEELER, W. M.: *The Social Insects.* New York: Harcourt, Brace, 1928.

J. P. SCOTT

24   Critical Periods in Behavioral Development

In this article, J. P. Scott reviews many different studies on critical periods in three different areas of behavioral development: socialization (see reading 23), infantile stimulation, and learning.

Reprinted from *Science*, Vol. 138, pp. 949–958, 30 November 1962, with the permission of the author and the American Association for the Advancement of Science. Copyright 1962 by the American Association for the Advancement of Science. Three figures have been omitted.

A number of years ago I was given a female lamb taken from its mother at birth. My wife and I raised it on the bottle for the first 10 days of life and then placed it out in the pasture with a small flock of domestic sheep. As might have been expected from folklore, the lamb became attached to people and followed the persons who fed it. More surprisingly, the lamb remained independent of the rest of the flock when we restored it to the pasture. Three years later it was still following an independent grazing pattern. In addition, when it was mated and had lambs of its own it became a very indifferent mother, allowing its offspring to nurse but showing no concern when the lamb moved away with the other members of the flock (1).

Since following the flock is such a universal characteristic of normal sheep, I was impressed by the extensive and permanent modification of this behavior that resulted from a brief early experience. The results suggested that Freud was right concerning the importance of early experience, and pointed toward the existence of critical periods in behavioral development. As I soon discovered, there is considerable evidence that a critical period for determining early social relationships is a widespread phenomenon in vertebrates; such a critical period had long been known in ants (2).

The theory of critical periods is not a new one in either biology or psychology. It was strongly stated by Stockard in 1921, in connection with his experiments on the induction of monstrosities in fish embryos, although he gave credit to Dareste for originating the basic idea 30 years earlier (3). In experimenting with the effects of various inorganic chemicals upon the development of *Fundulus* eggs, Stockard at first thought one-eyed monsters were specifically caused by the magnesium ion. Further experiments showed him that almost any chemical would produce the same effect, provided it was applied at the proper time during development. These experiments and those of Child (4) and his students established the fact that the most rapidly growing tissues in an embryo are the most sensitive to any change in conditions, thus accounting for the specificity of effects at particular times.

Meanwhile Freud had attempted to explain the origin of neuroses in human patients as the result of early experience and had implied that certain periods in the life of an infant are times of particular sensitivity. In 1935, Lorenz (5) emphasized the importance of critical periods for the formation of primary social bonds (imprinting) in birds, remarking on their similarity to critical periods in the development of the embryo, and McGraw soon afterward (6) pointed out the existence of critical periods for optimal learning of motor skills in the human infant.

Since then, the phenomenon of critical periods has excited the imagination of a large group of experimenters interested in human and animal development. In describing this fast-moving scientific field, I shall point out some of the most significant current developments. More detailed information is available in some excellent recent reviews (7, 8).

To begin with, three major kinds of critical-period phenomena have been discovered. These involve optimal periods for learning, for infantile stimulation, and for the formation of basic social relationships. The last of these has been established as a widespread phenomenon in the animal kingdom and consequently receives major attention in this article.

Periods Are Based on Processes

In the dog, the development of behavior may be divided into several natural periods marked off by important changes in social relationships (Table 24–1). Only a few other species have been studied in sufficient detail for making adequate comparisons, but enough data have been accumulated to show that similar periods can be identified in other mammals and in birds (9, 10). I originally expected to find that the course of postnatal development, like that of embryonic development, would be essentially similar in all vertebrates, and that while the periods might be extended or shortened, the same pattern of development would be evident in all (11). However, comparison of only two species, man and the dog, shows that the periods can actually occur in reverse order, and that there is an astonishing degree of flexibility in behavioral development (12).

This leads to the conclusion that the important part of each developmental period is not time sequence but the fact that each · represents a major develop-

mental process. Thus, the neonatal period is chiefly characterized by the process of neonatal nutrition — nursing in mammals and parental feeding in many birds. The transition period is characterized by the process of transition to adult methods of nutrition and locomotion and the appearance of adult patterns of social behavior, at least in immature form. The period of socialization is the period in which primary social bonds are formed. If we consider processes alone, it is apparent that they are not completely dependent on each other and that they can therefore be arranged in different orders. It is also apparent that certain of these processes persist beyond the periods characterized by them. For example, a mammal usually retains throughout life the ability to suck which characterizes the neonatal period, although in most cases this ability is little used.

Process of Primary Socialization

Since one of the first acts of a young mammal is to nurse, and since food rewards are known to modify the behavior of adult animals, it once seemed logical to suppose that the process of forming a social attachment begins with food rewards and develops as an acquired drive. However, the experimental evidence does not support this extreme viewpoint. Brodbeck reared a group of puppies during the critical period of socialization, feeding half of them by hand and the other half by machine, but giving all of them the same degree of human contact (13). He found that the two sets of puppies became equally attached to people. This result was later confirmed by Stanley and his coworkers (14), who found that the only difference in response between the machine-fed and the hand-fed puppies was that the latter yelped more when they saw the experimenter. Elliot and King (15) fed all their puppies by hand but overfed one group and underfed another. The hungry puppies became more rapidly at-

TABLE 24-1

Periods of development in the puppy and song sparrow. The six periods of development described by Nice (10) for the song sparrow correspond to the first four periods in the puppy, as indicated in the table. The young of the two species are born or hatched in an immature state, require intensive parental care and feeding, and go through much the same stages before becoming independent. Development is much more rapid in the bird than in the puppy, although small mammals such as mice mature at about the same rate as birds.

PUPPY			SONG SPARROW		
NAME OF PERIOD	LENGTH OF PERIOD (WEEKS)	INITIAL EVENT	NAME OF PERIOD	LENGTH OF PERIOD (DAYS)	INITIAL EVENT
I. Neonatal	0–2	Birth, nursing	Stage 1 (nestling)	0–4	Hatching, gaping
II. Transition	2–3	Eyes open	Stage 2	5–6	Eyes open
III. Socialization	3–10	Startle to sound	Stage 3	7–9	Cowering—first fear reactions
			Stage 4 (fledgling)	10–16	Leaving nest— first flight
			Stage 5	17–28	Full flight
IV. Juvenile	10–	Final weaning	Stage 6 (juvenile)	29–	Independent feeding

tached to the handlers. We can conclude that, in the dog, food rewards per se are not necessary for the process of socialization, but that hunger will speed it up.

Fisher (16) reared fox terrier puppies in isolation boxes through the entire socialization period. The puppies were fed mechanically (thus, food was entirely eliminated as a factor in the experiment), but they were removed from the boxes for regular contacts with the experimenter. One group of puppies was always rewarded by kind social treatment. A second group was sometimes rewarded and sometimes punished, but in a purely random way. Still a third group was always punished for any positive approach to the experimenter. The puppies that were both rewarded and punished showed most attraction and dependency behavior with respect to the experimenter, and the puppies that were always punished showed the least. After the treatment was discontinued, all puppies began coming toward the experimenter, and the differences rapidly disappeared. This leads to the surprising conclusion that the process of socialization is not inhibited by punishment and may even be speeded up by it.

At approximately 3 weeks of age—that is, at the beginning of the period of socialization—young puppies begin to bark or whine when isolated or placed in strange places. Elliot and Scott (17) showed that the reaction to isolation in a strange place reaches a peak at 6 to 7 weeks of age, approximately the midpoint of the critical period, and begins to decline thereafter. Scott, Deshaies, and Morris (18) found that separating young puppies overnight from their mother and litter mates in a strange pen for 20 hours per day produced a strong emotional reaction and speeded up the process of socialization to human handlers. All this evidence indicates that any sort of strong emotion, whether hunger, fear, pain, or loneliness, will speed up the process of socialization. No experiments have been carried out to determine the effects of pleasant types of emotion, such as might be aroused by play and handling, but these were probably a factor in Brodbeck's experiment with machine-fed puppies.

The results of these experiments on dogs agree with evidence from other species. While they were going on, Harlow (19) was performing his famous experiments with rhesus monkeys isolated at birth and supplied with dummy "mothers." When given the choice between a comfortable cloth-covered mother without a nipple and an uncomfortable mother made of wire screening but equipped with a functional nursing bottle, the young rhesus monkeys definitely preferred the cloth-covered models from which they had received no food rewards. Harlow concluded that the acquired-drive theory of the origin of social attachment could be discarded.

Later, Igel and Calvin (20) performed a similar but more elaborate experiment with puppies. These animals had more opportunity to choose, being provided with four kinds of mother models: comfortable and uncomfortable, each type with and without nipples. Like the rhesus monkeys, the puppies preferred the comfortable "mother" but usually chose one with a nipple. Thus, it appears that food rewards do contribute something to the social relationship, although they do not form its prime basis.

Since then Harlow (21) has raised to maturity the monkeys raised on dummy mothers, has mated them, and has observed their behavior toward their own young. They become uniformly poor mothers, neglecting their offspring and often punishing them when they cry. In spite of such rejection, the young rhesus infants desperately crawl toward their mothers and give every evidence of becoming attached to them, although perhaps not as strongly as in the normal relationship. Here again punishment does not inhibit the formation of a social bond.

The hypothesis that the primary social bond originates through food rewards had already been shown to be invalid in the precocial birds, many of which form attachments prior to the time when they begin to feed. Lorenz (5) was the first to point out the significance of this phenomenon, which he called "imprinting." He also stated that it differed from conditioning, primarily in that it was very rapid and apparently irreversible. However, rapid formation and great persistence are also characteristic of many conditioned responses and other learned behavior. Fabricius (22) pointed out that no sharp line can be drawn between imprinting and conditioning, and Collias (23) concluded that imprinting is a form of learned behavior that is self-reinforcing.

The process of imprinting in young ducklings and chicks has since been experimentally analyzed in much detail, with results that invariably confirm the conclusion that it takes place without any obvious external rewards or reinforcement. Hess (24) found that if he caused young ducklings to follow a model over varying distances or over hurdles, the ducklings which had to make the greater effort became more strongly imprinted. He also found that the drug meprobamate and its congener carisoprodol, which are muscle relaxants as well as tranquilizers, greatly reduce imprinting if given during the critical period. James (25) found that chicks would become attached to an object illuminated by a flickering light, even though they were not allowed to follow, and Gray (26) later showed that they will become attached to a motionless object illuminated by a steady light and viewed from an isolation box. It is therefore apparent that chicks can become imprinted without following, although muscular tension may still be important.

Guiton (27) found that chicks allowed to follow a model in a group become less strongly imprinted than chicks exposed singly, and he attributed the results to the greater fear shown by the isolated chicks. Recently, Pitz and Ross (28) subjected young chicks following a model to a loud sound and found that this increased the speed with which they formed a social bond. Hess (29) (with the apparatus shown in Fig. 1) has given a mild electric shock to chicks following a model and finds that this also increases the strength of imprinting. Instead of avoiding the model, the distressed chick runs after it more closely.

For example, birds often retain newly formed eggs in their bodies overnight, thus incubating them for several hours before laying. By chilling duck eggs just before placing them in an incubator (thus killing all embryos except those in the earliest stages of development) Gottlieb (31) was able to time the age of ducklings from the onset of incubation rather than from hatching and found that variation in the timing for the critical period was much reduced. No such exact timing studies have been

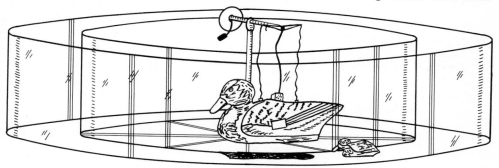

FIG. 1. Hess's apparatus for measuring the following response in ducklings and chicks. A decoy revolves on a circular path, the young duckling staying nearby. Other revolving objects may be substituted for the decoy, which is wired for sound. The following response is a major positive timing mechanism that initiates the critical period for imprinting; it is also an indicator that an attachment has been formed. [From a photo by E. H. Hess.]

We may conclude that these young birds become attached to any object to which they are long exposed during the critical period, even when their contact is only visual. We may also conclude that the speed of formation of a social bond is dependent upon the degree of emotional arousal, irrespective of the nature of that arousal. Whether attachment is the result of the emotion itself or of the reduction of emotion as the chick or duckling approaches the model is still a matter of conjecture (30).

The basic timing mechanisms for developmental periods are obviously the biological processes of growth and differentiation, usually called maturation. For various reasons, these are not precisely correlated with age from birth or hatching.

made in mammals, but I have estimated that there is at least a week's variation in development among puppies at 3 weeks of age, and the variation among human infants must be considerably greater (32).

Another approach to the problem is to try to identify the actual mechanisms which open and close a period. Since an important part of forming a primary social relationship appears to be emotional arousal while the young animal is in contact with another, it is obvious that the critical period for socialization could be timed by the appearance of behavioral mechanisms which maintain or prevent contact, and this indeed is the case. There are demonstrable positive mechanisms, varying from species to species, which bring young animals close to other members of their kind:

the clinging response of young rhesus monkeys; the following response of chicks, ducklings, and lambs and other herd animals; the social investigation, tail wagging, and playful fighting of puppies; and the visual investigation and smiling of the human infant (33). These are, of course, accompanied by interacting responses from adult and immature members of the species: holding and clasping by primate mothers, brooding of mother hens and other birds, calling by mother sheep, investigation and play on the part of other young puppies, and the various supporting and nurturing activities of human mothers.

If contact and emotional arousal result in social attachment, there must be negative mechanisms which prevent such attachment once the critical period is past. Perhaps the most widespread of these is the development of a fear response which causes the young animal to immediately leave the vicinity of a stranger and hence avoid contact. This developing fear response is found in young chicks (7), ducklings (22, 34), dogs (35); ...., rhesus monkeys (36), and in many other birds and mammals. Even in children there is a period between the ages of 5 and 12 months in which there is a mounting fear of strangers (37), sometimes called "8-months anxiety" (38). As already pointed out, there is a time in development when certain fear responses actually facilitate imprinting, but, as they grow stronger, the escape reaction follows so quickly that it prevents contact altogether.

Another sort of negative mechanism is the rejection of strange young by adult sheep, goats, and many other herd animals (39). In these species the mothers become strongly attached to the young within a few hours after birth and refuse to accept strangers thereafter .... This indicates that the rapid formation of emotional bonds is not limited to young animals.

These timing mechanisms all depend primarily on the development of social behavior patterns, but both sensory and motor development can also influence timing. For example, a very immature animal cannot maintain contact by following, and in slowly developing altricial birds such as jackdaws and doves (5, 40), the period of imprinting comes much later than it does in the precocial species. In the human infant the process of socialization begins before the adult motor patterns develop, but contact is maintained by visual exploration and by the smiling response to human faces (33). Thus, understanding the process of socialization and its timing mechanisms in any particular species requires a systematic study of the development of the various capacities which affect the time of onset and the duration of the critical period. These include sensory, motor, and learning capacities as well as the ability to perform essential patterns of social behavior.

The fact that emotional arousal is so strongly connected with the process of primary socialization suggests that the capacity to produce emotional reactions may also govern the time of onset of a critical period. Figure 2 summarizes the results of a study of emotional development in the dog during the critical period. If puppies are kept in large fields, totally isolated from people, fear and escape responses toward human beings very nearly reach a maximum by the time the puppies are 14 weeks old—a finding that fixes the upper limit of the period of socialization (35). On the other hand, the peak of the emotional response to isolation in a strange place occurs when puppies are approximately 6 to 7 weeks old, as does the peak of the heart-rate response to handling. At this age, such emotional arousal actually contributes to the strength of the social bond. Fuller (41) was unable to condition the heart-rate response consistently until puppies were 5 weeks old. This indicates that one of the factors that brings the critical period to a close may be the devel-

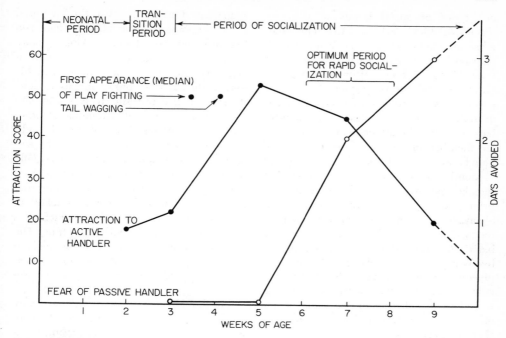

FIG. 2. Timing mechanisms for the critical period in puppies (see 35). The period is initiated by positive behavior mechanisms, such as playful fighting, which result in attraction to a strange individual, and it is brought to a close by the development of a fear response which causes the attraction to decline. The optimum period for rapid and permanent socialization comes shortly after the appearance of prolonged avoidance reactions.

oping ability of the young puppy to associate fear responses with particular stimuli.

All this suggests that if the development of the escape response to strangers could be held in check, the critical period might be extended indefinitely. Raising puppies in small isolation boxes during the critical period inhibits the development of the escape response, but they still show obvious signs of fear when they are first removed from their cages. Fuller (42) reports some success in socializing these older pups by overcoming their fear responses, either by careful handling or through the use of tranquilizing drugs.

Fear responses thus have the dual effect of facilitating the formation of the social bond during the critical period (along with other emotions) and of bringing the period to a close. This is understandable because the type of fear which

terminates the critical period is a developing fear of strange animals. In the early part of the critical period the escape reaction is either lacking or is momentary and weak. At the close of the period it is strong enough to prevent contact altogether.

Formation of Affectional Bonds in Adult Life

Until recently, most investigators have concentrated their attention on the critical period for primary socialization or imprinting and few have gone on to study similar phenomena in later development. This field of investigation is just beginning to open up, though many related facts have long been known. For example, many birds form strong pair bonds which are maintained as long as both members survive. In studying the development of various types of social bonds in differing species of ducks, Schutz (43) finds that, while attachments to particular individuals may be formed in the early critical period from 12 to 17 hours after hatching, the critical period for the attachment to the species may not come until sometime later, in some cases as late as 30 days after hatching, and the attachment to a particular member of the opposite sex, or the pair bond, does not come until the age of 5 months or so. Schutz also finds that female mallards cannot be sexually imprinted with respect to other species but always mate with other mallards no matter what their earliest experience has been. A similar phenomenon is reported by Warriner (44), who finds that male pigeons prefer to mate with birds whose color is similar to that of the parents who reared them, whether of the same or another color from themselves, but females show no preference.

Certain species of mammals, such as foxes (45), form long-lasting mating bonds. It is possible that the violence of the sexual emotions contributes to the formation of the adult bond, just as other sorts of emotional arousal are important to the primary socialization of the infant. Klopfer (46) has suggested that the rapid formation of the social bond in a mother goat toward her kid is the result of the high degree of emotional arousal which accompanies the birth of the offspring.

In short, it seems likely that the formation of a social attachment through contact and emotional arousal is a process that may take place throughout life, and that although it may take place more slowly outside of certain critical periods, the capacity for such an attachment is never completely lost.

At this point it may be remarked that, in attempting to analyze the development of affection and social bonds objectively, scientists have often tried to simplify the problem by postulating various unitary, unromantic, and sometimes unesthetic ex-

planations. One of these was the "acquired drive" hypothesis—that children love you because you feed them. Taking a more moderate view Harlow (19) has emphasized "contact comfort" as a major variable —that the young monkey begins to love its mother because she feels warm and comfortable—but that a number of other factors are involved. As this article indicates, evidence is accumulating that there is a much less specific, although equally unromantic, general mechanism involved —that given any kind of emotional arousal a young animal will become attached to any individual or object with which it is in contact for a sufficiently long time. The necessary arousal would, of course, include various specific kinds of emotions associated with food rewards and contact comfort.

It should not be surprising that many kinds of emotional reactions contribute to a social relationship. The surprising thing is that emotions which we normally consider aversive should produce the same effect as those which appear to be rewarding. This apparent paradox is partially resolved by evidence that the positive effect of unpleasant emotions is normally limited to early infancy by the development of escape reactions.

Nevertheless, this concept leads to the somewhat alarming conclusion that an animal (and perhaps a person) of any age, exposed to certain individuals or physical surroundings for any length of time, will inevitably become attached to them, the rapidity of the process being governed by the degree of emotional arousal associated with them. I need not dwell on the consequences for human behavior, if this conclusion should apply to our species as well as to other animals, except to point out that it provides an explanation of certain well-known clinical observations such as the development by neglected children of strong affection for cruel and abusive parents, and the various peculiar affectional relationships that develop between prisoners and jailors, slaves and masters, and so on. Perhaps the general adaptive nature of this mechanism is that since the survival of any member of a highly social species depends upon the rapid development of social relationships, a mechanism has evolved which makes it almost impossible to inhibit the formation of social bonds.

Critical Periods of Learning

Unlike the process of socialization, the phenomenon of critical periods of learning was first noticed in children rather than in lower animals. McGraw's (47) famous experiment with the twins Johnny and Jimmy was a deliberate attempt to modify behavioral development by giving one of a pair of identical twins special early training. The result varied according to the activity involved. The onset of walking, for example, was not affected by previous practice or help. Other activities, however, could be greatly speeded up — notably roller skating, in which the favored twin became adept almost as soon as he could walk. In other activities performance was actually made worse by early practice, simply because of the formation of unskillful habits. McGraw (6) concluded that there are critical periods for learning which vary from activity to activity; for each kind of coordinated muscular activity there is an optimum period for rapid and skillful learning.

In an experiment with rats, Hebb (48) used the technique of providing young animals with many opportunities for spontaneous learning rather than formal training. Pet rats raised in the rich environment of a home performed much better on learning tasks than rats reared in barren laboratory cages. Since then, other experimenters (49) have standardized the "rich" environment as a large cage including many objects and playthings and have gotten similar effects.

Forgays (see 50) finds that the age at which the maximum effect is produced is limited to the period from approximately 20 to 30 days of age, immediately after weaning. A similar experience in adult life produces no effect. In rats, at any rate, the critical period of learning seems to coincide with the critical period of primary socialization, and it may be that the two are in some way related. Candland and Campbell (51) find that fearful behavior in response to a strange situation begins to increase in rats between 20 and 30 days after birth, and Bernstein (52) showed earlier that discrimination learning could be improved by gentle handling beginning at 20 days. It may well be that the development of fear limits the capacity for future learning as well as the formation of social relationships.

In addition to these studies on motor learning and problem solving, there are many experiments demonstrating the existence of critical periods for the learning of social behavior patterns. It has long been known that many kinds of birds do not develop the characteristic songs of their species if they are reared apart from their own kind (53). More recently, Thorpe (54) discovered a critical period for this effect in the chaffinch. If isolated at 3 or 4 days of age, a young male chaffinch produces an incomplete song, but if he hears adults singing, as a fledgling 2 or 3 weeks old or in early juvenile life before he sings himself, he will the next year produce the song characteristic of the species, even if he has been kept in isolation. In nature, the fine details of the song are added at the time of competition over territory, within a period of 2 or 3 weeks, when the bird is about a year old. At this time it learns the songs of two or three of its neighbors, and never learns any others in subsequent years. The critical period for song learning is thus a relatively long one, but it is definitely over by the time the bird is a year old. There is no obvious explanation for its ending at this particular time, but it is possible that learning a complete song pattern in some way interferes with further learning.

King and Gurney (55) found that adult mice reared in groups during youth fought more readily than animals isolated at 20 days of age. Later experiments showed that most of the effect was produced in a 10-day period just after weaning, and that similar experience as adults produced little or no effect (56). Thus, there appears to be a critical period for learning to fight through social experience, and this experience need be no more than contact through a wire. In this case the effect is probably produced by association with other mice before the fear response has been completely developed. Similarly, Fisher (16) and Fuller (57) inhibited the development of attacking behavior in fox terriers by raising them in isolation through the critical period for socialization. The animals would fight back somewhat ineffectually if attacked, but did not initiate conflicts. Tinbergen (58) found a critical period in dogs for learning territorial boundaries, coinciding with sexual maturity.

The results of corresponding experiments on sexual behavior vary from species to species. In mice, rearing in isolation produced no effects (59). Beach (60) found that male rats reared with either females or males were actually slower to respond to sexual behavior than isolated males, and he suggested that habits of playful fighting established by the group-reared animals interfered with sexual behavior later on. In guinea pigs, contact with other young animals improves sexual performance (61).

On the other hand, young chimpanzees (62) reared apart from their kind can only be mated with experienced animals. Harlow (21) discovered that his rhesus infants reared on dummy mothers did not develop normal patterns of sexual behavior, and he was able to obtain matings only by exposing females to experienced males . . . . Normal behavior can be developed by allowing 20-minute daily play periods with other young monkeys, but if rhesus infants are reared apart from all other monkeys beyond the period when they spontaneously play with their fellows, patterns of both sexual and maternal behavior fail to develop normally. These results suggest that play has an important role in developing adult patterns of social behavior in these primates, and that the decline of play behavior sets the upper limit of the critical period during which normal adult behavior may be developed.

Such great changes in the social environment rarely occur in humans even by accident, but Money, Hampson, and Hampson (63) have studied the development of hermaphroditic children who have been reared as one sex and then changed to the other. They find that if this occurs before 2½ years of age, very little emotional disturbance results. Thus, there is a critical period for learning the sex role, this capacity persisting unchanged up to a point in development which roughly corresponds to the age when children begin to use and understand language. Perhaps more important, this is the age when children first begin to take an interest in, and play with, members of their own age group.

It is difficult to find a common factor in these critical periods for learning. In some species, such as rats, mice, dogs, and sheep, certain critical periods for learning coincide with the period for primary socialization and seem to be similarly brought to a close by the development of fear reactions. Other critical periods, in chaffinches and dogs, coincide with the formation of adult mating bonds. However, the critical period for sexual learning in the rhesus monkey comes later than that for primary socialization (64), as do critical periods for various kinds of learning in human beings.

Part of this apparent inconsistency arises from our ignorance regarding timing mechanisms. One such mechanism must be the development of learning capacities, and we have evidence in dogs (65), rhesus monkeys (66), and human infants (12) that learning capacities change during development, sometimes in a stepwise fashion. One element in these capacities is the ability to learn things which facilitate subsequent learning.

It is equally possible, however, to "learn not to learn," and such a negative learning set may act to bring the critical period to a close. At this point, we can only state a provisional general hypothesis: that the critical period for any specific sort of learning is that time when maximum capacities—sensory, motor, and motivational, as well as psychological ones—are first present.

Critical Periods for Early Stimulation

Experiments to determine the effects of early stimulation have been mainly performed on infant mice and rats, which are usually weaned at about 21 days at the earliest, and have been concerned with the effect of stimulation during this pre-weaning period. All investigators beginning with Levine (67) and Schaefer (68), agree that rats handled during the first week or 10 days of life have a lessened tendency to urinate and defecate in a strange "open field" situation, learn avoidance behavior more readily, and survive longer when deprived of food and water. In short, early stimulation produces an animal that is less timorous, learns more quickly, and is more vigorous. Levine found that the effect could be obtained by a variety of stimuli, including electric shock and mechanical shaking as well as handling. This ruled out learned behavior as an explanation of the effect, and Levine, Alpert, and Lewis (69) discovered that animals handled in the early period showed a much earlier maturation of the adrenocortical response to stress. Levine interpreted these results as indicating that the laboratory environment did not pro-

vide sufficient stimulation for the proper development of the hormonal systems of the animals. This interpretation is in agreement with Richter's finding (70) that laboratory rats are quite deficient in adrenocortical response as compared with the wild variety. Schaefer, Weingarten, and Towne (71) have duplicated Levine's results by the use of cold alone, and have suggested temperature as a possible unitary mechanism. However, their findings are not necessarily in disagreement with those of Levine, as the hormonal stress response can be elicited by a variety of stimuli, and temperature may simply be another of the many kinds of stimuli which produce the effect.

According to Thompson and Schaefer (72) the earlier the stimulation the greater the effect. If the hormonal mechanism is the chief phenomenon involved, we can say that there is a critical period during the first week or 10 days of life, since the adrenal response in any case matures and becomes fixed by 16 days of age.

Denenberg (73) takes a somewhat different approach, pointing out that there should be optimal levels of stimulation, so that either very weak or very strong stimulation would produce poor results. He suggests that there are different critical periods for the effect of early stimulation, depending on the intensity of stimulation and the kind of later behavior measured. Working within the critical first 10 days, Denenberg found that the best avoidance learning was produced by stimulation in the second half of the period, whereas the best survival rates were produced by stimulation in the first half. Weight was approximately equally affected, except that there was little effect in the first 3 days (74).

Analyzing the effect on avoidance learning, Denenberg (75) and his associates found that both unhandled controls and rats handled for the first 20 days performed poorly, the former because they were too emotional and the latter because they were too calm to react quickly. An intermediate amount of emotional response produces the best learning, and this can be produced by handling only in the first 10 days of life; handling during the second 10 days has a lesser effect. No handling produces too much emotionality, and handling for 20 days results in too little. Irrespective of the effect on learning, the data lead to the important conclusion that emotional stimulation during a critical period early in life can lead to the reduction of emotional responses in later life.

More precisely, there appear to be two critical periods revealed by research on early stimulation of rats, one based on a physiological process (the development of the adrenal cortical stress mechanism) and extending to 16 days of age at the latest, the other based on a psychological process (the reduction of fear through familiarity) (51), beginning about 17 days when the eyes first open and extending to 30 days. The effects of handling during these two periods are additive, and many experiments based on arbitrary time rather than developmental periods undoubtedly include both.

The deleterious effects of excessive stimulation in the life of the infant may also be interpreted as a traumatic emotional experience. Bowlby (76), in studying the group of juvenile thieves, found that a large proportion of them had been separated from their mothers in early infancy, and he postulated that this traumatic emotional experience had affected their later behavior. Since this conclusion was based on retrospective information, he and his coworkers have since studied the primary symptoms of separation and have described in detail the emotional reactions of infants sent to hospitals, and thus separated from their mothers (77). Schaffer (78) found a difference in reaction to separation before 7 months and separation afterward. Both sets of infants were disturbed, .but they were disturbed in different ways. Infants show increasingly severe emotional reactions to adoption from 3 through 12 months of age (33). It seems logical to place the beginning of the critical period for maximum emotional disturbance at approximately 7 months— at the end of the critical period for primary socialization, which Gray (79) places at approximately 6 weeks to 6 months. Infants whose social relationships have been thoroughly established and whose fear responses toward strangers have been fully developed are much more likely to be upset by changes than infants in which these relationships and responses have not yet been developed.

However, not all apparently "traumatic" early experiences have such a lasting effect. Experimental work shows that young animals have a considerable capacity to recover from unpleasant emotions experienced in a limited period in early life (80), and that what is traumatic in one species may not be in another. While young rats become calmer after infantile stimulation, young mice subjected to excessive auditory stimulation later become more emotional (81). At this point it is appropriate to point out that critical periods are not necessarily involved in every kind of early experience. Raising young chimpanzees in the dark produces degeneration of the retina, but this is a long and gradual process (82).

Another approach to the problem is to stimulate emotional responses in mothers and observe the effect on the offspring. Thompson (83) and other authors (84) have shown that the offspring of rats made fearful while pregnant are more likely to be overemotional in the open-field situation than the offspring of animals not so stimulated. Since any direct influence of maternal behavior was ruled out by cross-fostering experiments, it seems likely that the result is produced by modification of the adrenocortical stress mechanism — in this case, by secretion of maternal hormones acting on the embryo rather than by stimulation after birth of the young animal itself. No precise critical period for the effect has been established, but it is probably confined to the latter part of pregnancy. Similar effects have been obtained in mice (85), and if such effects can be demonstrated in other mammals, the implications for prenatal care in human beings are obvious.

It is interesting to note that, whereas shocking the mother both before and after parturition has the effect of increasing emotional responses in the young, the emotional responses of young rats are *decreased* when the treatment is applied directly to them. The explanation of this contradiction must await direct experiments on the endocrine system.

General Theory of Critical Periods

There are at least two ways in which experience during critical periods may act on behavioral development. The critical period for primary socialization constitutes a turning point. Experience during a short period early in life determines which shall be the close relatives of the young animal, and this, in turn, leads the animal to develop in one of two directions —the normal one, in which it becomes attached to and mates with a member of its own species, or an abnormal one, in which it becomes attached to a different species, with consequent disrupting effects upon sexual and other social relationships with members of its own kind.

The concept of a turning point applies equally well to most examples of critical periods for learning. Up to a certain point in development a chaffinch can learn several varieties of song, but once it has learned one of them it no longer has a choice. Similarly, the human infant can learn either sex role up to a certain age, but once it has learned one or the other, changing over becomes increasingly difficult. What is learned at particular points limits and interferes with subsequent

learning, and Schneirla and Rosenblatt (86) have suggested that there are critical stages of learning—that what has been learned at a particular time in development may be critical for whatever follows.

A second sort of action during a critical period consists of a nonspecific stimulus producing an irrevocable result, not modifiable in subsequent development. Thus, almost any sort of stimulus has the effect of modifying the development of the endocrine stress mechanism of young rats in early infancy.

Is there any underlying common principle? Each of these effects has its counterpart in embryonic development. Up to a certain point a cell taken from an amphibian embryo and transplanted to a new location will develop in accordance with its new environment. Beyond this turning point it develops in accordance with its previous location. Some cells retain a degree of lability, but none retain the breadth of choice they had before. Similarly, specific injuries produced by nonspecific causes are also found in embryonic development: damage to an embryonic optic vesicle results in a defective eye, no matter what sort of chemical produces the injury. It is obvious that the similarity between this case and the critical period for early stimulation can be accounted for by the single common process of growth, occurring relatively late in development in the case of the endocrine stress mechanism and much earlier in the development of the eye. The effects are nonspecific because of the fact that growth can be modified in only very limited ways, by being either slowed down or speeded up.

Both growth and behavioral differentiation are based on organizing processes. This suggests a general principle of organization: that once a system becomes organized, whether it is the cells of the embryo that are multiplying and differentiating or the behavior patterns of a young animal that are becoming organized through learning, it becomes progressively more difficult to reorganize the system. That is, organization inhibits reorganization. Further, organization can be strongly modified only when active processes of organization are going on, and this accounts for critical periods of development.

Conclusion

The concept of critical periods is a highly important one for human and animal welfare. Once the dangers and potential benefits for each period of life are known, it should be possible to avoid the former and take advantage of the latter.

The discovery of critical periods immediately focuses attention on the developmental processes which cause them. As these processes become understood, it is increasingly possible to deliberately modify critical periods and their results. For example, since the development of fear responses limits the period of primary socialization, we can deliberately extend the period by reducing fear reactions, either by psychological methods or by the use of tranquilizing drugs. Or, if it seems desirable, we can increase the degree of dependency of a child or pet animal by purposely increasing his emotional reactions during the critical period. Again, if infantile stimulation is desirable, parents can be taught to provide it in appropriate amounts at the proper time.

Some data suggest that for each behavioral and physiological phenomenon there is a different critical period in development. If this were literally true, the process of development, complicated by individual variability, would be so complex that the concept of critical periods would serve little useful purpose. Some sort of order can be obtained by dealing with different classes of behavioral phenomena. For example, it can be stated that the period in life in which each new social relationship is initiated is a critical one for the determination of that relationship. Furthermore, there is evidence that critical-period effects are more common early in life than they are later on, and that the critical period for primary socialization is also critical for other effects, such as the attachment to particular places (87), and may overlap with a critical period for the formation of basic food habits (88).

We may expect to find that the periods in which actual physiological damage through environmental stimulation is possible will turn out to be similarly specific and concentrated in early life.

A great deal of needed information regarding the optimum periods for acquiring motor and intellectual skills is still lacking. These skills are based not merely on age but on the relative rate of maturation of various organs. Any attempt to teach a child or animal at too early a period of development may result in his learning bad habits, or simply in his learning "not to learn," either of which results may greatly handicap him in later life. In the long run, this line of experimental work should lead to greater realization of the capacities possessed by human beings, both through avoidance of damaging experiences and through correction of damage from unavoidable accidents (89).

REFERENCES

AND NOTES

1. SCOTT, J. P.: *Comp. Psychol. Monogr.* **18**, 1 (1945).
2. FIELDE, A. M.: *Biol. Bull.* **7**, 227 (1904).
3. STOCKARD, C. R.: *Am. J. Anat.* **28**, 115 (1921).
4. CHILD, C. M.: *Patterns and Problems of Development* (Univ. of Chicago Press, Chicago, 1941).
5. LORENZ, K.: *J. Ornithol.* **83**, 137, 289 (1935).
6. McGRAW, M. B.: In *Manual of Child Psychology*, L. C. Carmichael, Ed. (Wiley, New York, 1946), pp. 332–369.
7. HESS, E. H.: In *Nebraska Symposium on Motivation* (Univ. of Nebraska Press, Lincoln, 1959), pp. 44–77.
8. MOLTZ, H.: *Psychol. Bull.* **57**, 291 (1960);

J. L. Gewirtz: In *Determinants of Infant Behaviour*, B. M. Foss, Ed. (Methuen, London, 1961), pp. 213–299.

9. Scott, J. P.: In *Social Behavior and Organization in Vertebrates*, W. Etkin, Ed. (Univ. of Chicago Press, Chicago, 1964), pp. 231–255.

10. Nice, M. M.: *Trans. Linnaean Soc. N. Y.* 6, 1 (1943).

11. Scott, J. P., and M. V. Marston: *J. Genet. Psychol.* 77, 25 (1950).

12. Scott, J. P.: *Child Develop. Monogr.*, 28, 1 (1963).

13. Brodbeck, A. J.: *Bull. Ecol. Soc. Am.* 35, 73 (1954).

14. Stanley, W. C.: Private communication (1962).

15. Elliot, O., and J. A. King: *Psychol. Repts.* 6, 391 (1960).

16. Fisher, A. E.: Thesis, Pennsylvania State Univ. (1955).

17. Elliot, O., and J. P. Scott: *J. Genet. Psychol.* 99, 3 (1961).

18. Scott, J. P., D. Deshaies, and D. D. Morris: "Effect of emotional arousal on primary socialization in the dog," address to the New York State Branch of the American Psychiatric Association, 11 Nov. 1961.

19. Harlow, H.: *Am. Psychologist* 13, 673 (1958).

20. Igel, G. J., and A. D. Calvin: *J. Comp. Physiol. Psychol.* 53, 302 (1960).

21. Harlow, H. F., and M. K. Harlow: Personal communication (1962).

22. Fabricius, E.: *Acta Zool. Fennica* 68, 1 (1951).

23. Collias, N.: In *Roots of Behavior*, E. L. Bliss, Ed. (Harper, New York, 1962), pp. 264–273.

24. Hess, E. H.: *Ann. N. Y. Acad. Sci.* 67, 724 (1957); in *Drugs and Behavior*, L. Uhr and J. G. Miller, Eds. (Wiley, New York, 1960), pp. 268–271.

25. James, H.: *Can. J. Psychol.* 13, 59 (1959).

26. Gray, P. H.: *Science* 132, 1834 (1960).

27. Guiton, P.: *Animal Behavior* 9, 167 (1961).

28. Pitz, G. F., and R. B. Ross: *J. Comp. Physiol. Psychol.* 54, 602 (1961).

29. Hess, E. H.: "Influence of early experience on behavior," paper presented before the American Psychiatric Association, New York State Divisional Meeting, 1961.

30. Moltz, H., L. Rosenblum, and N. Hali-

kas: *J. Comp. Physiol. Psychol.* 52, 240 (1959).

31. Gottlieb, G.: *Ibid.* 54, 422 (1961).

32. Scott, J. P.: *Psychosomat. Med.* 20, 42 (1958).

33. Caldwell, B. M.: *Am. Psychol.* 16, 377 (1961).

34. Hinde, R. A., W. H. Thorpe, and M. A. Vince: *Behaviour* 9, 214 (1956).

35. Freedman, D. G., J. A. King, and O. Elliot: *Science* 133, 1016 (1961).

36. Harlow, H. F., and R. R. Zimmermann: *Ibid.* 130, 421 (1959).

37. Freedman, D. G.: *J. Child Psychol. Psychiat.* 1961, 242 (1961).

38. Spitz, R. A.: *Intern. J. Psychoanalysis* 31, 138 (1950).

39. Collias, N. E.: *Ecology* 37, 228 (1956).

40. Craig, W.: *J. Animal Behavior* 4, 121 (1914).

41. Fuller, J. L., and A. Christake: *Federation Proc.* 18, 49 (1959).

42. Fuller, J. L.: Private communication.

43. Schutz, F.: Private communication.

44. Warriner, C. C.: Thesis, Univ. of Oklahoma (1960).

45. Enders, R. K.: *Sociometry* 8, 53–55 (1945).

46. Klopfer, P. H.: *Behavioral Aspects of Ecology* (Prentice-Hall, New York, 1962).

47. McGraw, M. B.: *Growth: a Study of Johnny and Jimmy* (Appleton-Century, New York, 1935).

48. Hebb, D. O.: *Am. Psychologist* 2, 306 (1947).

49. Forgays, D. G., and J. W. Forgays: *J. Comp. Physiol. Psychol.* 45, 322 (1952).

50. Forgays, D. G.: "The importance of experience at specific times in the development of an organism," address before the Eastern Psychological Association (1962).

51. Candland, D. K., and B. A. Campbell: Private communication (1962).

52. Bernstein, L.: *J. Comp. Physiol. Psychol.* 50, 162 (1957).

53. Scott, W. E. D.: *Science* 14, 522 (1901).

54. Thorpe, W. H.: In *Current Problems in Animal Behaviour*, W. H. Thorpe and O. L. Zangwill, Eds. (Cambridge Univ. Press, Cambridge, 1961).

55. King, J. A., and N. L. Gurney: *J. Comp. Physiol. Psychol.* 47, 326 (1954).

56. King, J. A.: *J. Genet. Psychol.* 90, 151 (1957).

57. Fuller, J. L.: "Proceedings, International

Psychiatric Congress, Montreal," in press.

58. TINBERGEN, N.: *The Study of Instinct* (Oxford Univ. Press, Oxford, 1951).

59. KING, J. A.: *J. Genet. Psychol.* **88**, 223 (1956).

60. BEACH, F. A.: *Ibid.* **60**, 121 (1942).

61. VALENSTEIN, E. S., W. RISS, and W. C. YOUNG: *J. Comp. Physiol. Psychol.* **47**, 162 (1954).

62. NISSEN, H.: *Symposium on Sexual Behavior in Mammals, Amherst, Mass.* (1954), pp. 204–227.

63. MONEY, J., J. G. HAMPSON, and J. L. HAMPSON: *Arch. Neurol. Psychiat.* **77**, 333 (1957).

64. HARLOW, H.: In *Determinants of Infant Behaviour*, B. M. Foss, Ed. (Wiley, New York, 1961), pp. 75–97.

65. FULLER, J. L., C. A. EASLER, and E. M. BANKS: *Am. J. Physiol.* **160**, 462 (1950); A. C. CORNWELL and J. L. FULLER: *J. Comp. Physiol. Psychol.* **54**, 13 (1961).

66. HARLOW, H. F., M. K. HARLOW, R. R. RUEPING, and W. A. MASON: *J. Comp. Physiol. Psychol.* **53**, 113 (1960).

67. LEVINE, S., J. A. CHEVALIER, and S. J. KORCHIN: *J. Personality* **24**, 475 (1956).

68. SCHAEFER, T.: Thesis, Univ. of Chicago (1957).

69. LEVINE, S., M. ALPERT, and G. W. LEWIS: *Science* **126**, 1347 (1957).

70. RICHTER, C. P.: *Am. J. Human Genet.* **4**, 273 (1952).

71. SCHAEFER, T., JR., F. S. WEINGARTEN, and J. C. TOWNE: *Science* **135**, 41 (1962).

72. THOMPSON, W. R., and T. SCHAEFER: In *Functions of Varied Experience*, D. W. Fiske and S. R. Maddi, Eds. (Dorsey, Homewood, Ill., 1961), pp. 81–105.

73. DENENBERG, V. H.: In *The Behaviour of Domestic Animals*, E. S. E. Hafez, Ed.

(Bailliere, Tindall and Cox, London), 109–138.

74. DENENBERG, V. H.: *J. Comp. Physiol. Psychol.* **55**, 582–589 (1962).

75. DENENBERG, V. H., and G. G. KARAS: *Psychol. Repts.* **7**, 313 (1960).

76. BOWLBY, J.: *Intern. J. Psychoanalysis* **25**, 19, 107 (1944).

77. HEINICKE, C. M.: *Human Relations* **9**, 105 (1956).

78. SCHAFFER, H. R.: *Brit. J. Med. Psychol.* **31**, 174 (1950).

79. GRAY, P. H.: *J. Psychol.* **46**, 155 (1958).

80. KAHN, M. W.: *J. Genet. Psychol.* **79**, 117 (1951); A. BARON, K. H. BROOKSHIRE, and R. A. LITTMAN: *J. Comp. Physiol. Psychol.* **50**, 530 (1957).

81. LINDZEY, G., D. T. LYKKEN, and H. D. WINSTON: *J. Abnormal Soc. Psychol.* **61**, 7 (1960).

82. RIESEN, A. H.: In *Functions of Varied Experience*, D. W. Fiske and S. R. Maddi, Eds. (Dorsey, Homewood, Ill., 1961), pp. 57–80.

83. THOMPSON, W. R.: *Science* **125**, 698 (1957).

84. HOCKMAN, C. H.: *J. Comp. Physiol. Psychol.* **54**, 679 (1961); R. ADER and M. L. BELFER: *Psychol. Repts.* **10**, 711 (1962).

85. KEELEY, K.: *Science* **135**, 44 (1962).

86. SCHNEIRLA, T. C., and J. S. ROSENBLATT: *Am. J. Orthopsychiat.* **31**, 223 (1960).

87. THORPE, W. H.: *Learning and Instinct in Animals* (Methuen, London, 1956).

88. HESS, E. H.: In *Roots of Behavior*, E. L. Bliss, Ed. (Harper, New York, 1962), pp. 254–263.

89. Part of the research described in this article was supported by a Public Health Service research grant (No. M-4481) from the National Institute of Mental Health.

25   Letters:

I. "Critical Periods" in the Development of Behavior

T. C. SCHNEIRLA and JAY S. ROSENBLATT

II. Reply to Schneirla and Rosenblatt

J. P. SCOTT

Science thrives on controversy. Provided that opposing theories are testable, nothing stimulates research better than disagreement. The careful reader will have noted in the two previous readings that Scott's ideas about the critical period hypothesis differ somewhat from those of Schneirla and Rosenblatt. In response to Scott's article in *Science* (reading 24), Schneirla and Rosenblatt wrote a protest published in the "Letters" section of that journal, in which Scott's reply was also published. Both letters are reproduced here with the kind permission of Doctors Schneirla, Rosenblatt, and Scott, and the American Association for the Advancement of Science.

Reference: *Science*, Vol. 139, pp. 1110–1116, 15 March 1963. Copyright 1963 by the American Association for the Advancement of Science. Reprinted by permission.

I.
"Critical Periods" in the Development of Behavior

Scott's interesting article (1) on "critical periods" in behavioral development merits a thoroughgoing critical review bearing on the validity of his general conceptions of behavioral ontogeny basic to the idea which he has extrapolated from embryology to the study of behavior. Here, however, we comment specifically on certain inferences that might be drawn from his allusion to our recent article on behavioral development in cats (2).

In discussing his concept of critical periods, Scott reports us as having "suggested that there are critical stages of learning—that what has been learned at a particular time in development may be critical for whatever follows."

Although we are not disposed to dispute this broad statement, it is not ours. In our view, any such sentence should have a more comprehensive context, to the effect that what the young animal may attain in behavior at any phase of ontogeny depends upon the outcome of earlier development in its every aspect. The point we wish to emphasize here, however, is that our position might be seriously misunderstood in at least two important respects from Scott's allusion to our article. (i) Although, as our study of social behavior in newborn kittens (2, 3) indicated strongly, learning is involved at all phases in behavior development, our findings have broader and very different implications for social ontogeny than might be gathered from Scott's mention of the work. (ii) The context indicates that Scott has misunderstood the criticisms we have

287

offered (2, 3) of his "critical periods" concept.

The gist of our objection is not that we favor describing three critical periods of social development, corresponding to the three main stages in the ontogeny of social-feeding behavior in kittens for which we found evidence, or whatever number of critical periods might be advanced as an alternative. We were interpreting our results from a viewpoint definitely at odds with Scott's notion of "critical periods" when we wrote (2): "These considerations favor a very different view of the concept of 'critical periods' from the one now held by many writers. In the social development of the cat, we are led to the idea that striking changes in the essential progression are grounded not only in the growth-dependent processes of maturation but also, at the same time, in opportunities for experience and learning arising in the standard female-litter situation. This conception of social ontogeny encourages stressing not just one or a few chronologically marked changes in the behavior pattern, but rather indicates that normally each age period is crucial for the development of particular aspects in a complex progressive pattern of adjustment." We consider the implications of this theoretical viewpoint for developmental research very different from those of Scott's concept.

Evidence supporting our view demonstrated that in kittens, at all age periods, social approaches preliminary to feeding behavior undergo a course of development in the litter situation significantly different from the behavior of kittens reared under conditions of isolation and fed from an "artificial mother" (2, 3). No evidence was found for any time interval in which the different conditions of rearing failed to produce a pattern of feeding approaches and suckling in kittens reared in isolation that was significantly different from that in normally reared kittens of corresponding ages. This result had

been predicted from the theory of social ontogeny (4) which guided our work.

Those who examine this theory (4, 5) and related considerations (2, 6, 7) will find an emphasis upon the fusion of maturation (growth-contributed) and experience (stimulation-contributed) processes at different stages in behavior ontogeny, together with the contention that the contributions both of maturation and of experience (the latter including, but not confined to, conditioning and learning), as well as the interrelations of these contributions, may differ greatly according to stage in any animal. This theory thus differs sharply from Scott's, with its emphasis (see 8) upon factors of maturation presumably specific for "critical periods" and its apparent assumption that "learning" is a distinct and probably a delayed contributor.

From our theory of behavioral development (4–6), we conclude that factors of maturation may differ significantly in their influence upon ontogeny, both in the nature and in the timing of their effects, according to what relations to the effects of experience are possible under the existing conditions. We found, in support of this view, that gains in suckling made by kittens reared in isolation differed greatly from gains made by litter mates reared by the mother, and that the kittens reared in isolation were, at best, only partially adapted to the demands of social feeding and suckling of the mother at the time of their return to the litter. The differences between the experimental animals and the control litter mates were striking. In no single phase of development during the first 2 months of life did these two very different conditions of rearing — with mother and litter or isolated, with an "artificial mother"—fail to have very different effects on the development of suckling responses, despite the presumable equivalence of potential factors of maturation for kittens in the two groups. The results indicate that the actual effects of maturation differed considerably in the two cases. We do not find such evidence compatible with the meaning of *maturation* that would seem to follow from the critical-period hypothesis.

What is social behavior? Scott states (1) that in puppies the period of socialization begins at approximately 3 weeks of age. We submit, however, that much of the evidence he cites bears only tangentially on the question of when socialization really begins. Although his article is mainly concerned with social behavior, it does not deal primarily with *intra*species behavorial relationships, but deals, instead, with the responses of puppies to human handlers, of young birds to artifacts, and the like. Under the heading, "Process of primary socialization" we find, for example, citations of tests in which machine-fed and hand-fed puppies "became equally attached to people . . .," hand-fed puppies "yelped more when they saw the experimenter . . .," "hungry puppies became more rapidly attached to the handlers . . .," and "separating young puppies overnight from their mother and litter mates . . . speeded up the process of socialization to human handlers."

The degree of equivalence between such results and the ontogeny of interactions among species mates may prove to be appreciable, but it has not been determined. We suggest that Scott, in basing his principal treatment of social development upon experimental interventions featuring responses to conditions other than association with species mates has been led astray. In our studies of the social-feeding behavior of kittens we were able to distinguish early forms of intraspecies social responses not evident in reactions to human handlers or to artifacts such as the "artificial mother." A dependence upon the latter two sources of evidence might have led us to neglect aspects of intraspecies behavior which we found crucial for the understanding of social ontogeny.

With due emphasis upon intraspecies behavioral relations, we maintain that processes of socialization and formation of the social bond begin at birth, if not earlier (2–6). Kittens make consistent progress from an hour or two after birth in becoming oriented to their environment and to species mates, in becoming adjusted to the litter situation and the "home area," and in making individual, distinctive responses to particular nipples. Such aspects of behavior concern reciprocal relations of dependency with the mother and with litter mates, hence are social.

Because Scott was concerned with giving an account of the critical-period concept and illustrating it, evidence centered on the ontogeny of intraspecies responses may not have seemed relevant to him. Yet, because his reference to our article might imply that it supports his own concepts of behavioral development, we assert that there is an important difference between his view and our own.

T. C. SCHNEIRLA
JAY S. ROSENBLATT

REFERENCES

1. SCOTT, J. P.: *Science* **138**, 949 (1962).
2. SCHNEIRLA, T. C., and J. S. ROSENBLATT: *Am. J. Orthopsychiat.* **31**, 223 (1960).
3. ROSENBLATT, J. S., G. TURKEWITZ, and T. C. SCHNEIRLA: In *Determinants of Infant Behaviour*, B. M. Foss, Ed. (Methuen, London, 1961), pp. 51–74.
4. SCHNEIRLA, T. C.: In *L'Instinct dans le Comportement des Animaux et de l'Homme* (Masson, Paris, 1956), pp. 387–452.
5. SCHNEIRLA, T. C.: *J. Abnormal Soc. Psychol.* **41**, 385 (1946).
6. SCHNEIRLA, T. C.: In *Problems of Infancy and Childhood*, M. J. Senn, Ed. (Josiah Macy, Jr. Foundation, New York, 1951), pp. 81–124.
7. THOMAS, A., H. G. BIRCH, S. CHESS, and M. E. HERTZIG: In *Proc. World Congr. Psychiat. 3rd, Montreal* (1962), pp. 722–726.
8. SCOTT, J. P.: *Psychosomat. Med.* **20**, 42 (1958).

II.
Reply

Statements of contrasting theoretical positions are useful if they stimulate the collection of additional data, leading in turn to the modification and evolution of theory. I am sure that the comments of Schneirla and Rosenblatt were offered in this spirit, as is my reply.

The points raised in their letter go far beyond the scope of my original article. I believe that most of them are complementary rather than contradictory.

1) Failure to find a critical period for primary socialization in the cat. In order to thoroughly understand the development of behavior in a given species, one should have timed data on the development of basic behavioral capacities, including sensory, motor, and learning capacities, as well as on the development of patterns of social behavior. In addition, one should have a description of adult social organization, to which behavioral development seems to be strongly related. In the absence of such general background information for the cat, I have been unable to evaluate Schneirla and Rosenblatt's data in terms of evidence for the existence or nonexistence of a critical period for primary socialization. Although cats are not highly social animals, I would be surprised if there were no such period in this animal, in view of the wide occurrence of the phenomenon in social birds and mammals, and even in insects.

2) Role of learning in behavioral development. With respect to the importance of learning in behavioral development, our points of view are supplementary rather than antithetic. Where Schneirla and Rosenblatt emphasize the fusion of maturation and learning, I would add that the learning process also changes with time and can itself be thought of as a developmental process. Much evidence indicates that the rate of development of the capacity for learning varies widely from species to species, but additional information is badly needed along these lines. To my knowledge, in no species, not even the human, has a study of any simple learning capacity been carried completely through the stages of early development.

3) Nature of the process of socialization. Schneirla and Rosenblatt have concerned themselves with the point at which the process begins; my article dealt with the period during which the process proceeds most rapidly. Both kinds of information are necessary for understanding the process. As I said in the article, processes are not necessarily limited to the periods in which they are most prominent.

4) Experimental methodology. Two principal methods of studying the development of social behavior have been used: cross-fostering between species (or upon models) and social isolation. The two methods produce quite different results. In general, cross-fostering transfers social relationships but often has little effect on the development of social behavior patterns. Social isolation prevents the development of social relationships and may distort or inhibit the development of certain social behavior patterns. Both methods contribute to our understanding of the process of socialization. Schneirla and Rosenblatt observe that the cross-fostering method is more likely to reveal the existence of critical periods; this method has not yet been applied in the cat.

5) The nature of behavioral development. Two testable hypotheses can be stated (in stating them I do not ascribe either extreme of the two viewpoints to Schneirla and Rosenblatt). (i) Behavioral development is a unitary process, and what takes place in one period of development is dependent on everything that went before. (ii) Behavioral development may be composed of many different processes having a considerable degree of independence, both within the individual and between species. The actual facts

probably lie somewhere between these two viewpoints.

Behavioral development is an extremely complex phenomenon. In interpreting any given set of data it is important that alternative hypotheses be considered and eventually tested.

J. P. SCOTT

VICTOR H. DENENBERG

26   An Attempt to Isolate Critical Periods of Development in the Rat*

Recent experimentation has shown that handling an infant organism will affect its later behavior. Victor H. Denenberg, a frequent contributor to the literature on behavioral development, reports an effort to specify the critical period for such stimulation in the rat.

Reference: *Journal of Comparative and Physiological Psychology*, 1962, **55**, 582–589. Reprinted by permission of the author and the American Psychological Association.

An examination of the critical-period literature shows that two related but different approaches have been followed by researchers. One approach is to ask whether the same stimulation at different ages in early life has the same effect; if not, this has been considered proof that there are critical periods in development. The other approach is to try to find certain limited periods in development during which a particular stimulus will have rather profound effects. This approach stems directly from the embryological meaning of critical periods, and it is in this context that Scott (1958; Williams & Scott, 1953) has used the term.

A number of studies have shown that the same stimulation at different ages will have different effects in adulthood (e.g., Denenberg & Bell, 1960; Denenberg & Karas, 1960, 1961). There have been fewer studies which have been able to

* This investigation was supported in part by Research Grant M-1753 from the National Institute of Mental Health of the National Institutes of Health, United States Public Health Service.

demonstrate the second meaning of critical periods (Levine & Lewis, 1959). The purpose of this experiment was to stimulate Ss for brief intervals during the first 10 days of life to see whether evidence supporting either or both concepts of critical periods could be found. The first 10 days was chosen for investigation since prior work has shown that stimulation throughout this interval had significant effects upon avoidance learning, body weight, and survival time (Denenberg & Karas, 1960, 1961), the variables in this experiment.

Method

The procedures followed were identical in all respects to those of Denenberg and Karas (1960, Experiment III; 1961) and may be briefly summarized.

SUBJECTS

Sixty-nine Harvard Wistar rats from 12 litters were used. They were born in cages measuring 9 in. by 9 in. by 15 in. Litters were reduced to eight pups as soon as discovered. No litter containing less than four pups was used. After a litter was born, the shavings in the cages were never changed.

INFANTILE EXPERIENCE

Two litters were randomly assigned to each of the following experimental treatments: handling on Days 1 to 3, 3 to 5, 1 to 5, 6 to 8, 8 to 10, or 6 to 10. Handling consisted of removing the young from the cage once daily, placing each S individually into a 1-gal. tin can partially filled with shavings, leaving the Ss in the cans for 3 min., and then returning them to the cages. At 21 days the Ss were weaned, earpunched, sexed, weighed to the nearest .1 gm., and placed in small cages with like-sexed litter mates. Food and water were always present until the terminal phase of the experiment.

ADULT TESTING

The avoidance learning apparatus consisted of an interchangeable start box and escape box, and a center chamber. A constant-current shock unit, set at .8 ma., was used. The current was randomly distributed over the bars of the grid by means of a scrambler.

Starting at 60 days the Ss were habituated to the apparatus for 2 days, followed by 8 days of avoidance training with five trials per day. The S was placed in the starting chamber at the beginning of each trial. At the same time that the door in front of the start box opened, an auditory CS began and a Standard Electric timer started. The CS terminated 4 sec. later and shock began. Entrance into the escape chamber turned off the timer. If S entered the escape chamber within 4 sec., both the CS and timer were terminated, and this was scored as an avoidance response.

At 69 days after the last set of learning trials the Ss were weighed and placed on terminal food and water deprivation. Hours until death occurred were recorded.

Results and Discussion

The data consist of the body weights at 21 and 69 days, number of avoidance responses, and survival time for the six groups. Data for Ss which received no handling in infancy and for Ss which were handled for the first 10 days of life are also presented as reference values. These values were obtained from other experiments by Denenberg and Karas (1960, Experiments II and III; 1961) in which the identical procedure was followed and which overlapped the present experiment in time. Table 26–1 summarizes the pertinent statistics.

DAY 21 WEIGHT

The analysis of variance of these data found no significant differences among the six experimental groups. This is consistent with the previous finding (Denenberg & Karas, 1961) that the control group and Group 1–10 did not differ significantly.

AVOIDANCE LEARNING

The analysis of variance of number of avoidance responses yielded an overall F ratio of 3.97, $p < .01$. Further analyses determined that Group 6–10 was significantly superior in avoidance learning to all other experimental groups; the remaining five groups did not differ among themselves. When compared with the two reference groups, Group 6–10 was significantly better than the control group ($p < .05$) and did not differ from Group 1–10. The difference between Group 1–5 and the control group approached significance ($p < .08$).

DAY 69 WEIGHT

The body weights were subjected to an analysis of variance after classification by experimental groups and sex. The six groups differed significantly among themselves and sex was significant as well (both

TABLE 26-1

Means and N for the six experimental groups and the two reference groups on the four variables

GROUP	N	21-DAY WT. (GM.)	AVOIDANCE LEARNING	69-DAY WT. (GM.)[a]	HOURS SURVIVAL
1–3	10	41.35	8.50	170.84	265.40
3–5	13	38.81	8.62	199.27	344.92
1–5	12	37.81	8.50	193.24	393.58
6–8	11	35.61	13.45	185.78	256.78[b]
8–10	12	39.52	11.17	198.30	311.67
6–10	11	36.85	20.91	202.14	316.64
Control[c]		37.50	13.85	176.64	175.79
		(46)	(18)	(24)	(24)
1–10[c]		38.63	18.85	205.10	255.52
		(50)	(18)	(25)	(25)

a Means equally weighted for sex.

b $N = 9$ for survival time; 2 Ss escaped.

c Ns given in parentheses; from Denenberg & Karas (1960, 1961).

beyond the .01 level), but the interaction between sex and experimental groups was not significant. The 69-day-weight means in Table 26–1 are equally weighted for sex.

Further analyses of the significant treatment difference revealed that Group 1–3 weighed significantly less than all other groups. In addition, Group 6–10 was heavier than Group 6–8 ($p < .05$) but did not differ from the remaining four groups. Comparisons of these six means with those of the reference groups showed that Group 1–3 had essentially the same mean weight as Ss which received no stimulation in infancy while the means of the other groups were similar to the Group 1–10 mean.

SURVIVAL TIME

The analysis of these data yielded an F of 5.67 ($p < .01$). Group 1–5 survived significantly longer than all other groups except Group 3–5. Comparisons within the first 5 days of life indicated that Group 3–5 survived longer than Group 1–3

($p < .01$), but there were no significant differences within the second 5 days. All six experimental groups survived significantly longer than the control Ss. Four groups were found to survive significantly longer than Group 1–10: Groups 3–5, 1–5, 6–10, and 8–10.

NUMBER OF DAYS OF HANDLING AND PERFORMANCE

Another way to analyze these data is to examine the relationship between number of days of handling and performance, disregarding when S was stimulated. Since the experimental conditions were the same, the present results were combined with the previous work of Denenberg and Karas (1960, Experiments II and III; 1961) yielding five durations of stimulation: 0 (controls), 3, 5, 10, and 20 days. Figure 1 presents curves relating 21- and 69-day body weight, avoidance learning, and survival time to number of days of handling. With the possible exception of the 21-day weight curve, the general function

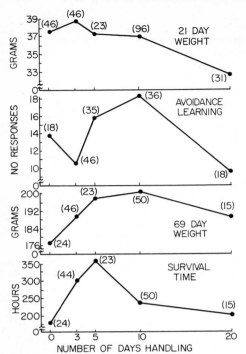

FIG. 1. Weight at 21 days, avoidance learning, weight at 69 days, and survival time as a function of number of days of handling in infancy. (Numbers in parentheses indicate the N for each point.)

of these data may be described by an inverted U curve (Denenberg, 1959).

The data amply demonstrate that both Ss' age when handled and the number of days of handling are significant parameters affecting later behavior. If one considers the demonstration of an age effect in early life to be proof of critical periods, then these data support the critical-period hypothesis. However, the data do not support the concept of critical periods if one thinks of this term in a manner analogous to its use in embryology, namely, that only during certain limited periods of development will a particular stimulus have an effect. The finding that handling on Days 6 to 10 was sufficient to improve learning scores while 3 days of stimulation was not sufficient may be considered to be

a demonstration of the second use of this concept. However, more recent research (Denenberg & Kline, unpublished) has found that this "critical period" is strictly a function of intensity of stimulation; when Ss are shocked rather than handled, the critical period disappears. The present data, in combination with other research (Denenberg & Bell, 1960; Denenberg & Karas, 1960, 1961), strongly indicate that, for the rat and mouse at least, there may be as many critical periods as there are combinations of independent-variable parameters and dependent-variable measures. It appears to be more fruitful to study the functional relationships among these variables than to try to isolate specific critical periods in development.

Summary

In an attempt to isolate critical periods in development, infant rats were handled on Days 1–3, 3–5, 1–5, 6–8, 8–10, or 6–10. They were weighed at 21 days, received avoidance training from 60 to 69 days, were weighed at 69 days, and were then placed on a terminal deprivation schedule until death occurred. Significant differences among the groups were obtained on all measures except 21-day body weight. It was concluded that both Ss' age and the number of days of handling are critical parameters affecting later behavior.

REFERENCES

DENENBERG, V. H.   The interactive effects of infantile and adult shock levels upon adult learning. *Psychol. Rep.*, 1959, **5**, 357–364.

DENENBERG, V. H., and R. W. BELL   Critical periods for the effects of infantile experience on adult learning. *Science,* 1960, **131**, 227–228.

DENENBERG, V. H., and G. G. KARAS   Interactive effects of age and duration of infantile experience on adult learning. *Psychol. Rep.*, 1960, **7**, 313–322.

DENENBERG, V. H., and G. G. KARAS   Interactive effects of infantile and adult experiences upon weight gain and mortality in the rat. *J. comp. physiol. Psychol.*, 1961, **54**, 685–689.

LEVINE, S., and G. W. LEWIS   Critical period for effects of infantile experience on maturation of stress response. *Science*, 1959, **129**, 42–43.

SCOTT, J. P.   Critical periods in the development of social behavior in puppies. *Psychosom. Med.*, 1958, **20**, 42–54.

WILLIAMS, E., and J. P. SCOTT   The development of social behavior patterns in the mouse, in relation to natural periods. *Behaviour*, 1953, **6**, 35–64.

WILLIAM A. MASON

27   The Effects of Social Restriction on the Behavior of Rhesus Monkeys: I. Free Social Behavior*

The behavior of animals has always fascinated man, particularly the behavior of animals that are big, dangerous, or unusual. This interest led to the capture and display of animals in zoos and circuses. But how much of the behavior of captive animals is "normal" for the species? How does the behavior of an animal that has matured in the wild compare with that of a restricted animal? In the following reading, William A. Mason investigates this problem by comparing the social behavior of feral and laboratory-born rhesus monkeys.

This report originally appeared in the *Journal of Comparative and Physiological Psychology*, 1960, **53**, 582–589. It is reprinted here with the permission of the author and the American Psychological Association.

The present researches are part of a series of experiments investigating the effects of restricted social experience on the social behavior of rhesus monkeys. The principal comparisons in these experiments are between monkeys living under free-ranging conditions until captured, and laboratory-born monkeys separated from their mothers in early infancy and raised under conditions which limited the nature and extent of early social experience.

To insure uniform and controlled living conditions and provide ready access to infant Ss for testing, early maternal sep-

* Support for this research was provided through funds received from the Graduate School of the University of Wisconsin, Grant G6194 from the National Science Foundation, and Grant M-722 from the National Institutes of Health.

aration is virtually essential to the effective conduct of a major psychological research program utilizing infant monkey Ss. Such a program has been in progress at the University of Wisconsin since 1953, and a large number of infant monkeys have been separated from their mothers and housed in individual living cages at the Primate Laboratory.

When maintained in accordance with the general recommendations of van Wagenen (1950), there is no indication that early maternal separation adversely affects the growth and viability of the infant macaque. However, the reduction in intraspecies social contacts and the routine and relatively impersonal nature of the caretaking methods employed in the laboratory create an impoverished social environment which approaches the more extreme forms of institutional environments for human children.

Investigations assessing the effects of institutionalization on human personality development and social behavior have been summarized by Bowlby (1952), and the findings indicate that deprivation of normal socialization experiences in human children results in a wide range of personal and social deficiencies and aberrations including affective disorders, limited capacity for sustained and effective social relationships, and psychopathic tendencies.

Although there exist no comparable data on the effects of similar restrictions on the development of social behavior in the nonhuman primates, field workers have generally assumed that prior socialization experience is of fundamental importance in the development of orderly and efficient patterns of social interaction characteristic of nonhuman primate socities (Carpenter, 1942; Imanishi, 1957). Because of formidable practical difficulties, however, careful longitudinal studies have not been completed under field conditions, and the process of socialization in free-ranging primates has not been fully described. The available evidence indicates that under natural conditions there is ample time and opportunity for complex social learning to occur. The period of infantile dependency in Old World monkeys is relatively long, extending in most forms for approximately two years. Following this there is a period of several years during which the tie to the mother gradually weakens and the individual has the status of a juvenile which associates with other young monkeys and does not participate fully in adult functions and activities. Adult status is probably not attained by the male before its sixth year; females mature somewhat earlier.

During these early years the young monkey has considerable social mobility, providing a wide range of social contacts and many opportunities to observe and participate in a variety of activities with peers and with adults of both sexes. It is probable that basic social attachments binding the individual to the group are established and strengthened during this time and many of the essential patterns of social intercourse are developed and refined. Thus, restriction upon the nature and extent of early socialization experience might be expected to produce inadequacies in subsequent relations.

The present research investigated differences in the form and frequency of spontaneous social interactions of feral and laboratory-raised rhesus monkeys.

Experiment 1: Intragroup Comparisons of Feral and Socially Restricted Monkeys

METHOD

Subjects. The Ss were two groups of six adolescent monkeys. One group of three males and three females, the Restricted group, was born in the laboratory. They were separated from their mothers before the end of the first month of life and were housed in individual cages which allowed them to see and hear other young monkeys, but which prevented physical contact between them. Opportunities for more extensive intraspecies social contacts were confined to a few brief periods during the first year of life. Interspecies social experience was limited almost entirely to daily contacts with human beings in connection with routine caretaking and testing activities. At the start of the experiment three Ss were 28 months of age and three were 29 months old.

The second group of three males and three females, the Feral group, was captured in the field. Immediately following their arrival in Madison they spent approximately 3 months on a zoo monkey island with about 20 other monkeys of similar age and background and the next 3 months with the same animals in a large group living cage in the basement of the zoo's primate building. This section is not on exhibition. The entire group was shifted to the laboratory when the 6 Ss later used in this study were about 20 months old. They were housed in pairs for 8 months. At the time of separation, one month before the start of the experiment, none was caged with any other member of the group of 6. During the month before the experiment began and throughout the period covered by this research, the Ss lived in individual cages. They were selected from the larger group to match the Ss of the Restricted group in sex, weight, and dentition. It is estimated the age differences among Ss were no greater than one month.

Apparatus. The test chamber, constructed of gray plywood, measured 6 ft. by 6 ft. by 6 ft. and was illuminated from above by a 150-w. bulb. Two opposing walls contained one-way observation panels, and in each of the other walls was a large hinged door fitted with a smaller sliding door through which the Ss entered the chamber from an adjacent carrying cage. Behavior was recorded on a multiple-category keyboard which operated the pens of an Esterline-Angus recorder, giving a continuous record of the frequency, duration, and temporal patterning of social interactions. By appropriate wiring of the keyboard a total of 11 response categories were available for each member of a test pair.

Procedure. Once a day for 14 days each S was individually placed in a carrying cage at the entrance to the chamber and was allowed 3 min. in which to enter and explore the room. This was followed by seven daily 3-min. sessions in which entry was forced for all Ss not entering the room during the first few seconds of the session.

In the social testing which followed these individual adaptation sessions, Feral and Restricted monkeys were paired only with the other members of their group. Each of the 15 pairs obtainable from each group was observed in a series of 16 social test sessions each 3 min. long. To initiate a session, the sliding door on

the O's right was raised and when the S had entered the room, the second sliding door was raised. When both Ss were in the chamber, the Esterline-Angus recorder was started. A timer automatically stopped the recorder at the end of the test period. The testing schedule was so arranged that all pairs were tested once every two days with the restriction that no S participated in two successive test sessions. For each pair the order of testing and the side

TABLE 27-1

Definitions and reliability of response categories

1. Approach: Moves to within 6 in. of other monkey (75%).
2. Aggression: Includes intense vocalization (barks, growls), biting, pulling. Threat or bluff (Chance, 1956) was not scored as aggression. No occurrence during reliability check.
3. Groom: Systematically picks through another's fur with hands (95%).
4. Mount: Characteristically, grasps the partner's hips with hands, and feet clasp her legs (96%).
5. Play: Tumbling, mauling, wrestling, and nipping. Less vigorous and intense than aggression, is not accompanied by intense vocalization, and rarely elicits squealing or other evidence of pain in partner (79%).
6. Sexual presentation: Assumption of female mating posture. Hindquarters are elevated and turned toward the partner (60%).
7. Social facilitation of exploration: Activity of one animal with respect to some inanimate feature of the room elicits approach, observation, or display of similar behavior from another (59%).
8. Social investigation: Close visual, manual, and/or oral investigation of the partner. Particular interest toward apertures. No occurrence during reliability check.
9. Thrusting: Piston-like movements usually accompanying mounting (95%).
10. Visual orientation: Passive observation of other (66%).
11. Withdrawal: Abrupt movement away from other. Not scored during play or aggression unless it terminated interaction (65%).

from which the Ss entered the chamber were counterbalanced over sessions.

The behavior of each S was separately recorded by depressing the appropriate response-keys during the period of behavioral occurrence. To provide an estimate of the reliability of the method, two Os were present and independently recorded the social interactions of 15 pairs on a total of 90 sessions. Table 27–1 presents definitions of the response categories and their corresponding reliability values for frequency measures. Reliability is expressed in terms of per cent agreement:

$$\frac{\text{Frequency of agreements}}{\text{Frequency of agreements} + \text{disagreements}}$$

RESULTS

To conserve space only the response categories of play, grooming, aggression, and sexual behavior are analyzed in detail. Among the other response measures, differences between groups in the frequency of approaches, withdrawals, and social investigation were not statistically significant. The frequency of visual orientation responses was higher among Feral Ss, and socially facilitated exploration occurred more frequently in the Restricted group. These differences were statistically significant, p being .01 for each of these comparisons. Unless otherwise indicated these and all subsequent statistical comparisons were based on t tests performed on total individual scores.

Play. Although the form of play behavior was similar in both groups, play occurred more frequently among Restricted Ss. The mean total incidence of play was 342.0 and 179.8 for Restricted and Feral groups, respectively. Although the difference between groups is substantial, it falls short of significance at the .05 level, principally because within each group there were large and consistent sex differences in the incidence of play. Both males and females of the Feral group had lower scores than like-sexed Ss in the Re-

stricted group, and all females showed less play behavior than did males. Mean play scores for females were 115.7 and 29.0 in Restricted and Feral groups, respectively, whereas corresponding values for males were 568.2 and 330.7. Play behavior did not occur in female pairs in the Feral group and occurred in female pairs of the Restricted group in only six sessions. The difference between sexes in the frequency of play for the combined groups is significant at the .001 level.

Grooming. The incidence of grooming was relatively low in both groups, occurring in three Ss in the Restricted group in 10 sessions and in four Ss in the Feral group in 25 sessions. Grooming was observed in seven Feral pairs and in five Restricted pairs. These differences were not statistically significant.

Grooming episodes tended to be substantially longer in Feral pairs and occasionally occupied nearly the entire test period. The mean duration of grooming behavior, determined by dividing total duration by number of occurrences, was 1.6 sec. and 25.3 sec. for Restricted and Feral groups, respectively, and this difference is significant at the .05 level.

Qualitative differences between groups were observed in the response to grooming. While being groomed members of the Feral group were characteristically passive and immobile, whereas the Ss in the Restricted group showed no specific or consistent complementary responses.

Aggression. The mean total frequency of aggression for Restricted and Feral groups was 11.7 and 2.0, respectively, and this difference is significant at the .05 level. Eleven pairs in the Restricted group engaged in aggression in at least one session and seven pairs fought in more than one session. In the Feral group, aggression occurred in six pairs, and in only two of these pairs did fighting occur in more than one session.

Aggressive episodes tended to be longer in the Restricted group, the mean duration being 4.87 sec. for these Ss, as compared with 1.21 sec. for Feral Ss. This difference, however, was not statistically significant. Although there were no apparent differences between groups in the form of individual aggressive responses, it was characteristic of the Ss in the Restricted group, particularly during the early phases of the experiment, to respond with aggression when attacked, whereas Feral Ss generally withdrew from attack or submitted passively and without retaliation.

Sexual behavior. A striking difference was apparent between Feral and Restricted males in the frequency and integration of sexual behavior. Mean total frequencies are presented in Figure 1, and it

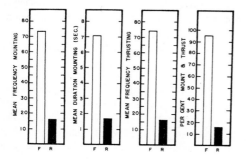

FIG. 1. Comparisons of sexual behavior of Restricted (R) and Feral (F) males.

is evident that Feral males showed more mounting and thrusting and had sexual episodes of substantially longer duration. All differences were significant at the .05 level. The incidence of mounting was negligible among females in both groups.

Gross qualitative differences in the organization of the male sexual act were present. Males in the Restricted group never clasped the partner's legs with their feet during mounting and would frequently assume inappropriate postures and body orientation. Many responses by these males could not be categorized as sexual until thrusting was observed, hence mounting was not scored for 64% of the total

thrusting responses. Inasmuch as the presence of thrusting presumably implies some attempt to mount, the mounting scores of the Restricted males were subsequently increased by the number of thrusting responses in which mounting was not recorded. This raised their mean total mounting score from 16.0 to 23.3. The difference between groups was still statistically significant ($p = .05$).

Ejaculation was not observed in either group. Menstrual cycles in the females were absent or irregular, and there was no apparent relationship between male sexual behavior and cyclic activity of the females.

With the exception of one highly dominant female in the Feral group, assumption of the female sexual posture (presentation) occurred in all Ss. Mean total frequency of sexual presentation was 23.5 and 12.2 in Feral and Restricted groups, respectively. Males in both groups made this response less frequently than females, accounting for 28% and 10% of total presentations in Feral and Restricted groups, respectively. Differences between groups and between sexes in the frequency of sexual presentation were not statistically significant.

Sexual presentation was notably more stereotyped for Feral animals of both sexes. In this group presentation was occasionally preceded by gazing intently at the partner while making rapid movements of the lips, and it was virtually always accompanied by postural adjustments, including flexing of the legs as the partner mounted. These behaviors were never observed among Restricted Ss.

To provide further evidence on the nature of the differences between groups in the male sexual pattern, a second experiment was run in which the males from Feral and Restricted groups were tested with the same socially experienced females, thus eliminating differential social experiences of the sexual partner as a factor contributing to differences in male sexual performance.

Experiment 2: Behavior of Restricted and Feral Males with Socially Experienced Females

METHOD

Subjects. The Ss were the three Feral and three Restricted males previously described, and three adolescent females captured in the field and without prior contact with any of the males. During the six-month period between Experiments 1 and 2, each male participated about 10 hr. in the social tests of gregarious tendencies and food competition. The males lived in individual cages throughout the period covered by the preceding experiments, and all Ss were individually housed during the present research.

Apparatus and procedure. The apparatus and the testing and recording procedures were the same as those described in Experiment 1. In the present experiment, however, only male-female pairs were tested. Following five individual 3-min. adaptation sessions for all Ss, each male was tested in ten 3-min. sessions with each female. Males participated in one test session a day and each female was used in two sessions. No female was tested in two successive sessions. The response categories used in Experiment 1 were extended and modified to provide further information on the integration of the male sexual

pattern. Response categories retained from Experiment 1 without modification included aggression, approach, groom, play, sexual presentation, thrusting, and withdrawal. Measures of visual orientation and social facilitation were not obtained in the present experiment. Mounting was classified as follows: "Appropriate mounting orientation" — longitudinal axes of the bodies are aligned during mounting, with the Ss facing in the same direction. "Inappropriate mounting orientation" — all attempts at mounting not scored as appropriate mounting. Additional categories included: "Hip clasp"—within 5 sec. before mounting the male places both hands on partner's hips. "Foot clasp"—male grasps female's legs with both feet during mounting. "Anogenital investigation" — visual, manual, and oral investigation of partner's anogenital region.

RESULTS

Mean and individual totals for frequency of nonsexual responses in males are presented in Table 27–2. None of the differences is significant, although what differences there are tend to be in the same direction as in Experiment 1.

The sexual responsiveness of the Restricted males showed a striking increase relative to their performance levels in Experiment 1. In the present experiment the mean incidence of mounting per session,

TABLE 27-2

Nonsexual responses of feral and restricted males in Experiment 2

RESPONSE	FERAL S				RESTRICTED Ss			
	331	336	337	MEAN	3	4	5	MEAN
Aggression	1	1	0	0.7	0	0	0	0.0
Approach	368	293	38	233.0	641	228	358	409.0
Groom	9	14	0	7.7	0	1	0	0.3
Dur. groom (sec.)	4.8	15.4	0	6.7	0	1.0	0	0.3
Play	114	47	0	53.7	144	79	129	117.3
Withdrawal	26	7	15	16.0	14	2	21	12.3

TABLE 27-3

Sexual responses of feral and restricted males in Experiment 2

MEASURE	FERAL S				RESTRICTED S				p
	331	336	337	MEAN	3	4	5	MEAN	
Approp. mount	64	53	1	39.3	25	30	18	24.3	ns
Inapprop. mount	0	0	0	0.0	60	40	47	49.0	.01
% approp. mount	100	100	100	100.0	29	43	28	33.3	.01
Mounting dur. (sec.)	4.2	5.3	10.0	6.5	2.4	2.5	2.7	2.5	ns
Thrusting	65	53	1	39.7	69	55	42	55.3	ns
% mount + thrusting	100	98	100	99.3	81	79	68	76.0	.01
Foot clasp	63	53	1	39.0	0	7	0	2.3	ns
% mount + foot clasp	98	100	100	99.3	0	10	0	3.3	.01
Hip clasp	49	47	0	32.0	24	30	14	22.7	ns
% mount + hip clasp	66	81	0	49.0	16	34	9	19.7	ns
Anogenital investig.	27	21	0	16.0	4	2	5	3.7	ns

including both appropriately and inappropriately oriented responses, was 2.44 as compared with 0.20 in Experiment 1. Similarly, the mean frequency of thrusting increased from 0.13 per session to 1.84. These changes are significant at the .02 level as determined by t tests for correlated measures. Although the higher frequency of mounting behavior might conceivably be related to modification of scoring categories between Experiments 1 and 2, the same interpretation would not apply to measures of thrusting. A more reasonable hypothesis is that the behavior of the socially experienced female partner and/or experience gained by Restricted males in the social tests intervening between Experiments 1 and 2 contributed to this increase in sexual responsiveness.

Comparative data on the sexual performance of Restricted and Feral males in the present experiment are presented in Table 27-3. The differences between groups in the frequency of mounting and thrusting were not statistically significant. Interpretation of this outcome is complicated by the fact that Feral Male No. 337 mounted only once in this test series, as compared with 83 mounts in Experiment 1. The remaining animals in this group

showed no evidence of lowered sexual responsiveness relative to their performance in Experiment 1. There is no indication, however, that these animals differed reliably from Restricted males with regard to frequency of thrusting and mounting (appropriate and inappropriate mounting orientations combined), which provides further evidence of enhanced sexual responsiveness of Restricted males in the present experiment.

In spite of more frequent sexual responses the sexual performance of the Restricted males was poorly integrated (see Fig. 2). Only 33% of total mounts in this group were appropriately oriented, 76% of total mounts were accompanied by thrusting and only 3%, included clasping the partner's legs. Comparable values for the Feral males exceeded 98% and the differences between groups were significant at the .01 level. The duration of mounting was again substantially shorter among Restricted males, mounting was less frequently preceded by grasping the partner's hips and the incidence of anogenital investigation was lower. These differences, however, were not statistically significant. Ejaculation was not observed in either group.

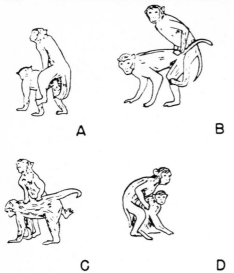

A   B

C   D

FIG. 2. Sexual behavior of Feral and Restricted males with socially experienced female partners. *A*. Rear view of Feral male in typical copulatory position. *B*. Side view of Feral male in typical copulatory position. *C*. Restricted male attempting to mount from the side. Note elevation of left foot. *D*. Sexual behavior of a Restricted male. Although mounting orientation is appropriate (as defined herein), the hands are placed high on the female's trunk and she remains sitting. The male is thrusting against the female's back. All figures were traced from moving-picture film.

The behavior of the females clearly suggested that they were not responding equivalently to the two groups of males. Females frequently failed to assume appropriate receptive postures in response to sexual advances of Restricted males (see Fig. 2D), and made fewer approaches to these animals. Furthermore, the high incidence of cowering and grimaces in the presence of Restricted males suggested that the females were afraid. This impression receives support from the finding that their withdrawal scores were higher with Restricted partners (Mean totals: Restricted, 210.7; Feral, 66.0). This difference was significant at the .01 level as determined by Wilcoxon tests performed on individual trial totals.

Discussion

The results of Experiment 1 indicate that restriction of intraspecies social experience of rhesus monkeys during the first two years of life retards the development of integrated social responses and orderly patterns of social interaction. Fighting was more frequent and prolonged among Restricted monkeys. They groomed less frequently, and grooming episodes were shorter. Sexual behavior in Restricted Ss was brief and showed gross deficiencies in organization, which were particularly evident in the behavior of males. The extent to which the performance of the Restricted monkeys was influenced by the brief social contacts provided them during the first year of life cannot be determined, but unpublished data on animals whose social experience was even more severely restricted suggest that this early social experience had some effect. Although the members of the Feral group in Experiment 1 were not strangers, the absence of any major changes in the social behavior of Feral males between Experiments 1 and 2 strongly suggests that possible pre-experimental contacts among members of the Feral group did not appreciably influence the present results.

The data on sexual behavior of Restricted males suggest that the components of the male copulatory pattern are differentially dependent upon social experience. The tendency to approach and bring the genitalia in contact with the partner was present from the first tests, as evidenced by the fact that all Restricted males attempted to mount on the first day of Experiment 1. Grasping the partner with the hands also appeared early in testing, but throughout the present experiments this response was less stereotyped and precise among Restricted males and was often accompanied by nipping, tugging, or other playful behaviors. Foot clasping was particularly deficient in Restricted males. This response was never observed among Restricted males in Experiment 1. In Experiment 2, only one of these males ever succeeded in grasping the partner's legs with both feet simultaneously, and this occurred only 7 times in 70 mounting attempts. A second male in this group occasionally raised its feet alternately as though attempting to place them, but never grasped with both feet simultaneously (see Fig. 2C). Closely related to this deficiency was the absence of efficient and appropriate postural orientation with regard to the sexual partner.

The data on sexual behavior are consistent with previous observations (Bingham, 1928; Foley, 1935; Maslow, 1936; Yerkes & Elder, 1936), and support the generalization that among nonhuman primates social experience is relatively more important to male than to female sexual behavior (Ford & Beach, 1952). Had more sensitive measures of female sexual behavior been used, however, there is little doubt that deficiencies would also have been demonstrated in the performance of Restricted females, although it is unlikely that these were sufficient to prevent effective coitus with an experienced male.

Social organization among nonhuman primates is characteristically orderly and efficient. Presumably, regular social relationships are dependent upon stable interindividual stimulus-response tendencies. Sexual presentation, presentation for grooming, grasping the hips preparatory to mounting, and the threat pattern are a few of the highly stereotyped responses described for rhesus monkeys which ordinarily function as social cues, eliciting appropriate reciprocal responses from other animals. These stimulus-response relationships form the basis for social coordination, communication, and social control in feral groups (Carpenter, 1942; Chance, 1956; Maslow, 1936). Insofar as the present findings bear on this problem, they suggest that among animals whose socialization has been restricted, the cue function of many basic social responses is poorly established if not absent altogether.

Summary

1. Comparisons were made of the spontaneous social interactions of monkeys raised in a socially restricted laboratory environment and Feral monkeys captured in the field.

2. Pairs of Restricted monkeys showed more frequent and prolonged fighting and fewer and less prolonged grooming episodes than Feral pairs. Differences between groups were found in the frequency, duration and integration of sexual behavior, which were particularly evident in the behavior of males.

3. Restricted and Feral males were subsequently tested with the same socially experienced females, thus eliminating inadequacies in the sexual partner as a factor contributing to the differences in male sexual performance. Gross differences in the organization of the male copulatory pattern were still apparent.

4. In addition to differences between groups in the form and frequency of these basic social responses, the data suggest that responses to social cues are poorly established in monkeys with restricted socialization experience.

REFERENCES

Bingham, H. C. Sex development in apes. *Comp. psychol. Monogr.,* 1928, **5,** 1–165.
Bowlby, J. *Maternal care and mental health.* Geneva: World Health Organization, 1952.
Carpenter, C. R. Societies of monkeys and apes. *Biol. Sympos.,* 1942, **8,** 177–204.
Chance, M. R. A. Social structure of a colony of *Macaca mulatta. Brit. J. anim. Behav.,* 1956, **4,** 1–13.
Foley, J. P., Jr. Second year development of a rhesus monkey *(Macaca mulatta)* reared in isolation during the first eighteen months. *J. genet. Psychol.,* 1935, **47,** 73–97.
Ford, C. S., and F. A. Beach *Patterns of sexual behavior.* New York: Harper, 1952.
Imanishi, K. Social behavior in Japanese

monkeys, *Macaca fuscata. Psychologia,* 1957, **1**, 47–54.

MASLOW, A. H. The role of dominance in the social and sexual behavior of infra-human primates: III. A theory of sexual behavior of infra-human primates. *J. genet. Psychol.,* 1936, **48**, 310–338.

VAN WAGENEN, G. The monkey. In E. J. Farris (Ed.), *The care and breeding of laboratory animals.* New York: Wiley, 1950. Pp. 1–42.

YERKES, R. M., and J. H. ELDER Oestrus, receptivity, and mating in chimpanzee. *Comp. psychol. Monogr.,* 1936, **13**, 1–39.

HARRY F. HARLOW

28   The Heterosexual Affectional System in Monkeys*

Harry F. Harlow has long been known to psychologists for his studies on learning sets and on the reinforcing properties of exploration and manipulation. His most recent experimental efforts, however, have been in a different field: the effects of early experience on the behavior of the monkey. By painstaking examination of several "affectional systems," Harlow identifies the ones that are important for the normal development of monkey behavior.

Reprinted from the *American Psychologist,* 1962, **17**, 1–9, with the permission of the author and the American Psychological Association. Several figures have been omitted.

The inspiration for this address came from observational data obtained from seven guinea pigs—two males and three females in a colony and two females brought in temporarily. Observations were provided by my ten-year-old daughter Pamela. These observations were made with love and endearment, and the behavior observed was endearment and love. Furthermore, these observations were made at a level of objectivity difficult for an adult to attain in this field.

Male and female guinea pigs are very fond of each other. They stare blissfully into the limpid pink or ruby or midnight-blue pools of each other's eyes. They nuzzle and they cuddle and the end production is not characterized by rush or rape.

° This research was supported by funds received from the Graduate School of the University of Wisconsin, from the Ford Foundation, and from Grant M-4528, National Institutes of Health.

After all, one does not have to hurry if there is no hurry to be had. This, Pamela has witnessed several times. A caged, virgin adult female was brought by a friend for mating. Twirp, Pamela's large, black, gentle male, was put into the cage with the new female. He purred, nuzzled her, brushed up against her, smelled and licked her, and gradually conquered the frightened animal. A half-hour later they were snuggled up next to each other, peaceful and content, and they lived in bliss for several weeks until another friend brought in her female and Twirp repeated his patient, gentle approach. Twirp has convinced me that some male guinea pigs, at least, are endowed with an innate sense of decency, and I am happy to say that this is the way most male monkeys behave. I presume that there are some men who have as deep a depth of dignity as guinea pigs.

The guest stands, unfortunately, ended

peaceful coexistence in the colony. For many months the five adult guinea pigs had lived amiably in one large cage, with Twirp in command and the second male playing second fiddle. While Twirp was host to the visiting females, White Patch commanded the permanent harem. When Twirp was reintroduced to the colony cage, it took but ten seconds to discover that he would not be tolerated. White Patch bared his teeth and lunged at Twirp, and to save the males, a new cage was acquired.

This led to various divisions of the females and led Pamela to discover particular male guinea pigs like particular female guinea pigs, and they squeal piteously when separated, even when the female is so bulging with babies that she can offer the male nothing in terms of drive reduction. Particular female guinea pigs like particular male guinea pigs. Tastes seem fairly stable, for even after weeks of peaceful residence with the unfavored male, the female will still attempt to get to her favorite male, and after weeks of quiet residence with unfavored females, the male will still try to get to his favorite female.

The females, like the males, defend their rights. In the happy one-cage days two females were separated from the group to care for their litters. White Thrush, in an advanced stage of pregnancy, lived alone with the males. When Chirp was returned to the colony cage after three weeks of maternal chores, both males approached enthusiastically, making friendly gestures. But Hell hath no fury like a female guinea pig spurned, and White Thrush would not tolerate infidelity. She hissed at Chirp, and lunged, and as Chirp fled from the cage, White Thrush pursued, teeth bared. The males also pursued, clucking and purring in anticipation. The males won, and White Thrush sulked the rest of the day. Guinea pigs apparently have a well-developed heterosexual affectional system.

Sex behavior in the guinea pig has been intensively investigated, and there are ex-haustive studies on what has been called the sex drive, but I know of no previous mention of or allusion to the guinea pig's heterosexual affectional system. No doubt this stems from the paradigm which has been established for research in this area.

In a typical experiment a male guinea pig and a female guinea pig in estrus are taken from their individual cages, dropped into a barren chamber, and observed for 15 minutes. In such a situation there is a high probability that something is going to happen and that it will happen rapidly and repeatedly. The thing that happens will be reliable and valid, and all that one needs to do to score it is to count. It is my suggestion that from this time onward it be known as the "flesh count." Sometimes I wonder how men and women would behave if they were dropped naked into a barren chamber with full realization that they had only fifteen minutes to take advantage of the opportunities offered them. No doubt there would be individual differences, but we would obtain little information on the human heterosexual affectional system from such an experiment.

Sex is not an adventitious act. It is not here today and gone tomorrow. It starts with the cradle, and as a part of the human tragedy it wanes before the grave. We have traced and are tracing the development of the heterosexual affectional system in monkeys.

We believe that the heterosexual affectional system in the rhesus monkey, like all the other affectional systems, goes through a series of developmental stages—an infantile heterosexual stage, a preadolescent stage, and an adolescent and mature heterosexual stage. Although these stages are in considerable part overlapping and cannot be sharply differentiated in time, we would think of the infantile stage as lasting throughout the first year and being characterized by inadequate and often inappropriate sexual play and posturing. The preadolescent stage, beginning in the second year and ending in the third year in the female and fourth year in the

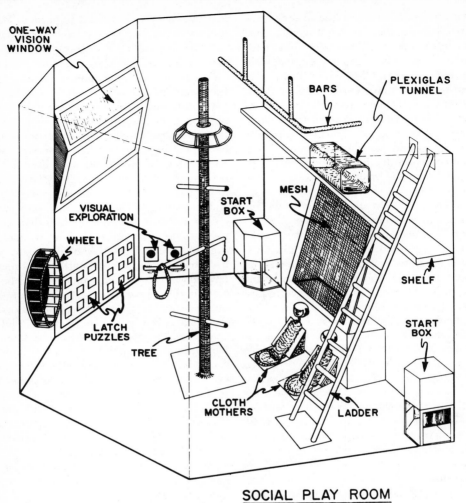

FIG. 1. Playroom test situation.

male, is characterized by adequate and appropriate sexual play and posturing, but incompleteness. The adolescent and adult stage is characterized by behaviors which are similar in form but give rise to productive outcomes which are also reproductive.

Since in this paper sex is an unavoidable issue, we present illustrations of normal adult macaque monkey sex behavior. Sexual invitation may be initiated by the female, . . . by a present pattern with buttocks oriented toward the male, tail elevated, and the female looking back-

ward with a fear-grimace (not threat) pattern involving flattened ears and lip smacking. . . . This pattern need not involve rape nor even rush on the part of the male. The male may also solicit, as in the case of the animal in the foreground of [an omitted] figure; this animal has assumed a posture soliciting either grooming or more intimate favors. These patterns seldom elicit violent, uncontrolled, reflex behaviors. Normal male and female overt sex behavior is shown in [an omitted] figure, the male having assumed the complex sex posture involving ankle clasp, dorsoventral mounting, and clasp of the female's buttocks. The partner demonstrates the complete female sexual pattern of elevating the buttocks, lowering the head, and looking backward. There have been millions of rhesus monkeys for millions of years, and there will be more in the future.

We have traced the development of the infantile heterosexual stage during the first year of life in two test situations using observational techniques. One is our playroom, illustrated in Figure 1, which consists of a room 8 ft. high with 36 feet of floor space. In this room are a platform, ladder, revolving wheel, and flying rings to encourage the infants' adaptation to a three-dimensional world, and there is an assortment of puzzles and toys for quieter activities. Two groups of four infants each, half of each group male and half female, have been observed in the playroom daily over many months. The second apparatus is shown in Figure 2. This is the playpen situation, and it consists of four large living cages and adjoining pens. Each living cage houses a mother and infant, and a three-

inch by five-inch opening in the wall between cage and playpen units enables the infants to leave the home cage at any time but restrains the mothers. The playpen units are separated by wire-mesh panels which are removed one or two hours a day to allow the infants to interact in pairs during the first 180 days and both in pairs and in groups of four during the next half-year of life. Again, we are referring to data gathered from two playpen setups, each housing four infants and their real or surrogate mothers. Insofar as the infantile heterosexual stage is concerned, it makes little or no difference from which situation we take our data.

The outstanding finding in both the playroom and playpen is that male and female infants show differences in sex behavior from the second month of life onward. The males show earlier and more frequent sex behavior than do females, and there are differences in the patterns displayed by the sexes. The males almost never assume the female sex-posture patterns, even in the earliest months. The females, on the other hand, sometimes dis-

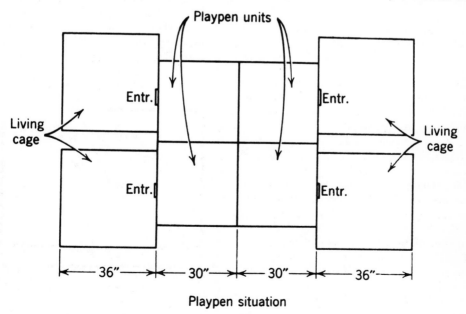

FIG. 2. Playpen test situation.

play the male pattern of sex posturing, but this is infrequent after ten months of age. Predominantly, females show the female pattern and exceptional instances are to other females, not males. Frequency of sex behavior for both males and females increases progressively with age. There is no latency period—except when the monkeys are very tired.

The early infantile sexual behaviors are fragmentary, transient, and involve little more than passivity by the female and disoriented grasping and thrusting by the male. Thus, the male may thrust at the companion's head in a completely disori-

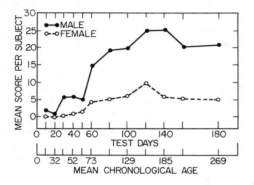

FIG. 3. Frequency of threat responses by males and females in the playroom.

ented manner or laterally across the midline of the body. . . . However, it is our opinion that these behaviors are more polymorphous than perverse.

Thus, as soon as the sexual responses can be observed and measured, male and female sexual behaviors differ in form. Furthermore, there are many other behaviors which differ between males and females as soon as they can be observed and measured. Figure 3 shows the development of threat responses by males and females in the playroom, and these differences are not only statistically significant, but they also have face validity. Analysis of this behavior shows that males threaten other males and females but that females are innately blessed with better manners;

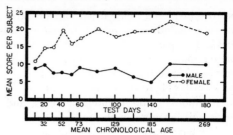

FIG. 4. Frequency of withdrawal responses by males and females in the playroom.

in particular, little girl monkeys do not threaten little boy monkeys.

The withdrawal pattern—retreat when confronted by another monkey—is graphed for the playroom in Figure 4 and the significance is obvious. Females evince a much higher incidence of passive responses, which are characterized by immobility with buttocks oriented toward the male and head averted, and a similar pattern, rigidity, in which the body is stiffened and fixed.

In all probability the withdrawal and passivity behavior of the female and the forceful behavior of the male gradually lead to the development of normal sex behaviors. The tendency for the female to orient away from the male and for the male to clasp and tussle at the female's buttocks predisposes the consorts to assume the proper positions. The develop-

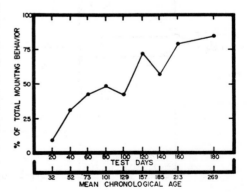

FIG. 5. Percentage of all male mounts (immature and mature) in the playroom that shows dorsal orientation (mature pattern).

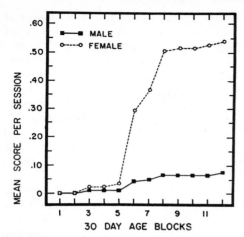

FIG. 6. Frequency of grooming responses made by males and females in the playroom.

ment of the dorsally oriented male sex-behavior pattern as observed in the playroom situation is shown in Figure 5 and may be described as a composite yearning and learning curve.

Infant male and female monkeys show clear-cut differences in behavior of far greater social significance than neonatal and infantile sex responses. Grooming patterns, which are basic to macaque socialization, show late maturation, but as is seen in Figure 6, when they appear, they sharply differentiate the two sexes. Caressing is both a property and prerogative of the females. Basic to normal macaque

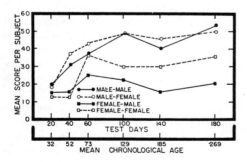

FIG. 7. Frequency of play-initiations by males and females to monkeys of the same (male-male, female-female) and other sex (male-female, female-male). Observations are from the playroom.

socialization is the infant-infant or peer-peer affectional system, and this arises out of and is dependent upon the play patterns which we have described elsewhere and only mention here. As is shown in the solid lines of Figure 7, play behavior in the playroom is typically initiated by males, seldom by females. However, let us not belittle the female, for they also serve who only stand and wait. Contact play is far more frequent among the males than the females and is almost invariably initiated by the males. Playpen data graphed in Figure 8 show that real rough-and-tumble play is strictly for the boys.

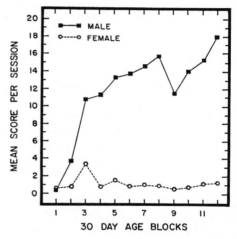

FIG. 8. Frequency of occurrence of "rough-and-tumble" play for two males and two females in the playroom through the first year of life.

I am convinced that these data have almost total generality to man. Several months ago I was present at a school picnic attended by 25 second-graders and their parents. While the parents sat and the girls stood around or skipped about hand in hand, 13 boys tackled and wrestled, chased and retreated. No little girl chased any little boy, but some little boys chased some little girls. Human beings have been here for two million years, and they'll probably be here two million more.

These secondary sex-behavior differences probably exist throughout the primate order, and, moreover, they are innately determined biological differences regardless of any cultural overlap. Because of their nature they tend automatically to produce sexual segregation during middle and later childhood, but fortunately this separation is neither complete nor permanent. Behavioral differences may very well make it easy through cultural means to impose a sexual latency period in the human being from childhood to puberty. We emphasize the fact that the latency period is not a biological stage in which primary sex behavior is suppressed, but a cultural stage built upon secondary behavioral differences.

We believe that our data offer convincing evidence that sex behaviors differ in large part because of genetic factors. However, we claim no originality for the discovery of intersex behavioral differences. In 1759 Laurence Sterne in his book *Tristam Shandy* described male and female differences at the most critical period in Tristam Shandy's development; indeed, it would not be possible to conceive of a more critical period.

"Pray, my dear, quoth my mother, *have you not forgot to wind up the clock?* ———— *Good G———! cried my father, making an exclamation, but taking care to moderate his voice at the same time———— Did ever woman, since the creation of the world, interrupt a man with such a silly question?"*†

Men and women have differed in the past and they will differ in the future.

It is possible that the listener has been dismayed by the frequent reference to sex and the relatively infrequent reference to affection. Out of these infantile behavior patterns, both sexual and non-sexual, develop the affectional bonds and the social ordering that appear to be important or

† Sterne, Laurence. *The life and opinions of Tristram Shandy, Gentleman.* J. A. Work (Ed.), New York: The Odyssey Press, 1940, p. 5.

even essential to the full development of the heterosexual affectional system of macaques. Traumatic affectional errors, both transient and prolonged, may have devastating effects upon subsequent social and sexual behaviors.

For some years we have been attempting to establish experimental neuroses in infant monkeys by having them live on unfriendly and inconsistent mother surrogates. One preparation was a rejecting mother that on schedule or demand separated her baby when a wire frame embedded in her spun-nylon covering was displaced violently upward and backward. The baby was disturbed, but as soon as the frame was returned to its resting position, the baby returned to cling to its surrogate mother as tightly as ever. Next we developed an air-blast mother with a series of nozzles down the entire center of her body which released compressed air under high pressure—an extremely noxious stimulus to monkeys. The blasted baby never even left the mother, but in its moments of agony and duress, clung more and more tightly to the unworthy mother. Where else can a baby get protection? Apparently our infant had never read Neal Miller's theory that avoidance gradients are precipitous and approach gradients gradual and tenuous, for love conquered all.

We next devised a shaking mother, which on schedule or demand shook her infant with unconscionable violence until its teeth chattered. The infant endured its tribulations by clinging more and more tightly. At the present time we believe we may be on the threshold of success through Jay Mowbray's creation of the porcupine mother, which extrudes brass spikes all over its ventral surface. Preliminary studies on two infants suggest that they are emotionally disturbed. Whether or not we eventually succeed, the fact remains that babies are reluctant to develop experimental neuroses, and at one time we even wondered if this were possible.

During the time that we were producing these evil mothers, we observed the monkeys which we had separated from their mothers at birth and raised under various mothered and nonmothered conditions. The first 47 baby monkeys were raised during the first year of life in wire cages so arranged that the infants could see and hear and call to other infants but not contact them. Now they are five to seven years old and sexually mature. As month after month and year after year have passed, these monkeys have appeared to be less and less normal. We have seen them sitting in their cages strangely mute, staring fixedly into space, relatively indifferent to people and other monkeys. Some clutch their heads in both hands and rock back and forth—the autistic behavior pattern that we have seen in babies raised on wire surrogates. Others, when approached or even left alone, go into violent frenzies of rage, grasping and tearing at their legs with such fury that they sometimes require medical care.

Eventually we realized that we had a laboratory full of neurotic monkeys. We had failed to produce neurotic monkeys by thoughtful planning and creative research, but we had succeeded in producing neurotic monkeys through misadventure. To err is human.

Because of housing pressures some of these monkeys and many of our surrogate-raised monkeys lived in pairs for several years while growing to sexual maturity, but we have seldom seen normal sex behavior, and we certainly have not had the validating criterion of newborn baby monkeys. Instead, these monkeys treat each other like brother and sister, proving that two can live in complete propinquity with perfect propriety as long as no one cares.

Their reason for being, as we saw it, was to produce babies for our researches, and so at this point we deliberately initiated a breeding program which was frighteningly unsuccessful. When the older, wire-cage-raised males were paired with the females at the peak of estrus, the introduction led only to fighting, so violent and vicious that separation was essential to survival. In no case was there any indication of normal sex behavior. Frequently the females were the aggressors; even the normal praying mantis waits until the sex act is completed.

Pairing such cloth-surrogate-raised monkeys as were sexually mature gave little better end results. Violent aggression was not the rule, and there was attempted sex behavior, but it was unreproductive since both the male and female behaviors were of the infantile type we have already described.

At this point we took the 17 oldest of our cage-raised animals, females showing consistent estrous cycles and males obviously mature, and engaged in an intensive re-education program, pairing the females with our most experienced, patient, and gentle males, and the males with our most eager, amiable, and successful breeding females. When the laboratory-bred females were smaller than the sophisticated males, the girls would back away and sit down facing the males, looking appealingly at these would-be consorts. Their hearts were in the right place, but nothing else was. When the females were larger than the males, we can only hope that they misunderstood the males' intentions, for after a brief period of courtship, they would attack and maul the ill-fated male. Females show no respect for a male they can dominate.

The training program for the males was equally unsatisfactory. They approached the females with a blind enthusiasm, but it was a misdirected enthusiasm. Frequently the males would grasp the females by the side of the body and thrust laterally, leaving them working at cross purposes with reality. Even the most persistent attempts by these females to set the boys straight came to naught. Finally, these females either stared at the males with complete contempt or attacked them in utter frustration. It became obvious that they, like their human counterpart, prefer maturer men. We realized then that we had established, not a program of breeding, but a program of brooding.

We had in fact been warned. Our first seven laboratory-born babies were raised in individual cages while being trained on a learning test battery. William Mason planned to test their social behaviors subsequently, and great care had been taken to keep the babies socially isolated and to prevent any physical contacts. Neonatal baby monkeys require 24-hour-a-day care, and infant monkeys need ministrations beyond a 40-hour week. We had assigned the evening care to Kathy, a maternal bit of fluff who had worked for several years as a monkey tester while studying to become an elementary school teacher.

Checking on his wards one night near 10 P.M., Mason found Kathy sitting on the floor surrounded by seven baby monkeys, all eight of the primates playing happily together. Before the horrified scientist could express his outrage, Kathy had risen to her full height of five feet two. Already anticipating the carping criticisms which he was formulating, she shook her finger in his face and spoke with conviction: "Dr. Mason, I'm an education student and I know that it is improper and immoral to blight the social development of little children. I am right and you are wrong!"

Although we were angry with Kathy, we did think there was a certain humor in the situation and we did not worry about our monkeys. We simply transferred Kathy to an office job. Alas, she could not have been more right and we could not have been more wrong! We have already described the social-sexual life of these 7 monkeys and the next 40 to come.

Two years later we had more than theoretical reasons to be disturbed because Mason tested 'a group of these isolation-raised monkeys, then between 2.5 and 3.5 years of age, and found evidence of severe social abnormalities, which might be described as sociopathic syndrome. He matched the laboratory-raised monkeys on the basis of weight and dentition patterns

with monkeys that had been born and raised in the wild for the first 12 to 18 months, then captured and subjected to various kinds of housing and caging treatments for the next year or two. In the test situations the laboratory-raised monkeys, as compared with feral monkeys, showed infantile sexual behavior, absence of grooming, exaggerated aggression, and absence of affectional interaction as measured by cooperation.

We are now quite certain that this sociopathic syndrome does not stem from the fact that the baby monkeys were raised in the laboratory but from *how* they were raised in the laboratory. Our infants raised in the laboratory by real monkey mothers and permitted opportunity for the development of normal infant-infant affection demonstrate normal male and female sexual behavior when they enter the second year of life. Furthermore, our playroom and playpen studies show that infant monkeys raised on cloth mothers but given the opportunity to form normal infant-infant affectional patterns, also develop normal sexual responses.

In a desperate attempt to assist a group of 18 three- to four-year-old cloth-surrogate-raised monkeys, half of them males and half females, we engaged in a group-psychotherapy program, placing these animals for two months on the monkey island in the Madison Zoo. . . . Their summer vacation on the enchanted island was not without avail, and social grooming responses rapidly developed and were frequent in occurrence. After a few days of misunderstanding, patterns of social ordering developed, and a number of males and females developed friendship patterns. Unfortunately, sexual behavior was infrequent, and the behavior that was observed was completely inadequate—at least from our point of view. In desperation we finally introduced our most experienced, most patient, and most kindly breeding male, Smiley . . ., and he rapidly established himself as king of the island and prepared to take full advantage of the wealth of opportunity which surrounded him. Fortunately, the traumatic experiences he encountered with unreceptive females have left no apparent permanent emotional scars, and now that he has been returned to our laboratory breeding colony, he is again making an important contribution to our research program. If normal sexual behavior occurred, no member of our observational team ever saw it, and had a female become pregnant, we would have believed in parthenogenesis.

But let us return to the monkeys that we left on the island and the older ones that we left in their cages. A year has passed, and the frustrations that both we and our monkeys experienced are in some small part nothing but a memory. We constructed larger and more comfortable breeding cages, and we designed a very large experimental breeding room 8 feet by 8 feet by 8 feet in size with appropriate platforms and a six-foot tree. Apparently we designed successful seraglios for I can report that not all love's labors have been lost. It does appear that the males are completely expendable unless they can be used in a program of artificial insemination. Certainly we can find no evidence that there is a destiny that shapes their ends unless some Skinnerite can help us with the shaping process. We have, however, had better success with some of the females, particularly the females raised on cloth surrogates.

Even so, one of the wire-cage-raised females is a mother and another is pregnant. Three cloth-surrogate females are mothers and four or five are expectant. We give all the credit to three breeding males. One, Smiley, does not take "no" for an answer. Smiley has a way with females. Patient, gentle, and persuasive, he has overcome more than one planned program of passive resistance. One female did not become pregnant until the fifth successive month of training. Month after month she has changed, and now she is mad about the boy. Male No. 342 behaves very much like Smiley. Even when females threaten

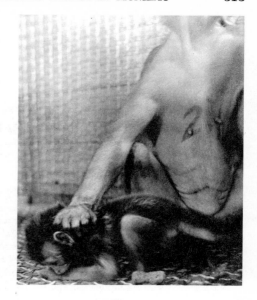

FIG. 9. Typical behavior of unmothered mother toward her infant. Mother is looking upward while crushing her baby against the cage floor.

him, he does not harm them. Given time, he has been able to overcome more than one reluctant dragon, and he is a master of the power of positive suggestion.

Breeding male No. 496 has helped us greatly, particularly with the younger, cloth-surrogate-raised females. His approach differs from that of Smiley and No. 342. His technique transcends seduction, and in contract bridge terms it may be described as an approach-forcing system.

Combining our human and male-monkey talents, we are winning the good fight and imparting to naive and even resistant female monkeys the priceless gift of motherhood. Possibly it is a Pyrrhic victory. As every scientist knows, the solution of one scientific problem inevitably leads to another, and this is our fate (Figure 9). Month after month female monkeys that never knew a real mother, themselves become mothers — helpless, hopeless, heartless mothers devoid, or almost devoid, of any maternal feeling.

29 The Effect of Early Social Experience on Male Sexual Behavior of Androgen Injected Turkeys*

In reading 15, the distinction was made between the prenatal and postnatal functions of sex hormones. Prenatally, they are thought to participate in the *organization* of particular neural centers. Postnatally, their function is the *activation* of these centers so that sexual behavior occurs. Therefore, if a prepubertal animal is given the proper sex hormones, mating behavior should occur. In the following selection, Schein and Hale show that this precocious sexual behavior can be induced in the turkey. They also show, however, that the *object* toward which courting responses are directed depends on the early experience of the animal.

Reprinted from *Animal Behaviour*, 1959, **7**, 189–200, with the permission of the authors and the publisher: Baillière, Tindall, and Cox, Ltd.

A number of studies indicate that the degree of social experience may affect the expression of male sexual behaviour. However, the specific aspect of behaviour modified often is equivocal. Sexual behaviour may be described qualitatively in terms of motor *patterns* or measured quantitatively in terms of frequency or *levels* of expression. Further, the *stimuli* which elicit the behaviour may be described qualitatively or measured quantitatively in terms of their releasing value. Although the three components do not operate independently, each may be modified independently and in turn may or may not affect the expression of the others.

Beach (1958) with rats and Wood-Gush (1958a) with chickens found no differences in the percentage of isolated and socially reared individuals exhibiting completely organised sexual patterns on the very first trial. In contrast, Valenstein, Riss

* Publication No. 2366 in the journal series of the Pennsylvania Agricultural Experiment Station.

& Young (1955) observed deficiencies in the level of sexual behaviour of isolation reared male guinea pigs and concluded that the sexual behaviour of these animals had not been organised into an effective pattern. Similarly, fish reared in complete isolation exhibited a reduced level of sexual behaviour and aberrant mating patterns when compared to others raised with varying degrees of social experience (Shaw, 1957). Rosenblatt & Aronson (1958) indicated that the development of the mating pattern and level of behaviour of male cats depends upon sexual experience in combination with high androgen levels. In line with this thesis, the levels of sexual expression of isolation reared fish (Shaw, 1956) and chickens (Fisher & Hale, 1957) tended to increase upon repetitive testing.

With respect to the stimuli which release sexual behaviour of animals reared in isolation, the literature contains equally contradictory reports. Beach (1958) and Wood-Gush (1958a) found that such individuals (rats and chickens, respectively) react sexually to normal appropriate intra-specific stimuli, while Fisher & Hale (1957), Raber (1948) and Craig (1914) (chickens, turkeys and ring doves, respectively) reported that sexual responses of birds raised in isolation were directed to biologically inappropriate stimuli.

Some of the above differences may be attributed to species differences, while others may be engendered by differences in the degree of isolation. As Klopfer (1959) points out, external influences may be operative earlier than has been suspected, so that isolation starting as early as 1 day of age still may be quite different from isolation before birth or hatching. One also wonders whether part of the differences might lie in using levels as a measure of presence or absence of patterns, and the difficulty of determining optimal stimuli for isolated animals. In addition, disorientated behaviour might be interpreted as "aberrant patterns" when in fact a stimulus directing orientation simply is not present.

The object of the present study was to determine the effect of early social experience on the organisation of patterns of sexual behaviour, the stimuli releasing sexual behaviour, and the levels of sexual response.

Materials and Methods

Sexual behaviour was induced precociously in turkey poults by androgen injections. The feasibility of the technique was demonstrated by Hanford & Hale (1959) and has the advantage of providing data within a relatively short period of time. In addition the need for housing large birds in individual compartments for long periods of time is circumvented.

The experiments herein reported were first done by one author and then repeated by the other, with another group of birds. Since each worked independently, slight differences in techniques and testing routines were involved; hence, the designation "Trial 1" and "Trial 2" will be used where appropriate.

HATCHING

Trials 1 and 2. Four days before expected hatching, incubating White Holland turkey eggs were covered with aluminum containers in a manner permitting free circulation of air around each egg, yet providing complete visual and tactile isolation of each hatchling. Poults were banded for individual identification within three to four hours after hatching, and transported in individual closed containers to randomly determined places in the brooder boxes.

BROODING

Trials 1 and 2. Eight brooding sections 5 ft. × 1 ft. × 10 in. high, were used. Four of the eight sections were partitioned into 1 ft. × 1 ft. × 10 in. compartments, each housing one bird. (Fig. 1 illustrates the two types of brooder compartments.) Thus there were initially 20 birds in individual compartments and four groups of 5 birds each in the remaining compartments (except for one group of 10 birds in Trial 1).

Heat necessary for brooding was provided continuously by a naked light bulb, and food and water were available *ad libitum* for each bird. Visual isolation was

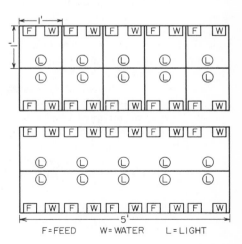

FIG. 1. Diagram of the "isolation" (upper) and "group" (lower) boxes used for brooding, as viewed from above.

obtained by using solid ½ in. plywood partitions. The tops and bottoms of the boxes were constructed of ½ in. mesh hardware cloth in order to accustom the birds to the observer. However, visual isolation was maintained when birds were removed for injection or testing by temporarily covering all boxes with plywood. It should be emphasised that "isolation", as used in this report, is only with respect to visual and tactual stimulation from other birds.

INJECTIONS

Precocious male sexual behaviour was induced by daily injections of 1 mg. testosterone propionate (Schering's Oreton). In Trial 1, injections were administered intramuscularly into the thigh region from the 6th through 35th day of age. In Trial 2, injections were administered subcutaneously into the neck region, from the 7th day of age until the animal was killed.

TREATMENTS

In order to study the effect of different social experiences the birds were either: (1) grouped, (2) grouped and then isolated, or (3) isolated. Minor variations from these treatments are noted below.

Trial 1. (38 surviving birds).

Grouped: 15 birds remained in small groups for the 32-day experimental period;

Group-isolated: 5 birds were moved from the initial 10-bird group to individual isolation compartments at 10 days of age and the other 5 at 20 days of age;

Isolated: 8 birds remained in isolation compartments for the 32-day experimental period; 5 others were moved from isolation to group compartments at 20 days of age.

At 32 days of age, all birds were removed from their compartments and released together into a 12 ft. × 10 ft. community pen. The genetic sex of each bird was determined on the basis of morphological characteristics at sexual maturity or by autopsy of those birds that died before reaching maturity.

Trial 2. (31 surviving birds).

Grouped: 13 birds remained in small

groups for the entire experimental period;

Group-isolated: 6 birds were moved from group to isolation compartments at 11 days of age;

Isolated: 8 birds remained in isolation compartments for the entire experimental period;

Supplementary: 4 birds, in irregular categories, were observed but are not included in the data.

At the end of the testing routine, birds were sacrificed and sexed by gross anatomical examination.

TEST MODELS

Previous studies on domestic turkeys (Schein & Hale, 1957, 1958a) indicated that a dummy female's head alone serves as an adequate arousal stimulus for normally reared, sexually active males. Some 3-week-old, androgen injected, turkeys strutted and displayed to a dummy head in adult-like fashion (Schein & Hale, 1958b). On the basis of these and other observations, the following objects were used as sexual releasers for both Trials.

Poult head: a poult of approximately the same age as the experimental birds was killed and stuffed with cotton. The head was removed and mounted on a stiff wire base so that it could be presented separately in an upright position.

Poult body: the stuffed body of the killed poult, presented without a head.

Human hand: the observer's hand placed on the floor of the test box, palm up (Trial 1) or down (Trial 2). A hand was used since it is possible that some of the animals became imprinted to the observer during the course of the experiment.

Inanimate objects: a small wooden block, an unlit lightbulb, or an inverted feed cup.

Behaviour and Testing Procedures

RESPONSES

In both Trials 1 and 2, responses of the poults to the introduced stimuli were classified as follows:

Escape, the bird tried to escape from its box when the stimulus object was present;

Avoidance, the poult avoided the stimulus object but made no effort to escape from the box;

No Response, avoidance was reduced to zero, and the bird showed no evidence of sexual behaviour;

Strutting, courtship display similar to that shown by sexually active adult males;

Copulatory movements, the poult "mounted" and "trod" the model in adult-like fashion; poults presented with a head trod the area immediately around the head, pressing the breast against the model.

TESTING PROCEDURE

Trial 1. Testing was done in the bird's home environment. Thus, the isolated poults were tested singly in their own boxes, while the grouped ones were tested collectively in their group box. Collective testing has previously been used satisfactorily with chickens (Fisher & Hale, 1957).

Qualitative tests: responses scored in terms of escape, avoidance, no response, strutting, or copulatory movements as noted above.

Single stimulus: head.

First, Age 17-18 days. All birds were confronted with a dummy head for at least a 5-minute period or until "mounting" occurred.

Second, Age 23-24 days. All birds were presented a dummy head combined with the dummy body for at least a 5-minute period or until "mounting" occurred. However, there was no evidence that the presence of the body modified the results, so this test was treated as a head test in the analysis.

Preference: head, body, and hand.

Age 35 days. Three days after the birds had been grouped together in a community pen, each was tested in the same pen in the absence of its penmates. In this test, the head, body and hand were placed on the floor of the pen approximately 2 ft. apart at the points of an imaginary equi-

lateral triangle. The bird was released in the middle of the triangle and its behaviour noted for at least 5 minutes or until "mounting" occurred. In the event of a sexual response to one stimulus object, an effort was made to transfer the response to the other stimuli. For example, if a bird made copulatory movements to the hand, the hand was moved slowly to the head and to the body, and then away again. However, in no case was it possible to transfer the response from one stimulus to the other.

Trial 2. All birds were tested individually in 2 ft. $\times$ 2 ft. $\times$ 1 ft. boxes except for a few limited tests with three poults (Nos. 230, 241, 250) at 19 days of age in their home box.

Qualitative tests: responses scored as in Trial 1.

Single stimulus: head, body or hand.

First, Age 32-35 days. Poults were placed in the test boxes 1 to 12 hours before testing. All birds were tested for 5 minutes with each model. Three birds, one from each treatment category, were tested at the same time in adjoining test boxes (in so far as numbers permitted), with presentation of the three stimulus objects counterbalanced.

Second, Age 40-43 days. In order to determine the repeatability of the initial test in Trial 2 and to measure any changes in behaviour, 1-minute tests were given to all birds except for grouped females. Birds were placed in the test boxes immediately prior to testing. Poults were tested as in the first test but with presentation of the stimuli in a different sequence, for a given bird, than in the initial tests. In the interval between the first and second tests, the poults had been given short tests with several other live poults.

In addition to tests with the usual stimulus objects, five of the grouped poults and all other birds also were given 1-minute tests with the inanimate objects.

Quantitative tests: scored in terms of the amount of time spent in sexual activity.

Single stimulus: head, body or hand.

Age 50-56 days. In the qualitative tests

TABLE 29–1

Responses of poults to various stimulus objects

(Legend: − − = Escape; − = Avoidance; O = No Response; S = Strutting;
C = Copulatory Movements)

BIRD NO.	STRUTTING NON-TEST	HEAD TEST FIRST	HEAD TEST SECOND	BODY TEST FIRST	BODY TEST SECOND	HAND TEST FIRST	HAND TEST SECOND	PREFERENCE TEST
				GROUPED POULTS				
males								
249	often	S	O(C)c	S	O(S)	−	−(S)	
250	often	S	O(C)	S	O(S)	S	O(S)	
182	often	S	−					−
176	often	S	−					−
251	often	− −	−(C)	− −	− −(S)	S	−(S)	
189	often	−	−					−
187	rare	−	−					−
257		− −	O	− −	O	− −	−	
females								
247	rare	O	S	O	S	−	S	
188	rare	−	−					O
186	rare	−	−					O
246		O	O	O	O	−	−	
248		O	O	O	O	−	− −	
255		O	O	O	O	− −	−	
254		O		−		− −		
256		O		O		− −		
253		−	−	O	−	− −	− −	
245		−		−		− −		
252		− −		−		− −		
Also 9 females (Trial 1) which consistently avoided.								
				GROUP-ISOLATED POULTS				
males								
243	often	C	C(C)	C	C(C)	S	S(S)	
262	often	C	C(C)	C	C(C)	S	S(S)	
155	often	C	C					C to head
158a	often	Sa	C					C to head
168	rare	C	C					C to head
167	rare	C	C					C to head
152a		−a	− −					−
females								
164		C	C					C to head
160a		−a	S					C to hand
261		S	O	S	S	O	S	
258		O	O	C	C	−	O	
260		−	C	−	S	−	S	
159a	rare	−a	O					O
259	rare	−	O	O	O	O	S	
163		O	O					−
170a		−a	O					−

TABLE 29-1—Continued

ISOLATED POULTS

males								
157	often	C	C					C to hand
228	often	S	S(S)	S	C(C)	C	C(C)	
241	often	S	S(S)	S	S(S)	S	S(S)	
166	often	– –	– –					C to hand
153	often	– –	S					S to hand
230	often	–	O(–)	–	–(–)	S	S(S)	
156	rare	– –	– –					S to hand
225	rare	–	–	–	–	–	–	
175b	rare	– –						O
286		–	–	– –	–	– –	– –	
240		– –	– –	– –	–	– –	– –	
females								
171b	often	C						C to hand
151	rare	S	S					S to hand
169	often	– –	S					S to hand
154	often	– –	– –					S to hand
165	rare	– –	O					O
172b		– –						–
239		– –	–	–	– –	– –	–	
232		–	– –	– –	– –	– –	–	
173b		– –						O
174b		– –						O

a Isolated at 20 days of age; first test made under group conditions.
b Grouped at 20 days of age.
c Response in parentheses refers to qualitative results in quantitative test, Trial 2.

some birds reacted to several stimulus objects. In order to evaluate the relative stimulus value of the various objects for these birds, quantitative tests were carried out with several males. Tests of 5 minutes duration each were given with head, body and hand, starting when the poults were 50 days old. To obtain maximum response levels, all birds were maintained in isolation for at least seven days before the testing started. Only one test was given per day and each bird was tested at least twice with each stimulus object. The total time spent in strutting or copulatory movements was determind by recording the activity of the bird during successive 5-second periods. These were summed to give the total activity during the 5-minute test. The one test per day procedure was adopted since a rapid response decrement had been observed in sequential tests.

Paired contests with other poults: At various times following the initial test, poults were tested in brief paired contests with other poults. These included pairings with both strutting poults and threatening or attacking poults.

Results

Data on all birds usd in both Trials are presented in Table 29–1. The birds within each treatment category are listed by genetic sex, and individual poults are arranged in approximate order from the most to the least sexually reactive. Birds in Trial 1 are numbered in the 100 series, and those in Trial 2 in the 200 series.

During the normal course of feeding, watering and injecting, many individuals were observed casually to strut in the absence of specifically presented stimuli. Isolated birds strutted openly in the presence of the observer, while grouped birds more often were observed covertly (usually, all except the most reactive grouped birds stopped strutting and exhibited avoidance when the observer was in view). Strutting behaviour was observed for the first time in a few birds as early as four days after the injections were started. Birds displaying in the absence of specifically presented stimuli are listed in Column 2 of Table 29–1 in order to provide an estimate of the potential population of sexually responding poults. Some birds were seen strutting often, others only rarely.

Qualitatively, the reaction of a bird to a stimulus situation was generally consistent from test to test. Birds responding sexually in one test tended to respond sexually in most or all of the test situations. Others were similarly consistent in avoiding or in not responding to the stimulus objects. Identical results were obtained on the first and second tests in 52 per cent. of the 69 tests in Trial 2, while 38 per cent. differed by only one response classification. Only seven pairs of results differed by more than one response classification: one group-

isolated female (260) accounted for three of the differences, and three grouped birds were represented in the other four differences. The grouped poults were the most variable, while group-isolated and isolated males were quite stable and gave identical results in 83 per cent. of the tests.

PATTERNS OF BEHAVIOUR

Prior to the initial test and during their first test with the various stimulus objects, at least some poults in each treatment category were seen to display. In both sexes the display pattern (Fig. 2) was similar to adult male courtship display in that the neck was held in a tight "S" shape, head close to the body, snood elongated, back feathers raised and fluffed, wing feathers spread and drooped slightly, and the tail raised, fanned and angled toward the stimulus object.

Upon the presentation of appropriate stimuli during the initial test, fully organised copulatory patterns were exhibited by some birds in the isolated and group-isolated categories, but not in the grouped category. In all instances the copulatory movements (Fig. 2) were miniature rep-

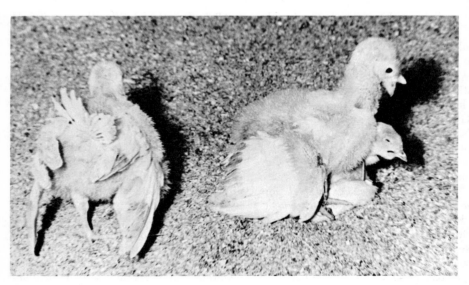

FIG. 2. Androgen-injected poult making copulatory movements on a dummy model; another poult struts nearby.

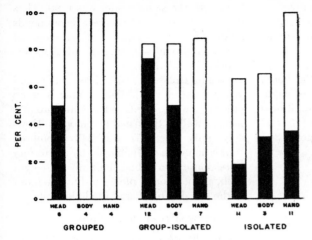

FIG. 3. Percentage of sexually reactive poults exhibiting sexual responses to a given model (copulatory movements in black, strutting in white). The number of birds involved is indicated under each model.

licas of adult patterns and included mounting, treading and trampling the models, and lowering the tail with a quivering motion. Copulatory patterns exhibited by individuals in their first test situation were not visibly different from those exhibited in subsequent tests.

There was no evidence of a gradual maturation of sexual behaviour with repetitive testing. *A priori*, the probability would appear greater that repeated testing might contribute more to the organisation of sexual behaviour in the isolated and group-isolated poults rather than in the grouped ones. Nevertheless, seven of the males in the former categories exhibited copulatory behaviour during initial tests with an appropriate model and only two of the remaining males (158, 166) in these categories showed this behaviour for the first time in later tests. Of five other poults which exhibited copulatory behaviour for the first time in later tests, three were grouped males and two were group-isolated females.

On rare occasions dramatic transitions in behaviour were observed over a period of seconds. One poult in a supplementary category avoided a head model for two minutes, then approached it without strutting and abruptly started copulatory movements which continued for three minutes. Another tried to escape for more than 4

minutes and suddenly moved to a dummy body in courtship display.

Intromission was precluded by the nature of the models, and actual mounting could not occur when the head model was used. Variations in affective neuromuscular co-ordination of copulatory patterns were not assessed. Actually, the effectiveness of normally reared adult males in completing copulations is so variable that a rather large population would be necessary to establish minor treatment differences (Hale, 1955).

STIMULI RELEASING BEHAVIOUR PATTERNS

Rearing conditions up to 10 days of age had a marked effect in determining the stimuli which released sexual behaviour. Responses of isolated birds in the Preference test were all to the observer's hand. In contrast, all but one of the reacting group-reared birds responded to the head model. None of the poults in any treatment category reacted to the body in the Preference test. However, under single stimulus test conditions in Trial 2 the body model did provide some sexual stimulation.

Only those poults responding sexually in at least one test situation serve to delineate the effective stimuli. Six grouped, 12 group-isolated, and 11 isolated poults fit this criterion. Stimuli releasing sexual behaviour in these poults are shown in Fig. 3. Since not all poults were tested with each model, the numbers of birds involved are noted under each stimulus object. Data are presented in terms of the percentage of tested poults responding to a given model. For example, 6 of the 12 group-isolated birds were tested with the body. Of these, 3 (50 per cent.) exhibited copulatory movements, and two additional poults strutted, making a total of 5 (83 per cent.) exhibiting sexual responses.

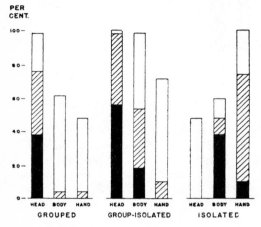

FIG. 4. Percentage of time during 5-min. quantitative tests in which poults exhibited copulatory movements (black), mounted or pressed against model (cross hatch) or strutted (white) in response to various models.

Trends in the quantitative test for those poults reacting to all three models were very similar to the qualitative observations presented in Fig. 3. The quantitative data are presented in Fig. 4 for three grouped (249, 250, 251), two group-isolated (243, 262) and two isolated (228, 241) poults.

Test scores were computed for the quantitative tests by multiplying the time spent exhibiting copulatory movements by two and adding this to the time engaged in all aspects of sexual behaviour. Thus a bird attempting copulation for the full 5-minute period was scored $(5 \times 2) + 5 = 15$, and one strutting the entire period scored $(0 \times 2) + 5 = 5$. Observed scores ranged from 0 to 15 and the correlation between scores on the two quantitative

tests with the same model was 0·90. Thus the high reliability of this test recommends its use for more extensive measurements of the variability of releasing stimuli in experimental populations.

Some isolated (157, 228, 241) and group-isolated (243, 260) poults, but no grouped poults, displayed to inanimate objects as well as the usual test models. However, only Nos. 157 and 243 attempted copulation with such objects: by the former in response to a rubber ball, an unlit light bulb, and a wooden block, and by the latter to the wooden block and the light bulb.

LEVELS OF SEXUAL BEHAVIOUR

Sex differences in sensitivity to the hormone were readily apparent. In the non-test observations 85 per cent. of the males in contrast to only 26 per cent. of the females were observed in courtship display. During the various tests, 46 per cent. of the males attempted copulation as compared with only 13 per cent. of the females.

The frequency or level of sexual responses to appropriate stimuli might have been modified through experience (as were the effective stimuli) even though the motor patterns were not affected. Results summarised in Table 29–1 clearly indicate over all differences in *apparent* levels of response for birds in the various treatment categories. Not only did a greater percentage of group-isolated poults respond sexually, but the frequency of "copulatory" behaviour was markedly higher than in any other group. Under the test conditions of this experiment, the rating for levels of sexual behavior as determined from an inspection of Table 29–1 would be, from highest to lowest: group-isolated, isolated, grouped.

However, it should be re-emphasised that isolated and group-isolated birds were maintained in individual quarters while grouped poults were in contact with other poults (or at best separated for a few hours) prior to testing. When three grouped poults (249, 250, 251) were isolated for one week prior to the quantitative tests,

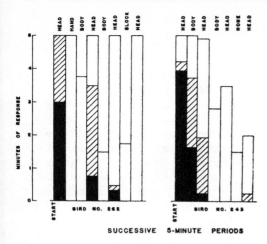

FIG. 5. Response decrement during continuous testing with various models (legend same as in Fig. 4).

levels of response increased sharply and were comparable to the most reactive birds in other categories.

Evidence of a marked response decrement in the continued presence of stimulus objects was obtained by subjecting two group-isolated poults (243, 262) to continuous testing for more than 30 minutes (Fig. 5). Each model was presented for 5 minutes, removed and another introduced. The number of minutes during which various aspects of sexual behaviour were exhibited is indicated for each successive 5-minute period. These poults were predominantly head reactors and it will be noted that although there was usually an increment in sexual behaviour each time the head was introduced, the response was considerably less than that observed during the previous head presentation. Similar decrements were observed with other poults during the routine 5-minute quantitative tests.

RELATIONSHIP OF AGGRESSION TO LEVELS
OF SEXUAL BEHAVIOUR

In tests with other poults, grouped and group-isolated males gave the courtship display and continued to strut even when attacked by other birds, except that occa-

sionally one of the less sexually reactive males would stop strutting and return the attack. Females in these treatment categories attacked introduced poults so consistently that fighting behaviour was a fairly reliable indication of the sex of the bird. After initial threats some of these females appeared to give a sexual crouch. Thus, those birds with the lowest male sex drive were most prone to show aggressive behaviour.

Wood-Gush (1958a, 1958b) observed an inverse relationship between aggressive and mating behaviour in sexually-inexperienced cocks. He suggested that this may mean that the aggressive drive masks the sexual drive, or that aggressive behaviour is aroused because sex drives are only weakly activated. Results with the poults in the present study support the second interpretation.

Discussion

An observed relationship between a behaviour and the degree of social experience often is accepted as *prima facie* evidence that the organisation or maturation of the behaviour is modified through experience. In the present study there was a relationship between sexual behaviour and social experience, in that the grouped birds showed less apparent sexual behaviour than the isolated or group-isolated birds. Following the line of reasoning mentioned above, one might conclude that early social experience *interfered* with the organisation and maturation of sexual behaviour. However, the expression of sexual behaviour in test situations may be modified strongly by factors other than the actual capacity for sexual behaviour. The actual capacity, or basic sexual potential of the population, is represented in Fig. 6. The diagram is an hypothetical representation of the frequency distribution of male sexual behaviour in males and females receiving a maximal dose of androgens, and is inferred from results described by Davis & Domm (1943), Beach (1948) and Hanford & Hale (1959).

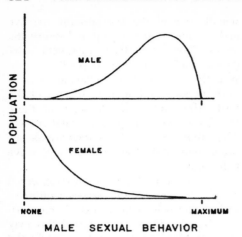

MALE SEXUAL BEHAVIOR

Three factors modifying the expression of sexual potential are: (1) avoidance; (2) transient effects of continuous stimulation on response potential; and (3) the appropriateness of the stimulus presented. A conceptual model based on these three factors is adequate to predict in a general way the behaviour of all birds used in this experiment. The effect of these factors on the expression of the basic sexual potential of the population is discussed below in terms of the conceptual model.

Avoidance. A primary assumption in the conceptual model is that escape-avoidance behaviour and sexual behaviour are *not* extremes on a single continuum. However, escape-avoidance completely masks sexual behaviour, and must be reduced to zero before the expression of sexual be-

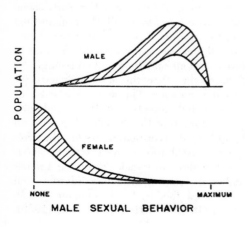

MALE SEXUAL BEHAVIOR

haviour can occur. If all animals avoided, there would be no overt expression of sexual behaviour although the basic sexual potential of the population would be unchanged. If avoidance were reduced by 50 per cent., then those animals in the unshaded portion of Fig. 7, representing *all* levels of responses, would show sexual responses, while the others would continue to avoid. Thus, an increase or decrease in the degree of avoidance would respectively decrease or increase the *number* of animals responding, but would not affect the *levels* of sexual responses of those birds which do respond.

The conceptual model contrasts with the concept of a balance between compet-

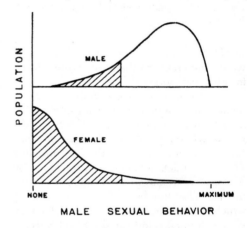

MALE SEXUAL BEHAVIOR

ing drives (Miller, 1944) which has been used so successfully in open field approach-avoidance situations. Use of the concept of balanced drives leads to a very different interpretation of the relationship between the masking effect of avoidance behaviour and the basic sexual potential of the population. Specifically, it implies that if avoidance is reduced by 50 per cent., sexual behaviour will be expressed only by those individuals with higher basic potentials (unshaded areas in Fig. 8), while those with lower potentials would continue to avoid (shaded areas). The concept of balance fails to explain certain aspects of the data in this experiment which are adequately accounted for in the conceptual model. The distinction between the two approaches is considered crucial in the interpretation of experimental findings.

Transient effects of continuous stimulation. This effect has been noted previously (Fig. 5 and attendant text) and is schematically presented in Fig. 9. A given stimulus is most effective at the initial time of presentation, and its effectiveness is markedly reduced during continuous presentation. Thus, an evaluation of the temporary response potential is essential for a valid analysis of the data.

Appropriateness of the stimulus. It has been noted previously (see Stimuli Releasing Behaviour Patterns in Results) that the effectiveness of a stimulus was strongly modified by early rearing conditions. Thus,

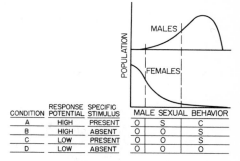

CONDITION	RESPONSE POTENTIAL	SPECIFIC STIMULUS	MALE SEXUAL BEHAVIOR		
A	HIGH	PRESENT	O	S	C
B	HIGH	ABSENT	O	O	S
C	LOW	PRESENT	O	O	S
D	LOW	ABSENT	O	O	O

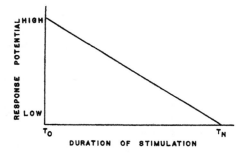

the stimulus value of a given model is not identical for all birds, and the difference must be taken into consideration in any critical examination of the data.

Evaluation of the data in terms of the conceptual model. At this point we may go back and revaluate the data in Table 29–1. As noted above, the avoidance evoking characteristics of the test situation affects the numbers of birds avoiding but does not affect the level of response of sexually reacting birds. Therefore those cases where avoidance occurred in a test may be ignored in considering the effect of treatments on levels of sexual behaviour. Only the other two factors, transient effects of continuous stimulation and appropriateness of the stimulus, affect the level of sexual response.

To illustrate, we may designate levels

of response on the continuum of male sexual behaviour (Fig. 6) in terms of no response (0), strutting (S), and copulatory movements (C). Four hypothetical test conditions (A, B, C, D) taking into account response potentials and specific releasing stimuli are listed in Fig. 10. Test condition A represents a population in an optimal test situation. Note that either a low response potential or the absence of an appropriate stimulus shifts the continuum to a lower level of male sexual behaviour (B or C). A deficiency of both at the same time shifts the continuum even further, to the point where no male sexual behaviour is evident (D).

The various tests that were used actually involved very different conditions depending upon interaction between treatment categories and test situations. Therefore, the relevant data in Table 29–1 have been reassembled and listed in Table 29–2 in terms of test conditions represented by the various test situations. Test conditions were specified as follows: predominantly head reacting birds (grouped, group-isolated) were classed as "stimulus present" in head tests and "stimulus absent" in hand tests; the converse held for hand reacting poults (isolated). In nontest strutting, grouped birds were classed as "stimulus present" (sexual stimulation provided by group mates) and group-isolated and isolated birds as "stimulus absent." Response potential was classified as "low" for the grouped birds since they were housed continuously in the presence of sexual stimulation provided by other poults. Response

TABLE 29-2

Effect of test conditions on level of sexual behaviour

TEST CONDITION[a]	TEST SITUATION	NO. OF TESTS IN WHICH POULTS RESPONDED WITH:					
		O	S	C	O	S	C
	Grouped birds	males			females		
A	Quantitative test, head	0	0	6			
B	Quantitative test, hand	0	6	0			
C	Non-test strutting	1	7	–	17	3	–
C	Qualitative test, head	3	4	0	9	1	0
C	Preference test				2	0	0
D	Qualitative test, hand	1	2	0	0	1	0
	Group-isolated birds						
A	Quantitative test, head	0	0	4			
A	Qualitative test, head	0	1	11	8	2	3
A	Preference test	0	0	4	1	0	2
B	Quantitative test, hand	0	4	0			
B	Non-test strutting	1	6	–	7	2	–
B	Qualitative test, hand	0	4	0	3	3	0
	Isolated birds						
A	Quantitative test, hand	0	4	2			
A	Qualitative test, hand	0	4	2			
A	Preference test	1	2	2	3	3	1
B	Quantitative test, head	0	4	0			
B	Non-test strutting	2	9	–	5	5	–
B	Qualitative test, head	1	5	2	1	3	1

a See text and Fig. 10.

potential was classed as "high" for isolated and group-isolated poults, and for the grouped poults following one week's isolation prior to the quantitative tests.

Hence in the qualitative head tests, group-isolated birds were in condition A, isolated birds in condition B, and grouped birds in condition C. On the other hand, grouped birds (which were in condition C for the qualitative head tests) changed to condition A for the quantitative head test resulting in a decided shift to a higher level of male sexual behaviour. These examples serve to emphasise that identical test situations do not necessarily represent identical test conditions.

Examination of the trends in Table 29–2 both within and between treatment categories indicates that the conceptual model presented in Fig. 10 has rather high predictive value with respect to the levels of response. In Table 29–3 the data are summarised in terms of the percentage distribution of sexual responses for the four test conditions without regard to treatment categories. The model adequately predicts the distribution of behaviour in all instances (except perhaps under condition D, where the number of tests is exceptionally small). These results strongly suggest that *transient test conditions* rather than *prolonged differential social experiences* are the primary factors contributing to the behavioural results presented in Table 29–1.

TABLE 29-3

Distribution (percentage) of sexual responses for the test conditions without regard to treatment categories

TEST CONDITION[a]	NO. OF TESTS	RESPONSE		
		O	S	C
		males		
A	43	2	26	72
B	44	9	86	5
C	15	27	73	0
D	3	33	67	0
		females		
A	23	52	22	26
B	30	53	43	4
C	32	87	13	0
D	1	0	100	0

= Predicted predominate behaviour.
  Predicted to occur but at a lower frequency.
[a] See text and Fig. 10.

One deviation of note is that under test condition A the isolated male poults showed a lower level of sexual response than those in the other treatment categories (Table 29–2). However, it is not possible to state conclusively that isolated poults are deficient in sexual behaviour, since at present there is no way to compare the relative stimulus value of the hand for isolated poults with the head for grouped poults. The fact that isolated poults reacted to a broader spectrum of stimuli with less differentiation (Figs. 3 and 4) lends support to the possibility that the hand is not an optimal stimulus. Therefore, it may be that the three test situations labelled "condition A" for the isolated poults (Table 29–2) should be intermediate between A and B. Hence, the deviation mentioned above might be the result of a sub-optimal test condition rather than a lower level of sexual expression.

The importance of the stimulus as a variable in measuring development of behaviour has frequently been ignored. In another context Hale & Almquist (1956) and Fisher (1958) have indicated that the level of sexual responses may be modified markedly by manipulation of stimulus conditions.

Stimulus specificity was most apparent in the grouped birds, which restricted copulatory movements to the head model and only strutted to the other stimuli. In this respect, their behaviour conforms to that of normally-reared adult males (Schein & Hale, 1957, 1958a). Less stimulus specificity was evidenced by the isolated and group-isolated birds, which gave copulatory movements to a wider range of stimulus objects. Indeed, one bird in each of these categories attempted matings with light bulbs, wooden blocks, upturned feeders, and a rubber ball.

The marked contrast between the apparent diversity of the results on first examination of Table 29–1 and the highly uniform results in Table 29–2 again suggests that many of the divergent results reported in the literature with various species may reflect differential test conditions rather than differential effects of experience. As noted in the foregoing discussion, standardised test situations may not represent the same test conditions for animals with different social experience.

Tests for the presence of organised patterns of behaviour demand optimal conditions for expression of sexual response, which are stated more readily than achieved. With isolated individuals the problem of reducing avoidance on the first test to a point which permits a true evaluation of sexual behaviour for all individuals in the experimental population may be impossible to resolve. In the present study the confined test area tended to trigger either sexual or avoidance behaviour almost immediately. Avoidance or strutting behaviour was typically exhibited within seconds, and copulatory movements usually started within half a minute. In a larger open field type testing area, avoidance behaviour might be expressed by distance with no overt expression of either avoidance or sexual behaviour. As familiarity with the test situation increases during prolonged testing, the actual avoidance distance might be decreased and accompanied by an increase in the expression of sexual behaviour. Thus an increase in sexual behaviour scores with repetitive or prolonged testing in an open field type situation may reflect a decrease in fear responses rather than maturation or organisation of sexual behaviour.

It is noteworthy that minor differences in techniques, including age at testing, mode of hormone administration, position of the observer's hand during a test, individual versus collective testing, or experience with other poults between tests did not influence the trend of the results.

Summary

The object of this study was to determine the effect of early social experience on the patterns and levels of sexual behaviour and on the stimuli releasing sexual patterns. Androgen injected male and female turkeys were studied from hatching through 5-8 weeks of age. Twenty-eight birds lived in grouped environments, while 21 others were reared under conditions of intraspecific visual isolation. Sixteen additional birds were raised in groups for a period of time posthatching, and then visually isolated for the duration of the experiment. Various stimulus objects were used as sexual releasers in several tests during the experiment. These included a poult head, a poult body without the head, the observer's hand, and several inanimate objects.

Complete strutting patterns were exhibited by some birds in each treatment category prior to or during their first test. Of 8 males in the isolated and group-isolated categories which showed fully organised "copulatory movements" at some time during the experimental period, 7 did so during their first test with an appropriate stimulus.

Further, the sexual reaction of a bird to a particular stimulus object generally was consistent and did not increase in repeated tests during the course of the experiment. Hence, it is concluded that the development of the pattern of sexual behaviour is not dependent upon early social or sexual experience.

Treatment differences were most notable with respect to the stimuli which released sexual behaviour. In a preference test, no bird in any treatment category responded preferentially to the headless body. Those birds with early group experience reacted predominantly to the head model, which is in accord with what has been observed in normally reared adult males. However, birds reared in isolation gave sexual responses predominantly to the observer's hand. Hence, it is concluded that early social experience markedly modifies the releasing value of sexual stimuli.

Under the test conditions of this experiment, ratings for levels of apparent sexual behaviour would be, from highest to lowest: group-isolated, isolated and grouped birds. However, it is pointed out that expression of the sexual potential of the population is dependent upon: (1) avoidance behaviour; (2) the appropriateness of the stimulus; (3) the temporary response potential resulting from the degree of recent stimulation. The data were re-evaluated in terms of a conceptual model which incorporated only these factors and the sex differences in sensitivity to androgen injections. Application of the model to the data strongly suggests that transient test conditions rather than prolonged differential social or sexual experiences contributed to the apparent differences in levels of response.

REFERENCES

BEACH, F. A., 1948 *Hormones and behaviour.* New York and London: Paul B. Hoeber, 368 pp.

BEACH, F. A., 1958 Normal sexual behaviour in male rats isolated at fourteen days of age. *J. comp. physiol. Psychol.,* **51,** 37–38.

CRAIG, W., 1914 Male doves reared in isolation. *J. anim. Behav.*, **4**, 121–133.

DAVIS, D. E., and L. V. DOMM, 1943 The influence of hormones on the sexual behaviour of domestic fowl. From *Essays in Biology*, Univ. of California Press, pp. 171–181.

FISHER, A. E., 1958 Effects of stimulus variation on sexual satiation in the male rat. *Amer. Psychol.*, **13**, 382 (abst.).

FISHER, A. E., and E. B. HALE, 1957 Stimulus determinants of sexual and aggressive behaviour in male domestic fowl. *Behaviour*, **10**, 309–323.

HALE, E. B., 1955 Defects in sexual behaviour as factors affecting fertility in turkeys. *Poult. Sci.*, **34**, 1059–1067.

HALE, E. B., and J. O. ALMQUIST, 1956 Effect of changes in the stimulus field on responsiveness of bulls to a constant stimulus animal. *Anat. Rec.*, **125**, 607 (abst.).

HANFORD, P. V., and E. B. HALE, 1959 Unpublished data.

KLOPFER, P. H., 1959 An analysis of learning in young anatidae. *Ecology*, **40**, 90–102.

MILLER, N. E., 1944 Experimental studies of conflict. In Hunt, J. McV., *Personality and behaviour disorders*. New York: Ronald Press.

RABER, H., 1948 Analyse des Balzverhaltens eines domestizieren Truthans *(Meleagris)*. *Behaviour*, **1**, 237–267.

ROSENBLATT, J. S., and L. R. ARONSON, 1958 The influence of experience on the behavioural effects of androgen in prepuberally castrated male cats. *Anim. Behav.*, **6**, 171–182.

SCHEIN, M. W., and E. B. HALE, 1957 The head as a stimulus for orientation and arousal of sexual behaviour of male turkeys. *Anat. Rec.*, **128**, 617–618 (abst.).

SCHEIN, M. W., and E. B. HALE, 1958a Stimuli releasing sexual behaviour of domestic turkeys. 16mm. Film, Psychological Cinema Register, PCR-114K, Pennsylvania State Univ.

SCHEIN, M. W., and E. B. HALE, 1958b Stimuli releasing sexual behaviour of turkeys. *Poult. Sci.*, **37**, 1240 (abst.).

SHAW, EVELYN, 1956 Sexual behaviour of male platyfish raised in individual aquaria. *Anat. Rec.*, **125**, 606 (abst.).

SHAW, EVELYN, 1957 Sexual behaviour of male platyfish reared in altered environments. *Anat. Rec.*, **128**, 621 (abst.).

VALENSTEIN, E. S., W. RISS, and W. C. YOUNG, 1955 Experiential and genetic factors in the organisation of sexual behaviour in male guinea pigs. *J. comp. physiol. Psych.*, **48**, 397–403.

WOOD-GUSH, D. G. M., 1958a The effect of experience on the mating behaviour of the domestic cock. *Anim. Behav.*, **6**, 68–71.

WOOD-GUSH, D. G. M., 1958b Genetic and experiential factors affecting the libido of cockerels. *Proc. roy. physiol. Soc., Edin.*, **27**, 6–8.

HOWARD MOLTZ and L. JAY STETTNER

30 The Influence of Patterned-Light Deprivation on the Critical Period for Imprinting*

This study is related to the "critical periods" controversy discussed in readings 23–25. Howard Moltz is one of many American psychologists who have become interested in problems posed by ethological research.

Reference: *Journal of Comparative and Physiological Psychology*, 1961, **54**, 279–283. Reprinted with the permission of the authors and the American Psychological Association.

* This investigation was supported by Research Grant M-2417 from the National Institutes of Health, United States Public Health Service.

Imprinting has been defined as the procedure of visually presenting to an animal a large moving object during the first several hours of its life under conditions that insure that the object is not associated with such conventional reinforcing agents as food and water. This procedure has been found to evoke a close following of the object in such precocial avian species as ducks, geese, coots, moorhens, and domestic fowl.

One reason that imprinting has generated so much interest is that its effectiveness in inducing following has been shown to be maximal during a brief and relatively specific period of ontogeny. For most precocial aves this period extends from about 8 hr. to about 20 hr. after hatching, with the incidence of subsequent following decreasing sharply if initial exposure to the test object occurs at a later age.

Two general suggestions have been offered regarding the conditions underlying the occurrence of the critical period for imprinting. On the one hand, Lorenz (1937), Hess (1959), and others have implied that the critical period is the direct result of a highly invariant sequence of maturational events which, as Hess states, ". . . has a counterpart in any of the innate responses at a reflexive or tropistic level" (p. 76). On the other hand, Moltz (1960) and Schneirla (1959) have suggested that the bird's readiness to respond to a moving object at one particular stage of its ontogeny and its lack of responsiveness when initial exposure occurs at a later stage are the result of changes brought about through the progressive interaction between the developing organism and its sensory environment.

Although these suggestions have not, of course, been formulated with sufficient precision to support a crucial experimental test, they do provide different points of departure with respect to studying the critical period. Thus, in accord with the "interaction viewpoint," we might begin by focusing experimental attention on the bird's early sensory environment, attempt-ing to manipulate that environment in a manner calculated to vary the age of imprinting effectiveness. A reasonable assumption would be that the animal's experience with patterned light—and thus its experience with visual forms—very early in ontogeny might function as an important determinant of the critical period. Indeed, even if the patterned-light environment were to contain no moving objects, the very presence of a structured or articulated perceptual environment might conceivably influence the animal's subsequent behavior toward the imprinting object. Of relevance here is the frequently reported observation that when initial exposure to the imprinting situation occurs after the critical period, the bird exhibits diffuse emotional excitement which presumably results in responses incompatible with following. Indeed, Hinde (1955) has suggested that the critical period is not a property of an inferred imprinting process but a consequence of the appearance of such conflicting response tendencies. Also of relevance are the results of studies (Hebb, 1946; McBride & Hebb, 1948; Melzack, 1952) of the genesis of emotional behavior in several vertebrate species which indicate that strong fear can frequently be elicited by strange, but innocuous, visual stimuli in the absence of specific avoidance conditioning. On this basis it seems reasonable to assume that the emotional excitement exhibited by a bird past the optimal age for imprinting occurs in response to the unfamiliar visual stimuli provided by the imprinting situation. Perhaps the time during which it was exposed to the structured sensory environment of the cage served to establish the visually "familiar" and, by thus rendering the test object and the apparatus "unfamiliar," contributed to the arousal of incompatible emotional responses and consequently reduced imprinting effectiveness. It would follow from this that the more perceptually naive S is at the time of initial introduction to the imprinting situation, the less likely it would be to display fear and the more likely it would be to pursue the test object. If such is indeed the case, then it does not appear unreasonable to suggest that the critical period for imprinting might be significantly extended if the bird's early visual experiences in the cage were reduced. The present experiment was designed in accord with this suggestion. More specifically, it includes an experimental group deprived of the opportunity to perceive visual forms prior to the first imprinting trial and a control group allowed patterned-light stimulation. The influence of these pre-exposure procedures on the effectiveness of imprinting at different ages was studied by delaying the occurrence of the first imprinting trial until S was either 12, 24, 48, or 72 hr. old.

Method

SUBJECTS

The eggs of 72 Peking ducks were hatched in a forced-air incubator placed in a dark room of the laboratory. Upon being removed from the incubator, each S was assigned at random to one of the treatment groups described below and then transferred to individual living cages having a floor area about 2 ft. square. All movement occurring outside the cage was eliminated from the animal's visual environment by covering the top and all but one side of each cage with sheet metal. The exposed side was placed 1 ft. from a wall to which a panel of light bulbs had been attached to provide illumination. Food, in the form of Purina Duck Startena pellets supplemented with yeast, and water were always available in the cage. In addition, a specially prepared wet mash was given each S.

APPARATUS

Since the apparatus has been described in previous reports (Moltz, Rosenblum, & Halikas, 1959; Moltz, Rosenblum, & Stettner, 1960), only the essential details will be presented. The apparatus consisted of an unpainted wooden alley 10 ft. by 2 ft. by 2 ft. Contained in the alley was a leather belt that passed around two pulleys set 9 ft. apart. A green cardboard object was suspended from the belt and made to travel down one side of the alley and up the other. A motor drove the pulleys and was adjusted so that the object moved at a constant speed of .4 ft/sec. Four Standard Electric timers were used to record the number of seconds that S spent following the object.

PROCEDURE

The Ss were removed from the incubator within approximately 4 hr. after hatching and assigned either to an experimental or to a control treatment. Each experimental S had a latex hood placed over its head, the hood having been fashioned so that it did not press against the corneas and did not hinder the bill from opening and closing freely. The transmission characteristics of the latex were such that it allowed the retinas of the duckling to be stimulated by brightness differences but prevented the perception of visual forms. Each control S was fitted with a hood in which a hole had been cut on either side to permit the retinas to receive normal patterned-light stimulation. In the case of both the experimental and control Ss, removal from the incubator and fitting the hood were performed in the dark.

The experimental and control groups were further divided into four subgroups, henceforth designated as the 12-, 24-, 48-, and 72-hr. subgroups, respectively. The subgroup designations indicate the mean age at which the first imprinting trial was administered. Thus, an S assigned to a 48-hr. subgroup, for example, was kept in its cage either under the diffuse-light condition imposed by the experimental treatment (E-48) or under the patterned-light condition imposed by the control treatment (C-48) until it was approximately 48 hr. old, at which time the hood was removed and S was placed in the alley for the start of the first imprinting trial. Subgroups E-12 and C-12 each contained 12 Ss; the additional 48 Ss were evenly distributed among the six remaining subgroups. As a matter of convenience, the age at which initial exposure occurred will henceforth be referred to as the "exposure age."

Each S was given two imprinting trials, the second trial being administered 24 hr. after the first. An imprinting trial consisted of a 25-min. period in the presence of the test object. The pattern of progression which the object described was as follows: 10-min. run, 5-min. pause, 10-min. run. At the termination of the first trial, S was taken from the alley and returned to its home cage. Its hood was not replaced, so that irrespective of subgroup membership it received patterned-light stimulation during the intertrial period. The weight of each S was recorded following the completion of the second trial.

SCORING

Previous results indicated that "attachment" to the object included not only following behind when the object was in motion, but also walking by the side of the object and frequently running ahead and then stopping to wait. A scoring procedure which appeared to reflect adequately these responses (such responses henceforth being designated as "following") involved activating the timer whenever S was either following the object within a distance of 1 ft. or was standing within a distance of 6 in. of any side of the object. For convenience, the number of seconds accumulated during the 20 min. that the object was in motion during a trial will be referred to as a "following-score." In addition to the scores, protocols of the animals' behavior were recorded for each trial.

Results

The average following-score each S obtained during the two imprinting trials was computed. Figure 1 shows the median of these average scores for each subgroup. Inspection of this figure reveals that the experimental and control subgroups were nearly equivalent with respect to strength

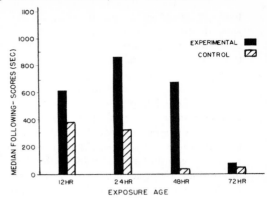

FIG. 1. Median following-scores obtained by experimental and control Ss after different exposure ages.

of following when first exposure to the test object occurred at 12 hr. of age, but were markedly different when first exposure occurred at either 24 or 48 hr. Indeed, an exposure age of 48 hr. resulted in the control subgroup's showing little following, while the same exposure age resulted in the experimental subgroup's showing as much following as that exhibited by experimental Ss run during the critical period (i.e., at 12 hr.). However, when an exposure age of 72 hr. was employed, the level of following attained by the experimental subgroup was almost equivalent to the level attained by its control counterpart.

In accord with the interpretation of Figure 1, no significant difference was found either between the 12-hr. subgroups ($U = 62$, $p > .50$) or between the 72-hr. subgroups ($U = 25$, $p > .25$), while a highly significant difference was found between the 24-hr. subgroups ($U = 10$, $p = .01$) and between the 48-hr. subgroups ($U = 2$, $p < .01$). None of the differences among E-12, E-24, and E-48 was significant. Comparisons among the control subgroups revealed that C-48 and C-72 each differed significantly from C-12 and C-24. It should be noted that, in the case of all the analyses presented, the same conclusions were reached when the score obtained by each S during either the first or second imprinting trial was substituted for its average score over both trials in computing the subgroup medians.

Mention must also be made of the protocols that were recorded, for they reveal important aspects of the animals' behavior not directly reflected in their scores. Of particular concern in the present experiment was the level of emotionality exhibited during the imprinting trials. Such indices of emotionality as avoidance of the test object, "distress calls," and startle responses were recorded. Figure 2 shows the percentage in each subgroup that displayed avoidance during the first 5 min. of exposure to the object. It can be seen that, with the exception of the 12-hr. subgroups, the control Ss showed a greater tendency to avoid than the experimental Ss. The Fisher exact probability test revealed that at exposure ages of 24, 48, and 72 hr. the differences between the experimental and control subgroups were highly significant ($p < .02$ for each comparison). The control Ss also tended to exhibit more distress calls and startle responses as compared with the experimental Ss. These results are clearly in accord with the anticipated effect of patterned-light deprivation upon emotionality.

It is perhaps worth noting that although the experimental Ss wore hoods which permitted only diffuse-light stimu-

lation, none of the experimental subgroups differed significantly from its control counterpart with respect to weight. In large measure this can be attributed to the procedure adopted to induce feeding, which entailed directing S's head for 30 or 40 sec. to its supplementary bowl of wet mash. However, the obtained distribution of weight scores makes it appear likely that despite the induced-feeding procedure, hood-wearing for a period of more than 72 hr. would have resulted in significant weight differences.

Discussion

The results indicate that depriving ducklings of the opportunity to experience a structured or articulated perceptual environment prior to their being exposed to the imprinting situation significantly extends the age at which the imprinting procedure proves effective in inducing following. The fact of this extension should raise doubt concerning the validity of conceiving the critical period to be exclusively a function of an invariant maturational sequence and should emphasize the importance of investigating the nature of the interaction between the developing organism and its sensory environment.

A finding of particular interest in the present study is that those experimental Ss whose initial imprinting trial occurred at 72 hr. of age did not follow. Although patterned-light deprivation resulted in vigorous pursuit of the test object when an exposure age of 48 hr. was employed, an additional 24 hr. under the same visual conditions resulted in little or no following. While it is of course conceivable that patterned-light deprivation for as long as 72 hr. might have damaged the visual system of the bird, it is unlikely that failure to follow was due to failure to adequately perceive the test object. Observations of the behavior of the experimental Ss while they were in the alley, as well as ophthalmoscopic examination of ducklings from another study that had been reared under

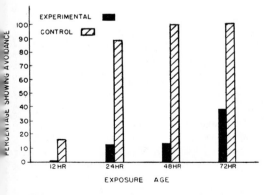

FIG. 2. Percentage of Ss in each subgroup that displayed avoidance during the first 5 min. of exposure to the test object.

diffuse light for 65 hr. from the occurrence of hatching, indicated no visual deficit.†

It is interesting to note that although the 72-hr. experimental Ss did not follow significantly more than their control counterparts, they did exhibit significantly less emotionality. Indeed, E observed that several 72-hr. experimental Ss stood quietly in the alley, attended to the object as it passed, but showed no tendency to follow. Their failure to follow, in view of the fact that they evinced little emotionality, raises the general question of why patterned-light deprivation was found to be effective in extending the critical period. It will be recalled that we suggested that a visually naive S would be less likely to display fear at the time of initial introduction to the imprinting situation and, consequently, would be more likely to pursue the test object. However, the behavior of the 72-hr. experimental Ss indicated that the relative absence of fear did not insure the occurrence of following. Thus, it now appears that although patterned-light deprivation indeed functioned to reduce emotionality, conditions other than reduced emotionality probably were involved in mediating the effectiveness of this treatment in the case of birds exposed at 24 and 48 hr. of age. For while these Ss also displayed little fear, they, unlike the 72-hr. experimental Ss, followed vigorously. At present, we can conclude only that the sensory experience of the animal prior to its initial introduction to the imprinting situation influences its behavior toward the test object. Much additional research will probably be required before the conditions underlying this influence become clear.

Summary

An experiment with Peking ducks was performed to determine whether the critical age for imprinting could be extended by depriving S of the opportunity to perceive visual forms prior to its initial introduction to the "imprinting" object. Accordingly, the experimental Ss were permitted only diffuse-light stimulation in their cages, while the control Ss received normal patterned-light stimulation. Both groups were further divided into four subgroups, designated as the 12-, 24-, 48-, and 72-hr. subgroups. The designations indicated the mean age at which the first imprinting trial was administered. An imprinting trial consisted of a 25-min. period of exposure to a green cardboard test object that moved in a 10-ft. alley. One such trial a day was given for two days.

It was found that the experimental Ss followed the test object considerably more than the control Ss when initial exposure occurred at 24 and 48 hr. of age. No significant difference was found either during the critical period (i.e., at 12 hr.) or at 72 hr.

It was concluded that depriving ducklings of the opportunity to experience a structured visual environment prior to their being exposed to the imprinting situation functions to extend the age at which the imprinting procedure proves effective in inducing following.

REFERENCES

HEBB, D. O.   On the nature of fear. *Psychol. Rev.*, 1946, **53**, 250–275.

HESS, E.   The relationship between imprinting and motivation. In M. R. Jones (Ed.), *Nebraska symposium on motivation.* Lincoln: Univer. Nebraska Press, 1959. Pp. 44–77.

HINDE, R. A.   The modifiability of instinctive behavior. *Advanc. Sci.*, 1955, **12**, 19–24.

LORENZ, K.   The companion in the bird's world. *Auk*, 1937, **54**, 245–273.

McBRIDE, A. F., and D. O. HEBB   Behavior of the captive bottle-nose dolphin *Tursiops trucatus. J. comp. physiol. Psychol.*, 1948, **41**, 111–123.

MELZACK, R.   Irrational fears in the dog. *Canad. J. Psychol.*, 1952, **6**, 141–147.

† Thanks are due William Battersby for performing the examinations.

MOLTZ, H. Imprinting: Empirical basis and theoretical significance. *Psychol. Bull.*, 1960, **57**, 291–314.

MOLTZ, H., L. ROSENBLUM, and NINA HALIKAS Imprinting and level of anxiety. *J. comp. physiol. Psychol.*, 1959, **52**, 240–244.

MOLTZ, H., L. ROSENBLUM, and L. STETTNER Some parameters of imprinting effective-ness. *J. comp. physiol. Psychol.*, 1960, **53**, 297–301.

SCHNEIRLA, T. C. An evolutionary and developmental theory of biphasic processes underlying approach and withdrawal. In M. R. Jones (Ed.), *Nebraska symposium on motivation.* Lincoln: Univer. Nebraska Press, 1959. Pp. 1–41.

section five

SENSORY PROCESSES, COMMUNICATION, AND ORIENTATION

Man has long been curious about the mental life of the creatures who share the earth with him, and he has posed many questions regarding the existence of "consciousness" and similar processes in animals. Although most of these questions are forever unanswerable, modern experimentation has conclusively demonstrated that many animals possess senses and means of communication and orientation that man does not have. In this section, you will read about bees that respond to ultraviolet light and to the polarization of light in the sky; fish that respond to changes in an electrical field which they themselves generate; newts that migrate long distances to a particular segment of a particular stream; and several examples of "ultrasonic" hearing and echolocation in mammals and insects.

Although experimentation on the topics included in this section is difficult and demanding, it can be most rewarding, for many of the most interesting problems in animal behavior are found in these areas.

Suggestions for Further Reading:

FRAENKEL, G. S., and D. L. GUNN, *The Orientation of Animals.* New York: Dover, 1961.

LANYON, W. E., and W. N. TAVOLGA, eds., *Animal Sounds and Communication.* American Institute of Biological Sciences, New York, 1960.

Physiological Mechanisms in Animal Behaviour. London: Cambridge University Press, 1950. Part I.

VON BUDDENBROCK, W., *The Senses.* Ann Arbor: University of Michigan Press, 1958.

M. J. WELLS

31 What the Octopus Makes of It:
Our World from Another Point of View

In this paper a noted English zoologist surveys the behavioral equipment of
that fascinating mollusk: the octopus. He finds that in terms of sensory and
motor potential, *Octopus* is "a very capable animal indeed." Yet, the octopus
does not respond to all the information that seems to be available to it, probably
because its brain is incapable of sufficient organization and integration of the
sensory information.

Originally, this article was the Darwin Lecture presented to the annual meeting of the British Association for the Advancement of Science at Cardiff, September 1960. It was first printed in *The Advancement of Science* (London),
January 1961, and subsequently reprinted in *American Scientist*, 1961, 49, 215–
227. It is reproduced here by permission of the author, the British Association for
the Advancement of Science, and the editors of *American Scientist*. Figure 1 and
two plates have been omitted.

If one is to find out how the brains of
animals work one must first discover what
they are built to do. At the highest, vaguest
level it is easy enough to define this; brains
sort out sensory information and deal with
the organisation of suitable reactions. At
any more detailed level we run into trouble
because we have to define, among other
things, the sensory information that is
being used, and this is not as easy as it
would at first appear to be. By examining
the properties of the sense organs that an
animal has—by recording off sensory nerves
and so on—we can discover only the limits
within which the animal is potentially capable of detecting changes in the world
around it. What we cannot find out by
such a study is whether the animal actually makes use of all the information provided by its sense organs—that is whether
the creature's performance is limited by
the properties of its sense organs or by
the integrative machinery of its central
nervous system.

To discover this we have to watch and
experiment upon the intact, living animal.

The account that follows deals with the
deductions that can be made from observations of the behaviour of individuals
of one particular species—the common octopus. It will be shown that in this animal
it is the central integrative and not the
sensory machinery that limits what the
animal can do—a fortunate state of affairs
since the very nature of the limitations
that we find gives us important and otherwise unobtainable clues about the way that
the integrative machinery must itself be
put together.

As an experimental animal the octopus
has a number of outstanding virtues. It is
easy to catch and easy to keep. It eats
crabs and pieces of fish, both of which are
easy to get. And its habits in the sea, where
it lives among rocks in a hole whence it
pounces out on passing prey, mean that
we can keep it under comparatively natural
conditions in the laboratory.

Octopus also has the advantage of
being of the right order of size. This is
important if we are to investigate the
properties of its central nervous system,

because it means that the animal is living in the physical environment to which we are ourselves accustomed. We can devise tests for the animal knowing that it will be operating under conditions that we ourselves understand—a situation that is not always true of invertebrate animals, particularly of very small invertebrate animals, in whose lives surface tensions and molecular forces generally assume an importance altogether foreign to our own experience of the world. By studying *Octopus*, an animal of about ⅟₁₀₀ of our own size, we avoid problems of this nature and, because we can ourselves appreciate, measure, and classify most of the environmental disturbances to which our experimental animal reacts, we can hope to build up a picture of what the world looks, tastes, and feels like to it. This animal has sense organs capable of detecting very much the same sorts of changes as our own, yet the picture of our world that an octopus must have can be shown to be very different from ours in several important ways that can only be due to fundamental differences in the make-up of its central nervous system.

Octopuses are primarily visual and tactile animals, like ourselves. The similarity of cephalopod and vertebrate eyes is often cited in textbooks as a classic instance of convergent evolution, the eye of an octopus being structurally so like the vertebrate eye that sections of it are a favourite catch-question in university scholarship examinations; it has a lens, iris, and retina arranged very much as in our own eye . . . . In detail, of course, the two differ both in function and in structure; focusing, for example, is by moving the lens in and out in *Octopus*, by altering the shape of the lens in man; the optic nerves depart from the outside of the retina in *Octopus*, from the inside (and out through the "blind spot") in ourselves. The important point for present purposes is that the octopod eye is capable of furnishing very much the same sort of information about things seen as our own.

Octopus has one other set of sense organs showing a remarkable convergence with our own. The octopod statocyst (the animal has two, one on either side of the head just below the brain) has an otolith hung on a set of sensory hairs (which we can compare with the macular gravity receptors of our own inner ear) and a line of sensory cells with loaded processes arranged in three planes at right angles inside a fluid-filled sac—an arrangement that is clearly capable of providing the same information about angular accelerations as the ampullae in our semicircular canals . . . .

Octopus has no specialised olfactory organs. There is a small pit, which seems likely from its position to be concerned with testing the water of the respiratory stream as it enters the gill chamber. But it has yet to be shown that removing it has any effect upon behaviour and its function remains problematic. Much more important is the chemical sensitivity, a "taste sense," which seems to be a property of the body surface generally and especially of regions such as the rims of the suckers which are particularly well supplied with sensory nerve endings. The sense organs concerned are difficult to identify; there are very many sensory nerve terminations in the skin, and some at least of these, buried below the surface, may be discounted as more likely to be mechanoreceptors reacting to compression or stretch than chemoreceptors. But others, with free endings projecting to the surface of the skin, may well be responsible for the animal's sensitivity to chemical substances in the water around it. The little we know about these structures tells us practically nothing about the nature of the information that they must provide; the nerves from them are too small to record from electrically with techniques at present available and we are forced to deduce their function from a consideration of the sort of stimuli to which the animal can be shown to react.

As well as this equipment for collecting information about the world around it, *Octopus* must have sense organs for telling it what is going on within its own body. It must, among others, have sense organs recording tension in the muscles of its arms, since it reacts to passive stretch by contraction; and in any case it is difficult to see how the animal could make the continual fine positional adjustments needed for clambering over the rocks among which it lives were there not some source of detailed information about the position of parts of the individual arms. It will be noticed that proprioceptive sense organs, though wholly internal, are nevertheless potentially capable of giving information about the outside world because the distribution of tension in the individual muscles must bear some relation to the surfaces over which the animal is traveling and to the shape and weight of any objects that it handles. We ourselves can distinguish the shape of objects by touch because we are aware of the relative position and movements of our fingers—we use proprioceptive information from receptors in our finger muscles and integrate this with information from more superficial tactile receptors in order to build up images of objects that we are handling.

Examination of the sensory equipment of *Octopus* gives us, then, some idea of the potential capacities of the animal—what it ought to be able to do were it able to use all the information collected to best advantage. Potentially it is a very capable animal indeed. It has flexible muscular arms, with suckers for grasping and manipulating objects and a set of sense organs capable of providing very much the same sorts of sensory information as our own. In principle there is no reason why this animal should not be capable of carrying out manipulative acts much as we do.

Yet it does not. Its brain is not organised to deal with the incoming sensory information in as elaborate a way as our own. It has several notable differences in organisation—deficiencies by our standards

—that limit the integrative capacity of the animal so that the perceptual world that an octopus lives in is a very different place from our own.

We can find out a little about this other world by watching octopuses in aquaria. The animal likes to sit in one corner of its tank, preferably amongst a heap of rocks or bricks. From this "home" the creature pounces out upon any small moving object; it will attack fingers dabbled in its tank (Aristotle said this showed it was a very stupid animal), and it collects food such as crabs or pieces of fish when these are dropped in, taking them home to devour at leisure. The octopus, looking out from its home, is clearly able to distinguish both the size and the range of objects that it sees. Large objects are not attacked, and very large objects elicit a special display . . . . in which the animal expands the interbrachial web, pales and flattens out, appearing suddenly much larger than it really is—one can assume that this serves to deter would-be predators in the sea. We can tell that size is distinguished as a quality of objects independent of the extent of the image that they make on the retina because small objects are recognised as such even when very close to the octopus, and animals that have been trained (see below) continue to discriminate between figures of similar shape but different size regardless of their distance.

Objects of different shape are also distinguished, and untrained octopuses, fresh from the sea, are more liable to attack some objects than others. All will attack crabs when they see them, and most individuals will go for a variety of less "natural" figures—geometrical shapes cut out of card and moved about on the end of a wire—generally preferring circles to rectangles, and elongate figures moving along their long axes to similar figures moving at right angles to their long axes.

Observations of this sort do not, however, tell us very much about the limits of the visual discrimination system, and very little about the way that objects seen are classified by octupuses. The fact that an animal reacts in the same way in two situations does not necessarily mean that it cannot distinguish between them. More probably it simply has no reason for doing so, and in order to pursue the matter further we have to provide incentives which will drive the creature to discriminate if it possibly can.

With many invertebrate animals this would be difficult. *Octopus,* however, is intelligent and readily trainable. It is also perpetually hungry (an octopus will eat sufficient to double its weight in a month if it is given the chance) so that it quickly learns to recognise any situation that yields food. If, for example, a crab and a geometric figure are shown together in its tank, the animal learns in three or four trials to come out and attack when the figure is shown alone. The difficulty is then to prevent the octopus from attacking all figures indiscriminately, and this can be done by punishment for attacks in inappropriate situations. Octopuses dislike small electric shocks, and a convenient form of punishment is a 6–9 volt A.C. electric shock, administered by touching the erring octopus with electrodes fixed to a probe. Using this reward and punishment technique octopuses can be taught to distinguish between a variety of figures. As one might expect, some discriminations prove more difficult for them than others; they take longer to learn these, and the accuracy of their performance never becomes as great as with simpler discriminations. We can use the number of errors that octopuses make in learning to discriminate as a measure of the difficulty of the problem set, and by training them to distinguish between objects that differ in only one definable way at a time we can discover which features of things seen are discriminable. We can, for example, show that octopuses are capable of distinguishing between figures that differ only in orientation, provided that the difference between the figures can be defined in terms of horizontal and vertical—mirror

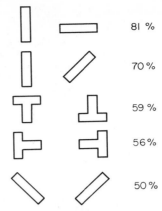

FIG. 1. Geometric figures that octopuses can be trained to distinguish by sight and the proportion of errors made over the first sixty trials of training to discriminate between them [from SUTHERLAND (1957), *Nature* (London), 179].

images are not distinguished (Fig. 1). Such a result tells us a number of things about the way that the animal's visual system must be organised. It shows, for example, that the octopus is *not* making use of any of the available "short cuts" to discrimination—it is not distinguishing shapes because they differ in area or because they differ in length of outline or because they have more or fewer corners (*cf.* insects such as bees, which classify shapes by their degree of irregularity of outline). *Octopus* must, in fact, be discriminating between objects much as we do, from the distribution of their masses in space. Apparently classification of shapes is in some way related to their distribution about the horizontal and vertical axes, since forms, such as the oblique, mirror-image rectangles of Fig. 1, which have similar distributions about these axes, are not distinguished. It is interesting that we, too (though possibly for rather different reasons), find mirror images and left/right relatively difficult to distinguish compared with horizontal/vertical and up/down.

Recent work has shown a possible anatomical basis for the octopus's tendency to classify objects in terms of their horizontal

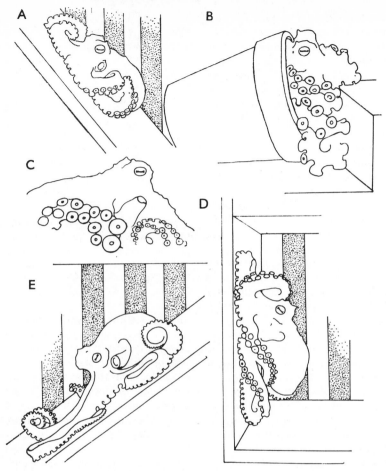

FIG. 2. Orientation of the eyes of the *Octopus* before [(A), (B), and (C)] and after [(D) and (E)] removal of the statocysts. The slit-like pupil normally remains horizontal over a wide range of bodily positions, but this constancy of orientation is lost when the statocysts are removed [from WELLS (1960), *J. exp. Biol.* 37].

and vertical extents; the elements of the retina itself, and the connections between the individual nerves in the outer layers of the optic lobes of the brain are both arranged in a predominantly horizontal and vertical manner. The retinal array can be said to be horizontal and vertical (rather than simply arranged along two axes at right angles) because the eyeball remains constantly oriented with respect to gravity over a wide range of bodily positions (Fig. 2). It can be shown moreover that this orientation depends upon the integrity of

the statocysts, and that after surgical removal of these gravity receptors the majority of trained animals cease to discriminate between figures differing only in orientation. A few individuals, however, continue to discriminate between the objects, though not always in the direction learned during preoperational training, and some animals make many more than random errors, consistently mistaking vertical for horizontal rectangles (and *v. v.*) in their postoperational training. This result was at first puzzling — a statocyst that is not there clearly cannot be producing the wrong information—until it was noticed that the perverse animals were all individuals that habitually sat in positions such that their retinae (as indicated by the angle of the slit-like pupils) lay at right angles to the position maintained during preoperational training. Evidently the orientation of an object can be distinguished because the image of the object falls in a constant relation to the horizontal/vertical axes of the retinal array, and the central machinery for learning to recognise figures is organised on the assumption that the eye remains in a constant position with respect to gravity.

By vertebrate standards this is a very curious way of doing things. Vertebrates, such as ourselves, recognise the orientation of objects whatever position the eyes happen to be in; our central nervous system correlates proprioceptive information about the position of the eyes relative to the head, and of the head relative to gravity, with the distribution of the image on the retina. Vertebrates can still tell which way up they are and recognise the orientation of figures after destruction of the gravity receptors in the labyrinth, presumably by integrating proprioceptive information about the distribution of tensions in their muscles with the visual input. This is something that octopuses cannot do. Although operated animals continue to feed and grow after statocyst removal, they never learn to orientate themselves correctly, and do not regain the capacity to discriminate between objects differing in orientation, although they can still learn simpler discriminations, such as between black and white discs.

A return to the question of nonuse of proprioceptive information in learning will be made below in consideration of the tactile system of *Octopus*. But first, what else can the animal discover about the world around it by using its eyes?

The question of whether octopuses can distinguish colours has been investigated but remains unsettled. It certainly looks as though *Octopus* can distinguish colours, but none of the conditioning experiments done so far have eliminated the possibility that the experimental animals were really distinguishing the coloured lights or objects on a basis of intensity of illumination rather than wavelength of transmitted or reflected light. A similar difficulty occurs in the interpretation of results which suggest that octopuses are able to distinguish another quality of light reaching the retina — its plane of vibration. Recent experiments with octopuses in aquaria show that they can be taught to distinguish between sources of light polarised in two directions at right angles—sources that look exactly alike to us. It has been claimed that this capacity is related to the fine structure of the retinal elements and that these detect the plane of polarisation directly—in which case the ability to learn the distinction presumably rests once again upon the constant orientation of the retinae. Alternatively, however, it is quite possible that the octopus is *not* detecting the plane of polarisation directly, but making the distinction indirectly from differences in the pattern of reflections from objects in its tank and from particles suspended in the water. In any case the use, if any, that *Octopus* makes of its capacity is unknown.

As might be expected, if only from the animal's excessive number of arms, *Octopus* has a well developed touch sense. We can investigate this systematically in much the same way as for the visual senses—by reward and punishment training experiments. The only differences in the technique arise out of having to use animals blinded by section of the optic nerves (a simple operation carried out under urethane anaesthesia) in order to eliminate the possibility of their learning to recognise the test objects by sight. The test objects are presented one at a time, by touching them against one of the arms of the octopus; the animal then grasps and either accepts the object, passing it in under the interbrachial web to the mouth, or rejects it, thrusting the object away. When it is rewarded for accepting one of a pair of objects, and punished for accepting the other, an octopus rapidly learns to discriminate between them (Fig. 4).

It is possible in this way to train octopuses to distinguish between shellfish of various species, and between live and dead shellfish of the same species—the dead ones being scrubbed clean and filled with sealing wax. Octopuses are thus able to make tactile discriminations on a basis of "taste" alone—we can call this a "chemotactile" sense—using receptors on the arms.

The chemotactile sense is difficult to investigate, but not because the animals are difficult to train. The difficulty arises rather from our own inability to measure and classify the stimuli—and until we can do this ourselves, we have very little hope of finding out how the octopus does it. It seems that the chemotactile sense organs on the arms of *Octopus* are sensitive to tastes that we would call sweet, bitter, and sour (not salt—the animal lives in the sea), but we do not know whether these tastes are alike to the animal. We do know that the sensitivity of the receptors is very high, the suckers on the arms detecting substances in concentrations comparable with the minimum concentrations detectable by the human tongue. And there the matter must rest until we can devise a practicable means of measuring the concentration of substances at the region of contact with the suckers of the octopus and a way of ensuring that our test objects continue to taste the same throughout the experiment.

It is easier to investigate *Octopus's* ability to distinguish the physical properties of objects touched because it is easier for us to classify and control the size, shape, and texture of objects than their chemical characteristics. As in the visual experiments, we can measure the similarity of any two objects to octopuses from the proportion of mistakes that they make in learning to discriminate between them. Doing this we discover something rather curious about the organisation of the tactile system of *Octopus*. It turns out that the animal is quite unable to distinguish the

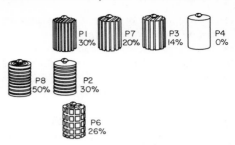

FIG. 3. Objects used in the experiments on the tactile sense of *Octopus*. The series is arranged so that there is a decreasing proportion of grooved to flat surface from left to right. This proportion is indicated as a percentage for each object. The objects in the top row differ only in the frequency of vertical grooves cut into them. P_2 differs from P_1 only in the orientation of the grooves cut into it. P_6 has very nearly the same proportion of groove as P_1, but the grooves are arranged to form a pattern of squares. Octopuses find P_1, P_2 and P_6 difficult or impossible to distinguish, but can be taught to discriminate between the members of the top row and between P_8 and P_4 relatively easily [from WELLS and WELLS (1957), *J. exp. Biol.* 34].

shape of objects, or indeed to distinguish anything about them other than their surface texture and even this is rated in a rather curious way. It seems that the animal can detect the presence of surface irregularities, but cannot distinguish anything about their distribution. The members of the series of objects shown in Fig. 3, for instance were only distinguished when they varied in what could be described as "roughness"—in the proportion of smooth surface cut away to make the grooved patterns on them; the nature of the pattern—whether the grooves ran along or round the cylinders and so on—was apparently quite irrelevant and not available to *Octopus* as a means of distinguishing between them. Evidently there is no central projection of the tactile sensory field in octopuses and the relative position of the tactile sense organs is not taken into account in building up an image of what an object handled is like. This is quite unlike ourselves where the relative position of receptors is most important in building up a picture of things we touch.

All of which returns us to something already implied by the consequences of statocyst removal on visual discrimination; *Octopus* seems unable to use proprioceptive information about the position of parts of its own body in learning.

We can confirm this peculiar feature of the organisation of *Octopus* by yet another sort of discrimination experiment. We can try to train octopuses to distinguish between objects of different weight. They cannot do it (Fig. 4). The result of these experiments is the more peculiar because *Octopus* quite obviously compensates for the weight of objects when it handles them. A heavy object is grasped in the normal way by an arm, which is passively extended by the weight of the object (blind animals generally sit on the sides of their aquaria); the octopus "takes up the slack" as it were,

contracting its arm muscles, and then handles the object, passing it to the mouth or rejecting it in the normal way. A human observer can tell which object the animal is handling simply by watching the octopus, but the animal itself is not capable of learning to recognise that holding one object requires more muscle contraction than holding the other.

It seems, then, that although *Octopus* is capable of integrating information from the various sense organs detecting outside events, it cannot learn to combine information from these external receptors with information from internal ones. It cannot, moreover, learn to recognise external events signalled by internal receptors. This is not to say that internal information remains unused. The animal must, of course, make fine adjustments to the position of parts of its own body as a result of information from internal receptors, or it would be unable

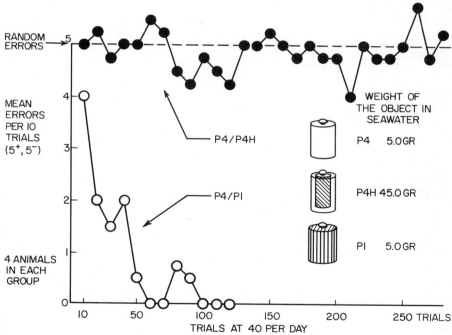

FIG. 4. Tactile discrimination by octopuses. Four animals were trained to distinguish between the smooth perspex cylinder P₄ and the grooved cylinder P₁, learning this discrimination rapidly (the experimental results are plotted O—O). Four other animals trained in exactly the same way, failed to learn to distinguish between P₄ and P₄H, which was smooth like P₄, but nine times as heavy (results plotted ●—●) (WELLS unpublished results).

to move about as it does. But the whole business of postural adjustment seems to be dealt with at an automatic, reflex level. We have already seen how the eyes are kept horizontal by a reflex mechanism operating on information arising from the statocysts, and it appears that similar more or less inflexible mechanisms look after details of all the motor responses that the animal makes; for instance, well-integrated taking and rejecting movements — those that blind animals use when responding to objects that they touch—can be carried out even by isolated arms, chopped off from the body of the octopus. Distribution of organisation of responses to proprioceptive inputs has obvious administrative advantages, and it is possibly the only economical way of organising such a highly complex and flexible animal. *Octopus* has no skeleton, so that movements of parts are not restricted as in vertebrates, and this very flexibility would pose a horrific problem of integration for any wholly central mechanism. Even in ourselves where movements are restricted by the skeleton there is a tendency to simplify the brain's problem by delegating a good deal of postural adjustment to a spinal level, and in *Octopus* this tendency has apparently proceeded to the extreme where *all* the proprioceptive information needed for fine adjustments is dealt with in lower nervous centres — centres that do not themslves take part in the determination of which a repertoire of responses by the animal as a whole shall be made in reply to any particular set of stimuli from the outside world.

Quite how this extreme state of affairs has come about is uncertain. It is possibly a consequence of descent from pelagic ancestors—octopuses are exceptional among cephalopod molluscs in that they live on the bottom, making extensive use of tactile stimuli; the rest, with few exceptions (*Sepia*, the cuttlefish and its close relatives) live in the open waters of the deep sea. Whatever the origin, the administrative economy of a largely reflex adjustment of posture has disadvantages for the pres-

ent-day bottom-living *Octopus*. It means, as we have seen, that the animal cannot derive additional information about the things that it touches from the relative positions of the receptors stimulated by the contact. And it means that, despite Pliny's attractive story about the stone and the oyster, there is no possibility of the animal learning to make skilled movements.

From our point of view these limitations are a virtue. *Octopus* has a nervous system that does many of the things that our own does—the animal learns readily, to mention just one aspect of nervous organisation that we should like to know about—but it is a great deal less complicated. The octopus collects much the same sort of information about the world as we can ourselves, but it apparently makes different and far more limited use of this information. And because, in particular, it seems unable to use positional information, the brain of an octopus may prove to be a very great deal easier to analyse than the brain of any vertebrate.

But whatever we eventually hope to find out, the first stage in this analysis must be to discover what the octopus makes of the world around it.

REFERENCES

BOYCOTT, B. B., 1954 "Learning in Octopus vulgaris and other Cephalopods," *Pubbl. Staz. zool. Napoli*, **25**, 67–93. (How to catch and keep octopuses and details of experimental techniques.)

SUTHERLAND, N. S., 1960 "Theories of shape discrimination in *Octopus*," *Nature, Lond.*, **186**, 840–844. (Mechanism of visual discrimination in octopus.)

WELLS, M. J., 1958 "Nerve structure and function," *Advanc. Sci., Lond.*, **57**, 449–57. (The relation of the work on octopuses to other lines of research on brain mechanisms—a review of the Section D proceedings at Dublin, 1957.)

YOUNG, J. Z., 1960 "Learning and form discrimination by *Octopus*," *Biol. Rev.*, **36**, 60, 74–94. (A review of the results of training experiments.)

K. VON FRISCH and M. LINDAUER

32   The "Language" and Orientation of the Honey Bee*

Karl von Frisch's ingenious experiments have resulted in many remarkable discoveries on the behavior of bees and other lower animals. As Donald Griffin (author of reading 37) pointed out in his Foreword to von Frisch's *Bees: Their Vision, Chemical Senses, and Language* (Cornell, 1950), the early discoveries of von Frisch on the language of the honey bee were so startling that many scientists simply did not believe them. Only after several independent confirmations had been published was the validity of von Frisch's work recognized. Von Frisch seems to have been untroubled by this skepticism, and Griffin quotes his comment, "No competent scientist *ought* to believe these things on first hearing."

The following reading is reprinted from the *Annual Review of Entomology*, 1956, 1, 45–58, with the permission of the authors and the publisher.

Suggestions for further reading: Lindauer, M., *Communication among Social Bees*. Cambridge, Mass.: Harvard University Press, 1961. Von Frisch, K., *The Dancing Bees*. New York: Harcourt, 1953.

We have been asked to report upon the latest results of our study of the "language" and orientation of bees. The knowledge we had up to 1950 has been presented in a series of lectures entitled "Bees" and given by the senior author on the occasion of an invitational tour of the United States. These lectures have been edited in book form by von Frisch (11), and a bibliography up to the year 1950 is to be found in this booklet. The present review is concerned primarily with developments since that time.

The "language" of the bees is not a verbal one. It depends on the senses of touch and smell. Their words are rhythmic movements and scents. Before going into details we should like to restate the means by which the bees communicate with each other.

A bee informs her hive companions of a new, rich food source (nectar, sugar solution, or pollen) found in the close vicinity of the hive by means of a round dance (see Fig. 2a). Those of the bees which are in

* The survey of the literature pertaining to this review was completed in April, 1955.

a co-operative mood follow the returned bee closely during the dance on the honeycomb and learn that there is a profitable source of food. By the special form of dance, which gives no indication of direction, they are taught that it is to be found close to the hive. The specific scent of the visited plant sticking to the body of the dancer, to the pollen, or to the nectar tells them for which kind of flower to search.

If the food is farther away than 50 to 100 m., the round dance is replaced by the waggle dance (Fig. 2c). With its help the hive mates following the dancer are informed not only of the existence of a promising source of food and of its characteristic scent, they even learn at what distance and in which direction from the hive to seek it. The distance is taught by the measure (rhythm) of the dance [von Frisch (11)]. The direction is given in relation to the position of the sun. If the feeding place is to be found exactly in the same direction in which the sun lies at the time, the dancer indicates this on the vertical honeycomb of the hive by orientating the straight wagging of the dance vertically upwards. If the feeding place lies at an angle of 60° to the left of the sun, the straight part within the dance will also be carried out at an angle of 60° to the left of the vertical, and so forth. They transpose thus the angle to the sun, that has to be made while flying to the food source, into the field of the gravity when dancing on the honeycomb [von Frisch (11, Fig. 44, p. 77)]. The hive mates which have accompanied the dance fly out and will find the source of food according to the communications they have received.

The food gathering bees dance after each flight, as long as it is advantageous to draw further gatherers to the exploited feeding place. As soon as the food becomes scarce, they stop dancing, although they continue collecting, and from then on this worker group does not increase anymore. By these means the principle of relations between supply and demand is applied to the behaviour of bees.

Certain objections have been raised to our use of the word "language" to describe these means of communication [Révész (37)]. It is evident that the mental principles of communication between bees are quite different from those of the human language. In order to underline this difference we write the word "language" in quotation marks. There is, however, no doubt that the language of the bees is on a higher level than the means of communication among birds and mammals with the exception of man. Warning or attracting calls and mating songs among birds express only the animal's motivation. This can convey itself to other members of the species. The dances of bees, however, transmits the knowledge of significant facts [von Frisch (14, 17)].

The Indication of Distance

With increasing distance between feeding place and hive the number of straight runs within the waggle dance decreases, the rhythm of the dance becomes slower. At the same time the number of abdominal waggles during the straight run increases. It cannot be determined from the beginning whether the number of straight runs in a given time, or the number of waggles, indicate the distances. The latter are so quick that one can only approximately estimate their number by direct observation. Relying on such data [von Frisch (9, p. 20)] Haldane & Spurway (20) suggest that the number of waggles is the principal means by which distance is conveyed. We think, however, that before coming to this conclusion we must count the mean number of waggles per distance as accurately as possible. For this reason, we have made slow-motion pictures of dances at varying distances from the feeding place. The evaluation of this work has not yet been completed.

Two important observations have been made which might answer the problem of how a bee is able to estimate the distance she has flown. If the bee has a head wind on its outword journey to the feeding place she indicates in her dance a greater distance than when there is no wind. Similarly she indicates a shorter distance than normal when she had the wind in her favour [von Frisch (10, p. 15)]. If she has to fly uphill on her way to the feeding place she will, when dancing in the hive convey a greater distance than when she flies the same length on the level. And if she has to fly downhill she will communicate a shorter distance still [Hern & Wanke (23)]. It seems, therefore, that the time or energy spent on the flight from hive to feeding place† are very important, instead of the actual distance. Probably the main factor in the evaluation of distance is the energy spent on the flight; the experiments concerning this problem, however, are not yet finished.

The following experiment shows how accurately the dancer's indication of dis-

† All given data on the dance concern the flight to the feeding place, none the flight homewards to the hive.

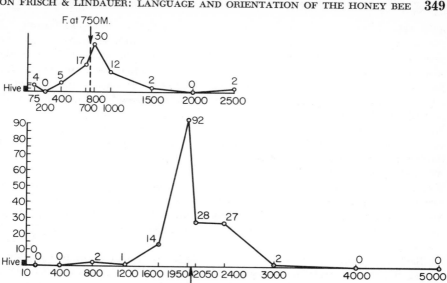

FIG. 1. Experiments concerning the reaction to the indication of distance. The distances of the scent plates from the hive are indicated on the abscissa in meters. The numbers on the points of the graph correspond with the number of bees which have come to each scent plate.

(Above) Trial of June 27, 1949. Distance between feeding place (F) and hive is 750 m. Duration of the experiment: 90 min.

(Below) Trial of July 20, 1952. Distance to feeding place is 2000 m. Duration of experiment: 3 hr.

tance is understood and followed by the other bees. Several bees individually numbered with coloured dots are, at a certain distance from the hive, fed with a sugar solution to which a scent, for example lavender oil, was added. Upon their return to the hive, the numbered gatherers dance, and during the dance the hive companions smell the lavender and search for this specific odour when flying out. On the direct line from the hive to the feeding place and even further away "scent plates" are placed at various distances. They emit the scent, but offer no food. The bees looking out for this odour at the indicated distance are attracted by the scent plates if they come near them. They fly around them and finally alight on them and are thereupon counted by an observer. In Figure 1 we show the results of two such experiments. In the first trial the feeding place was at a distance of 750 m. and in the second at 2000 m. from the hive. The data given for the different points of the graph indicate how many of the searching bees came to each scent plate during the time of observation. The graphs show that the indication of distance given by the dancer is quite accurate and has been well understood by the other bees [von Frisch (13, 17)].

The Indication of Direction

Normally the bees dance on the vertical honeycomb. In the dark hive they show the direction to be flown in order to indicate the feeding place to their companions by transposing the angle to the sun at which they flew from hive to food into the vertical plane. Sometimes, however, it happens that the returning bee dances outside the hive on the horizontal landing plank, in the daylight. In that case she points directly towards the goal during the straight wagging runs of the dance [von Frisch (11, Fig. 50, p. 87)]. This kind of communication of direction is the simpler one and more easily understood, as many insects possess a light-compass-reaction. They can register the position of the sun during their excursions or flights and keep thus a straight line of movement always maintaining the same angle to the sun. During her flight the bee also memorises the position of the sun and upon her return to the hive she maintains on the horizontal surface the same memorised angle to the sun, when performing the straight run of the dance. Thus she points directly towards the feeding place during the wagging dance.

Based on these observations we presumed that the dancing on a horizontal surface and in daylight was the more primitive and phylogenetically older form of indication of direction. It was, therefore, important to investigate the behaviour of other species of bees such as *Apis florea* Fabricius the dwarf honey bee. Its behaviour is comparatively primitive. The nest consists of one honeycomb only and possesses no nest cover. The honeycomb is built in the open air, suspended from a bush, the top of the comb being attached to a branch. The upper end of the honeycomb forms a broadened horizontal platform. The homecoming bees go immediately onto this platform where they convey, by a horizontal wagging dance in the same manner as our honey bees, what they found and whereabouts. They indicate the direction to be flown according to the position of the sun or the polarized light rays of the blue sky. If the honeycomb is turned around its horizontal or its vertical axis, the dancers walk always to the top in order to find a horizontal surface for dancing [Lindauer (unpublished observations)]. The hypothesis that the dancing on a horizontal surface is the original and more primitive means of communication among bees is considerably strengthened by these observations.

It is rather difficult to conceive how in their social evolution the bees have ac-

quired the possibility of transposing their orientation to the sun into an orientation to gravity for the vertical dance in the dark hive. But some new observations show that among other insects such translations are also to be found, although biologically they appear to be pointless.

Vowles (41) working in a dark room on a horizontal plane forced ants into a motion of flight. As long as a lamp burnt the ants always maintained the same angle to the light source while in flight (light-compass-movement). When the light was turned out, and the surface put in a vertical position, the ant would run at approximately the same angle to the field of gravity as it formerly had taken to the light on the horizontal plane. Birukow (6) found a similar behaviour in the dung beetle, *Geotrupes silvaticus* Panz., in *Coccinella septempunctata* Linn., and in *Melasoma populi* Linn. The conformity with the behaviour of the bees, however, is not complete. The ants do indeed maintain the same angle to gravity when on a vertical surface as they had kept to the light but with four possibilities of choice: they run at the same angle either upwards to the right or to the left, or downwards to the right or to the left. *Geotrupes* translates correctly not only the angle but even the direction to the light into the direction to gravity, with the difference that it identifies the downward direction with the direction to the sun and the upwards direction with the one leading away from the sun. The bees, on the other hand, direct their waggle dance to the zenith when they fly towards the sun and to the nadir when they fly away from the light. This latter behaviour can also be found in some other beetles (*Coccinella* and *Melasoma*). But when these ran, e.g., 20° to the left towards the light, they can in the dark and on a vertical plane run either 20° to the left or the right against the field of gravity [Teuckhoff, after Birukow (6)]. There is little doubt that with further research other insects will be found which transpose exactly in the same way as the bees. This, however, is not so very important. The essential fact is that there seems to exist a primary capacity of the nervous centers to transpose a given angle to the light into an action of the sense organ of gravity as soon as the optical stimulus ceases to act [Birukow (6)]. Rothschild (38) comes in a more philosophic way to the same conclusion. Therefore we need not suppose that on a conference of the workers union the bees agreed to adopt a certain key reaction in order to transpose the angle to the light into the angle to gravity. The fact that during their evolution they were able to make such a correct and unmistakable use of their primary faculty of transposition is miraculous enough.

We tried in vain to find an expression for "upwards" and for "downwards" in the "language" of the bees. We carried a hive to a deep valley setting it up in the middle of the steep slope. Then two feeding places were put out, both being in exactly the same direction from the hive and at the same distance, but one being on the valley floor, the other exactly above it on a bridge. The dancing bees were unable to inform their hive mates whether they meant them to fly to the upper or the lower feeding place. In another experiment the feeding place was exactly above the opening platform of the hive on a broadcasting tower. The dancers could not convey the vertical direction of flight to the other bees and performed round dances thus sending their

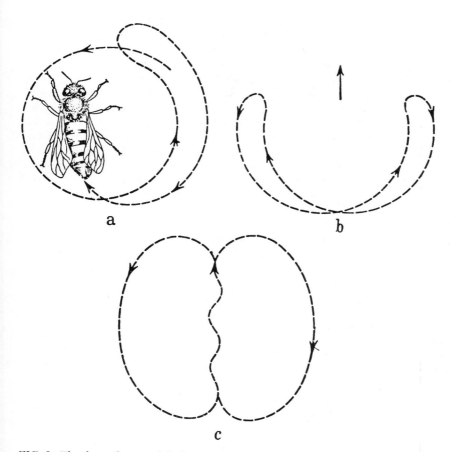

a

b

c

FIG. 2. The dance figures of the bees. (a) The round dance. (b) The sickle dance. (c) The waggle dance.

companions out into the surrounding meadows instead of upwards to their own feeding place [von Frisch, Heran & Lindauer (18)].

"Dialects" in the Bees Language

The bees belonging to the *carnica* race (*Apis mellifera* var. *carnica* Polm.) perform round dances (Fig. 2a) when the feeding place is closer than 50 to 100 m. from the hive. Baltzer and Tschumi found that Swiss bees execute another form of dancing, the sickle dance (Fig. 2b), when the feeding place is in the neighbourhood of the hive. Whereas the round dance of *A. m. carnica* does not indicate the direction for feeding places in the immediate neighbourhood this sickle dance shows the direction to be flown. The axis of the danced semicircle (arrow in Fig. 2b) gives the appropriate direction to be followed, exactly in the same way as the straight part indicates this in the true waggle dance. According to Tschumi (40) the Swiss bees perform the sickle dance for as short a distance as 10 m. The same behaviour has been observed among Dutch bees by Hein (21).

This latter form of dancing seems to be a special character of the subspecies. In populations crossbred from the dark *A. m. carnica* and the yellow striped Italian bee (*Apis mellifera* var. *ligustica* Spin.) representatives of the dark race were to be found in the same hive with bees having the yellow abdominal segments of the Italian subspecies. Upon their return from a food source 10 m. distant the dark *carnica* bees performed mairly round dances, whereas the yellow bees of the same population performed sickle dances [von Frisch (13)]. Further experiments with such cross-breeds have, however, shown that the form of the dance is not always coupled with the pigmentation of the dancer in this way. The pure Italian breed differs clearly however from the pure *carnica* colonies because of the large number of sickle dances performed at short feeding distances.‡ Even the indication of distance reveals variations

between these subspecies. At a given distance the Italian bees dance slower than the bees of *A. m. carnica* [Baltzer (2); von Frisch (13) and other unpublished experiments].

More important differences than those among the subspecies of our common honey bee have been found among the various species of *Apis* which Lindauer (unpublished data) was able to study on Ceylon.

Apis indica Fabr., closely related to *Apis mellifera* and often interpreted as one of its subspecies, indicates distance and direction in the same way as our honey bee but possesses the peculiarity that sickle dances indicating direction begin at a distance of 0.5 m. between the hive and source of food and that well directed waggle dances are performed as soon as the distance is above 2 m. The dance rhythm, for the indication of distance is slower than in *Apis mellifera*, although otherwise the graphs obtained from distance indication follow a very similar course. The dances of *A. dorsata* Fabr., the giant honey bee, differ from those of *A. m. carnica* only in that the direction-indicating waggle dances begin at as short a distance as 3 m. and that the dance rhythm for a given distance is slower. We have already mentioned that *A. florea* uses a horizontal surface for its dances. We would, however, like to add here that they perform round dances up to a distance of 5 m. between hive and food. As soon as the distance is longer they switch over to the waggle dance.

The Dances of Swarming Bees

The goal which the dancers indicate is normally a rich source of food. But during the search for a new nesting site exactly the same dances are carried out to convey information of good housing possibilities. Not only the daily bread but also favourable breeding conditions are highly impor-

‡ The colonies in which Tschumi and Hein observed the sickle dances were, as was discovered later, crossbred with Italian bees.

tant for the survival of a colony of bees.

A short time after a swarm has left the mother hive and formed a cluster in its neighbourhood, some bees may be seen dancing on the cluster. Now they are not food gatherers but scouts which have found a nesting site and indicate their discovery to the clustered, waiting colony. By close observation of these dances it is possible to predict the direction in which the swarm will finally fly and over what distance, sometimes several kilometers. On three occasions merely through the reading of the scout's dances we succeeded in finding, even before the colony moved to it, the new, hardly visible site.

At the beginning the scouts indicate several nesting sites to the cluster, as they search everywhere at the same time. Each scout advertises his own discovery. Before the cluster moves into a new nest an agreement is, however, found, and the bees will fly to the best of all the proposed nesting sites. If on a small island or in a wide plain, with few or no natural sites, artificial nesting places are offered to a swarm, we are able to detect which qualities of a nesting site are favourably and which are adversely appraised by the scouting bees. Among other qualities the distance between nesting site and mother hive, the size of the nest cavity, its protection against wind, and its thermal insulation seem to be very important in their choice of the nesting place.

Those of the scouts which find an especially favourable site, dance much longer and more energetically than those which find a place of lesser value. In this way the attention of the clustered bees is mainly drawn to the best proposition. The bees that take part in the dances fly out and inspect the proposed nesting site. These, on their return to the cluster, also dance and make further propaganda for it.

We must add that those scouts that find an inferior site change their mind if other bees having found a better place dance very energetically near them. Attracted by these vigorous dancers they follow the latter and inspect the better place. Upon

their return these also will dance in favour of the new goal.

We were also able to observe which of the bees became scouts. They are levied among the experienced field bees, which change their activity during the swarming time. These seasoned bees stop gathering when all the cells of the hive contain sealed brood, nectar, and pollen. Every apiarist knows that on such occasions the bees remain lazily and inactively in the hive and cluster in the form of a beard at the flight hole. He interprets his observation correctly as a sign for an approaching swarm emission. Under such circumstances, when there is no need for other activities some of the old bees take the initiative and reconnoiter new nesting sites. At this point the preparations for the swarming have begun. Thus the preliminary activities for swarming begin early, several days before the swarm leaves the hive [Lindauer (27, 28, 30)].

The Perception of the Sun through a Clouded Sky

It is much more important for bees than for man to know always where the sun stands. This knowledge is indispensable for their own orientation and for the communication with their hive mates concerning feeding possibilities. In consequence they are much better equipped for such an accomplishment than we human beings.

They are even able to detect the position of the sun through the entirely covered sky. This can easily be shown if we put an experimental hive into a horizontal position and give the bees a view of the covered sky through a glass window. On the horizontal honeycomb the bees dance correctly. Their waggle lines point directly towards the goal, but only if they can see the point in the clouded sky behind which the sun is hidden. Their dance lacks orientation if they can not look in this direction, even if the other parts of the sky are visible.

This ability of detection is not attributable to the perception of infrared rays. To our great astonishment experiments with filters have shown that the ultraviolet rays between 3000 and 4000 A are decisive for the bees' view of the sun when it is concealed behind the clouds [von Frisch (16); Heran (22)].

The Perception of Polarized Light

If the sun is hidden behind a forest, a mountain, a house or even below the horizon, the bees are still able to orientate themselves and to convey correctly their findings under the condition that the sky, or only a small spot of it, is clear and blue. The light coming out of the blue sky is partially polarized, and its plane of vibration is in direct correlation with the position of the sun. The bee's eye is able to recognise the plane of vibration of polarized light and can in consequence detect the position of the unseen sun if a spot of blue sky is visible [see von Frisch (11, pp. 88–109)].

Autrum suggests that each ommatidium of the compound eye is able to analyse polarized light by its eight radially arranged sensory cells [see von Frisch (11, Fig. 55, p. 98)]. He strongly supported his hypothesis by carrying out electrophysiological experiments on eyes of bees and flies. The magnitude of the exposure potentials depends on the light intensity, if an ommatidium of a cut off head§ is exposed. The rotation of a polarizer put in front of the eye does not influence the magnitude of the potentials. In consequence the ommatidium does not possess a common polarizer. If this were the case maxima and minima would appear. Autrum found, however, that the exposure of an ommatidium with polarized light gives clearly higher

§ The head was put on a fine steel pin (indifferent electrode). The different electrode was a second pin stuck into the eye. The exposure of a single ommatidium was made possible by a source of light the angle of vision of which under the given conditions was considerably smaller for the eye than the angle of aperture of the ommatidium.

potentials than the exposure with unpolarized light of the same intensity. This result corresponds very well with his hypothesis. In polarized light the intensity of the light becomes much stronger within the plane of its vibration when compared with unpolarized natural light of the same fundamental intensity. As a result of this fact the effective intensity becomes higher in those sensory cells of an ommatidium which are the most sensitive to the light of the given plane of vibration. It is irrelevant that the other sensory cells of the same ommatidium contribute a lower potential because the highest potential within the lot is decisive for the entire effect [Autrum & Stumpf (1)].

Optical research on the effect of polarization carried out with eyes of bees and flies have produced results which agree with these findings. Light arriving vertically on the ommatidium is not doubly refracted either by the corneal lens or by the crystalline cone. When the visual cells of an ommatidium are investigated in the direction of their axis, the rhabdomeres, however, show double refraction. Theoretically it is to be supposed that one of the two directions of vibration of double refracted light is suppressed in the visual cell. The small size of the elements in question has not made it possible to prove this [Menzer & Stockhammer (31)]. It has been proved, however, that for flies (*Calliphora et al.*) the planes of vibration of the speedier rays are radially arranged and correspond thus with the position of the visual cells themselves.

Reactions to the direction of vibration of polarized light have, since their discovery among bees, been proved among many other Arthropoda: such as ants [Schifferer, see von Frisch (12, p. 220); Carthy (7); Vowles (41)], among flies [Autrum & Stumpf (1) for *Calliphora;* Wellington (45) for *Sarcophaga;* Stephens, Fingerman & Brown (39) for *Drosophila*], among beetles [Birukow (5) for *Geotrupes*], among larvae of Lepidoptera and Hymenoptera [Wellington, Sullivan & Green (46)], among larvae of Diptera [Baylor & Smith (3)], among crustaceans [Kerz (24) for *Eupagurus*], among *Amphipoda* [Pardi & Papi (33, 35, 36) for *Talitrus*], among several *Cladocera* [Baylor & Smith (3); Eckert (8)], among spiders for the wolf spider *Arctosa* [Papi (32)], among mites for *Hydrachna* [Baylor & Smith (3)] and finally in *Agalena* [Görner (unpublished data)] and in *Limulus* [Waterman (42, 43, 44)].

Some authors think that the reactions to polarized light, which they were able to observe, can be explained by a double refraction in the dioptric system. Such an explanation is however only possible if the effective light rays arrive obliquely (to the longitudinal axis of the ommatidium) on the eye [see Berger & Segal (4); Stephens, Fingerman & Brown (39); Baylor & Smith (3)]. It is possible that the reactions to polarized light of those Anthropoda which have been examined are not all attributable to the same type of function. For bees and flies, at least, we cannot agree with the above mentioned supposition.

The results obtained by Autrum & Stumpf, by Menzer & Stockhammer, and by Stockhammer indicate that there is a double refraction within the visual cells of each ommatidium. Furthermore the bees are able to analyse the direction of vibration of polarized light extremely well, even when the experimental conditions are such that we cannot assume the participation of obliquely arriving rays.

The Importance of the Sun As a Means of Orientation

It is not difficult to conceive that the sun can be used as a compass when the bees take a short flight. By flying at a constant angle to the sun they are able to keep on a straight course. Furthermore we have seen that they use the angle to the sun in order to indicate the direction of a goal to their hive mates. Even this is easily comprehensible for short periods of activity.

During recent years we found that bees are capable of using the sun for orientation over periods of many hours during which the sun's position continually changes. They seem to be acquainted with the movement of the sun and to possess a well developed time sense which enables them to calculate the change of the solar position and to cor-

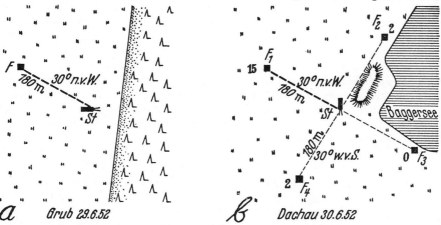

FIG. 3. Displacement test indicating ability of honey bee to allow for change in solar position. (a) Position of hive (St) and feeding place (F) on afternoon of June 29, 1952 near Grub. The marked bees were fed during this afternoon. (b) New position of hive and feeding places (F_1 to F_4) on the following morning (June 30) near Dachau. The numbers to the left of each feeding place indicate the numbers of previously marked bees collected at each feeding place this morning. Every arriving bee is immediately caught so that the other bees at the hive cannot be informed of the change in the situation.

rect accordingly their direction of flight. The proof that they possess this faculty was first obtained by a displacement test [von Frisch (12); von Frisch & Lindauer (19)]. As an example we show here the method and its results.

An experimental hive was brought into a region entirely unknown to the colony. On the afternoon of June 29, 1952 we opened the flight hole and fed some of the numbered and thus individually known bees until the evening. The feeding place was 180 m. from the hive in the direction 30° north of west (Fig. 3a). On the following morning the hive was taken to another entirely unknown landscape of different structure. The bees, therefore, found no familiar landmarks for their orientation during flight. The sun stood in the east, whereas during the preceding afternoon it had been in the west. Furthermore the hive had a different position. Thus the position of the flight hole could not help in the orientation of the bees. All around the hive at a distance of 180 m. we put up feeding plates. Notwithstanding the different landscape, the different position of hive and sun and in spite of the different time, the known bees, with few exceptions, flew to the feeding place 30° north of west which they had found and visited during the preceding afternoon. The other feeding places were almost completely ignored (Fig. 3b). In their search for the previously known feeding place in this unknown territory the bees can only have been helped by the sun. In order to use the sun as a means of orientation bees must be able to calculate the solar movements.

This capability is, however, shown in a much more surprising fashion by the following observation. Gathering bees do not dance for a longer time than 1 or 2 min. They start afterwards for a new flight. Some of the scouts become nonstop-dancers, when they find a nesting site for a preparing swarm, performing for hours their orientated waggle dance. During that time they slowly correct the direction of their dance according to the change of the sun's position. Even when they dance in a hive, set up in a closed room, so that they can see neither sun nor sky, they change their dance accordingly. They hereby demonstrate most impressively their knowledge of the solar position for every hour of the day and this even in a completely closed room [von Frisch (15); Lindauer (29)].

There is no doubt that among the Arthropoda the honey bees with their complicated instincts are on a very high rank of evolution. It is, however, remarkable that the use of the sun as a compass in correlation with a perfect time sense apparently does not necessitate a very high development of the mental faculties, because the same means of orientation is known to exist among crustaceans and spiders. *Talitrus saltator,* a crustacean which belongs to the Amphipoda, lives on the seashore. If by a storm or a human hand this animal is carried out of the region of moist sand which it inhabits and is put down on dry land, it makes his way hastily back to the shore. Even if it is carried many miles inland it takes exactly the same direction which would normally bring it from dry sand back to the moist sand of its habitat. This occurs only under the condition that it is given the opportunity of detecting the solar position, either directly or with the help of the polarized light from the blue sky. It finds this definite direction at every hour of the day even if it has previously been kept for hours in a dark room [Pardi & Papi (33, 35, 36)]. The same means of orientation has been found in *Tylos latreillii,* a crustacean belonging to the Isopoda, which is also an inhabitant of the moist sand of beaches [Pardi (34)] and in the wolf spider *Arctosa perita,* which lives on the shores of the sea and lakes [Papi (32)]. It is surmisable that the sun serves also as a compass for the long distance migrations of insects such as butterflies. This method of orientation, is however, not only known among the Arthropoda but even among birds. Birds can use the sun in connection with the time of day as a guide for their migrations [Kramer (25, 26)].

The Relative Importance of Landmarks and the Solar Compass

It has been known for a long time that bees use conspicuous landmarks such as trees, rocks, houses, etc. for their orientation in the landscape. But as we have seen, they orientate themselves as well by the position of the sun and by polarized light. In order to find out which of the two, the terrestrial or the celestial clue, is the more important for the bee, we set them in competition in the following experiment.

We trained bees to find a feeding place 180 meters to the south of their hive. The arrangement was such that on their way from hive to food source the bees flew along the edge of a forest running from north to south. On the following day we transplanted the colony in a new unknown landscape with a similar edge of forest, this time running from east to west. The bees did not look for the feeding place in the trained direction to the south of the hive, but flew along the edge of the forest 180 m. to the west. The very conspicuous landmark won the competition over the solar compass. In another set of conditions, however, when the edge of the forest was 200 m. lateral to the course to be flown, the forest being at an angle of vision of 3 to 4°, after their transplantation the bees followed in the majority of cases the clue given by the celestial compass.

In the same way as an adjacent forest edge, a shore line or a road is a superiour means of orientation when compared to solar orientation. When geographic characters are used it appears to be most important that the course to be flown follow a continuous and unbroken landmark. Correspondingly experiments have shown that a single high tree or an isolated cluster of bushes were not instrumental in deviating the bees from their accustomed direction of flight after a transplantation into a new landscape [von Frisch & Lindauer (19)].

Our method of investigation is time consuming but it gives us the possibility of judging the relative importance of the different means of orientation in bees.

REFERENCES

1. AUTRUM, H., and H. STUMPF: *Z. Naturforsch.*, 5b, 116–22 (1950).
2. BALTZER, F.: *Archiv Julius Klaus-Stift. Vererbungsforsch., Sozianthropol. u. Rassenhy.*, 27, 197–206 (1952).
3. BAYLOR, E. R., and F. E. SMITH: *Am. Naturalist*, 87, 97–101 (1953).
4. BERGER, P., and M. I. SEGAL: *Compt. rend.*, 234, 1308–10 (1952).
5. BIRUKOW, G.: *Naturwissenschaften*, 40, 611–12 (1953).
6. BIRUKOW, G.: *Z. vergleich. Physiol.*, 36, 176–211 (1954).
7. CARTHY, J. D.: *Behaviour*, 3, 275–303 (1951).
8. ECKERT, B.: *Českoslov. Biol.*, 2, 76–80 (1953).
9. VON FRISCH, K.: *Österr. zool. Z.*, 1, 1–48 (1946).
10. VON FRISCH, K.: *Naturwissenschaften*, 35, 12–23, 38–43 (1948).
11. VON FRISCH, K.: *Bees—their Vision, Chemical Senses and Language* (Cornell University Press, Ithaca, N. Y., 119 pp., 1950).
12. VON FRISCH, K.: *Experientia*, 6, 210–21 (1950).
13. VON FRISCH, K.: *Naturwissenschaften*, 38, 105–12 (1951).
14. VON FRISCH, K.: *Psychol. Rundschau*, 4, 235–36 (1953).
15. VON FRISCH, K.: *Verhandl. deut. Zool. Ges. Freiburg 1952*, 58–72 (Leipzig, Germany, 1953).
16. VON FRISCH, K.: *Sitzber. bayr. Akad. Wiss., Math.-naturw. Kl.*, 197–99 (München, Germany, 1954).
17. VON FRISCH, K.: *Festrede bayr. Akad. Wiss.* (Verlag bayr. Akad. Wiss., München, Germany, 1955).
18. VON FRISCH, K., G. HERAN, and M. LINDAUER: *Z. vergleich. Physiol.*, 35, 219–45 (1953).
19. VON FRISCH, K., and M. LINDAUER: *Naturwissenschaften*, 41, 245–53 (1954).
20. HALDANE, J. B. S., and H. SPURWAY: *Insectes Sociaux (Paris)*, 1, 247–83 (1954).
21. HEIN, G.: *Experientia*, 6, 142 (1950).
22. HERAN, H.: *Z. vergleich. Physiol.*, 34, 179–206 (1952).

23. HERAN, H., and L. WANKE: Z. vergleich. Physiol., 34, 383–93 (1952).

24. KERZ, M.: Experientia, 6, 427 (1950).

25. KRAMER, G.: Ibis, 94, 265–85 (1952).

26. KRAMER, G.: Verhandl. deut. Zool. Ges. Freiburg 1952, 72–84 (Leipzig, Germany, 1953).

27. LINDAUER, M.: Naturwissenschaften, 38, 509–13 (1951).

28. LINDAUER, M.: Naturwissenschaften, 40, 379–85 (1953).

29. LINDAUER, M.: Naturwissenschaften, 41, 506–7 (1954).

30. LINDAUER, M.: Z. vergleich. Physiol., 37, 263–324 (1955).

31. MENZER, G., and K. STOCKHAMMER: Naturwissenschaften, 38, 190–91 (1951).

32. PAPI, F.: Z. vergleich. Physiol., 37, 230–33 (1955).

33. PAPI, F., and L. PARDI: Z. vergleich. Physiol., 35, 490–518 (1953).

34. PARDI, L.: Z. Tierpsychol., 11, 175–81 (1954).

35. PARDI, L., and F. PAPI: Naturwissenschaften, 39, 262–63 (1952).

36. PARDI, L., and F. PAPI: Z. vergleich. Physiol., 35, 459–89 (1953).

37. RÉVÉSZ, G.: Psychol. Rundschau, 4, 81–83 (1953).

38. ROTHSCHILD, F. S.: Schweiz. Z. Psychol. u. ihre Anwendungen, 12, 177–99 (1953).

39. STEPHENS, G. C., M. FINGERMAN, and F. A. BROWN: Ann. Entomol. Soc. Amer., 46, 75–83 (1953).

40. TSCHUMI, P.: Schweiz. Bienenzeitung, 129–34 (1950).

41. VOWLES, D. M.: J. Exptl. Biol., 31, 341–55 (1954).

42. WATERMAN, T. H.: Science, 111, 252–54 (1950).

43. WATERMAN, T. H.: Proc. Natl. Acad. Sci. U. S., 40, 258–62 (1954).

44. WATERMAN, T. H., and C. A. G. WIERSMA: J. Exptl. Zool., 126, 59–85 (1954).

45. WELLINGTON, W. G.: Nature, 172, 1177 (1953).

46. WELLINGTON, W. G., C. R. SULLIVAN, and G. W. GREEN: Can. J. Zool., 29, 330–51 (1951).

H. W. LISSMANN

33   Electric Location by Fishes

In this reading, H. W. Lissmann, a Cambridge zoologist, presents a summary account of his experiments on the remarkable "electric sense" possessed by certain fishes.

Scientific American, March 1963, 208, 50–59. Reprinted by permission of author and publisher. Copyright © 1963 by Scientific American, Inc. All rights reserved. Several figures have been omitted.

Study of the ingenious adaptations displayed in the anatomy, physiology and behavior of animals leads to the familiar conclusion that each has evolved to suit life in its particular corner of the world. It is well to bear in mind, however, that each animal also inhabits a private subjective world that is not accessible to direct observation. This world is made up of information communicated to the creature from the outside in the form of messages picked up by its sense organs. No adaptation is more crucial to survival; the environment changes from place to place and from moment to moment, and the animal must respond appropriately in every place and at every moment. The sense organs transform energy of various kinds — heat and light, mechanical energy and chemical energy — into nerve impulses. Because the human organism is sensitive to the same kinds of energy, man can to some extent visualize the world as it appears to other living things. It helps in considering the behavior of a dog, for example, to realize that it can see less well than a man but can hear and smell better. There are limits to this procedure; ultimately the dog's sensory messages are projected onto its brain and are there evaluated differently.

Some animals present more serious obstacles to understanding. As I sit writing at my desk I face a large aquarium that contains an elegant fish about 20 inches long. It has no popular name but is known to science as *Gymnarchus niloticus*. This same fish has been facing me for the past 12 years, ever since I brought it from Africa. By observation and experiment I have tried to understand its behavior in response to stimuli from its environment. I am now convinced that *Gymnarchus* lives in a world totally alien to man: its most important sense is an electric one, different from any we possess.

From time to time over the past century investigators have examined and dissected this curious animal. The literature describes its locomotive apparatus, central nervous system, skin and electric organs, its habitat and its family relation to the "elephant-trunk fishes," or mormyrids, of Africa. But the parts have not been fitted together into a functional pattern, comprehending the design of the animal as a whole and the history of its development. In this line of biological research one must resist the temptation to be deflected by details, to follow the fashion of putting the pieces too early under the electron microscope. The magnitude of a scientific revelation is not always paralleled by the degree of magnification employed. It is easier to select the points on which attention should be concentrated once the plan is understood. In the case of *Gymnarchus*, I think, this can now be attempted.

A casual observer is at once impressed by the grace with which *Gymnarchus* swims. It does not lash its tail from side to side, as most other fishes do, but keeps its spine straight. A beautiful undulating fin along its back propels its body through the water — forward or backward with equal ease. *Gymnarchus* can maintain its rigid posture even when turning, with complex wave forms running hither and thither over different regions of the dorsal fin at one and the same time.

Closer observation leaves no doubt that the movements are executed with great precision. When *Gymnarchus* darts after the small fish on which it feeds, it never bumps into the walls of its tank, and it clearly takes evasive action at some distance from obstacles placed in its aquarium. Such maneuvers are not surprising in a fish swimming forward, but *Gymnarchus* performs them equally well swimming backward. As a matter of fact it should be handicapped even when it is moving forward: its rather degenerate eyes seem to react only to excessively bright light.

Still another unusual aspect of this fish and, it turns out, the key to all the puzzles it poses, is its tail, a slender, pointed process bare of any fin ("gymnarchus" means "naked tail"). The tail was first dissected by Michael Pius Erdl of the University of Munich in 1847. He found tissue resembling a small electric organ, consisting of four thin spindles running up each side to somewhere beyond the middle of the body. Electric organs constructed rather differently, once thought to be "pseudo-electric," are also found at the hind end of the related mormyrids.

Such small electric organs have been an enigma for a long time. Like the powerful electric organs of electric eels and some other fishes, they are derived from muscle tissue. Apparently in the course of evolution the tissue lost its power to contract and became specialized in various ways to produce electric discharges [see "Electric Fishes," by Harry Grundfest; *Scientific American*, October, 1960]. In the strongly electric fishes this adaptation serves to deter predators and to paralyze prey. But the powerful electric organs must have evolved from weak ones. The original swimming muscles would therefore seem to have possessed or have acquired at some stage a subsidiary electric function that had survival value. Until recently no one had found a function for weak electric organs. This was one of the questions on my mind when I began to study *Gymnarchus*.

I noticed quite early, when I placed a new object in the aquarium of a well-established *Gymnarchus*, that the fish would approach it with some caution, making what appeared to be exploratory movements with the tip of its tail. It occurred to me that the supposed electric organ in the tail might be a detecting mechanism. Accordingly I put into the water a pair of electrodes, connected to an amplifier and an oscilloscope. The result was a surprise. I had expected to find sporadic discharges co-ordinated with the swimming or exploratory motions of the animal. Instead the apparatus recorded a continuous stream of electric discharges at a constant frequency of about 300 per second, waxing and waning in amplitude as the fish changed position in relation to the stationary electrodes. Even when the fish was completely motionless, the electric activity remained unchanged.

This was the first electric fish found to behave in such a manner. After a brief search I discovered two other kinds that emit an uninterrupted stream of weak discharges. One is a mormyrid relative of *Gymnarchus;* the other is a gymnotid, a small, fresh-water South American relative of the electric eel, belonging to a group of fish rather far removed from *Gymnarchus* and the mormyrids.

It had been known for some time that the electric eel generates not only strong discharges but also irregular series of weaker discharges. Various functions had been ascribed to these weak discharges of the eel. Christopher W. Coates, director of the New York Aquarium, had suggested that they might serve in navigation, postulating that the eel somehow measured the time delay between the output of a pulse

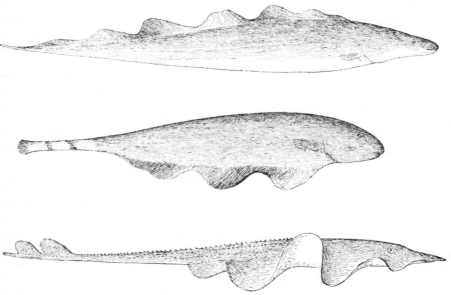

FIG. 1. Unusual fins characterize *Gymnarchus (top)*, a gymnotid from South America *(middle)* and sea-dwelling skate *(bottom)*. All swim with spine rigid, probably in order to keep electric generating and detecting organs aligned. *Gymnarchus* is propelled by undulating dorsal fin, gymnotid by similar fin underneath and skate by lateral fins resembling wings.

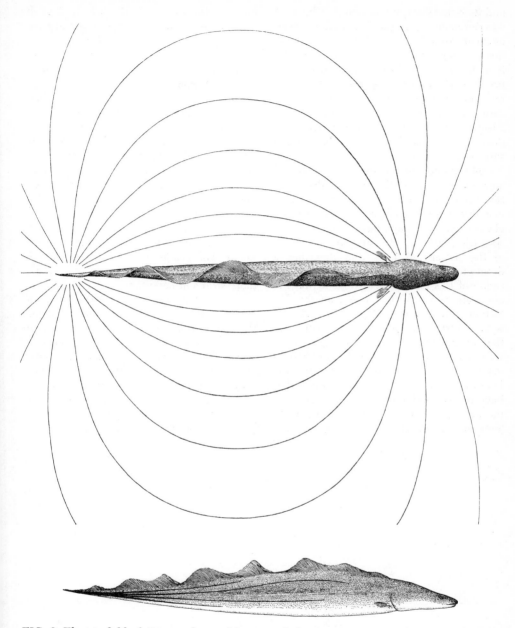

FIG. 2. Electric field of *Gymnarchus* and location of electric generating organs are diagramed. Each electric discharge from organs in rear portion of body . . . makes tail negative with respect to head. Most of the electric sensory pores or organs are in head region. Undisturbed electric field resembles a dipole field, as shown, but is more complex. The fish responds to changes in the distribution of electric potential over the surface of its body. The conductivity of objects affects distribution of potential.

and its reflection from an object. This idea was untenable on physical as well as physiological grounds. The eel does not, in the first place, produce electromagnetic waves; if it did, they would travel too fast to be timed at the close range at which such a mechanism might be useful, and in any case they would hardly penetrate water. Electric current, which the eel does produce, is not reflected from objects in the surrounding environment.

Observation of *Gymnarchus* suggested another mechanism. During each discharge the tip of its tail becomes momentarily negative with respect to the head. The electric current may thus be pictured as spreading out into the surrounding water in the pattern of lines that describes a dipole field [Figure 2]. The exact configuration of this electric field depends on the conductivity of the water and on the distortions introduced in the field by objects with electrical conductivity different from that of the water. In a large volume of water containing no objects the field is symmetrical. When objects are present, the lines of current will converge on those that have better conductivity and diverge from the poor conductors [Figure 3]. Such objects alter the distribution of electric potential over the surface of the fish. If the fish could register these changes, it would have a means of detecting the objects.

Calculations showed that *Gymnarchus* would have to be much more sensitive electrically than any fish was known to be if this mechanism were to work. I had observed, however, that *Gymnarchus* was sensitive to extremely small external electrical disturbances. It responded violently when a small magnet or an electrified insulator (such as a comb that had just been drawn through a person's hair) was moved near the aquarium. The electric fields produced in the water by such objects must be very small indeed, in the range of fractions of a millionth of one volt per centimeter. This crude observation was enough to justify a series of experiments under more stringent conditions.

In the most significant of these experiments Kenneth E. Machin and I trained the fish to distinguish between objects that could be recognized only by an electric sense. These were enclosed in porous ceramic pots or tubes with thick walls. When they were soaked in water, the ceramic material alone had little effect on the shape of the electric field. The pots excluded the possibility of discrimination by vision or,

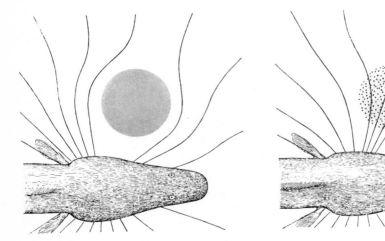

FIG. 3. Objects in electric field of *Gymnarchus* distort the lines of current flow. The lines diverge from a poor conductor (*left*) and converge toward a good conductor (*right*). Sensory pores in the head region detect the effect and inform the fish about the object.

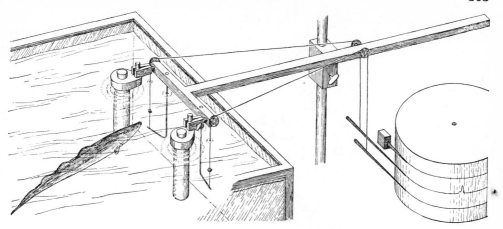

FIG. 4. Experimental arrangement for conditioned-reflex training of *Gymnarchus* includes two porous pots or tubes and recording mechanism. The fish learns to discriminate between objects of different electrical conductivity placed in the pots and to seek bait tied to string behind the pot holding the object that conducts best. *Gymnarchus* displays a remarkable ability to discriminate.

because each test lasted only a short time, by a chemical sense such as taste or smell.

The fish quickly learned to choose between two pots when one contained aquarium water or tap water and the other paraffin wax (a nonconductor). After training, the fish came regularly to pick a piece of food from a thread suspended behind a pot filled with aquarium or tap water and ignored the pot filled with wax [Figure 4]. Without further conditioning it also avoided pots filled with air, with distilled water, with a close-fitting glass tube or with another nonconductor. On the other hand, when the electrical conductivity of the distilled water was matched to that of tap or aquarium water by the addition of salts or acids, the fish would go to the pot for food.

A more prolonged series of trials showed that *Gymnarchus* could distinguish mixtures in different proportions of tap water and distilled water and perform other remarkable feats of discrimination. The limits of this performance can best be illustrated by the fact that the fish could detect the presence of a glass rod two millimeters in diameter and would fail to respond to a glass rod .8 millimeter in diameter, each

hidden in a pot of the same dimensions. The threshold of its electric sense must lie somewhere between these two values.

These experiments seemed to establish beyond reasonable doubt that *Gymnarchus* detects objects by an electrical mechanism. The next step was to seek the possible channels through which the electrical information may reach the brain. It is generally accepted that the tissues and fluids of a fresh-water fish are relatively good electrical conductors enclosed in a skin that conducts poorly. The skin of *Gymnarchus* and of many mormyrids is exceptionally thick, with layers of platelike cells sometimes arrayed in a remarkable hexagonal pattern. . . . It can therefore be assumed that natural selection has provided these fishes with better-than-average exterior insulation.

In some places, particularly on and around the head, the skin is closely perforated. The pores lead into tubes often filled with a jelly-like substance or a loose aggregation of cells. If this jelly is a good electrical conductor, the arrangement would suggest that the lines of electric current from the water into the body of the fish are made to converge at these pores, as if

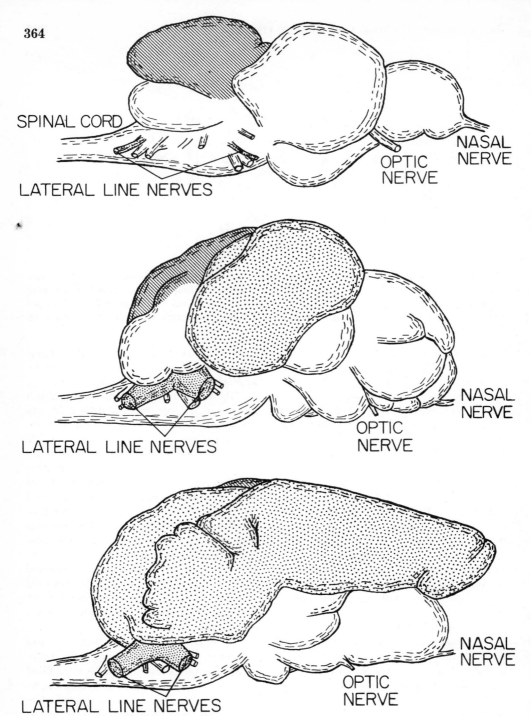

SPINAL CORD

LATERAL LINE NERVES

OPTIC NERVE

NASAL NERVE

LATERAL LINE NERVES

NASAL NERVE

OPTIC NERVE

LATERAL LINE NERVES

OPTIC NERVE

NASAL NERVE

FIG. 5. Brain and nerve adaptations of electric fish are readily apparent. Brain of typical non-electric fish *(top)* has prominent cerebellum (striped). Regions associated with electric sense (stippled) are quite large in *Gymnarchus (middle)* and even larger in the mormyrid *(bottom)*. Lateral-line nerves of electric fishes are larger, nerves of nose and eyes smaller.

focused by a lens. Each jelly-filled tube widens at the base into a small round capsule that contains a group of cells long known to histologists by such names as "multicellular glands," "mormyromasts" and "snout organs." These, I believe, are the electric sense organs.

The supporting evidence appears fairly strong: The structures in the capsule at the base of a tube receive sensory nerve fibers that unite to form the stoutest of all the nerves leading into the brain. Electrical recording of the impulse traffic in such nerves has shown that they lead away from organs highly sensitive to electric stimuli. The brain centers into which these nerves run are remarkably large and complex in *Gymnarchus,* and in some mormyrids they completely cover the remaining portions of the brain [Figure 5].

If this evidence for the plan as well as the existence of an electric sense does not seem sufficiently persuasive, corroboration is supplied by other weakly electric fishes. Except for the electric eel, all species of gymnotids investigated so far emit continuous electric pulses. They are also highly sensitive to electric fields. Dissection of these fishes reveals the expected histological counterparts of the structures found in the mormyrids: similar sense organs embedded in a similar skin, and the corresponding regions of the brain much enlarged.

Skates also have a weak electric organ in the tail. They are cartilaginous fishes, not bony fishes, or teleosts, as are the mormyrids and gymnotids. This means that they are far removed on the family line. Moreover, they live in the sea, which conducts electricity much better than fresh water does. It is almost too much to expect structural resemblances to the fresh-water bony fishes, or an electrical mechanism operating along similar lines. Yet skates possess sense organs, known as the ampullae of Lorenzini, that consist of long jelly-filled tubes opening to the water at one end and terminating in a sensory vesicle at the other. Recently Richard W. Murray of the Uni-

versity of Birmingham has found that these organs respond to very delicate electrical stimulation. Unfortunately, either skates are rather uncooperative animals or we have not mastered the trick of training them; we have been unable to repeat with them the experiments in discrimination in which *Gymnarchus* performs so well.

Gymnarchus, the gymnotids and skates all share one obvious feature: they swim in an unusual way. *Gymnarchus* swims with the aid of a fin on its back; the gymnotids have a similar fin on their underside; skates swim with pectoral fins stuck out sideways like wings [Figure 1]. They all keep the spine rigid as they move. It would be rash to suggest that such deviations from the basic fish plan could be attributed to an accident of nature. In biology it always seems safer to assume that any redesign has arisen for some reason, even if the reason obstinately eludes the investigator. Since few fishes swim in this way or have electric organs, and since the fishes that combine these features are not related, a mere coincidence would appear most unlikely.

A good reason for the rigid swimming posture emerged when we built a model to simulate the discharge mechanism and the sensory-perception system. We placed a pair of electrodes in a large tank of water; to represent the electric organ they were made to emit repetitive electric pulses. A second pair of electrodes, representing the electric sense organ, was placed some distance away to pick up the pulses. We rotated the second pair of electrodes until they were on a line of equipotential, where they ceased to record signals from the sending electrodes. With all the electrodes clamped in this position, we showed that the introduction of either a conductor or a nonconductor into the electric field could cause sufficient distortion of the field for the signals to reappear in the detectors.

In a prolonged series of readings the slightest displacement of either pair of electrodes would produce great variations in the received signals. These could be smoothed to some extent by recording not the change of potential but the change in the potential gradient over the "surface" of our model fish. It is probable that the real fish uses this principle, but to make it work the electrode system must be kept more or less constantly aligned. Even though a few cubic centimeters of fish brain may in some respects put many electronic computers in the shade, the fish brain might be unable to obtain any sensible information if the fish's electrodes were to be misaligned by the tail-thrashing that propels an ordinary fish. A mode of swimming that keeps the electric field symmetrical with respect to the body most of the time would therefore offer obvious advantages. It seems logical to assume that *Gymnarchus*, or its ancestors, acquired the rigid mode of swimming along with the electric sensory apparatus and subsequently lost the broad, oarlike tail fin.

Our experiments with models also showed that objects could be detected only at a relatively short distance, in spite of high amplification in the receiving system. As an object was moved farther and farther away, a point was soon reached where the signals arriving at the oscilloscope became submerged in the general "noise" inherent in every detector system. Now, it is known that minute amounts of energy can stimulate a sense organ: one quantum of light registers on a visual sense cell; vibrations of subatomic dimensions excite the ear; a single molecule in a chemical sense organ can produce a sensation, and so on. Just how such small external signals can be picked out from the general noise in and around a metabolizing cell represents one of the central questions of sensory physiology. Considered in connection with the electric sense of fishes, this question is complicated further by the high frequency of the discharges from the electric organ that excite the sensory apparatus.

In general, a stimulus from the environment acting on a sense organ produces a sequence of repetitive impulses in the sensory nerve. A decrease in the strength of the stimulus causes a lower frequency of impulses in the nerve. Conversely, as the stimulus grows stronger, the frequency of impulses rises, up to a certain limit. This limit may vary from one sense organ to another, but 500 impulses per second is a common upper limit, although 1,000 per second have been recorded over brief intervals.

In the case of the electric sense organ of a fish the stimulus energy is provided by the discharges of the animal's electric organ. *Gymnarchus* discharges at the rate of 300 pulses per second. A change in the amplitude—not the rate—of these pulses, caused by the presence of an object in the field, constitutes the effective stimulus at the sense organ. Assuming that the reception of a single discharge of small amplitude excites one impulse in a sensory nerve, a discharge of larger amplitude that excited two impulses would probably reach and exceed the upper limit at which the nerve can generate impulses, since the nerve would now be firing 600 times a second (twice the rate of discharge of the electric organ). This would leave no room to convey information about gradual changes in the amplitude of incoming stimuli. Moreover, the electric organs of some gymnotids discharge at a much higher rate; 1,600 impulses per second have been recorded. It therefore appears unlikely that each individual discharge is communicated to the sense organs as a discrete stimulus.

We also hit on the alternative idea that the frequency of impulses from the sensory nerve might be determined by the mean value of electric current transmitted to the sense organ over a unit of time; in other words, that the significant messages from the environment are averaged out and so discriminated from the background of noise. We tested this idea on *Gymnarchus* by applying trains of rectangular electric pulses of varying voltage, duration and frequency across the aquarium. Again using the conditioned-reflex technique, we determined the threshold of perception for the different pulse trains. We found that the fish is in fact as sensitive to high-frequency pulses of short duration as it is to low-frequency pulses of identical voltage but correspondingly longer duration. For any given pulse train, reduction in voltage could be compensated either by an increase in frequency of stimulus or an increase in the duration of the pulse. Conversely, reduction in the frequency required an increase in the voltage or in the duration of the pulse to reach the threshold. The threshold would therefore appear to be determined by the product of voltage times duration times frequency.

Since the frequency and the duration of discharges are fixed by the output of the electric organ, the critical variable at the sensory organ is voltage. Threshold determinations of the fish's response to single pulses, compared with quantitative data on its response to trains of pulses, made it possible to calculate the time over which the fish averages out the necessarily blurred information carried within a single discharge of its own. This time proved to be 25 milliseconds, sufficient for the electric organ to emit seven or eight discharges.

The averaging out of information in this manner is a familiar technique for improving the signal-to-noise ratio; it has been found useful in various branches of technology for dealing with barely perceptible signals. In view of the very low signal energy that *Gymnarchus* can detect, such refinements in information processing, including the ability to average out information picked up by a large number of separate sense organs, appear to be essential. We have found that *Gymnarchus* can respond to a continuous direct-current electric stimulus of about .15 microvolt per centimeter, a value that agrees reasonably well with the calculated

sensitivity required to recognize a glass rod two millimeters in diameter. This means that an individual sense organ should be able to convey information about a current change as small as .003 micromicroampere. Extended over the integration time of 25 milliseconds, this tiny current corresponds to a movement of some 1,000 univalent, or singly charged, ions.

The intimate mechanism of the single sensory cell of these organs is still a complete mystery. In structure the sense organs differ somewhat from species to species and different types are also found in an individual fish. The fine structure of the sensory cells, their nerves and associated elements, which Ann M. Mullinger and I have studied with both the light microscope and the electron microscope, shows many interesting details. Along specialized areas of the boundary between the sensory cell and the nerve fiber there are sites of intimate contact where the sensory cell bulges into the fiber. A dense streak extends from the cell into this bulge, and the vesicles alongside it seem to penetrate the intercellular space. The integrating system of the sensory cell may be here.

These findings, however, apply only to *Gymnarchus* and to about half of the species of gymnotids investigated to date. The electric organs of these fishes emit pulses of constant frequency. In the other gymnotids and all the mormyrids the discharge frequency changes with the state of excitation of the fish. There is therefore no constant mean value of current transmitted in a unit of time; the integration of information in these species may perhaps be carried out in the brain. Nevertheless, it is interesting that both types of sensory system should have evolved independently in the two different families, one in Africa and one in South America.

The experiments with *Gymnarchus*, which indicate that no information is carried by the pulse nature of the discharges, leave us with a still unsolved problem. If the pulses are "smoothed out," it is difficult to see how any one fish can receive information in its own frequency range without interference from its neighbors. In this connection Akira Watanabe and Kimihisa Takeda at the University of Tokyo have made the potentially significant finding that the gymnotids respond to electric oscillations close in frequency to their own by shifting their frequency away from the applied frequency. Two fish might thus react to each other's presence.

For reasons that are perhaps associated with the evolutionary origin of their electric sense, the electric fishes are elusive subjects for study in the field. I have visited Africa and South America in order to observe them in their natural habitat. Although some respectable specimens were caught, it was only on rare occasions that I actually saw a *Gymnarchus,* a mormyrid or a gymnotid in the turbid waters in which they live. While such waters must have favored the evolution of an electric sense, it could not have been the only factor. The same waters contain a large number of other fishes that apparently have no electric organs.

Although electric fishes cannot be seen in their natural habitat, it is still possible to detect and follow them by picking up their discharges from the water. In South America I have found that the gymnotids are all active during the night. Darkness and the turbidity of the water offer good protection to these fishes, which rely on their eyes only for the knowledge that it is day or night. At night most of the predatory fishes, which have well-developed eyes, sleep on the bottom of rivers, ponds and lakes. Early in the morning, before the predators wake up, the gymnotids return from their nightly excursions and occupy inaccessible hiding places, where they often collect in vast numbers. In the rocks and vegetation along the shore the

ticking, rattling, humming and whistling can be heard in bewildering profusion when the electrodes are connected to a loudspeaker. With a little practice one can begin to distinguish the various species by these sounds.

When one observes life in this highly competitive environment, it becomes clear what advantages the electric sense confers on these fishes and why they have evolved their curiously specialized sense organs, skin, brain, electric organs and peculiar mode of swimming. Such well-established specialists must have originated, however, from ordinary fishes in which the characteristics of the specialists are found in their primitive state: the electric organs as locomotive muscles and the sense organs as mechanoreceptors along the lateral line of the body that signal displacement of water. Somewhere there must be intermediate forms in which the contraction of a muscle, with its accompanying change in electric potential, interacts with these sense organs. For survival it may be important to be able to distinguish water movements caused by animate or inanimate objects. This may have started the evolutionary trend toward an electric sense.

Already we know some supposedly nonelectric fishes from which, nevertheless, we can pick up signals having many characteristics of the discharges of electric fishes. We know of sense organs that appear to be structurally intermediate between ordinary lateral-line receptors and electroreceptors. Furthermore, fishes that have both of these characteristics are also electrically very sensitive. We may hope one day to piece the whole evolutionary line together and express, at least in physical terms, what it is like to live in an electric world.

REFERENCES

LISSMANN, H. W. "Ecological Studies on Gymnotids," in *Bioelectrogenesis: A Com-*

parative Study of its Mechanisms with Particular Emphasis on Electric Fishes. American Elsevier Publishing Co., Inc., 1961.

LISSMANN, H. W. "On the Function and Evolution of Electric Organs in Fish," in *Journal of Experimental Biology*, Vol. 35, No. 1, pages 156–191; March, 1958.

LISSMANN, H. W., and K. E. MACHIN "The Mechanism of Object Location in Gymnarchus Niloticus and Similar Fish," in *Journal of Experimental Biology*, Vol. 35, No. 2, pages 451–486; June, 1958.

MACHIN, K. E., and H. W. LISSMANN "The Mode of Operation of the Electric Receptors in Gymnarchus Niloticus," in *Journal of Experimental Biology*, Vol. 37, No. 4, pages 801–811; December, 1960.

VICTOR C. TWITTY

34 Migration and Speciation in Newts

The Preface to this book has stressed the interdisciplinary nature of the science of animal behavior. Men with greatly different academic training have contributed to it. In the following reading, a distinguished embryologist describes a fascinating series of experiments on homing behavior in newts. Note that the reproductive isolation, discussed in the last section of the article, appears to be due to behavioral differences between the species. Reading 5 concerns the evolution of such behavioral isolating mechanisms.

Reprinted from *Science*, Vol. 130, pp. 1735–1743, 25 December 1959, with the permission of the author and the American Association for the Advancement of Science. Several figures have been omitted.

I have chosen to deal in this article with the subject that is of most interest to me personally—namely, the working relationship I have enjoyed for over twenty-five years with my favorite animals, the newts of California. When I first went to Stanford University in the early thirties and began what I thought was the hopeless task of finding an adequate substitute in the West for the classical *Amblystoma punctatum* that was the mainstay of experimental morphologists in the eastern United States, I stumbled across three or four new species and subspecies of the California newt in the course of collecting material for embryological studies from various parts of the state. And the work that I have done since then has been largely shaped by the amphibian friendships I formed at that time. Having discovered these new species, and given them names (it was someone else, however, who named one subspecies *twittyi*

—later declared invalid!), I have developed a proprietary interest, and maybe a feeling of obligation to them, that has influenced my choice of experiments ever since, including some that are quite far afield from my original interest and training.

As a student of Ross G. Harrison, I was of course at the time looking for things that I could get my iridectomy scissors into, and the first thing that struck me was the markedly different pigment patterns that distinguished the larvae of the species of California newts.

The neural-crest origin of the pigment cells was just in the process of being established at that time by DuShane, and as a confirmed heteroplastic grafter it was inevitable that I would soon begin switching neural crest and related tissues back and forth between the embryos of the species; by this method, and also through the use of tissue culture, I was able eventually to analyze in considerable detail the developmental basis of the hereditary differences in pigment patterns. This led in turn to studies on the problem of cell migration per se, and if I were writing this article five or six years ago it would undoubtedly deal with cell patterns or cell movements, or some other related embryological topic.

But in the meantime my interest has been diverted to other aspects of the biology of California newts, and instead of dealing with the movements of salamander cells, this account will deal mostly with the migrations of the adult newts themselves. This may seem to be a surprising transfer of emphasis, but from the time I first came to know these animals and began to experiment with their embryos, certain collateral questions arose that have continued to intrigue me. For example, I had learned shortly after discovery of the species that artificially produced hybrids were completely viable, but at the time methods had not been developed for rearing California newts, whether normal or hybrid, to maturity in the laboratory, and so I did not know whether the hybrids were fertile. Also, in working out the life histories of the different species I became aware of some interesting differences in their behavior. For example, one species would lay its eggs singly, another in flat clusters, another in round clusters; one would choose quiet water for spawning, another rapid mountain streams; and so on. To make a long story short, I had always wanted to undertake some experiments—merely as a sideline, I thought at the time—to learn whether artificially produced hybrids would grow to maturity if released in nature, and if so, whether they would be fertile—would perhaps even interbreed with the native parental populations, with all of the interesting possibilities that that would present—and also to learn how hybridization might affect some of the behavioral differences I have mentioned.

An opportunity to test these somewhat visionary questions came in 1953 when I obtained permission from the owners to establish a field station on a large ranch in the coastal mountains of Sonoma County about 100 miles north of San Francisco.° Western newts require four or five years to reach sexual maturity, and needless to say the answers to the questions will be slow in coming. The last couple of years we have begun to get some very encouraging results, however, and later I shall indicate briefly where we stand.

But it is principally some of the unexpected by-products of the project with which I should like to deal at present.

Migration Studies

When we began planting young hybrids in a selected experimental stream on the ranch, the alarming thought struck us that even if the hybrids did survive to maturity they might scatter over the whole countryside and eventually select for breeding an entirely different stream — maybe in the next county.

And so we were immediately faced with the question: Do newts have a fixed home range throughout their lives, or are their yearly movements to and from the water of a random nature, perhaps carrying them to new breeding sites each year? I had never anticipated that I would become involved in such unfamiliar issues as this, but I can say that the study of the problem has been just as fascinating—and just as involved and difficult—as the study of the migrations of salamander cells.

And so, as briefly as possible, let me outline what we have learned and what remains to be learned.

° I wish to thank Mr. and Mrs. T. L. Hedgpeth and more recent owners of the ranch, particularly Mr. and Mrs. Stanley Richardson, Jr., for the facilities and courtesies they have generously extended to me. The project has been supported in part by grants from the National Science Foundation.

Taricha rivularis† is the species that is most abundant at the ranch, and is the one that we have used for the migration studies. *Taricha granulosa* is also present there, but in much smaller populations. The other two forms, *T. torosa* and *T. t. sierrae*, are native to other regions of the state. In one part or another of California, *T. granulosa* is sympatric with the other three forms, but the latter are not known to be sympatric with one another.

There are several streams on the ranch, but we have selected for our work one that is called Pepperwood Creek, a tributary of the Wheatfield Fork of the Gualala River. Pepperwood Creek is a small stream, but it is literally crawling with newts during the breeding season. To give you some idea of the size of the population we are working with, I might mention that since the project began we have, by systematic collecting, removed from a 1½-mile stretch of this stream—the portion we have set aside for our studies—a total of over 24,000 females, partly for use in the hybridization experiments. That is a lot of "water-dogs," as they are called in California. The effects of this inroad on the size and on the sex ratio of the *rivularis* population is an incidental problem of considerable interest in itself, and one that we are following in some detail.

. . . [An omitted] contour map prepared from a U.S. Forest Service aerial photograph, shows the course of the experimental stream and the topography of the adjoining terrain. For recording our results, the portion of the stream selected for the study was marked off into a series of 58 "stations" or intervals, each 50 yards in length and identified by numerals painted on trees or boulders along the stream.

The great majority of the population inhabits the mountainous and heavily

† The genus was formerly designated *Triturus*.

wooded slope to the south, and from here each spring the newts descend to the stream for breeding. At the end of the mating season they leave the water abruptly and redistribute themselves over the mountainside, where they spend the dry summer months underground.

When the rains begin in the autumn or winter the animals emerge again and forage on the forest floor, often high upon the mountainside. Since the terrain they traverse in returning to the stream as the breeding season approaches is very rugged and irregular, cut by many gullies and ravines, one wonders whether a given animal returns to the same segment of stream where it had bred the year before, or whether it is perhaps diverted to a new point of entry. In other words, are we dealing in this study with a single, shifting population within which there is relatively free mixing and interbreeding of individuals throughout the experimental area, or is it perhaps instead a more or less stable mosaic of relatively isolated sub-populations, each with its own "home area" and restricted segment of the experimental stretch, to which the same group of individuals returns year after year for mating and reproduction?

To find the answer we have marked literally thousands of animals for subsequent recognition, and I shall cite the results of only a few representative series.

In 1953 we collected 262 males from a single pool at station 9, marked them, and returned them to the same pool. The first observations on this series were made two years later, and observations have been made each year subsequently (Fig. 1). As you will note, year after year virtually all of the animals recaptured were taken at or very near the pool where they were originally collected and marked. This was as true this past season, after six years, as it was in the beginning. The percentage of recaptures has also been high, over 60 percent the first year and still about 40 percent this last year. (In fact, a total of

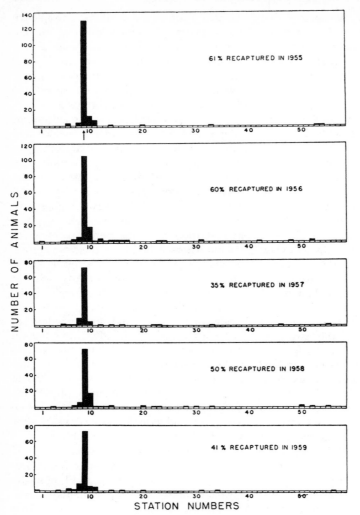

FIG. 1. In 1953 adult newts were collected from a pool at station 9, marked to permit their subsequent recognition, and released in the same pool. The graphs show the locations where they were recaptured in later years, beginning in 1955. For recording the recaptures the stream was marked off into 50-yard segments or "stations."

85 percent has been recaptured over the years, but never that many during any single season.) Incidentally, this speaks for the longevity of the species and also for the low rate of mortality in the adult population.

To appreciate these results one must bear in mind that these are animals that in many cases have moved relatively great distances up and down the mountainside between successive breeding seasons.

Figure 2 shows the results, over a period of four years, of two additional series of marking experiments. These animals were collected from longer segments of stream, one series from the upper part of the experimental stretch and the other from the lower end of it. In each case they

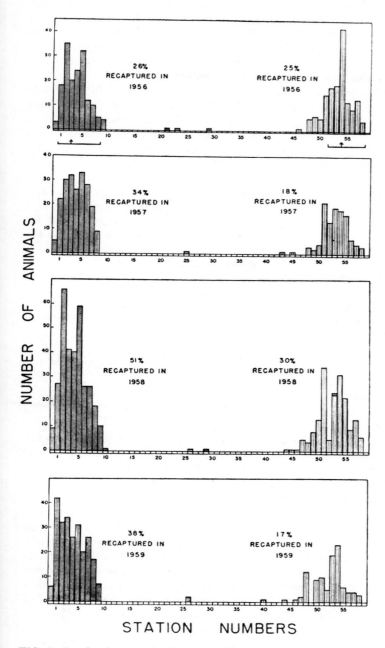

FIG. 2. Graphs showing the locations of recaptures over a four-year period for two series of marked newts. The brackets and arrows indicate where each series was collected and released, respectively, in 1955.

were all released in a single pool, near the middle of the segment in which they had been collected. The graphs showing their recapture in subsequent years are self-explanatory, and it is as evident as it was in the preceding series that the animals find their way back to the home segment of stream year after year with almost

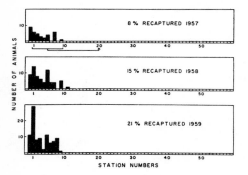

FIG. 3. Graphs showing the return to the home segment of the stream of newts that had been displaced in 1956 to a point about half a mile downstream.

monotonous regularity and fidelity. In our daily patrol of the entire experimental stretch throughout the breeding season the location where these animals will be recaptured is so predictable that we are almost grateful when we encounter an exception—as we very seldom do.

The next experiments show that this behavior is based on a very positive affinity or sense of identification that the animals develop for their home segment of stream, and an ability to relocate it and recognize it after they have been displaced to foreign segments.

In the series represented in Fig. 3, adults were collected from the upper segment of the experimental stream, marked, and released downstream at station 20, about half a mile away. The graphs show the recaptures during the three succeeding years. Without exception, all of the animals recaptured had successfully relocated the home segment of stream.

It is true that the percentage of recaptures is lower than before, only 8 percent the first year. But you will note that the percentage has increased each year subsequently. This must mean that some of these animals had retained a memory of the home area, and the ability to recognize it, for at least three years. During that period, while still searching for their home base, they were unwilling to settle for any other segment of the stream. In a sense, then, the very ability to reproduce is dependent upon association with the home area. Why they should be so fussy and selective is difficult to see. One part of the stream is inherently as suitable for reproduction as another, as shown by the fact that the population breeds throughout the entire stretch.

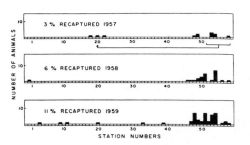

FIG. 4. Graphs showing the return, with a few scattered exceptions, of newts to the home segment of stream after displacement in 1956 to a point about one mile upstream.

similar series in which the animals were displaced for approximately a mile, from the lower end of the experimental stretch to station 20. The results are the same as before, except that the percentage of successful returns is lower, and there are a few animals that have apparently tossed in the sponge and settled for other than the home segment of stream. It is as if they have finally decided that the home stretch is simply out of reach and have resigned themselves eventually to acceptance of the breeding ground that is nearest at hand.

Incidentally, I should stress that these homing returns are made, not by way of the stream channel itself, but overland between breeding seasons; this, in view of the rugged nature of the terrain, makes the journey even longer and tougher.

One wonders how much further these animals could be displaced and still find their way home. Have we, in this last series, almost approached the "point of no return"? Until this year I would have been inclined to say so, but it appears that this is not the case.

In 1956 about a thousand females collected during the season from the experimental stretch were marked and released in a stream in a deep canyon on the other side of the mountain ridge that rises to the south of Pepperwood Creek. The release point is perhaps three miles from the experimental stretch and is so inaccessible that we have not revisited it since the animals were transferred there. The ridge separating the two streams rises a good thousand feet above them, and frankly, I never expected to hear from these displaced animals again. However, near the end of this past spawning season they began to show up, and we recorded 18 individuals that were clearly members of the series. Next year I am sure we shall find more. There is not time to discuss the implication of this, or of other related experiments we have made, except to point out that whether it reflects a true homing search or not, as I am confident it does, it is a remarkable achievement by animals as relatively sluggish and slow-paced as newts. Considering the size of newts and their rate of locomotion, the distances involved are really very great.

The next question is whether the animals we have displaced from one part of the experimental stretch to another find their way back home by random search or by oriented migration involving some form of true navigation.

Thus far, we have tested this in the following manner.

[An omitted figure] shows a star-shaped enclosure that we constructed of wire mesh near the streamside, about midway along the experimental stretch. The black line and arrow parallel the axis of the nearby stream and indicate the direction of flow of the stream. At the tip of each arm of the enclosure there is an opening into an escape-proof trap. In the center is a release box from which animals can escape by a spiral ramp through an opening in the lid of the box. Animals are placed in this box, usually in late afternoon, and the traps are checked for captured animals the following morning. Animals are collected from the water, either upstream or downstream from the enclosure, and placed in the release box, and the traps are examined the next morning to see whether the newts have started back in the right or in the wrong direction.

To summarize the results as briefly as possible, we found that if the animals are taken from distances not exceeding about 700 yards, then a very great majority, consistently 80 to 95 percent, orient their movements in the right direction. When they are taken from greater distances, their initial movements appear to be in random directions. We have tested this repeatedly and with large numbers of animals.

To evaluate the homing series described above in terms of these results with the "star-trap," the implication is that animals displaced more than about half a mile from their home area are stimulated by the displacement to initiate a searching behavior that is at first lacking in orientation. However, once they are carried by these random movements within striking distance of the home territory, they pick up signals or landmarks that enable them to navigate the remainder of the distance with remarkable directness.

Nature of the Signals

The next question, of course, is: What is the nature of the signals or landmarks, and what are the senses employed in their recognition?

One thinks first of all, perhaps, of the visual recognition of familiar landmarks or topographical features, since vision is so important in the homing behavior of certain other animals.

For reasons I shall not go into it is not simple to test this critically by the star-trap method, but we have tested it in another, perhaps even more direct and convincing, way.

We again collected a series of animals from the extreme upper end of the experimental stretch and displaced them to station 20. In this case, however, before they were displaced they were completely and permanently blinded by the surgical removal of both eyes. Figure 5 shows the recaptures a year later. Without exception all were back in the segment of the stream from which they had been taken. We were not too confident that these blinded animals would even survive, and when we found that their homing behavior was unimpaired we were admittedly surprised and impressed. Only 10 percent of the animals were recaptured, but this is as high—in fact a bit higher—than the first-year recaptures with the comparable series of normal or sighted animals described

above. At the very least, this series shows that recognition of the home territory, once the animals relocate it, is certainly not accomplished through any visual associations that they have developed.

Another possibility that we have considered is that the animals orient their movements and identify the home segment of stream, or its bordering terrain, through kinesthetic memory — if there is such an expression. Any one of us, very conceivably, if we tramped repeatedly over an area of irregular terrain, might come to memorize its topographical features or pattern so completely that we could subsequently recognize any given spot within the area and orient our route accordingly in any chosen direction—even if we were blinded. Likewise the newts: During the rainy months preceding the breeding season they forage actively on the forest floor, and over the years they very possibly encompass and come to memorize the topographical pattern of a fairly large area of terrain extending upstream and downstream from the more restricted point where they eventually enter the water to breed.

We have tested this possibility, or have tried to test it, in the way described below, and the results indicate that, just as

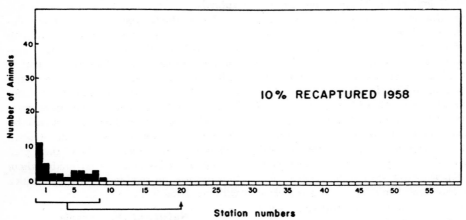

FIG. 5. Graph showing the return of newts to the home segment of the stream a year after they had been blinded by the removal of both eyes and displaced to a point about half a mile downstream.

vision is not the means by which migration is oriented, neither is kinesthetic sense.

First of all, we simply covered the floor of the star-trap with a carpeting that would erase or conceal any of the natural irregularities of the terrain within the test enclosure. For this we used a plastic sheeting, known commercially as "Visqueen." However, animals tested under these conditions oriented their movements just as well, or seemingly as well, as when the floor of the enclosure was left in its natural state.

A somewhat fancier test and one that permits more refined analysis was performed by construction of a large platform (30 by 6 feet) that could be adjusted at different heights above the ground and could be tilted at different angles. A release box was placed at its center and a trap at each end . . . . The platform was installed near the creek, with its long axis parallel to the stream. Near the end of the past breeding season it was placed in operation in a sharply tilted position, with the downstream end elevated about five feet above the opposite or upstream end. Mixed groups of animals, half of them collected from downstream locations and half from upstream, were placed in the release box. In spite of the tilt, which presents an entirely new and foreign "topography" to the animals, the two groups sorted themselves out with very few errors, each moving in the direction of the home segment of stream. It seems clear from these tests that the animals do not "feel their way home" through recognition of familiar features of the immediate terrain in areas to which they have been displaced.

What are the possibilities that remain? I think that hearing can be discounted, and this leaves principally olfaction or related chemical senses. Do these animals smell their way home, and when they get there, does home—to them—mean a familiar and distinctive set of odors peculiar to the soil and vegetation along the streamside at that particular point? In animals as

earth-bound as salamanders, living throughout their terrestial phase in such intimate association with humid soil and all its products, I suppose it is not unlikely that the chemistry of their environment looms larger in their experience than do impressions of sight and sound. We do know that these newts have a remarkable sense of smell, or of chemical detection. It is by means of scent that the males detect the presence and location of females when the females enter the stream for breeding. A female, or even a sponge soaked in water in which females have been stored, dipped briefly in the water will excite and attract males situated many yards down-current.

When we plug the nasal passages with Vaseline, as can be very effectively done by injecting barely melted Vaseline into the nares, and test the animals in the star-trap, orientation does seem to disappear or at least be greatly reduced. In fact, most of the animals fail to migrate at all and remain in the release box. However, the effects of a badly stuffed-up nose may prove to be merely traumatic or disturbing in nature and not due to the loss of the sense of smell as such.

So next year we plan to concentrate on a rather elaborate study of the possible role of odor, and I hope we shall be able to settle the matter. As I have told the chaplain at Stanford, if it proves not to be a question of odor, then the whole problem really lies more in his realm than in mine, and I will gladly assign it to one of his theology majors.

The Home Area

But whatever the sensory mechanism (or mechanisms) proves to be, I think the most interesting thing about the whole business is the simple biological fact that identification with the home area seems to mean so much to the salamanders. To them there is clearly "no place like home."

There are, of course, certain well-recognized advantages or consequences of spatial localization within animal populations. It tends to stabilize and equalize distribution of the members of a population, and accordingly to reduce competition. It assures the selection of suitable—that is, already tested—spawning sites and hence minimizes gametic wastage such as would occur if eggs were laid in portions of streams that go underground during the summer before the tadpoles could metamorphose. Since it reduces the effective size of breeding populations, it also minimizes the swamping of mutant genes that may arise, and thereby facilitates genetic differentiation or speciation.

It must also carry its penalties, however, since, as we have seen, animals are reluctant to enter an unfamiliar segment of stream—even though it may be completely suitable for breeding. This means, in effect, that accidental displacement can be tantamount to reproductive death, if the animals are unable to relocate—or are in any way prevented from relocating—the home area.

But in any case, good or bad, it is a refinement of behavior that somehow I never expected to find so highly developed in animals that, until now, I must confess, I had always considered to be among the least discerning of vertebrates. In any event, I shall never again think of salamanders as mere egg-laying machines, created for the special benefit of the experimental embryologist.

Genetic Testing Ground

And now to turn briefly to another phase of the program. As I indicated above, in its inception the project at the ranch was designed to throw some light on the genetics and speciation of California newts, not on their ethology.

When one becomes involved in the systematics of a genus there are certain important questions that inevitably arise. Do or can the species form viable and fertile hybrids? If so, why do sympatric pairs of species preserve their separate identities—that is, what are the isolating mechanisms that prevent interbreeding? In the case of species that are *not* sympatric, would they, if it were not for their geographical isolation, prove capable of interbreeding successfully — and if so, what would the ultimate consequences be?

To test these and related questions we have attempted to convert the experimental stream at the ranch into a sort of genetic testing ground, or genetic melting pot. Since 1953 we have produced by artificial hybridization, and introduced into the experimental stretch as young tadpoles, some 200,000 hybrids of three different interspecific combinations. In addition, we have introduced tadpoles of the species that are not native to that part of the state. In other words, as I am sure some systematists will feel, we are really messing up nature rather badly in poor little Pepperwood Creek.

As I said earlier, it is too soon to know what the ultimate genetic consequences may be, if any. In order to have completed the program myself, I should have initiated it many years earlier. But we are beginning to learn a few things, and I shall run through some of them very briefly.

We have recaptured only a few mature hybrids as yet, but enough to know that they *can* survive and return to the breeding stream as adults.

Moreover, we have shown that the hybrids of the California species of newts are fertile—in both sexes. With the hybrids recaptured in nature, and others reared to maturity simultaneously in the laboratory, we have tested fertility by backcrossing the hybrids to the parental species by artificial fertilization. We have tested several interspecific combinations, and all have proved fertile, although we shall need to accumulate more data before it can be determined whether there is possibly some reduction in fertility.

This shows that hybrid inviability or infertility are not the reproductive barriers that isolate pairs of newt species that occur together in California. In the case of such species, that breed in the same bodies of water at the same season of the year, we believe that the barriers to interbreeding have instead a behavioral or psychological basis, and through a detailed study of courtship patterns in the different species we are attempting to determine the nature of these ethological blocks to successful interspecific mating.

Thus far we have been unable to induce either sympatric or allopatric pairs of species to interbreed voluntarily, either in the laboratory or when confined together in escape-proof enclosures constructed in the stream itself. There is some indication, however, that these behavioral barriers to interbreeding disappear with hybridization. In the one case tested, when an adult hybrid male was placed in a mating enclosure with a female of the maternal species, successful mating and ovulation ensued. This suggests the possibility that if we can establish sizable populations of hybrids in the experimental area, introgression and consequent modification of the native population may occur.

The species of California newts have striking differences in larval pigment pattern, as I mentioned above, and when the hybrids of these species are backcrossed to the parental species, the offspring show a clear genetic segregation in their pigmentary characteristics.

Figure 9 [omitted, Ed.] shows a young larva of torosa with its sharp pigment band, and a larva of rivularis with its uniformly dispersed pigmentation. Between the two is a hybrid of the two species, and as one can see, it is roughly intermediate in its pigment pattern.

If we backcross an adult of the hybrid to one of the parent species the offspring show a spectrum of pigment patterns ranging between those characteristic of the hybrid and those characteristic of the backcross parent. . . . [An omitted figure] shows three such backcross offspring, one with a hybrid-type pattern, one with a rivularis-type pattern, and a third with an intermediate pattern. Other characters, such as the presence and size of the balancer and the size of the dorsal fin, also segregate in the backcrosses, and they segregate independently of one another and of pigment pattern. The ratios of segregation indicate that the numbers of genes that differentiate the species with respect to these characters are not very large.

There is not space to deal with the corresponding results of backcrosses involving other species combinations.

These are elementary genetic experiments, but since they involve my California newts, and since I have been for years uncertain of the feasibility of making any type of genetic analysis at all with these animals, the results are of special interest to me personally.

Conclusion

In presenting this account I am well aware that developmental biologists will possibly react with the feeling, "there goes another embryologist down the drain," and animal behaviorists will point with gratification, on the other hand, to the evidence that here is an embryologist who has finally seen the true light—even though he sees it dimly and is still an amateur. In any case, the reader in whose mind problems of speciation are uppermost, especially during this much celebrated Darwin Centennial year, can consider himself fortunate that he is not using experimental animals that yield genetic information as slowly as do California newts.‡

‡ This article is adapted from a presidential address delivered before the American Society of Zoologists at the 1959 meetings held at Pennsylvania State University, University Park, Pennsylvania.

G. V. T. MATTHEWS

35 The Orientation of Pigeons as Affected by the Learning of Landmarks and by the Distance of Displacement

G. V. T. Matthews has made outstanding contributions to our knowledge of the homing abilities possessed by certain birds. His *Bird Navigation* (Cambridge University Press, 1955) is a standard reference in the field. In this more recent article, Matthews analyzes the methods used by pigeons to "home" from various distances. The "T" numbers mentioned in the article refer to the Tests listed in Table 35–1.

Reprinted from *Animal Behaviour*, 1963, 11, 310–317, with the permission of the author and the publisher: Baillière, Tindall and Cox, Ltd.

Introduction

It has recently been demonstrated (Matthews, 1961) that non-migratory Mallard (*Anas p. platyrhynchos*) have a strong tendency to fly in one direction, unrelated to any homing ability. Further it has been found that different stocks of Mallard have different directional tendencies (Matthews, 1963a). The relevance of these findings to experiments on the orientation of the non-migratory homing pigeon has been discussed in the papers cited. In particular the work on pigeons at Wilhelmshaven, Germany, and Durham, North Carolina (summarized by Kramer, 1957, 1959 and 1961) appears to have been bedeviled by an immediate northward "nonsense" orientation often simulating homeward navigation. By contrast pigeons, at Cambridge, England, showed no such tendencies (summary in Matthews, 1955b). These conflicting results could have been due to a real difference in stocks or to the different initial training given. The German/American birds were given initial experience by a

few short flights in several directions; the English birds were flown repeatedly at increasing distances from one direction. Unless this direction coincided with that of the stocks' "nonsense" orientation the latter would be weakened and eventually eliminated. Hoffmann (1959) had the opportunity to discriminate between these possibilities when he raised English and German pigeons at the Cambridge loft, using the German technique of training. Although investigating directional tendencies he did not report on the directions in which his pigeons flew. Instead he relied on their homing times, when their average homing "speed" was around 9 miles per hour from distances of no more than 14 miles.

In these circumstances it is felt that some work done with the English stock, discussed at a conference at Duke University in April 1955 and mentioned in brief outline by Matthews (1955b) should be set out in full. The aim was to examine the importance of landmarks and their use in relation to some subtle form of navigation. Kramer, Hoffmann and their colleagues tended to dismiss the impor-

380

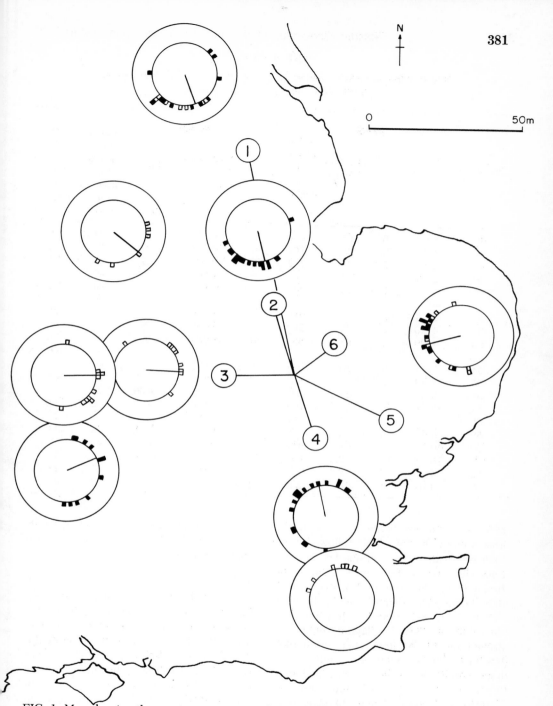

FIG. 1. Map showing the previous experience of the pigeons. The scatter diagrams record the vanishing points of birds from Team A, □ and Team B, ■ when released previously for the first time at an unknown point in sunny conditions and without experimental interference. The release points used in the present tests are indicated by the numbered circles connected to the home loft at Madingley.

TABLE 35-1

The sequence of releases undertaken with the same individual pigeons
(Team A, 12 birds; Team B, 18 birds)

TEST	DATE 1953/55	POINT	DISTANCE (MILES)	HOME BEAR- ING (DE- GREES)	CLOUD (EIGHTHS)	WIND DIRECTION AND FORCE	TEAM	AV. DEVIA- TION FROM HOME BEARING (DE- GREES)	AV. TIME IN SIGHT (MIN- UTES)
40	8/14	6	25	342	0	W/1	B	71	3.9
47	11/10	2	25	162	0	SW/2	B	59	4.3
48	12/5	2	25	162	8	ENE/1	B	73	5.1
49	1/14	2	25	162	4	WSW/4	B	40	4.0
50	4/7	2	25	162	1	NW/1	A	88	5.1
							B	26	3.1
51	4/14	2	25	162	2	W/3	B	24	3.0
52	4/20	2	25	162	8	E/2	B	22	3.9
53	4/29	3	23	088	0	NW/1	A	68	4.0
							B	84	5.0
54	5/11	9	10	251	1	W/1	A/B	47	3.0
55	8/14	11	5	331	2	Nil	A/B	65	4.8
56	8/16	10	2.5	335	3	Nil	A/B	21	3.5
57	8/26	12	10	031	1	Nil	A/B	52	3.8
58	8/31	7	5	138	1	WSW/2	A/B	33	3.7
59	9/23	5	35	292	0	SW/2	A/B	79	3.6
60	10/11	1	79	166	0	W/3	A/B	40	3.8
61	10/16	10	2.5	335	2	W/2	A/B	18	3.1
62	4/1	8	2.5	222	8	Nil	A/B	31	4.5
63	4/11	4	18	230	2	NW/3	A/B	54	4.4

tance of landmark learning even in the area around the loft. This followed from their observation that well-marked orientations observed a few miles from home broke down when the sky was overcast, as does homeward orientation at a distance. However, it now appears possible that their pigeons were displaying "nonsense" orientation. In Mallard such orientation has been demonstrated 2 - 5 miles from home (Matthews, 1962) and is definitely based, by day, on the sun's position (Matthews, 1963b). While the conclusion that the short distance "nonsense" orientation of pigeons is likewise not based on landmarks is unexceptional, there is less justification for asserting on those grounds that landmarks play no part in the true homing process.

MATERIAL

One of the difficulties of using homing pigeons for navigation studies is the great variation in orientation/homing ability not only between stocks but between individuals (Matthews, 1953b). It is clearly not practical to select out, by an exhaustive series of field tests, sufficient pigeons of near-identical ability. Instead the present series of tests were carried out using the *same individual pigeons* throughout, discarding all previous records of any that were lost. Thirty birds were used which by age and experience may be considered as two teams. Team A was of 12 birds reared in 1952 and trained from the west before being given critical tests in other directions. Team B of 18 birds was reared in 1953 and trained north/south before their critical tests. Both teams were then used for breeding at the loft at Madingley Field Station, Cambridge. The releases in sunny conditions at 50 miles and over in which these pigeons had taken part for the first time and without experimental interference are shown by orientation diagrams superimposed on the map in Fig. 1. The tests concerned have been described by Matthews (1953a and 1955a). From this it will be seen that the birds had a very wide experience of homing from many directions and distances. Including early training flights they had all returned home at least fifteen times after transportation, as well as daily returns after exercise flights undertaken at their own volition. These were therefore far from naive birds; they had traversed wide areas and had demonstrated a firm desire to return home.

The pigeons were taken to the release points in covered baskets and liberated one at a time, each bird being followed to vanishing point in 16 × 40 binoculars. The bearing of that point and the time taken to reach it was recorded. In a number of tests intermediate bearings, at 15 seconds intervals, were recorded by an assistant. Numbered pins were placed in a large compass rose on which the observer stood, their position corresponding to a plumb-line hanging from his binoculars.

Table 35–1 gives the sequence of releases, the weather conditions, the average deviation of vanishing points from the home bearing and the average time in sight. Visibility was recorded as moderate to excellent for the tests, exceeding five miles in the worst conditions (T.47, 49, 57, 62).

REPEATED RELEASES AT THE SAME POINT

Landmark learning at the home site is difficult to study in that failure to home after a brief experience of the surroundings of the loft may be due to many other factors. Landmark learning at a release point is not necessarily the same process, but, using experienced homers, it is more open to investigation. Repeated releases at one point would be expected to lead to an improvement in orientation by recognition of landmarks, though only to a small extent if the bird obtains information as to its position relative to home by a true navigational system (e.g., sun navigation). Again, the birds may learn to fly in one direction by a process independent of landmarks (e.g., sun compass orientation). Landmarks would then play a secondary part only if the compass orientation was specific to the release point and not general on release. Landmark learning would become of primary importance if other navigational or directional clues were eliminated as sun navigation and sun-compass orientation are by thick, complete overcast. Such conditions therefore provide the critical tests. Matthews (1953a) had already shown that a second release within a week at the same point led to improvement if made in sunny conditions but not in cloudy conditions. The present tests were to probe the situation further.

Repeat releases in sunny conditions after longer periods gave little evidence of learning. Thus birds from Team A gave only a crude homeward tendency (average deviation 68°) when released (T.53) at Point 3, having been released there twice (in groups) in the course of a week 21 months previously. Team B released at Point 2 for a second time (T.47) after a group release there three months earlier gave little better results (Fig. 2). Team B was next released again (T.48) at the same point with complete overcast condi-

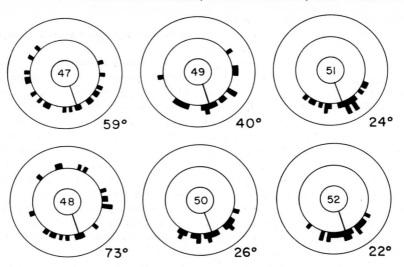

FIG. 2. Vanishing points in successive releases at the same point (2). Each 5° block represents the bearing on which a bird was lost from sight. The figure to the right of each circle is the average deviation of these bearings from that of home (indicated by the radial line). The central figure is the number of the Test. The critical tests, 48 and 52 were made under overcast. Landmarks had been learned by the latter release but not by the former.

tions. The resulting scatter was so wide as to be little better than random and the birds spent a long time flying near the release point. As three releases were clearly not sufficient for the learning of landmarks, the birds' experience of the point was doubled by three further releases in sunny conditions. One (T.49) was the following month. After a lapse of three months owing to the requirements of the breeding programme two further releases were made within a week (T.50, 51). As will be seen from Fig. 2 a distinct improvement in orientation resulted. A seventh, critical release (T.52) was now made in conditions of full overcast. In strong contrast to T.48 the birds now gave an excellent homeward orientation, though they showed some uncertainty in that the time in sight was somewhat longer than in the immediately preceding tests. There is no doubt that they had by this stage found and recognized sufficient landmarks to "map-read" themselves towards home. Hence six previous flights from this point

had been sufficient for the birds to learn the landmarks whereas two such flights had not. The minimal requirements will lie somewhere between and as the sixth release showed little improvement over the fifth it is probable that learning was about as advanced by then as it would ever likely to be.

Such relatively slow learning of landmarks is in accord with the results obtained by Matthews (1952) when pigeons were tested under laboratory conditions. There it was shown, however, that once learnt the information was retained excellently, for a matter of years. At the loft itself the learning of the surrounding landmarks in five daily exercise flights would seem quite a reasonable rate of progress. It may also be that more rapid learning may occur in that special circumstance. Pigeon fanciers are unanimous in their experience that it is much more difficult to resettle a pigeon in a new loft once it has been flown from that in which it was raised. The difficulty is greater still in the case of a bird that has itself bred in the old loft.

THE EFFECT OF OVERCAST

There is much evidence (Matthews 1955b for summary) that overcast causes breakdown in orientation and/or navigation of birds. The common sense interpretation is that the clouds prevent essential orientation clues from reaching the bird, notably those deriving from the sun's position. Pratt (1953) suggested that overcast might have a direct emotional effect on the birds, throwing out of action some subtle parapsychological phenomenon. This is discountenanced by the results of T.52. Where an adequate secondary means of orientation (learned landmarks) was present, homeward orientation was swiftly taken up despite thick overcast. This conclusion was checked at a later stage in this series by releasing the birds of both teams only 2 - 5 miles from the loft (Point 8, Fig. 4) under full overcast

(T.62, Fig. 5). Again good homeward orientation was achieved, again presumably by the use of learned landmarks.

THE EFFECT OF DISTANCE OF DISPLACEMENT

We have seen that pigeons released a second and third time in sunny conditions at points 23 - 25 miles from home show little evidence of orientation. Such as there was suggested "map-reading" by imperfectly remembered landmarks. This cannot occur when the birds are released for the first time at the point. Thus in T.50 Team A were having their first experience of Point 2. They scattered at random (Fig. 3) after much time spent nearby. This unorientated behaviour was the more noticeable as Team B (on their fifth release there) were giving during the same period a very marked (Fig. 2) and swift homeward orientation. For their part Team B birds had given a very wide scat-

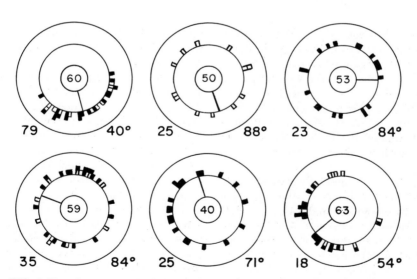

FIG. 3. Vanishing points at different distances from home. The figure to the left of the circle indicates the distance in miles.

Note. Homeward orientation is present at 79 miles, is not apparent at 35 down to 23 miles but reappears at 18 miles. All releases in sunny conditions.

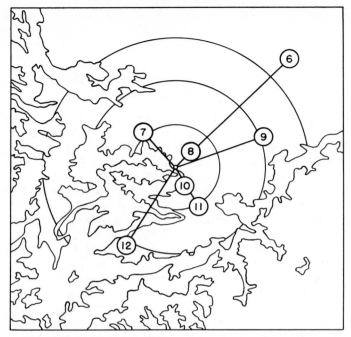

FIG. 4. Map showing release points used for short distance releases. The numbered circles are connected to the loft at Madingley. The 100, 200 and 400 foot contours are shown, also circles at 5, 10 and 15 miles. All releases in sunny conditions except T.62.

ter at their first release (T.40) at Point 4, at the same distance in the opposite direction (Fig. 3). Again when released for the first time at Point 3 to the west they gave (T.53) a random scatter and slow departure (Fig. 3). This test, incidentally, confirmed that repeated releases at Point 2 had not trained the birds to fly south on release, with reference to the sun's position.

Pigeons with unusually extensive experience in many directions thus appeared unable to recognize landmarks at points 23 - 25 miles from the loft. The other implication in their lack of orientation, that navigational information was not available at such distances either, will be considered later. For the moment the question was how far *did* the area of recognized landmarks extend from the loft. A series of releases· at short distances were there-

fore carried out from the points shown in Fig. 4. The orientation results are illustrated in Fig. 5.

Homeward orientation was apparent at 10 miles and very marked at 2 - 5 miles. The degree of orientation did not relate exactly with distance, nor would this be expected. Each landscape has features which would confuse as well as those which would assist orientation of a bird dependent on landmarks alone. Thus town-bred pigeons might fly to investigate a town, country-bred birds the reverse. Then the topography may be such as to permit better views of the home surroundings from one direction than another. Madingley lies at the northern foot of a low range of hills ringing the flat expanses of the Fens. It was no surprise that at 5 miles the better orientation was shown at Point 7 to the north-west rather than at

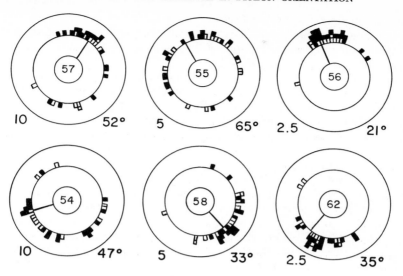

Point 11 to the south-east; at ten miles Point 9 north-east gave rather better results than Point 12 to the south-west. There is no need to call in directional tendencies or "position-effects" (with their mysterious implications) to explain these variations. Such probing of the landmark knowledge of these particular pigeons could have been continued indefinitely were it not for a limit to the number of suitable release points and to the fact that multiple close releases were increasing the birds' local knowledge all the time. A last release (T.63) at Point 6, 18 miles, showed that the birds had by then sufficient knowledge to orientate towards home at that distance and from that direction.

Now those same pigeons which had failed to orientate 25 miles from the loft had previously (Fig. 1) shown good homeward orientation from 50 miles in sunny conditions. An intermediate release (T.59) was therefore made in full sun at 35 miles, Point 5. The results (Fig. 3) were a near-random scatter. Lest for some obscure reason the birds had lost their ability to navigate they were given a distant, sunny release (T.60) at Point 1, 79 miles from the loft. They showed a homeward orien-

tation typical of such circumstances (Fig 3.)

Close to home then, these pigeons were dependent on learnt landmarks, the known area varying with the individual's experience but extending out in the present case as far as 18 miles in at least one direction. There was then an intermediate zone to beyond 35 miles in which the birds were not familiar with the landmarks and were not apparently able to orientate by any other means. Somewhere between 35 and 50 miles homeward orientation became possible and remained so at greater distances.

The present experiments thus support that group of theories which propound some form of navigational "grid" by which the bird "fixes" its position relative to home in two co-ordinates. This involves comparison of the values of two factors varying quantitatively in a regular way across the earth's surface, their gradients being angled to each other. Earlier evidence that homeward orientation from a distance breaks down under overcast would suggest that the factors concerned are those derived from the sun's position and movement, whether by the method originally postulated by Matthews (1951) or its modification put forward by Penny-cuick (1960). But whatever the nature of the stimuli there will be a lower limit below which the sense organs concerned cannot discriminate between the values pertaining at home and those being observed. The navigational system will then only provide the information that the bird is somewhere close to home. When, as in the present case, the area of known landmarks does not extend so far out, the bird must perforce fly at random until that area is reached. Wilkinson (1952) has shown that this can be quite an efficient process, especially at short distances. Moreover, if the bird's wanderings take it away from the home area it will reach the outer zone in which sensory discrimination of the navigational stimuli is possible and so be enabled to turn back towards home. Learning of landmarks in the home area is thus seen as an essential part of efficient homing. Such learning at the release points or en route are probably of minor importance except when birds are released repeatedly from one point and/or in the same direction — the circumstances of most pigeon races.

THE LACK OF DIRECTIONAL TENDENCIES AND OF IMMEDIATE ORIENTATION

Perusal of the orientation diagrams showing the bearings at which the birds were lost from sight at 12 release points provides clear evidence that these 30 pigeons were not hampered by a tendency to fly in any one direction, at least by the stage of training at which the study of their orientation began. In this respect their behaviour was consistent with that of Cambridge pigeons since these provided in 1949 the first unequivocal demonstration of bird navigation—by orientating towards home successively from 127 miles NNW, 79 miles WSW and 69 miles SSE (Matthews, 1951). The birds in the present experiments also conformed with the Cambridge pattern in that they showed no *immediate* orientation towards home. To illustrate this the bearings of the pigeons *one minute* after release are shown in Fig. 6. These may be compared with their final bearings (in Figs. 2, 3 and 5). In T.51 they were being released for the sixth time at this point and yet only the very crudest homeward orientation

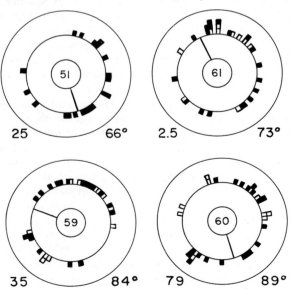

FIG. 6. Bearings one minute after release at a selection of points.

was apparent after one minute. Similarly in T.61 the birds were being released for a second time at a point only 2 - 5 miles 'from the loft, giving the tightest fan of vanishing points (average deviation 18°) yet recorded. Even so, at one minute there is only the beginning of a cluster round the home bearing and the overall deviation is near random. Both these results suggest that the birds may first test for clues on the navigational grid before looking for and recognizing landmarks; certainly it appears that the latter process is not immediately accomplished.

In T.59 the release at an unknown point 35 miles in the intermediate zone gave us randomly spread bearings at one minute as it did finally. T.60 is the classic case of birds released in the outer zone far from known landmarks but able to rely on navigational clues to pick up the direction of home. One minute after release the bearings of the birds were scattered at random. Indeed by 2 - 5 minutes they were still giving no statistical evidence of orientation (average deviation 78°). The birds were finally lost to sight in an average of 3 - 8 minutes when they then had an average deviation from the home direction of only 40°. All this confirms that the navigational procedure of these pigeons took some time to complete, sufficient for instance not to preclude observation of the sun's movement along its arc.

Summary

1. The same thirty pigeons of wide experience were used throughout the tests.

2. Repeated releases at one point showed that landmarks were learned sufficiently well to orientate by them after more than two but less than six releases.

3. The area of previously known landmarks extended up to 18 miles, at least in one direction.

4. Released 23 - 35 miles from home the birds showed no orientation, apparently not knowing the landmarks nor being able to navigate.

5. Released 50 - 79 miles, and further, orientation towards home was clearly shown.

6. These findings are in accord with navigation by a "grid", involving comparison of factors varying quantitatively across the earth's surface.

7. There were no indications of directional tendencies or immediate homeward orientation.

Acknowledgments

The work was carried out while I was in receipt of a grant from the Department of Scientific Research, experimental expenses were met by another grant from the Royal Society and the results written up while holding a post at the Wildfowl Trust financed by the Nature Conservancy. To all these bodies I express my gratitude. I am also grateful to Sir James Gray, F.R.S., for making the work possible and to Dr. W. H. Thorpe, F.R.S., for his constant interest and encouragement. The pigeons were maintained by Mr. G. E. Dunnett, helped by Miss E. M. Barraud. Miss J. Cooper assisted at many of the releases.

REFERENCES

HOFFMANN, K., 1959 Uber der Einfluss verschiendener Faktoren auf die Heimkehrleistung von Brieftauben. *J. Orn.*, **100**, 90–102.

KRAMER, G., 1957 Experiments in bird orientation and their interpretation. *Ibis*, **99**, 196–227.

KRAMER, G., 1959 Recent experiments on bird orientation. *Ibis*, **101**, 399–416.

KRAMER, G., 1961 Long distance orientation. Pp. 341–371 in *Biology and Comparative Physiology of Birds*, Vol. 2 (ed. A. J. Marshall). New York and London.

MATTHEWS, G. V. T., 1951 The experimental investigation of navigation in homing pigeons. *J. exp. Biol.*, **28**, 508–536.

MATTHEWS, G. V. T., 1952   The relation of learning and memory to the orientation and homing of pigeons. *Behaviour*, **4**, 202–221.

MATTHEWS, G. V. T., 1953a   Sun navigation in homing pigeons. *J. exp. Biol.*, **30**, 243–267.

MATTHEWS, G. V. T., 1953b   The orientation of untrained pigeons: a dichotomy in the homing process. *J. exp. Biol.*, **30**, 268–276.

MATTHEWS, G. V. T., 1955a   An investigation of the chronometer factor in bird navigation. *J. exp. Biol.*, **32**, 39–58.

MATTHEWS, G. V. T., 1955b   *Bird-Navigation.* Cambridge University Press.

MATTHEWS, G. V. T., 1961   "Nonsense" orientation in Mallard *Anas platyrhynchos* and its relation to experiments on bird navigation. *Ibis*, **103**a, 211–230.

MATTHEWS, G. V. T., 1963a   "Nonsense" orientation as a population variant. *Ibis*, **105**, 185–197.

MATTHEWS, G. V. T., 1963b   The astronomical bases of "nonsense" orientation. *Proc. XIII int. orn. Cong.*, in press.

PENNYCUICK, C. J., 1960   The physical basis of astro-navigation in birds; theoretical considerations. *J. exp. Biol.*, **37**, 573–593.

PRATT, J. G., 1953   The homing problem in pigeons. *J. Parapsychol.*, **17**, 34–60.

WILKINSON, D. H., 1952   The random element in bird "navigation." *J. exp. Biol.*, **29**, 532–560.

W. N. KELLOGG

36   Echo Ranging in the Porpoise

This summary article describes W. N. Kellogg's careful experiments that firmly established the porpoises' use of reflected sound to perceive objects in their environment.

For a more complete description of these experiments, as well as other fascinating facts about porpoises, see Kellogg's *Porpoises and Sonar* (Chicago: University of Chicago Press, 1961).

This article originally appeared in *Science*, Vol. 128, pp. 982–988, 24 October, 1958. Reprinted here with the permission of the author and the American Association for the Advancement of Science.

It has long been known that bats orient themselves in flight by the process of echo ranging or echolocation. That is, they emit a series of short high-frequency sound pulses, the echoes of which, upon their return to the bat's ears, are the means by which it avoids colliding with objects while in flight. An analysis of echo ranging in the bat undertaken by Griffin (1) indicates that bats may even find the flying insects which they eat in this manner. The basic principle behind the process is the same as that of Navy sonar and of the marine Fathometer or echo sounder.

That animals of the sea, especially the great whales and the porpoises, may employ a similar method to avoid colliding with objects in their pathway—as well as with the ocean bottom—has often been suggested but has never been conclusively demonstrated. Yet it is known that some of the dolphins and certain of the larger whales make many underwater noises (2). To date, these sounds have perhaps been most successfully studied in the case of the shallow-water porpoise, or bottlenose dolphin, *Tursiops truncatus* (Montagu). This animal, it should be noted, belongs to the order of Cetacea, suborder Odontoceti. It is one of the smaller of the toothed whales, of which the giant sperm whale is the largest representative. Kellogg, Kohler, and Morris (3) have made acoustical analyses of some of the submarine noises produced by *Tursiops* and have published a preliminary, although incomplete, frequency spectrum describing one class of sounds emitted.

Such facts as are at present available indicate the following:

1) The underwater noises made by the bottlenose dolphin satisfy fully the necessary acoustical and temporal requirements for echo ranging in water. Those of the short-pulse variety occur in trains or series, the individual pulses of which have a duration as short as 1 millisecond (3). These trains of repeated sound signals, like the cries of the bat, are particularly well suited to the production of a continuous series of echoes. In general, the pulses are complex in frequency pattern and contain many ultrasonic vibrations (3, 4). Although high frequencies are by no means essential for echo ranging, such frequencies would be particularly useful under certain conditions — for example, when there is a residual background of water and wave noise.

2) The acoustic receptor of the Odontoceti is remarkably well adapted for responding to sound vibrations in water. Its structure alone suggests a kind of supersensitivity to sound (5). Moreover, observations of the reactions to water-borne noises made by wild or noncaptive porpoises, such as the reactions reported by Fraser (6) and by Howell (7), imply that the sense of hearing in these animals is very acute indeed. So far as is known, however, the only extensive tests of hearing on these cetaceans are those attempted by Kellogg and Kohler (8) and by Schevill and Lawrence (9). The results show that *Tursiops truncatus* is capable of reacting to sound vibrations, in water, at least as high in frequency as 80 kilocycles per second—or two full octaves above the upper frequency threshold for hearing in man.

There seems little reason to doubt, therefore, that *T. truncatus* both emits and

can receive sound vibrations in water which possess the necessary characteristics for echolocation. It may consequently be said to possess an echo-ranging or a sonar system.

3) But even though this animal appears to have a kind of sonar system, there is as yet no direct evidence that he actually uses it as such. To investigate this matter further, it now becomes necessary to test captive porpoises for the avoidance and location of objects in water, after vision has been experimentally eliminated. This is, in fact, the object or purpose of the present research program. This article summarizes a series of investigations on underwater echo ranging conducted at the Marine Laboratories of Florida State University, 43 miles south of Tallahassee on the Gulf of Mexico (10).

Subjects and Equipment

The subjects were two bottlenose dolphins donated by the Marine Studios of Marineland, Florida, and transported 260 miles by truck to the university's laboratories. They were between seven and eight feet in length, and each was estimated to have a weight of around 300 pounds.

Although these animals are known to be both playful and intelligent (11), there are nevertheless marked variations in the behavior of different individuals. In the case of our own two subjects, for example, the male, a young adolescent, appeared to be quite dependent upon the more mature female and swam immediately to her side in times of stress or excitement. The female, in turn, displayed a certain reserve or sophistication by withdrawing, of her own choice, from active participation in two of the studies to be reported. As a consequence, the tests in two of the echo-ranging situations were confined to the behavior of one animal alone. In the remaining situations, both individuals took part. The animals were given the names of Albert and Betty.

The observations were made in a specially dredged pool or enclosure where the porpoises were maintained (12). The surface dimensions of the pool were 55 by 70 feet, and the depth was 5½ feet at low tide and 7 feet at high tide. The sides and bottom of the excavation were of soft marl or muck, which produced a poor reflecting surface for underwater sound signals. This material served, therefore, as a kind of natural baffle; its damping effect upon audio-vibrations was excellent for studies of echo ranging. The pool was connected to the nearby waters of Alligator Harbor through large concrete pipes which permitted a free tidal flow both into and out of the enclosure. A 30-inch boardwalk was built around the bank at the water level, and the land area nearby was fenced off some distance back from the excavation.

A natural advantage of this testing environment was the turbidity or opacity of the water. Shoal water in this part of the Gulf is generally brownish during the warmer months but clears somewhat during the winter. In addition, the mud in the pool itself was continually stirred by the swimming of the porpoises, and this reduced even further the penetration of light. Regular tests of the degree of light penetration were made with a Secchi disc, and the findings were confirmed by transparency measurements with a photoelectric colorimeter. The results showed the light penetration to be as low as 10 inches in some instances, although the average penetration was closer to 20 inches. Harmless dyes were available to reduce the underwater visibility even further should this become necessary, but these were never used except in an exploratory way. The possibility that the porpoises could locate objects in the water by vision was minimized, therefore, by this turbidity.

To facilitate the lowering of underwater gear into the water, a network of horizontal wires and cables, supported by rows of small telephone poles on the bank, was stretched across the entire area of the pool about 15 feet above the water. This network was a permanent installation and was used for supporting various sorts of running tackle, which could be manipulated by assistants from the shore. With suitable rigging of this kind, one or more objects could be lowered into the water or removed from it at any desired place or places. A heavy crane mounted on a short dock protruding into one end of the pool took care of unusually heavy equipment.

The electronic accessories used in this work included several varieties of hydrophones (or underwater microphones), a heavy underwater transducer (or speaker), preamplifiers, amplifiers, oscilloscopes and oscilloscope camera, tape recorders, and air speakers. These devices were used (i) for listening to the submarine noises made by the animals while they were being tested, (ii) for recording and photographing some of these sounds, and (iii) for projecting back into the water to the porpoises the recordings of their own noises made while they were performing at echo-ranging problems.

Reactions to Submerged Targets

In the wild or natural state, *T. truncatus* catches and eats live fishes, but in captivity it must learn to eat dead (although fresh) fish. With practice it can be trained to eat from the hand. Suppose that a test or "target" food fish is thrown into the pool in such a way as to strike the water 30 feet or so from the porpoises' positions. If the test is to be critical, the animals should not be able to see either the fish in the air or the motions of the thrower. The instant the bait enters the water, both animals immediately turn and race toward it at maximum speed, although before they can arrive at the spot, the fish, if fresh, will have sunk beneath the surface. The bait is by then not visible to human observers on the bank or to the animals, yet one or the other of the porpoises never fails to retrieve it and usually surfaces almost immediately with the fish in its mouth. The whole procedure takes but a few seconds. There is no exploratory or searching behavior whatever.

What, then, is the sensory mechanism for accomplishing this trick? Obviously it cannot be a visual mechanism in such turbid water. It cannot be an olfactory mechanism, for the sense of smell does not exist in these animals (13). The olfactory bulbs are missing altogether, and the nostrils or blowhole is closed during submersion. Gustatory reception seems highly improbable, since the chase and seizure are much too fast for any tasting to take place. The response is like that of a dog picking up a stick on the run. There remain the tactual and temperature senses, and audition. We are forced to infer by the process of elimination that the acoustic receptor must be the sensory channel which is employed.

A deduction of this kind is confirmed by underwater listening to the animals' sounds as the chase takes place. Although porpoise sound signals may be entirely absent before the target fish strikes the water, the noise of its splash produces a torrent of sputtering sound pulses as both animals dash toward the target. When the seizure is complete, the sounds again subside.

To investigate this phenomenon in a more systematic way, the following tests were conducted:

1) Objects of various sorts were thrown or lowered into the water so as to make a splash upon entering. These included BB shot, pebbles, fishes, and 4-foot poles. Such objects also served as echo-ranging targets after submersion.

2) Streamlined or "teardrop" objects were silently lowered into the water without surface noise, yet they served, upon submersion, as targets for reflected sound waves.

3) Surface splashes alone were pro-duced, but no underwater target was furnished. This was accomplished in several ways, although most effectively by dropping water in measured quantities upon the surface of the pool.

The major results obtained from these tests are enumerated below:

1) If the pool was perfectly quiet, even a single BB shot tossed into the water would elicit an underwater beaming response on the part of the porpoises.

2) Water dropped upon the surface which created a splashing noise sufficiently different from the background noise to be perceived was also followed by bursts of exploratory sound pulses, although these were likely to be of only momentary duration. A single drop of water from a medicine dropper did not cause enough surface noise to elicit this reaction. Under favorable conditions, however, a half-teaspoonful of water dropped from a height of 5 or 6 feet would elicit exploratory sound pulses. The splashing of a stream of water from a hose did the same thing. But since no echoes were returned after the porpoises' original sound bursts, the pattern of pulse signals in these cases was no more than exploratory and ended after a single burst.

3) A solid object immersed with complete quietness, on the other hand, produced no echo ranging until the animals happened to make sporadic exploratory ranging signals. A delay of 10 or 15 seconds might therefore result after a streamlined target had been lowered in this manner. Yet if the same target was dropped with a splash, this was at once followed by a continuous sound pattern. The splash appeared to serve as a cue for the production of the sound signals, and if echoes were returned from the original burst, the beaming continued.

The behavior of Albert, who learned to take fish from the hand (Betty would never consistently do this), was particularly significant in this connection. It was never necessary to signal or call the porpoise when a fish was inserted into the water—even from behind a screen which concealed all movement from the air. During feeding he would make occasional exploratory bursts of sound pulses which might be compared to "glancing" or "looking" in terms of vision. These bursts were usually from 1 to 2 seconds long and occurred every 10 seconds or so. He appeared to be "searching" for the fish. As soon as the fish was submerged (or as soon as the beaming signals produced echoes), the pattern of sounds would change. Discrete bursts of sound pulses would now be separated by intervals no longer than a second or two. As the porpoise moved toward the target, the intervals between bursts were eliminated altogether.

While making these sounds and approaching the target, the animal would continually oscillate its head or reorient its body from right to left through an arc of perhaps 10 degrees, as a human being might when employing binaural localization. If the target fish was moved laterally under the water as Albert approached, the porpoise immediately turned so as to keep the stimulus in his sagittal plane, continually making small head oscillations at the same time.

Avoidance of Obstacles

The ability to avoid submerged objects while swimming was examined in these animals by immersing a series of obstructions which completely bracketed the swimming area. The obstacles used in these tests were light poles or posts 52 inches long. They therefore subtended most of the vertical distance between the surface and the bottom. The poles were made of galvanized sheet metal and were triangular in cross section, each side being 2 inches wide. Thirty-six of these poles were suspended over the water by rigging attached to the overhanging cables and lowered simultaneously by assistants at a predetermined signal. The poles were arranged in a regular geometrical pattern, the rows and columns of which were 8 feet (about one porpoise length) apart.

Since these obstructions were of metal and were suspended freely from above, they were extremely sensitive to contact stimuli. If touched or struck lightly either in air or in water, they gave off a metallic, bell-like ring or ping. Metallic noises of this sort made under the water could be heard by means of the hydrophone and regular underwater acoustical gear. They could also be recorded on magnetic tape along with porpoise sound signals. The metallic sounds served therefore as a means of automatically recording the collisions which the porpoises made with any of the submerged obstacles.

In the first 20-minute session of this sort there was a total of four collisions for both animals. So far as we could tell, these were made after the body of a porpoise had actually passed an obstruction. It appeared that the horizontal tail flukes of one of these small whales must have touched an obstacle as the animal was in the process of turning into a new alley. The second session was better than the first, and all subsequent trials were perfect, showing no collisions whatever. It looked as though the subjects had rapidly *learned* to navigate through the maze of obstructions in the limited swimming space allowed them. In one series of observations made during the dark phase of the moon, in nearly total darkness at night, there were also no errors.

As a final test we broadcast back to the animals, while they were swimming through the field of obstacles, tape recordings of their own noises which had been made during an earlier session in the same situation. The sounds were projected by a heavy Navy transducer, type 1-K. But the projected noises seemed not to affect the accuracy or the speed of their swimming in any way. And there were no collisions.

The most reasonable interpretation of this result appears to be that the porpoises were able to distinguish their own sound signals from the artificially produced interference. This interpretation finds support in the recent observations of Griffin (14) and of Griffin and Grinnell (15) that distracting or jamming sounds do not seriously disturb the echo-ranging ability of the bat.

Fish Discrimination Experiment

At first our two subjects were fed on mullet, *Mugil cephalus* (Linnaeus), but they soon began to refuse this fish. It therefore became necessary to supply them with a fish called spot, *Leiostomus xanthurus* (Lacépède), which they ate readily. Mullet thrown into the water would be chased but rejected. If held in the hand, a mullet would be approached but not taken.

As a consequence of this behavior, the question arose whether the animals could discriminate between preferred fish (the spot) and nonpreferred fish (the mullet) without seeing either fish. The fish-discrimination experiment was planned to examine this possibility. The discrimination cues were differences in the sizes of the preferred and the nonpreferred stimuli. To this end, mullet were selected for the experiment which were about twice as large in over-all length as the spot.

The general arrangement of the experiment is shown in Fig. 1. A rectangular screen of marine plywood was mounted solidly at the end of a 15-foot dock which projected into the pool. The screen was placed in such a way that its bottom edge was 1 to 2 inches below the surface of the water. From behind the screen, which concealed visible movement in the air, a spot and a mullet were silently lowered into the water at the same time. The tail of the spot was held by the experimenter so that the body of the fish projected approximately 6 inches below the bottom of

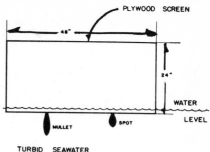

FIG. 1. Arrangement for presenting the stimuli in the fish-discrimination experiment. On any given trial, a spot (the preferred fish) and a mullet (the nonpreferred fish) were lowered simultaneously into the water from behind the plywood screen. The spot projected approximately 6 inches below the screen, the mullet 12 inches. A trial began when the fishes were submerged and ended when the porpoise took or touched either fish. The positions of the "positive" and "negative" fishes were randomly rotated from trial to trial.

the plywood screen. The mullet was held so as to project 12 inches below the screen. Every effort was made to eliminate all water noises as the fishes were inserted. That this was successfully accomplished was periodically checked by underwater listening. As in any discrimination experiment, the positions of the positive and negative stimuli were randomly rotated from trial to trial, although the absolute point of insertion of each fish was held constant with reference to the edges of the plywood screen.

Since the subject (Albert) was by this time well practiced in taking food fish from the hand, he would approach the end of the dock whenever human beings came near it and wait there to be fed. Generally he lay at the top of the water, 3 to 10 feet from the plywood screen, where he would ogle the experimenters first with one eye and then with the other, submerging for a few inches between breaths, which occurred rather rapidly in such instances. A regularly timed trial began with the immersion of the two stimuli and

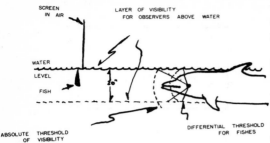

FIG. 2. The turbidity of the water acted somewhat like a one-way-vision screen. The experimenters above the water level could see sufficiently far beneath the surface to observe the porpoise's head and mouth, but the animal could not detect the target fishes in a horizontal direction. The difference between the absolute threshold for distance and the differential threshold—or the threshold of discrimination between the target fishes—is also illustrated in this figure.

ended when the porpoise took or touched either fish. If the spot was taken, this was counted a successful discrimination. The touching or taking of the mullet was scored as an error.

Because Albert did most of his approaching at or very near the surface, it was not difficult for observers on the dock above him to tell his position with reference to the target fishes, in spite of the turbidity of the water. At the same time, the subject himself could not detect the stimuli by visual means because of this turbidity. The situation in fact possessed some of the characteristics of a one-way-vision screen, the advantage being all in favor of the experimenters. The diagram in Fig. 2 should make this clear.

A distinct difference was found to exist between the limits of visibility, as measured by the Secchi disc, and the limits of discriminability between fishes of different size, as tested by human observers under water. The Secchi disc used in these studies was a circular white reflecting surface, 20 centimeters in diameter, which was submerged until it became in-

visible. The procedure gave an absolute threshold of visibility measured vertically in inches from the surface of the water.

By means of special observations made by skin-diving human beings, horizontal Secchi readings in the pool were compared with vertical readings. Similar tests were made of the maximum horizontal distance, under the water, from which it was possible for a human being to distinguish between a 12-inch mullet and 6-inch spot. The horizontal and vertical Secchi readings were on the whole equal, but the horizontal discrimination threshold was found to be about one-half the absolute Secchi threshold. A Secchi measurement of 20 inches read from the surface could be translated therefore into a horizontal differential threshold between the two fishes of approximately 10 inches. The manner in which this affected the visual capacity of the porpoise is shown schematically in Fig. 2.

Regardless of these limitations, how-

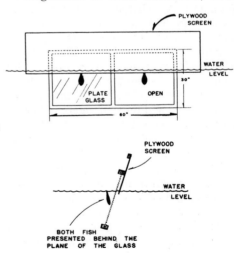

FIG. 3. (Top) Front view and (bottom) side view of the apparatus used in the window experiment. The porpoise was required to distinguish between two fish (spot) which were identical in visual appearance. The fish were presented simultaneously, but one was behind a sheet of plate glass. The glass was randomly shifted between the right and left windows.

ever, it soon became apparent that discrimination of a high order was taking place in the fish-discrimination experiment. In the first daily session of 16 trials, Albert committed four errors. The number of errors decreased irregularly upon successive sessions until none at all occurred. The final 140 trials—some made in near-total darkness at night—gave no errors whatever. The time per trial was not affected—that is, it was not increased —during the night sessions. If vision had played any part in the selection of the preferred fish, a reduction in illumination would certainly have made the task more difficult. It should consequently have increased the response time, and it might also have introduced errors.

Listening and underwater recording which were conducted throughout the experiment showed also that the porpoise reacted to the insertion of the fishes by increasing at once both the intensity and the continuity of his sound signals and by surging forward toward the targets as the signals increased.

Window Experiment

It may still be assumed by some that, in spite of the turbidity of the water, visual discrimination was not really excluded in these studies. Is it possible that Albert was able to distinguish between the fishes of different size by some superhuman ocular ability? To answer this objection, a new experiment was designed in which the use of vision would prove actually to be detrimental and confusing. This experiment is referred to in the present report as the window experiment.

Like the fish-discrimination experiment, the window experiment was also a discrimination experiment, but in this case the two stimuli to be discriminated were spot (preferred fish) identical in visual appearance. Both of the spot offered on any trial were equally visible, although one of them was unavailable or unattainable since it was presented behind a sheet of plate glass. The unavailable spot was the negative stimulus and the available spot the positive stimulus. A diagram of the apparatus which was used is shown in Fig. 3.

A rectangular frame of angle iron, 30 by 60 inches, contained a square plate-glass window which would slide to the right or left so as to fill one half of the rectangle. The position of the covering

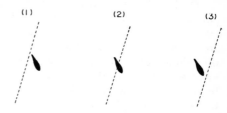

FIG. 4. Preliminary training was necessary in the window experiment in order to get the animal to insert its mouth through the aperture of the metal frame. Fish were first held in front of the frame as in (1), and on successive trials were gradually moved backward through the frame, as in (2) and (3). The glass was removed from the apparatus for these habituating trials.

glass on any trial was randomly determined. The target fishes were silently inserted from behind a plywood screen so that no movement from the air could be detected by the subject.

Both of the spot were held the same distance behind the plane of the glass, as indicated in Fig. 3 (bottom). In order to reach the available fish, it was necessary for Albert to insert his mouth several inches into the open aperture of the metal framework. An error or failure on any trial would consist of his bumping the plate-glass window or approaching very close to the glass.

To induce the porpoise to place a part of its head inside of the metal frame required a great deal of preliminary training, as might have been expected. All of this training was conducted with the window removed from the framework. Spot were sometimes offered in the right-hand opening and sometimes in the left. In the beginning, it was necessary for the experimenter to hold the fish in front of the plane of the plywood screen, exposing his submerged hand as well as the fish to Albert. By easy stages, the fish were gradually moved backward into and through the framework, as is indicated in Fig. 4.

During the experiment itself the window was adjusted at the beginning of the intertrial interval—that is, immediately after Albert had taken the fish for the preceding trial and while he was submerged and eating the fish (as revealed by underwater listening). In order to control for the sound caused by sliding the window, the movement of the glass was always made in two steps or stages. It was first pushed half way—that is, to the middle of the framework. From this central position it was subsequently moved either the rest of the way, in the same direction, or it was returned to its original position. This two-stage process produced the same sequence of apparatus noise following each trial, but the noise by itself gave no indication of the final location of the glass.

The trials were timed as in the fish-discrimination experiment, and records were made of the approximate starting position on each trial as well as of the direction and speed of swimming during a trial. In 202 trials recorded in this manner, there occurred not a single error, nor even what appeared to be the beginning of an error. No approaches whatever were made toward the fish behind the glass.

On the average it took Albert longer to complete a trial than it had in the fish-discrimination experiment, possibly because of his aversion to putting his nose within the metal frame. Later trials were somewhat faster than earlier trials, showing the effect of practice. Some sessions

were conducted in nearly complete darkness at night, but this again caused no change whatever in the accuracy of the performance or in the latency of responding.

The porpoise, in fact, ultimately came up with his own original version of how the problem should be solved. He developed the habit of stationing himself in front of the open window as soon as he had eaten the fish from the preceding trial and before the minimum intertrial interval set by the procedure had elapsed. He got ready, in other words, immediately after the movement of the glass and waited a few feet away for the available or "positive" fish to be submerged. He appeared to have learned through association or conditioning that the positive stimulus would come in the open window, and he distinguished at once the opened from the unopened. All this time the animal sputtered intermittently, as he made what might be termed "auditory glances" in listening for the forthcoming target fish.

Plexiglas Experiment

Even though these experiments dispose pretty well of the visual discrimination hypothesis, there remains the possibility that Albert may have been attracted to the target fishes by the chemical stimulus of taste and that his behavior should not, therefore, be accounted for in terms of echo ranging. The responses to submerged nongustatory targets discussed earlier in this article argue strongly against such a possibility. However, as a final check upon the notion that chemical substances in the water may have served as an uncontrolled variable in the window and fish-discrimination studies, an additional experiment was arranged in which food rewards were eliminated altogether. The motivating principle in this instance was avoidance or punishment. The general plan of the

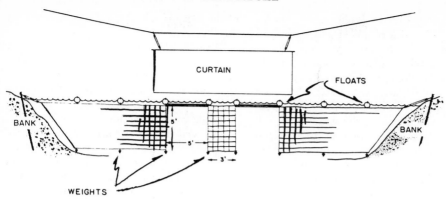

FIG. 5. The plan of the Plexiglas experiment. A steel net or fence was stretched tightly across the porpoise pool beneath the water, dividing it into two sections. The fencing was supported by floats at the surface and was weighted at the bottom. Two openings or doorways (5 feet wide) in the fence permitted the animals to swim from one section of the pool to the other. A heavy sheet of clear Plexiglas was used as a door to block one of the openings. The opaque plastic curtain, manipulated from the bank, could be raised or lowered to cover both openings. When it was raised, exposing the two doorways, this signaled the beginning of a trial. The Plexiglas door was moved from one opening to the other only when the curtain was down, thus concealing the movement.

experiment, which is here referred to as the Plexiglas experiment, is illustrated in Fig. 5. Both of the porpoises served as subjects in this situation.

A submerged net of wire fencing 5 feet in height was stretched tightly across the width of the pool at the center. It formed a fixed barrier or partition dividing the water area into two approximately equal parts. The wire in the fencing was ⅛ inch in diameter and was woven into squares 5 inches to the side. The net was suported by floats at the surface and was weighted at the bottom. Two openings 5 feet wide, located near the middle of the barrier, were the only passages or doorways from one half of the pool to the other. A large curtain of black war-surplus plastic suspended from above could be raised or lowered so as to block or cover both openings.

One of the openings could also be closed by a rigid sheet of clear Plexiglas, as is shown schematically in Fig. 6. Tackle from the shore permitted the Plexiglas to be moved laterally so as to block either

hole. With the black curtain raised, the porpoises were therefore confronted with a kind of choice apparatus which required them to distinguish between the doorways in the wire fencing, one of which was blocked by a solid but invisible Plexiglas door.

Two other nets—which might be called "motivating nets"—were placed at the ends of the pool, one at each end, parallel to the barrier net. These motivating nets were movable and were used to induce the animals to pass from one side of the barrier to the other. Since porpoises tend to avoid physical contact and will shy away from any strange or unusual object, they would avoid the motivating net behind them by escaping into the open area of the opposite side. The black curtain was then lowered, and the original motivating net floated back to its starting position. On the next trial the second motivating net, now behind the animals, was used to make them return to the original half of the pool. The subjects were gradually familiarized with the apparatus and conditions in several preliminary sessions with the Plexiglas removed and with both apertures free and unoccupied.

During the regular experimental trials, the Plexiglas door was adjusted in position only when the black curtain was submerged and completely covered both of the openings. As in the case of the window experiment, the lateral movement of the Plexiglas from one side to the other was performed in two stages. The Plexiglas was placed in the center position between the two door-

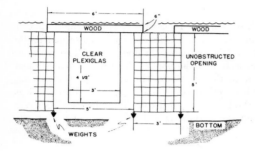

FIG. 6. The Plexiglas door in place in the Plexiglas experiment, whose over-all plan is shown schematically in Fig. 5. The door was moved laterally, by tackle operated from the shore, in such a way as to close or block one opening or the other on any given trial.

ways, and it was then given a final adjustment so as to fill one of the openings. In this way the apparatus noise was a two-stage affair and was always the same, even though the Plexiglas was moved away from an aperture and returned to its original position. The right-left sequence of the open doorway upon successive trials was randomly determined.

The timing of a trial began when the curtain was raised and the choice apparatus was exposed to the animals. The timing ended when the animals came up to blow or exhale on the opposite side of the barrier. Since the two porpoises could be readily identified by the observers, time scores were recorded separately for each. If a collision with the Plexiglas occurred, this could at once be detected by the shaking

of the net and the angular displacement of the Plexiglas itself.

Data in this experiment were obtained from 50 trials for each animal, or a total of 100 trials for both. The results showed that only two errors were committed in the entire series of 100 trials. The performance, in other words, was 98 per cent accurate. There was also evidence of learning or adaptation, as indicated by a gradual reduction in the time per trial. Underwater sound signals were again present in this experiment, as in the previous ones.

The conclusion seems inescapable that the porpoises avoided the solid but invisible Plexiglas door by means of echo-ranging. The selection of the open doorway took place, moreover, while the animals were passing through a net of ⅛-inch steel wire, which they also avoided. The location and discrimination of submerged objects by reflected sound signals is without doubt a necessary and a fundamental perceptual avenue for these cetaceans.

REFERENCES AND NOTES

1. GRIFFIN, D. R.: *Experientia* **7**, 447 (1951); *J. Acoust. Soc. Am.* **22**, 247 (1950).
2. FISH, M. P.: *Office Naval Research Tech. Rept. No. 49-30* (1944); B. KULLENBERG: *Nature* **160**, 648 (1947); A. F. McBRIDE: *Nat. Hist.* **45**, 16 (1940); W. E. SCHEVILL and B. LAWRENCE: *Science* **109**, 143 (1949).
3. KELLOGG, W. N., R. KOHLER, and H. N. MORRIS: *Science* **117**, 239 (1953).
4. MORRIS, H. N., R. KOHLER, and W. N. KELLOGG: *Electronics* **26**, 208 (1953).
5. KELLOGG, R.: *Quart. Rev. Biol.* **3**, 174 (1928); M. YAMATA: *Sci. Repts. Whales Research Inst.* **8** (1953); F. W. REYSENBACH DE HANN: *Acta Oto-Laryngol. Suppl. No. 134* (1957).
6. FRASER, F. C.: *Nature* **160**, 759 (1947).
7. HOWELL, A. B.: *Aquatic Mammals: Their Adaptations to Life in Water* (Thomas, Springfield, Ill., 1930).
8. KELLOGG, W. N., and R. KOHLER: *Science* **116**, 250 (1952); W. N. KELLOGG:

J. Comp. and Physiol. Psychol. **46**, 446 (1953).

9. SCHEVILL, W. E., and B. LAWRENCE: *J. Exptl. Zool.* **124**, 147 (1953).

10. These investigations were made possible by successive grants-in-aid from the National Science Foundation (grants No. G920 and G1730) and by additional financial and material assistance from the Research Council, the Oceanographic Institute, and the department of psychology of Florida State University. The porpoises were furnished through the kindness of F. G. Wood, Jr., curator of the Marine Studios at Marineland, Fla. Underwater acoustical equipment used in some of the observations was loaned by the Office of Naval Research (contracts No. Nonr531 and Nonr1502). I wish to thank Richard Durant, superintendent of the Marine Laboratories of the Oceanographic Institute, and Robert Kohler, Jr., electronics engineer, for invaluable assistance. I should also like to acknowledge the helpful cooperation of the university administration and the aid of numerous graduate students and graduate assistants who worked at different times on these experiments. This paper is contribution No. 106 from the Oceanographic Institute of Florida State University. More detailed analyses of the individual experiments are in preparation.

11. McBRIDE, A. F., and D. O. HEBB: *J. Comp. and Physiol. Psychol.* **41**, 111 (1948).

12. The entire porpoise facility has been described in more detail in W. N. KELLOGG: *J. Gen. Psychol.* **46**, 97 (1958).

13. REYSENBACH DE HANN, F. W.: *Acta Oto-Laryngol. Suppl. No. 134* (1957).

14. GRIFFIN, D. R.: *Listening in the Dark* (Yale Univ. Press, New Haven, Conn., 1958).

15. GRIFFIN, D. R., and A. D. GRINNELL: *Science* **128**, 145 (1958).

DONALD R. GRIFFIN,
FREDERIC A. WEBSTER,
and CHARLES R. MICHAEL

37   The Echolocation of Flying Insects by Bats

The previous reading described a careful series of experiments demonstrating echolocation in the porpoise. An equally ingenious experimental program, led by biologist Donald R. Griffin, has investigated similar phenomena in the bat. In this reading, Griffin, Webster, and Michael show that bats can detect and capture very small flying insects by means of echolocation.

Reprinted from *Animal Behaviour*, 1960, **8**, 141–154, with the permission of the authors and the publisher: Baillière, Tindall and Cox, Ltd.

Suggestion for further reading: Griffin, D. L.: *Listening in the Dark.* New Haven, Conn.: Yale University Press, 1958.

When bats are hunting insects they adjust the pattern and tempo of their high frequency orientation sounds in a way that seems quite appropriate for active echolocation of small moving targets but distinctly unsuited for the passive detection of insects by listening for their flight sounds (Griffin, 1953; 1958). The most obvious change is a marked rise in the pulse repetition rate just as the bat closes in on its prey. For example, *Eptesicus fuscus* often emits only four or five pulses per second in straight cruising flight, with silent intervals of 200 milliseconds between them; but during insect pursuit the same bat may shift to a "buzz" in which the pulses are separated by only five milliseconds. Similar flight patterns and vocal responses can be elicited by tossing into the vicinity of a hunting bat imitation insects such as pebbles or plagets of wet absorbent cotton. What little sound these make can scarcely resemble that of a real insect.

Yet this type of evidence is indirect and not wholly satisfactory, since some bats certainly do respond to the sounds made by buzzing insects (Moehres, 1950; Kolb, 1959). Studies of insect pursuit behaviour in the laboratory have recently enabled us to make four significant extensions of earlier studies under natural conditions: (1) a more detailed description of the bats' hunting tactics, (2) measurements of the high rates at which small insects are captured, (3) estimates of the minimum distances at which they are detected, and (4) selective masking experiments with low and high frequency noise which demonstrate conclusively that at least under some circumstances insects such as *Drosophila* are intercepted by echolocation.

It is convenient to distinguish three phases of insect hunting behaviour which appear always to be present with varying degrees of distinctness in bats of the family Vespertilionidae. The first or *search phase* is fairly straight flight in which the pulse repetition rate is relatively low, although the bat is evidently ready to attack flying insects. The second or *approach phase* begins when the bat first reacts to an insect, either by turning towards it, by increasing the pulse repetition rate, or both. Here the interval between pulses shortens progressively though often irregularly, as the bat apparently locates its prey more accurately and flies toward it. A *terminal phase* ensues when the bat is fairly close to the insect and emits a burst of pulses at a very high rate, the buzz. A similar buzz is emitted on dodging small wires or just before landing, but the buzz of an insect catch seems typically to last longer and to include more closely spaced pulses. In *Myotis lucifugus,* the species we have studied most thoroughly, the search phase involves pulse-to-

pulse intervals varying from about 50 to 100 milliseconds or more; in general the larger the room the longer the intervals in this phase. The approach phase has intervals between about 50 and 10 milliseconds, and in the buzz the pulses are separated by only 4 to 7 milliseconds. Intervals of more than 50 milliseconds are thus characteristic of cruising or search, 50 to 10 milliseconds approach, and less than 10 milliseconds the terminal phase of very close pursuit or actual capture of the insect.

Methods

Although small insects are apparently detected and pursued one at a time, the bats we have studied were much more likely to begin active hunting when large numbers of insects were on the wing. Even at best we have found that only a small fraction of the *Myotis lucifugus* released in rooms filled with flying insects undertake serious hunting; many will slowly starve and would doubtless die eventually in a room where other individual bats catch hundreds of insects every day. Two or three sessions of a half-hour or less on different days are usually sufficient to find the good catchers, provided that the bats are wide awake, warm, and active when tested. The 90 per cent. or more that did not show signs of hunting after several such sessions were released.

A good catcher identifies itself by making obvious interception manoeuvres, turning sharply, suddenly climbing or diving for a few inches, or merely by pulling up abruptly in the midst of fairly straight flight. Often the interfemoral membrane can be seen to turn upwards and forward, and the head may be thrust down into it very rapidly and out again. If the room is quiet, one can hear with the unaided ear the faint audible clicks which accompany each pulse of high frequency sound during the search or approach phases. The buzz accompanying the actual catching manoeuvre is usually more clearly audible.

With adequate lighting the actual capture of insects may be seen, but this has been much less obvious than the flight manoeuvres or the faint audible buzzes.

We have studied insect hunting in three different rooms, all about 8 feet high. The first, at the Vero Beach Laboratory of the Florida State Board of Health, was 8 ft. × 16 ft., the two used later in Cambridge, Massachusetts, were 12 ft. × 32 ft. and 11 ft. × 16 ft. All of these rooms had walls which reflected high frequency sound quite well, and in all cases the bats must have received strong echoes from walls, ceiling, and floor along with the much fainter echoes from their insect prey. This "clutter" may well have been what discouraged most bats from hunting indoors.

Sufficient numbers of insects might be obtained by light traps or other means of attracting wild insects, but we have reared mosquitoes and fruit flies by standard methods (Galtsoff, et al., 1959). It was necessary to stir the insects into flight every few minutes in order to elicit continuous hunting. The actual densities of flying insects varied widely, both in space and time; but the great majority of catches were probably made at densities of no more than three or four insects per cubic foot.

Since insect capture by bats is a rapid process, and since the small insect is often very difficult to see at all, we were anxious to record the hunting behaviour by single photographs and motion pictures. With single photographs, even when the insect as well as the bat is shown, it is difficult to be certain what part of a complex sequence of events is recorded. Multiple flash stroboscopic photographs have been very useful, and at a flashing rate of five to ten per second the successive images of a flying bat are sufficiently separated, except in turns or hovering manoeuvres. Insects can be photographed better with multiple than with single flashes, because a row of specks equal in number to the flashes is less likely to be confused with dust on the film. We have used both still and motion picture cameras in pairs, spaced 0·5 or 1 metre

apart, in order to obtain more accurate information about the positions of bat and insect, by simultaneous cross bearings.

In many experiments a tape recording was made of the bat's orientation sounds with a plastic dielectric condenser microphone (Kuhl et al., 1954), a suitable amplifier, band pass filter, and an Ampex tape recorder. Each flash of a strobe light can easily produce a recognizable electrical signal on the tape, so that when oscillograph pictures of the bat's sounds were later prepared from the tape recordings it was quite feasible to identify each flash and determine its time of occurrence relative to the recorded sounds from the bat.

Illumination and background surface are of great importance because bats are very dark and tend to blend into most backgrounds if photographed by reflected light. It is relatively easy to obtain silhouettes of flying bats against a white background, and if the background is marked off with a grid of contrasting lines, the bat's position can be determined with one camera by making parallax corrections (Grinnell & Griffin, 1958). If two lights are employed, the separation between the two shadows of a bat can be used to determine its distance from the wall. We were not able to use this method to photograph mosquitoes or *Drosophila*, however, and turned instead to a very dark background of black velvet with lateral illumination either by flood lamps or an electronic flash. By careful arrangement of the lamp or lamps it was possible to photograph both bats and individual fruit flies on 16 mm. film. The flies appeared only as specks, but in many cases a careful study of the film with a time motion study projector permitted unequivocal identification of the flies by their characteristic movement. Catches were recognized by the approach of a bat to a particular fly followed by the disappearance of the latter as the bat flew on. A dust speck could easily be mistaken for a single image of a fly, but dust varied randomly from frame to frame while flies remained in approximately the same place or moved progressively. Furthermore dust specks were not intercepted by the bats.

1. Hunting Tactics

Most of the pursuit and interception manoeuvres requires less than one second and are extremely difficult to observe directly. We therefore photographed the bats and insects and recorded simultaneously the pattern of the orientation sounds. Each of the catches for which full or fragmentary sound and position records were obtained was preceded by the customary search and approach phases defined above, although there were some catches or apparent catches of mosquitos without a full-fledged buzz. In such cases the pulse-to-pulse interval dropped from about 90 milliseconds in the search phase only to about 40 or 50 milliseconds. This shift from search to approach phases provides the best indication yet available of the distance by which a bat has already detected some small object, such as a wire or an insect. In two mosquito catches for which excellent records were obtained there was a clear drop in this interval at about 100 centimetres and at about 30 centimetres respectively from the probable position of the mosquito. That is, the interval showed a marked drop at these distances from the spot where, a fraction of a second later, the bat was to emit its sharp buzz. Mosquitos can therefore be detected at appreciable distances, but further discussion of this topic is best deferred to Section 3.

The manner in which the frequencies within each pulse varied during these catching manoeuvres is also of interest. In the search phase, before any apparent reaction to the insects, the pulses were about two milliseconds in duration, the intervals between pulses were roughly 80-100 milliseconds, and the frequency dropped in each pulse from about 75-85 kilocycles at the start to 37-45 kilocycles at the end. This is the typical octave of frequency sweep in a *Myotis* pulse, although the actual frequencies were slightly lower than on some other occasions. During the two pronounced buzzes mentioned above the pulse durations fell to 0·5 milliseconds, or sometimes a little less. The estimated frequencies within these and other very short pulses ranged from about 25 to 30 kilocycles. Our recent and technically much improved records thus require an important modification of the first description of frequency patterns during insect catching (Griffin, 1953). It is now clear both for *Myotis* and *Eptesicus* during the pursuit of real and imitation insects that in the terminal buzz the frequencies are distinctly *lower* than in the search phase (previously referred to as "cruising", an appropriate term for *Eptesicus* under natural conditions but much less apt for *Myotis* catching insects at high rates in a small space).

During the pursuit of an insect the actual lengths of the pulses of sound in air drop, in proportion to the pulse duration, from about 70 cm. to 15 cm. The distance travelled by the bat between pulses varies with its flying speed, but before and just after detection (indicated by the drop in pulse-to-pulse interval) the bats were flying at 2 to 3 metres per second, or 2 to 3 millimetres per millisecond. One of the longer intervals thus represents 200-300 mm. of travel, while during the two clearest buzzes the bat's speed was about 70 cm./second or 0·7 mm./millisecond. Since one pulse was emitted every 5 to 7 milliseconds, the bat was now travelling only about 3·5 to 5 mm. between pulses. The velocity of sound in air is about 340 mm./millisecond, so that the wave lengths of the orientation sounds were about 4 to 8 mm. in the search phase, but increased during the buzz. The catching manoeuvres and their relationship to the pattern of the buzz will be described in more detail in a later paper.

2. Rates of Insect Capture

A. MOSQUITOS

In April, 1958, at the invitation of E. T. Nielsen several bats were brought to his 8 ft. × 16 ft. flight chamber at Vero Beach,

TABLE 37-1

Rates of mosquito catching by bats at the Vero Beach Laboratory, April 1958. The average weight of six of the mosquitoes used (*Culex quinquefaciatus*) was 2.2 milligrams.

BAT	DATE	DURATION OF FLIGHT (MINUTES)	WEIGHT GAIN (MG.)	MOSQUITOES CAUGHT PER MINUTE
M. lucifugus Number 5 (Wt. 5.7 gr.)	April 1	30	350	5.3
	April 4	31	100	1.5
	April 4	9.5	73	3.5
	April 5	15	55	1.7
M. lucifugus Number 7 (Wt. 5.7 gr.)	April 2	10	125	5.7
M. subulatus leibii (Wt. 3.7 gr.)	April 2	21	77	1.7
	April 4	24	264	5
	April 5	15	312	9.5

Florida, which contained initially about 2,000 mosquitos (*Culex quinquefaciatus*). Several *Myotis lucifugus*, one *M. subulatus*, one *M. subulatus leibii*, two *Pipistrellus subflavus*, and two *Plecotus rafinesquii* were set free in this room for 10-15 minutes at a time, and certain of the *Myotis* hunted actively. These were left in the chamber overnight, and in the morning the mosquito population had fallen to roughly 200-300. Although none of the *Pipistrellus* or *Plecotus* was ever observed to hunt actively, a few of the *Myotis* were so successful that we could estimate the rate of insect capture not only by counting audible buzzes, but also by measuring the rate at which the bats gained weight (See Table 37-1). Many factors might reduce the weight gain —evaporation of water from skin or lungs, urination or defaecation — but since the bats were closely watched we could be sure that they did not eat or drink anything but insects caught on the wing. Their gain in weight thus represents a conservative mini-

mum estimate of the weight of insects captured.

It was not practicable to restore the population of mosquitos to its original level during these experiments, and on some of the subsequent days only a few hundred were present in the flight chamber. Yet in eight cases listed in Table 37-1 accurate weighing demonstrated high rates of mosquito catching. On other occasions the same bats gained very little, or even lost weight while flying in the same chamber. In these cases observation and listening for the faint audible components of the buzzes confirmed that they were hunting much less actively. The mosquito population was so low on 5th April that it was supplemented by releasing in the same room several dozen large crane flies (*Brachryprenna*). These weighed about 19 mg., but the bats usually dropped the legs and wings uneaten, and the bodies weighed only about 12 mg. During the 15 minutes when the *M. subulatus leibii* was observed to gain

372 mg. it was clearly observed to catch no more than 4 or 5 crane flies along with many mosquitos. It seems most likely that less than 60 mg. of its 372 mg. weight gain consisted of the crane flies, so that its rate of mosquito catching is listed in Table 37–1 as 312/15 or 21 mg. per minute. This bat was thus catching about ten mosquitos per minute or one every six seconds.

B. *Drosophila*

During the spring and summer of 1959 large numbers of *Drosophila* were reared in an 11 ft. × 16 ft. flight chamber and out of many *Myotis lucifugus* which were allowed to fly in this chamber, four, designated below as TR, S, B and TL, began active catching immediately when first allowed to fly in this room. The fruit flies were unfortunately not maintained in pure culture, but only two species were present, *Drosophila robusta* weighing 3 mg. on the average, and *D. melanogaster* with an average weight of 0·6 mg. On several occasions certain of these bats gained as much as 29 mg./minute while catching only fruit flies in this room. Sustained catching rates of 20 fruit flies per minute were observed, and two flies were often taken within one second (For details see below, especially Table 37–3). These rates of weight gain were in satisfactory agreement with the number of visible pursuit manoeuvres and audible buzzes which were often noticeable every few seconds, and are also quite similar to the estimates reported by Gould (1955; 1959) for the same species hunting under natural conditions.

3. Distances at Which Insects Are Detected

A. PROCEDURES

This subject was studied by a minor modification of the photographic method used to measure the distance at which small wires are detected (Grinnell & Griffin,

1958). Bats and fruit flies were photographed in an 11 ft. × 16 ft. flight room with bright lateral illumination against a dark velvet background with a 16 mm. Auricon sound-on-film camera. The bat's orientation sounds picked up by the microphone were rectified into low frequency clicks by a detector circuit, and supplied to the input of the sound camera. Each bat pulse was registered, on the same piece of film as the pictures, as a click which contained no information about the original frequency, only rough information about pulse duration and intensity, but accurate information about pulse repetition rate or interval between pulses. This camera operates at 24 frames per second, with its shutter open about 1/50th second. While the images were small and slightly blurred by the bat's motion, they sufficed to show its position within one or two inches every 24th of a second. Actually the position shown was the projection of the bat or fly against the opposite wall, and estimates of the distance between the two are subject to parallax errors in either direction. The apparent distance was greater than the actual distance when bat and fly were equally far from the camera, but less when one was behind the other. We could make only rough estimates of the bat's distance from the camera or the opposite wall, and hence we did not attempt to apply parallax corrections. But a long series of such single camera pictures allowed approximate estimates of the distance of detection and provided a most helpful background for more accurate determinations of bat and insect positions with paired cameras.

Detailed analyses were made of 34 catches or attempted catches by one *M. lucifugus*, S, 26 by another of the same species, B, and six by a *M. keenii septentrionalis*. In each of these 66 cases graphs were prepared showing, on a common time base, the pulse-to-pulse intervals, the vertical and horizontal positions of the bat and fly, and the apparent distance between them, that is, the distance between their images on the wall opposite the camera.

B. SPECIAL ASPECTS OF INSECT PURSUIT BEHAVIOUR RELEVANT TO MEASUREMENTS OF THE DISTANCE OF DETECTION

Before proceeding to analyse these data on distance of insect detection it is important to review certain aspects of the bat's behaviour during these insect catching manoeuvres. In several cases the bat began its pursuit by taking off from the wall where it had previously been resting, and flew out to catch a fly which may well have been detected before take-off. In many other instances, however, the detection clearly occurred while the bat was flying; often many flies were caught during a continuous flight; and sometimes the bat did not land until hundreds of catches had been made. When starts from the wall were eliminated along with cases where the bat was turning away from the wall, catching another insect, or executing some other special manoeuvre at the start of the search phase, the pulse-to-pulse interval during search varied from 48 to 85 milliseconds, with the range from 50 to 60 milliseconds predominating. On the average the first clear drop below 50 milliseconds occurred about 0·5 second before the catch; and after that time almost every approach phase included a steady drop in interval. In all cases the actual detection must have taken place somewhat earlier than the vocal reaction of shortening the pulse-to-pulse interval. But since we have no way of estimating the bat's reaction time we will conservatively consider that detection occurred at the moment when the first pulse was emitted after an interval significantly shorter than that characteristic of the search phase.

The actual number of pulses emitted during the approach phase varied between 4 and 22; the average for the two *M. lucifugus* was 8·1 and for the *M. keenii* 10·6. These pulses are presumably used to track the moving insect. The terminal buzz contained anywhere from 3 or 4 to 15 or 20 pulses separated by 5 to 10 milliseconds.

We have no way of determining whether the last pulse of the search phase served for detection, or whether several searching pulses at roughly 50-millisecond intervals were required. The number cannot be very large, however, because of the numerous cases described in the next section in which one catch was completed and a second detection and interception begun within a remarkably short period of time.

C. DOUBLE CATCHES

In six of the 66 cases selected for careful study there were two catches or attempted catches within less than one second. The actual period between catches was ¾ second for the *M. keenii*, ½ second for *M. lucifugus*, and three cases of about

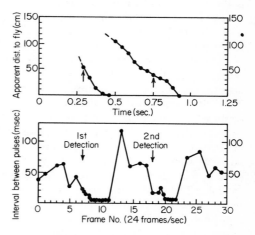

FIG. 1. A typical double catch within half a second. The upper graph shows as a function of time the apparent distance between the bat and the two *Drosophila*, that is, the separation between their images against the wall opposite the camera. Parallax errors may render these distances too high by 25 per cent. Each point on the lower graph shows on the same time base the interval separating one pulse of sound emitted by the bat from the previous pulse. Arrows mark the first vocal reaction to each fly, conservatively designed as the point of detection. During the two buzzes there were more pulses than could be plotted as separate points. Note that only four pulses were emitted in the search phase for the second catch (between 0.6 and 0.7 second).

½ second plus one of ¾ second for *M. luci-fugus* B. In all cases the two flies were intercepted by distinct manoeuvres, and it seems probable that the second insect was located only after the first had been seized. (In one of these six cases the first fly was attacked but missed.) Hence only a short interval of time and a few pulses are necessary for a successful search phase and detection. One of the clearest examples of double catches within one second is illustrated in Fig. 1. The positions of bat and fly were not clear until after the moment when the sound track first became adequate to show the tempo of the orientation sounds, but the latter part of the first approach phase was clearly photographed. The most significant aspect of this sequence is the time between the two catches. The next pulse to follow the first buzz came at a long interval (118 milliseconds) after the last pulse in the buzz. This is a common feature of these records, and it may well represent the time needed to remove the insect from interfemoral membrane where it is often "pouched" immediately upon capture or which it may strike before being seized in the teeth. Then three pulses were emitted at intervals of about 62 milliseconds, a value quite similar to the search phases just before and after the two catches. The next pulse came at an interval of only 17 milliseconds and clearly represented the beginning of the second approach phase. Only four pulses were emitted during the search phase between the two catches, hence the second fruit fly must have been detected by means of no more than four echoes. The reactions of these bats must thus be very rapid, and the information extracted from a very few pulses must suffice to locate the small target presented by a *Drosophila*.

D. RESULTS OBTAINED WITH ONE CAMERA

Almost every one of the 66 cases of fruit fly catches analysed graphically provided a clear indication of the point at which the search phase gave way to the

approach phase, thus demonstrating that the fly had already been detected. When the apparent distances of detection were averaged without parallax correction, the values were 73 cm. for the *Myotis keenii*, 55 cm. for *M. lucifugus* S, and 73 cm. for *M. lucifugus* B. The extreme values of these estimated distances of detection were 21 and 135 cm. Our next step was to average the individual values of pulse-to-pulse interval as a function of apparent distance

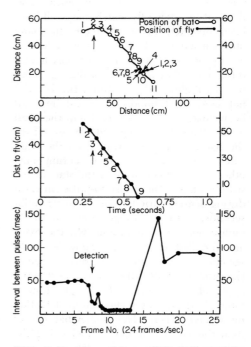

FIG. 2. Positions of bat and fruit fly and the pattern of orientation sounds during the catch. The upper graph shows a floor plan of part of the flight room some distance from the walls in which the zero point is arbitrarily selected to show the bat's position, and that of the fly, as determined by cross bearings from two motion picture cameras. The middle graph shows the distance separating bat and fly, and the numbers on the upper graph and middle graphs refer to frames of the film. The lower graph shows, on the same time base as the middle graph, the intervals between pulses. The arrow indicates the assumed point of detection. As in Fig. 1 the buzz contained more pulses than can be depicted individually.

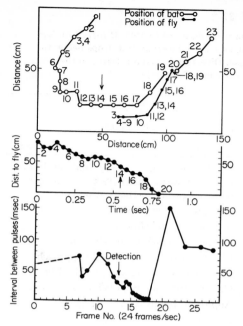

FIG. 3. Positions of bat and fly, together with the pattern of sound emission in another catch manoeuvre. For details see legend for Fig. 2.

E. MEASUREMENTS WITH TWO CAMERAS

After these records had been analysed we made a further effort to determine the distance of detection more accurately by using two 16 mm. motion picture cameras to photograph many *Drosophila* catches by two *M. lucifugus*, TL and TR, which were two of the better catchers under our experimental conditions. Both were Auricon sound-on-film cameras operated by synchronous motors at 24 frames per second. Each received the same input of rectified pulses from the microphone, and each photographed a clock with minute and second hands. To aid in correlating the two films, the field of each camera also included a clock hand that revolved once per second and an oscilloscope with the horizontal sweep set at 20 per second. Careful study of several hundred feet of paired films permitted the selection of 11 clear cases in which a *Drosophila* catch could be unequivocally located on both films, i.e., both bat and fly were depicted throughout

from the fly. The mean value of the interval thus obtained showed an increase out to a distance of about one metre. This might be interpreted as evidence that detection occurs at this distance, but the flight patterns and other circumstances such as proximity to the walls differed so much in these several cases that average curves are of somewhat doubtful significance. We therefore selected 16 cases where parallax errors seemed minimal, when the bat did not start from the wall, and when the search phase was relatively uncomplicated by immediately previous manoeuvres. On averaging these for each bat, the mean pulse-to-pulse interval was found to increase rather smoothly to reach a plateau value at 70 cm. for *M. lucifugus* S, 55 cm. for B, and 90 cm. for the *M. keenii*. Parallax errors render these values too high by perhaps 20 or 25 per cent. but detection at half a metre would appear to have been common, and an occasional detection may well have occurred at one metre.

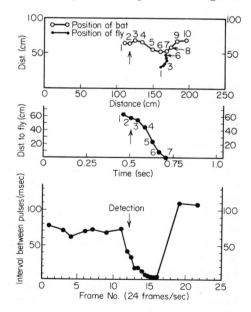

FIG. 4. Positions of bat and fly together with the pattern of sound emission in a third catch manoeuvre. For details see legend for Fig. 2.

TABLE 37–2

Distances and directions at which *Drosophila* were detected by two *Myotis lucifugus*.
Detection is assumed to occur when the pulse-to-pulse interval first drops below the
level characteristic of the search phrase. Direction is given relative to the
bat's flight direction at the time of detection.

CATCH NO.	BAT	DIST. OF DETECTION (CM.)	DIRECTION OF FLY AT TIME OF DETECTION (DEGREES)	REMARKS
1	TR	62	15°L.	Bat had just turned away from wall, fly moving toward bat, detection may have occurred earlier, perhaps at 80 cm.
2	TL	52	5°R.	Bat approaching at 90°
3	TL	68	60°R.	Approach from behind fly
4	TR	23	50°L.	Oblique approach from behind fly
5	TR	34	15°L.	Fly almost stationary, straight approach
6	TR	45	45°R.	Fly stationary, straight approach (Fig. 2)
7	TR	27	40°R.	Oblique approach from behind fly
8	TL	42	15°L.	Approach from behind fly (Fig. 3)
9	TL	83	35°R.	Fly approaching bat, detection may have been at about 90 cm.
10	TL	56	35°R.	Approaching at about 90° (Fig. 4)
11	TR	40	70°R.	Bat out of field of one camera during part of approach phase
Average distance of detection		48		

search, approach, and terminal phases, and there was no doubt concerning the matching of individual frames of the two films. In each pair of pictures the bat or fly appeared against the different spots on the grid on the opposite wall, and lines could be drawn on a floor plan of the room from the positions of the camera to these projections on the wall. The intersections of these lines located bat or fly within one or two inches. The same accuracy could equally well have been achieved in the vertical position, but in all eleven cases the bat and fly were either flying almost horizontally, or were diving or climbing too slowly to introduce appreciable errors when vertical movements were ignored.

For these eleven cases we thus obtained fairly precise plots of the positions of bat and fly every 24th of a second, and from these we could measure the distance from bat to fly. We could then plot the pulse-to-pulse interval on the same time base as the distance separating the bat from its target. Three samples of the resulting combined graphs are shown in Figs. 2, 3, and 4; these are representative, although they include more clear-cut shifts from search to approach phase than some of the other cases. All eleven cases permit fairly accurate estimates of the distance of detection, however, and these distances are listed in Table 37–2, along with the angular position of the fly relative to the bat's flight path at the time when the search phase ended and the approach phase began. It is quite evident that these more accurate measurements confirm the tentative conclusion reached above that detection commonly occurred at about half a metre. The shortest measured distance of detection was 23 and the longest 83 cm.

The motion pictures suggest that the bat turns towards its prey within a small fraction of a second after detection. It is also of considerable interest to note that many detections seem to have occurred at considerable distances even though the fly was not directly in front of the bat. Indeed there is little if any correlation between the angular position of the fly at the time of detection and the distance at which detection occurred. Since these bats usually seem to face in approximately the direction they are flying, at least in the search phase, this indicates that *Drosophila* can be detected from anywhere within a cone of perhaps 120°.

4. Selective Jamming Experiments with Low and High Frequency Noise

The evidence presented above suffices to show that small insects such as mosquitos and fruit flies are detected rapidly and at distances of about 50 cm. But even when taken together with the marked adaptation of the tempo of orientation sounds, this evidence does not prove conclusively that the insects are detected by means of echoes. It would still be logically possible to postulate that detection was achieved by hearing sounds of the insects' wingbeats. *Drosophila* were selected for the above experiments partly because their flight is very quiet, so that detection by passive listening would be more difficult than in the case of mosquitos or many of the larger flies and beetles. Furthermore, Williams & Galambos (1950) have measured the wave form of the flight sounds from a single *Drosophila funebris* beating its wings while attached to a small wire. The fundamental frequency under these conditions was about 180 cycles per second, and while the waves were complex enough to demonstrate the presence of strong harmonics, there do not appear to be any above the 10th at appre-

ciable amplitude. The sound of a single *Drosophila* is very faint; Williams & Galambos used a 640AA condenser microphone at 1·5 cm. from the fly but did not estimate the absolute sound pressure level.

We have measured the sounds emitted by *Drosophila melanogaster* when 20-30 at a time were placed in a small glass bottle (about 50 millilitres) covered at the top by gauze. When the flies were strongly agitated and buzzing vigorously the r.m.s. sound pressure level was 25-30 decibels above 0·0002 dyne/cm.^{2} at 15 cm. from the gauze covered end of the bottle. This sound level, measured with a calibrated 640AA microphone, must have been considerably higher than that from a single fly in flight at 50 cm. from a hunting bat; probably the level reaching the bat's ears at this typical distance of detection would have been below 20 decibels. The observed frequency was between 500 and 800 cycles/second which is considerably higher than that measured by Williams & Galambos. It seems probable that resonance phenomena associated with the bottle may have accounted for this difference, but for present purposes the important point is that 20 or 30 flies, aided by the bottle's resonance, produced such a low sound pressure level.

If these bats detect fruit flies by hearing their flight sounds, it should be possible to mask these low frequency and low intensity sounds from the fly without employing a masking noise of high enough frequency to interfere with the bat's echolocation. Our best microphones when used together with an ultrasonic spectrum analyser could detect no ultrasonic components in the flight sounds of *Drosophila*, even though adequate to reveal sounds as faint as 25-30 decibels, above 0·0002 dyne/cm.^{2} We can thus exclude the possibility that *Drosophila* are detected by hearing ultrasonic components of their flight sounds, unless these components lie below this level of intensity. For selective masking experiments we therefore set up a simple apparatus to generate noise over the frequency band from about 50-15,000 cycles/second. It consisted of a Grason-Stadler noise generator, a 20-watt high fidelity audio amplifier, and a combination of a standard 8-inch dynamic loudspeaker with an Electrovoice driver loudspeaker for the higher audible frequencies. This system filled the small flight room with a noise so loud that we had almost to shout when we wished to communicate. For comparison with this loud low frequency noise a rather weak thermal noise in the bat's frequency range was also used for certain experiments. It was generated by a General Radio type 1390A noise generator, a broad band amplifier which delivered into four Isophon electrostatic loudspeakers about 50 volts r.m.s. These loudspeakers gave a declining output above about 25 kilocycles/second, but still emit an appreciable signal to 55 kilocycles, ar.d a weaker signal at least over much of the range from 55 to 100 kilocycles. For some experiments electronic filters were used to restrict the frequency band of the low or high frequency noise. The low frequency noise sounded roughly equal in intensity throughout the small flight room used for observations of *Drosophila* catching, but the intensity of the high frequency noise undoubtedly varied widely from point to point, and it was not measured. Measurements with a calibrated 640AA microphone placed the overall sound pressure level of the 100-5,000 cycles/second band of the low frequency noise at +87 decibels re 0·0002 dyne/cm.² Its spectrum level did not vary greatly from 100-8,000 cycles/second as judged by ear and by measuring the level passed by a narrow band filter moved gradually across the frequency range from 100-10,000 cycles/second. The noise level was thus approximately 50 decibels per cycle bandwidth or 20-30 decibels more than the *overall* sound level of several *Drosophila* flying inside a small bottle.

When *Myotis lucifugus* which has previously been good fruit fly catchers were exposed to these two noises the results were consistent and unequivocal. The low

frequency noise had no noticeable effect; the bats continued to catch flies as rapidly in this noise as in the quiet. The high frequency noise, however, produced a marked decrease in the number of pursuit manoeuvres, the number of buzzes, and in the rate at which the bats increased weight while hunting. They did not stop hunting altogether, but usually made many fewer attempts to catch fruit flies, and then landed. If the high frequency noise was switched off they would often resume hunting almost at once. Excluding measurements obtained when the bat appeared tired or when the flies were scarce, the average rate of *Drosophila* capture was 9·5 per minute in the quiet and 11 per minute in the low frequency noise. Nor was there any appreciable difference between experiments in the dark and in the light. The results of the several experiments summarized in Table 37–3 thus provide strong evidence against the possibility that under these conditions fruit flies were intercepted by passive listening to their feeble flight sounds.

Discussion

When one watches a six-gramme bat chasing two-milligram fruit flies with dextrous, agile, and split-second manoeuvres, it is natural to wonder whether it obtains enough food from such tiny insects to equal metabolic energy required to catch them. Even the best catchers in our experiments have required supplementary feeding of mealworms, but this was primarily because we could not keep enough fruit flies on the wing to furnish a normal night's catch. The metabolic rate of a flying bat has been estimated as roughly 100 calories per gramme per hour or 600 calories per hour for a six-gramme bat (Griffin, 1958). The caloric value of a *Drosophila* does not seem to have been measured, but a reasonable approximation is probably the value of 2241 calories per gramme listed by Trager (1953) for newly emerged adults of the fly *Ophyra cadaverina*. When our bats were

TABLE 37-3

Rates at which *Myotis lucifugus* Captured *Drosophila* in Low and High Frequency Noise.
Rates of capture are based on the measured rate of weight gain divided by an assumed
average weight of 2 mg. for the fruit flies, and hence are minima.
Bat TR was used July 2-27, 1959, and bat TL August 23-24.

DATE AND TIME		CONDITIONS OF NOISE AND LIGHT		INTERVAL BETWEEN WEIGHINGS (MIN.)	RATE OF INSECT CAPTURE (FLIES PER MIN.)	REMARKS
July 2		0.05—5 kc.	dark	10	7.5	
July 18		0.05—5 kc.	light	10.5	11	
July 19		0.05—5 kc.	light	15	14.8	
July 20		0.05—5 kc.	light	12.8	4.7	
July 22	2:06	Quiet	light	12	6	
July 22	2:22	0.05—15 kc.	light	6.7	14.2	
July 27	1:40	0.1—15 kc.	light	3	13.5	
July 27	1:51	20—100 kc.	dark	3	—	Lost 1.7 mg./min.
July 27	2:00	Quiet	dark	3	11.7	
July 27	2:12	40—100 kc.	dark	3	1	
July 27	2:19	0.1—15 kc.	dark	3	3.8	Flies scarce
July 27	2:27	Quiet	dark	3	3.4	Flies scarce
Aug. 23	2:32	0.1—15 kc.	light	6	13.7	
Aug. 23	2:44	20—100 kc.	light	6	—	Lost 11 mg./min.
Aug. 23	2:56	Quiet	light	6	9.3	
Aug. 23	3:07	40—100 kc.	light	6	—	Lost 10 mg./min.
Aug. 23	3:18	0.1—15 kc.	light	6	6.9	
Aug. 23	3:31	Quiet	light	6	3.2	Bat tired
Aug. 24	4:00	0.1—15 kc.	light	3	13.1	
Aug. 24	4:13	20—100 kc.	light	4	—	Lost 29 mg./min.
Aug. 24	4:24	Quiet	light	4	10.9	
Aug. 24	4:32	40—100 kc.	light	4	—	Lost 7.5 mg./min.
Aug. 24	4:41	0.1—15 kc.	light	4	10.1	
Aug. 24	4:47	Quiet	light	4	7.8	Bat tired, flies scarce

catching ten fruit flies per minute (conservatively assumed to average 2 milligrams in weight) they were taking in food at a rate of roughly 2,700 calories per hour, provided the above assumptions are correct. Even though the supreme exertion of insect interception may require somewhat more than 600 calories per hour, the game does seem to be worth the candle.

Since *Myotis lucifugus* can detect echoes from *Drosophila* at 50 centimetres or more, it is appropriate to inquire what the intensity of such echoes would be. This will depend upon the sound level emitted by the bat, the frequency chosen for consideration, and the effective size of the fruit fly; but an approximate formula for the necessary computation is available (Griffin, 1958, p. 349). In the search phase the r.m.s. intensity of the outgoing pulse at 100 millimetres from the mouth of a *Myotis lucifugus* is about 100 decibels above the standard reference level of 0·0002 dyne/cm.[2] This is the maximum value when the pulse is at its highest amplitude, and this peak amplitude occurs at roughly 60-70 kilocycles, so that the strongest component of the echo corresponds to a wave length of about 5 mm. For simplicity let us assume that the *Drosophila* returns an echo of 5 mm. sound waves equal to that from a rigid sphere of 2 mm. radius, a rough approximation but one that we cannot improve upon until actual target cross sections of insects for bat pulses are measured. Making the above assumptions one can compute that the echo from a *Drosophila* would have an r.m.s. value of about 30 decibels at a distance from bat to fly of 50 cm., approximately the distance by which our records show detection to have occurred. This calculation assumes that the inverse square law applies to both the emitted sound beyond 10 cm. from the bat's mouth, and to the echo from the fruit fly. It also takes into account the 2½ decibels of atmospheric attenuation at 68 kilocycles over a round trip distance of 1 metre. If the fly were detected at one metre, rather than 50 cm. the echo would be reduced by sixteen fold, or by about 12 decibels. This, together with another 2½ decibels of atmospheric attenuation, would reduce the echo to 15 decibels, only slightly above the human auditory threshold at those frequencies where it is lowest.

Detection by bats of an echo having an intensity between 15 and 20 decibels appears plausible, except that the human auditory threshold of sound intensity rises sharply as the duration of a tone is decreased below about 200 milliseconds (Stevens, *et al.*, 1951, pp. 1,020-1,022). These data suggest that a 1-millisecond pulse might have a threshold 100 times, or about 20 decibels higher than one lasting 200 milliseconds. Since 0 decibels is approximately the human threshold under favourable conditions, it does not strain credulity to postulate that a bat could detect one-millisecond pulses at 15 decibels especially since there is good reason to believe that the auditory brains of bats are highly specialised for the detection of short pulses of high frequency sound (Grinnell & Griffin, 1959).

Another important question concerns the choice of 68 kilocycles, or a wavelength of 5 mm. as the most easily detectible portion of the echo. Other factors being equal, higher frequencies or shorter wavelengths would return somewhat stronger echoes, but higher frequencies are not present at as high intensities in the emitted pulse, they suffer more atmospheric attenuation, and furthermore in the case of spheres with a 2 mm. radius the increase in echo is not very rapid between 68 and 120 kilocycles, the highest observed frequency in *Myotis* pulses. Lower frequencies are actually used during the interception phase, down to about 25 kilocycles in some cases. But of course the distance is then much shorter, and to a first approximation the echo intensity varies inversely as the fourth power of the distance. While the echo of a 25 kilocycles component would be weaker than that of 68 kilocycles by a factor of about six, the shorter distance would more than offset this.

These echoes which the bat seems to detect at a level of about 30 decibels may come from any direction within a cone of roughly 120°. Nor is mere detection enough for the hungry bat; it must localise the direction from which the echo is coming and execute an appropriate turn within a fraction of a second. The probing pulse of sound emitted by a *Myotis* has a rather broad angular spread, although the higher frequencies at the start of the pulse are more sharply concentrated into the forward direction than the lower frequencies at the end. It is possible that in each of the cases shown in Table 37–2 where the angular position of the fruit fly was far removed from the flight path of the bat the animal happened to have its head turned in that particular direction at the moment of detection. But photographs of flying *Myotis* indicate that during the search phase the head is ordinarily pointed in the direction of flight, so that it seems more likely that echoes can be detected from anywhere within a fairly wide zone in front of the animal. The initial localization may not be precise, and the need for more accurate bearings may well explain the shortening of pulse-to-pulse interval during the approach phase. But an eventual understanding of the physiological mechanisms of echolocation must include not only the detection of insect echoes at a level of roughly 30 decibels, but their almost instantaneous localization as well.

Finally we should compare the difficulty of jamming the echolocation of small wires (Griffin & Grinnell, 1958) with the cessation of insect hunting in high frequency noise. It should be borne in mind that in the jamming experiments collisions with wires were presumably unpleasant enough to motivate their detection. But we have no way of ascertaining how strongly our bats were motivated to continue hunting when the noise was switched on. Insect hunting has been elicited only with difficulty, even in the quiet, and it is not surprising that high frequency noise would discourage it. In our jamming experiments with wires the bats preferred not to fly and they tried to avoid the difficult task of echolocating small wires in the noise. While we could make some of them do this by forcing them to fly in an array of wires, we have no comparable way of forcing bats to attempt insect catching in the noise. Furthermore, wires are larger in one dimension and are stationary, rather than moving targets. Bats often slow down on approaching wires, but insects are intercepted at flight speeds of at least one metre per second.

It is remarkable that our very loud low frequency noise did not reduce the rate of insect catching at all, and that the good catchers, TR and TL, caught approximately as many fruit flies in this noise as in the quiet. In human masking experiments low frequencies are found to mask higher tones more easily than the reverse, but the auditory system of a *Myotis* is clearly able to make sharp frequency discriminations (Grinnell & Griffin, 1959), and it must be able to distinguish 30 decibel echoes at 60 or 70 kilocycles from a noise covering the band from 0·1 to 10 or 15 kilocycles at a level of about 50 decibels per cycle bandwidth.

Another question might be phrased as follows: since bats can apparently hear echoes from wires at a signal-to-noise ratio of −35 decibels (Griffin & Grinnell, 1958), why not assume that they can also hear *Drosophila* wing beats 30 decibels below a 50 decibel per cycle bandwidth noise at lower frequencies? This question leads directly into the problem of critical bands for the hearing of bats, a problem discussed elsewhere (Griffin, 1958, pp. 373-375). But regardless of the uncertainties surrounding this problem, it is difficult to believe that bat hearing or *Drosophila* flight sounds could have so narrow a bandwidth as one cycle per second. Hence the noise effectively competing with the flight sounds must be greater than 50 decibels. Even if we assume that the overall level of the *Drosophila* flight sounds (about 20 db. re 0·0002 dyne/cm.²) is spread over as narrow a bandwidth as 10 cycles/second, the competing noise would have a level of 60 decibels or 40 decibels above the sound level from the fly.

It should be reiterated that we are not suggesting that all detection of insect prey by all bats under all conditions is based upon echolocation. The observations of Moehres (1950), Kolb (1959) and others are sufficient to demonstrate passive detection of relatively noisy insects, and we have also observed bats suddenly respond to a buzzing blow fly and turn towards it from a distance of several feet. Quite clearly both active echolocation and passive detection are important in the feeding behaviour of bats under natural conditions. We have considered only the former, because of its intrinsic interest, and because its importance had not been fully recognized heretofore.

Further experiments now in progress seem likely to throw additional light on the intricate and rapid flight manoeuvres executed during insect pursuit and interception, the ways in which the various membranes are employed, and the accuracy of localization of the insects. These studies will be reported elsewhere, together with a consideration of the information processing involved in the tracking of small moving targets.

Summary

1. Bats of the genus *Myotis* (*M. lucifugus, M. subulatus leibii* and *M. keenii septentrionalis*) have been studied while pursuing and capturing small insects under laboratory conditions. It is apparently important to provide fairly large numbers of such insects in order to elicit insect catching behaviour indoors.

2. Insect catches are individually directed pursuit manoeuvres; each insect is detected, located, and intercepted in flight within about half a second.

3. Certain individual bats caught mosquitos (*Culex quinquefaciatus*) and fruit flies (*Drosophila robusta* and *D. melanogaster*) at remarkably high rates which could be measured conservatively by the gain in weight of the bat. Sometimes a bat would average as many as 10 mosquitos or 14 fruit flies per minute during a period of several minutes. In four cases motion pictures showed two separate *Drosophila* catches within half a second.

4. The orientation sounds of the hunting bat are adjusted in a manner that seems appropriate for the echolocation of single insects one at a time. There is a *search phase* before the occurrence of any apparent reaction to the insect. In this phase the frequency drops from about 100 to 50 kilocycles during each pulse of sound, and the pulses are emitted by *M. lucifugus* at intervals of 50 to 100 milliseconds.

5. When an insect is detected the search phase gives way to an *approach phase* characterized by a progressive shortening of the pulse-to-pulse interval and, if necessary, a sharp turn towards the insect. In this phase the pulse duration may shorten somewhat, but the frequencies remain approximately the same as in the search phase or drop slightly.

6. When the bat is within a few centimetres of the insect there is a *terminal phase* in which the pulse duration and interval between pulses shorten to about 0·5 millisecond and 5 or 6 milliseconds respectively. Contrary to a conclusion reached earlier on the basis of much less adequate data (Griffin, 1953), the frequency *drops* in the terminal phase, sometimes to 25 or 30 kilocycles. This is the buzz, which also occurs in many cases when the bat is dodging wires or landing.

7. The distance from the insect at which detection occurs can be judged by the shift from search to approach patterns. This distance of detection is commonly about 50 cm. for *Drosophila,* and it occasionally may be as much as a metre with fruit flies or mosquitos.

8. Two *M. lucifugus* which had become adept at catching *Drosophila* in the laboratory were exposed to broad band thermal noise either at low frequencies (0·1-15 kilocycles) or high (20-100 kilocycles). The low frequency noise had an approximately uniform spectrum level of about 50 decibels per cycle band width (re 0·0002 dyne/cm.^{2}) from 0·1 to 8 kilocycles. It was thus very loud compared to the flight sounds of *Drosophila* which have a fundamental frequency of a few hundred cycles/second and a maximum sound pressure level of 20-25 decibels at the distances of detection by these bats. The high frequency noise was of low and varying intensity, but it discouraged or prevented insect catching. The low frequency noise, on the other hand, had no effect on insect catching; the bats gained weight in this noise (and in the dark) just as rapidly as in the quiet. Although bats sometimes detect insect prey by passive listening to sounds emanating from the insects themselves, these experiments appear to us to establish conclusively that small and relatively silent insects are often detected by echolocation.

Acknowledgments

We are happy to acknowledge much cooperation, assistance, and support without which these experiments would not have been possible. Financial support has been provided through a contract between the Office of Naval Research and Harvard University, and reproduction of this paper in whole or in part for the purposes of the United States government is authorized. Instrumentation and extremely helpful advice and suggestions have been contributed by the Lincoln Laboratory, Massachusetts Institute of Technology, especially by David A. Cahlender, J. J. G. McCue, and N. Durlach, and also by A. F. Lagon of the General Radio Company. The initial stimulus for these experiments came from Dr. E. T. Neilsen, and the first observations were made with his collaboration at the Vero Beach Laboratory, Florida State Board of Health. Mosquito eggs were supplied for subsequent experiments by Dr. Paul A. Wolk of the U. S. Public Health Service. In many experiments we were materially assisted by A. Boass, C. Gifford, and A. D. Grinnell. Our photographic recordings of bats and insects have depended to a large extent on stroboscopic lights developed by H. E. Edgerton, Massachusetts Institute of Technology.

REFERENCES

GALTSOFF, P. S., F. E. LUTZ, P. S. WELCH, and J. G. NEEDHAM (Eds.), 1959 *Culture methods for invertebrate animals.* New York: Dover Publications.

GOULD, E., 1955 The feeding efficiency of insectivorous bats. *J. Mammal.*, **36**, 399–407.

GOULD, E., 1959 Further studies on the feeding efficiency of bats. *J. Mammal.*, **40**, 149–150.

GRIFFIN, D. R., 1953 Bat sounds under natural conditions with evidence for the echolocation of insect prey. *J. exp. Zool.*, **123**, 435–466.

GRIFFIN, D. R., 1958 *Listening in the dark.* New Haven, Conn.: Yale University Press.

GRIFFIN, D. R., and A. D. GRINNELL, 1958 Ability of bats to discriminate echoes from louder noise. *Science*, **128**, 145–147.

GRINNELL, A. D., and D. R. GRIFFIN, 1958 The sensitivity of echolocation in bats. *Biol. Bull.*, **114**, 10–22.

GRINNELL, A. D., and D. R. GRIFFIN, 1959 The neurophysiology of audition in bats. *Anat. Rec.*, **134**, 574.

KOLB, A., 1958 Über die Nahrungsaufnahme einheimischer Fledermäuse vom Boden. *Verh. Deutsch. Zool. Gesellsch.* in Frankfurt a. M. 1958, pp. 162–168.

KUHL, W., G. R. SCHODDER, and F. K. SCHRODER, 1954 Condenser transmitters and microphones with solid dielectric for airborne ultrasonics. *Acustica*, **4**, 519–532.

MOEHRES, F. P., 1950 Aus dem Leben unserer Fledermäuse. *Kosmos*, **46** (7), 291–295.

STEVENS, S. S. (Ed.), 1951 *Handbook of experimental psychology.* New York: Wiley.

TRAGER, W., 1953 Chapter 14 in *Insect physiology* (K. D. Roeder, Ed.). New York: Wiley.

WILLIAMS, C. M., and R. GALAMBOS, 1950 Oscillographic and stroboscopic analysis of the flight sounds of *Drosophila. Biol. Bull.*, **99**, 300–307.

KENNETH D. ROEDER
and ASHER E. TREAT

38   The Detection and Evasion of Bats by Moths*

The evolution of a species occurs in relation to changes in the environment, including the evolutionary development of other species. Thus, when a predator develops a system for the capture of a certain prey, it should not be surprising that the prey, in turn, evolves mechanisms for the detection and evasion of the predator. In the previous reading, we observed that bats were capable of capturing insects by means of echolocation. The following reading presents one species' evolutionary "answer" to the bat. For more information on the neurophysiology of insect behavior, see Roeder, K. D., *Nerve Cells and Insect Behavior*. Cambridge, Mass.: Harvard University Press, 1963.

This article was reprinted from the *American Scientist,* 1961, **49,** 135–148, with the permission of the authors and the publisher. Four figures have been omitted.

A central objective of a large segment of biological and psychological research is to provide a physiological basis for behavior. The first step toward this objective is analytic, and consists of determining the structure and function of neural components after they have been isolated from their connections with the rest of the nervous system. There has been much progress in this direction, and it is now possible to describe in terms of input and output performance the operation of many isolated sense cells, neurons, and muscle fibers, even though the principles of their internal operation are mostly not understood.

The next step, the synthetic process of assembling this information on isolated neural components and relating it to the behavior of the intact animal, is hampered by two kinds of difficulty. The first appears to be methodological, but is somewhat hard to define. When one regards the ever-growing literature on the unit performance of sense cells, nerve cells, and muscle fibers, it is to experience that sense of dismay first

* Much of the experimental work reported in this paper was made possible by Grant E-947 from the U. S. Public Health Service.

encountered at a tender age when the springs, gears, and screws of one's first watch were strewn upon the table. The modus operandi of analysis or taking apart seems to come naturally, and the problems encountered are essentially technical in nature. Synthesis or the derivation of a system from its components seems to lack the a priori logic of analysis.

The second general difficulty is technical, and stems from the fact that even the simplest behavior of the higher animals and man is accompanied by the simultaneous activity of millions of sense cells, nerve cells, muscle fibers, and glands. Even if it were possible to register the traffic of nervous and chemical information generated and received by each and all of these neural elements during the behavior, it is doubtful whether the record would provide a meaningful description of the action.

Even though these problems cannot be solved directly at the present time, they become less formidable if the behavior selected for study is simple and stereotyped, and only a small number of nerve cells are concerned in its execution. These conditions are partly fulfilled by the sensory mechanisms whereby certain nocturnal moths detect the approach of insectivorous bats.

Echolocation and Countermeasure

Bats detect obstacles in complete darkness by emitting a sequence of high-pitched cries or chirps and locating the source of the echoes. As Griffin (1958) and others have shown, this form of sonar is unbelievably precise. By means of it, insectivorous bats locate and track flying moths, mosquitoes, and small flies (Griffin et al., 1960). North American bats, such as *Myotis lucifugus* and *Eptesicus fuscus,* emit chirps about 10 times a second when they are cruising in the open. Each chirp lasts from 10 to 15 milliseconds (msec.) with an initial frequency of 80 kilocycles (kc.) dropping about one octave in pitch toward its end. . . .

The frequencies in these chirps are ultrasonic, that is, inaudible to human ears, which cannot detect tones much above 15 to 18 kc. The higher frequencies used by bats make possible more discrete echoes from smaller objects. The chirps can be rendered audible by detecting them with a special microphone and rectifying the ultrasonic component. They then can be heard through headphones as a series of clicks. These clicks fuse into what Griffin has called a "buzz" when the bat is chasing an insect or avoiding an obstacle.

Several families of moths (in particular the owlet moths or Noctuidae) have evolved countermeasures enabling them to detect the chirps of bats. A pair of ultrasonic ears is found near the "waist" of the moth between thorax and abdomen. . . . An extremely thin eardrum or tympanic membrane is directed obliquely backward and outward into the recess (dark area) found at this point. . . . Internal to the eardrum is an air-filled cavity that is spanned by a thin strand of tissue running from the center of the eardrum to a skeletal support. . . . This tissue contains the sound-detecting apparatus,

consisting of two acoustic sense cells (A cells). A single nerve fiber arises from each A cell and passes close to the skeletal support, where the pair is joined by a third nerve fiber arising from a large cell (B cell) in the membranes covering the support. The three fibers continue their course to the central nervous system of the moth as the tympanic nerve.

The traffic of nerve impulses passing over the three fibers from A cells and B cell to the nervous system of the moth can be followed if a fine metal electrode is placed under the tympanic nerve. Another electrode is placed in inactive tissue nearby. As each impulse passes the site of the active electrode it can be detected as a small action potential lasting about 1 msec. Since the tympanic nerve contains only three nerve fibers, it is not difficult to distinguish and to read out the respective reports to the nervous system from the pair of A cells and the B cell. A similar experiment in a mammal is practically meaningless since the auditory nerve contains about 50,000 nerve fibers.

This method of detection shows that the A cells transmit organized patterns of impulses over their fibers only when the ear is exposed to sound (Roeder and Treat, 1957). The B cell transmits a regular and continuous succession of impulses that can usually be distinguished from the A impulses by their greater height. The B impulses are completely unaffected by acoustic stimulation, and change in frequency only when the skeletal framework and membranes lining the ear are subjected to steady mechanical distortion (Treat and Roeder, 1959). The B cell behaves in a manner similar to receptors found in other parts of the body that convey information about mechanical stress on joints, muscles, and skeleton. The role of such a receptor in the ear of a moth is unknown.

In the absence of sound, the A cells discharge irregularly spaced and relatively infrequent impulses. . . . A continuous pure tone of low intensity elicits a more regular succession of more frequent impulses in one of the A fibers. . . . The other fiber is not yet affected. Any slight increase in the intensity of the tone causes a corresponding increase in the impulse frequency of the active fiber. When the intensity of the tone is increased to about tenfold that producing a detectable response in the more sensitive A fiber, the second A fiber begins to respond in like manner. Its action potentials are superimposed on those of the first . . . by the method of recording, but actually reach the central nervous system over their own pathway. This experiment reveals two of the ways in which the moth ear codes sound intensity. It is like an instrument having a graded fine adjustment

(the intensity-frequency relation) and a coarse adjustment of two steps (the pair of A cells). Other ways of coding intensity will appear later.

The moth ear responds in this manner to tones from 3 kc. to well over 100 kc., but there is no evidence that it is capable of discriminating between tones of different frequency. It is most sensitive near the middle of its range, that is, to frequencies such as those contained in bat chirps.

In Plate 2, Figure 2 [omitted, ed.], it will be noticed that, in each of the recordings, the intervals between the successive impulses increase as the pure tone stimulus continues. In terms of the nerve code out-

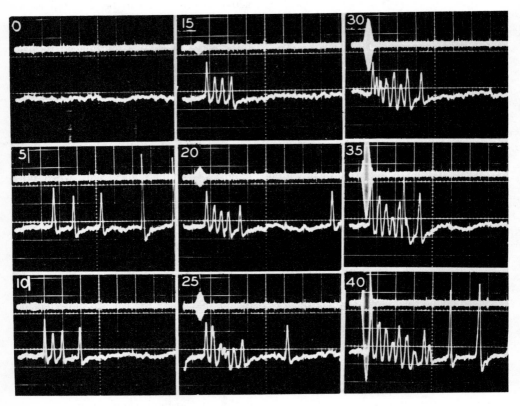

FIG. 1. Tympanic nerve responses (lower traces) of *Noctua* (= *Amathes*) *c-nigrum* to a 70 kc. sound pulse recorded simultaneously by a Granith microphone (upper traces). The numbers indicate the intensity of the sound pulse in decibels above a reference level (0). The threshold of the sensitive A cell lies between 0 and 5 db. The large spikes appearing in some of the records are from the B cell. The less sensitive A cell responds in the 25 db recording. Vertical lines, 4 msec. apart.

lined above, the A cells report that the sound is declining in intensity with time, although in fact it was kept constant. This adaptation to a constant stimulus occurs in most receptors registering changes in the outside world. In terms of our own experience, the impact of our surroundings would be shocking and unbearable if it were not distorted in this manner by sense organs. The brilliance of a lighted room entered after dark would continue to be blinding and the noise of a jet engine would remain unbearable. However, the A cells of the moth's ear adapt very rapidly to a continuous tone, and their full effectiveness as pulse detectors is revealed only when they are exposed to short tone pulses similar to bat chirps.

In the experiment illustrated in Figure 1, a tone pulse of 3 msec. duration was generated at regular intervals. It is similar to a bat chirp except for its regularity and the absence of frequency modulation. A microphone (upper trace) and moth ear (lower trace) were placed within range, and the intensity of the stimulus pulse was adjusted so that it just produced a detectable response in the most sensitive A fiber (0 db). The intensity was then increased by 5 decibel† (db) steps as each recording was made. It will be seen that the microphone begins to detect the sound pulse when it is about 10 db above the threshold of the most sensitive A cell in the moth's ear. As before, the increase in frequency of A impulses is evident if the 5 and 10 db records are compared, and a response of the less sensitive A cell appears first in the 25 db record where the extra peaks of its action potentials overlap those of the more sensitive A unit. In addition to these two ways of coding intensity, two more can now be recognized. If the interval between detection of the sound by the microphone and by the moth ear is compared at dif-

† The decibel (db) notation expresses relative sound pressures. An intensity of 20 db is tenfold that of the reference level (0 db), a 40-db sound is a hundredfold the reference level.

ferent sound intensities, it will be noticed that the tympanic nerve response occurs earlier and earlier on the horizontal time axis. In other words, the latency of the response decreases with increasing loudness. Also, the sense cells are seen to discharge impulses for some time after the sound has ceased, and this after-discharge becomes longer with increasing sound intensity.

The Detection of Bats

These experiments with artificial sounds suggest how the moth ear might be expected to respond to a bat cry. A few laboratory observations were made with captured bats. In one of these experiments, in collaboration with Dr. Fred Webster, the cries of a flying bat were picked up simultaneously by a moth ear and a microphone, and recorded on high-speed magnetic tape. . . . Interesting though they were, these experiments served mainly to show that the full potentialities of the moth ear as a bat detector could not be realized within the confines of a laboratory, and efforts were made to transport the necessary equipment to a spot where bats were flying and feeding under natural conditions.

Finally, about 300 pounds of equipment was uprooted from the laboratory and reassembled at dusk of a July evening on a quiet hillside in the Berkshires of western Massachusetts. Moths attracted to a light provided experimental material. The insect subject was pinned on cork so that one of its ears had an unrestricted sound field, and with the help of a microscope its tympanic nerve was exposed and placed on electrodes. After amplification, the action potentials were displayed on an oscilloscope. They were made audible as a series of clicks by means of headphones connected to the amplifier and were stored on magnetic tape for later study.

It was dark before all was ready, but bats immediately revealed their presence to the moth ear by short trains of nerve impulses that recurred about 10 times a second (Figure 2, A). The approach of a

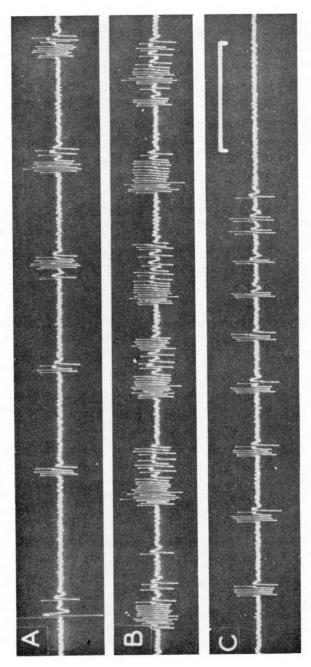

FIG. 2. Tympanic responses of *Noctua* (= *Amathes*) *c-nigrum* to the cries of bats flying in the field. (A) The approach of a cruising bat emitting pulses at about 10 per second. (B) Tympanic response to the original cry and its echo made by a bat cruising nearby. (C) A "buzz." Time line, 100 msec. (From Roeder and Treat, 1961.)

cruising bat from maximum range was coded as a progressive increase in the number and frequency of impulses in each train, first from one and then from both A fibers. It was not long before we learned to read something of the movements of the bats from these neural signals. Long trains, sometimes with two frequency peaks, suggested the chirps of nearby bats that echoed from the wall of a neighboring house (Figure 2, B). An increase in the repetition rate of the trains coupled with a decrease in the number of impulses in each train signified a "buzz" as the bat attacked some flying insect in the darkness (Figure 2, C).

All this was inaudible and invisible to our unaided senses. With a powerful floodlight near the nerve preparation we were able to see bats flying within a radius of 20 feet, and some attacks on flying insects could then be both seen and also "heard" through the "buzz" as coded by the moth's tympanic nerve. However, most of the sounds detected by the moth ear were made by bats maneuvering well out of range of the light. A rough measure of the sensitivity of the moth ear to bat chirps was obtained at dusk on another occasion when the bats could still be seen. The A cells first detected an approaching bat flying at an altitude of more than 20 feet and at a horizontal distance of over 100 feet from the moth—a performance that betters that of the most sensitive microphones.

Direction

Since differences in sound intensity are coded by the tympanic nerve in at least four different ways, the horizontal bearing of a bat might be derived from a comparison of the nerve responses to the same chirp in the right and left ears. A difference in right and left responses might be expected only if each ear had directional properties, that is, a lower threshold to sounds coming from a particular direction relative to the moth's axis.

Directional sensitivity was measured in an open area where echoes were minimal.

A source of clicks of constant intensity was placed on radii to the moth at 45° intervals. The source was moved in and out on each radius until a standard tympanic nerve response was obtained, and the distance from the moth noted. Horizontal distances along eight radii were combined to make a polar plot of sensitivity (Roeder and Treat, 1961). The plot showed that, although there was little difference in sensitivity fore and aft, a click on the side nearest the ear at about 90° relative to the moth's longitudinal axis was audible at about twice the distance of a similarly placed click on the far side.

This led to further field experiments in the presence of flying bats. The tympanic nerve responses from both ears of a moth were recorded simultaneously on separate tracks of a stereophonic magnetic tape. The tape was subsequently replayed into a two-channel oscilloscope and the traces photographed (Figure 3). In the upper record (A) the increase in number of impulses in each succeeding train suggests the approach of a bat. When the signals from right and left ears are compared, it is evident that the greatest difference exists when the signal is faintest, the first response of the series occurring in one ear only. When both ears respond, the differential nature of the binaural response can be seen first as a difference in the number of spikes generated in right and left ears, second in the differential spike frequency, and third in the latency of the response, which is greater on that side generating fewer spikes. It is also evident that, as the sound intensity increases (presumably due to the approach of the bat), the differential becomes less until the responses of right and left ears become almost identical. In another experiment, it was found that the tympanic nerve response saturates, i.e., becomes maximal, when the sound intensity is about 40 db (hundredfold) above threshold. From this it can be concluded that the moth's nervous system receives information that would enable it to determine whether a distant bat was to the right or left, but if the bat was at close quarters

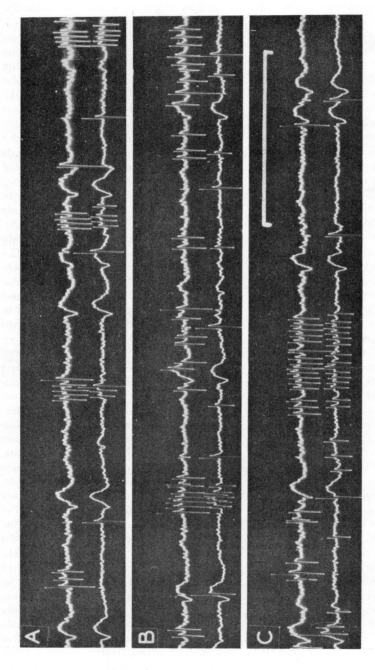

FIG. 3. Binaural tympanic responses of *Feltia* sp. to the cries of red bats flying in the field. The electrocardiogram of the moth also appears on both channels as slow waves. B impulses (large spikes) appear regularly in the records from both tympanic nerves. (A) An approaching bat. Differential response is marked at first (response latency, number of spikes) but has practically disappeared in the final train. (B) A "buzz" registered mainly by one ear. (C) A "buzz" registered by both ears. Time line, 100 msec.

this information would not be available. In Figure 3C, the "buzz" was picked up by one ear only, presumably because during this part of its performance the chirps of a bat are much less intense.

It is tempting to estimate just how close the bat must be before the moth fails to get information on its location. If it is assumed that a bat is first detected at 100 feet and approaches on a straight path at right angles to the moth's course while making chirps of constant loudness, the differential tympanic nerve response would diminish throughout the approach and disappear completely when the bat was 15 to 20 feet away. However, we have not yet determined how much of the information that we are able to read out of its auditory mechanism is actually utilized by the moth in its normal behavior.

The Evasive Behavior of Moths

Although the evasive behavior of moths in the presence of bats must have been witnessed hundreds of times, it is hard to find an adequate account of the maneuvers of either party. The contest normally takes place in darkness, and, even when it is illuminated by a floodlight, the action is too fast and complex to be appreciated by the eye. The flight path of the bat and its ability to intercept and capture its prey have been studied by Griffin (1958) and his students. More recently, Webster (in press) has shown by means of high-speed sound motion pictures that bats become adept at using echoes to plot an interception course with an object moving in a simple ballistic trajectory. Many people have noted the seemingly erratic dives and turns made by moths when bats are near, and similar behavior has been described when moths are exposed to artificial sources of ultrasound (Schaller and Timm, 1950; Treat, 1955).

In an effort to learn more about the behavior of moths under field conditions their flight was tracked photographically as they reacted to a series of ultrasonic pulses

simulating bat cries. The sounds were generated by the equipment used in the experiment shown in Figure 1. The pulses were similar in form to those shown, although longer in duration (6 msec.). Each pulse ranged from 50 to 70 kc. with a rise and fall time of about 1 msec. Pulse sequences up to 50 per second could be released on closure of a switch. The sounds were emitted by a plane-surfaced condenser loudspeaker mounted so as to project a fairly directional beam over an open area of lawn and shrubs illuminated by a 250-watt floodlight.

The observer sat behind the sound generator and floodlight, holding in one hand the cable release of a 35 mm. camera set on "bulb," and in the other the switch controlling the onset of the sound-pulse sequence. Many moths and other insects flew out of the darkness into this floodlight arena. A number were attracted directly to the light and were disregarded. Many others moved across the arena at various angles but without marked deviation toward the light. When one of these appeared to be in line with the loudspeaker the camera shutter was opened and the sound pulses turned on.

Two of the tracks registered by the camera as the illuminated moths moved against the night sky are shown in Figure 4. Many insects, including some moths, showed no change in flight pattern when they encountered the sound. In others, the changes in flight path were dramatic in their abruptness and bewildering in their variety. The simplest, and also one of the commonest reactions was a sharp power dive into the grass (Figure 4, left). Sometimes the dive was not completed and the insect flew off at high speed close to the ground. Almost as frequently the dive was prefaced or combined with a series of tight turns, climbs, and loops (Figure 4, right).

It is not known whether these maneuvers are selected in some random manner from the repertoire of individual moths, or whether they are characteristics of different species. However, Webster (in press)

FIG. 4. Flight tracks registered by various moths just before, and immediately following, exposure to a series of simulated bat cries. The dotted appearance of the tracks is due to the individual wingbeats of the moth. The beginning of each track appears in each photograph, and the moth finally flies out of the field.

has shown that bats soon learn to plot an interception course with food propelled through the air in a simple ballistic trajectory. The random behavior elicited by simulated bat cries in the natural moth population seems to be a natural answer to this predictive ability in bats, while the sharpness of the turns must certainly tax the maneuverability of the heavier predator.

The reacting moths shown in Figure 4 were mostly within 25 feet of the camera and sound source, and were exposed to an unknown but probably high sound intensity. Under these circumstances, the evasive behavior appeared to be completely unorientated relative to the sound source, as might be predicted from the binaural tympanic nerve recordings. In some instances, moths flying at a greater distance or only on the edge of the sound beam appeared to turn away from the area and fly off at high speed. This must be checked in future experiments.

The Survival Value of Evasion

In spite of the evidence that the moth ear is an excellent bat detector, and that acoustic stimulation releases erratic flight patterns, one may well ask whether this behavior really protects moths from attack by bats.

This question has been answered (Roeder and Treat, 1960) by observing with a floodlight 402 field encounters between moths and feeding bats. In each encounter we recorded the presence or absence of evasive maneuvers by the moth, and the outcome, that is, whether it was captured by the bat or managed to escape. From the pooled data we determined the ratio of the percentage of nonreactors surviving attack to the ratio of reactors surviving attack. Thus computed, the selective advantage of evasive action was 40 percent, meaning that for every 100 reacting moths that survived, there were only 60 surviving nonreactors.

This figure is very high when compared with similar estimates of survival value for other biological characteristics. It seems more than adequate to account for the evolution of the moth's ear through natural selection even if the detection of bats turns out to be its only function.

Conclusion

As with most investigations, this work raises more questions than it has answered. The role of the B cell remains completely obscure. There is no evidence to connect it with the auditory function even though it is located in the ear, and its regular impulse discharge is a characteristic feature of the tympanic nerve activity of many species of moth (Treat and Roeder, 1959. See also Figure 3). The manner in which the A cells transduce sound waves recurring 100,000 times a second into the much slower succession of nerve impulses remains a mystery, and the synaptic mechanisms whereby information from the A fibers is translated into action by the nervous system of the moth, await investigation.

During the field experiments it was noticed that many other natural sounds initiated impulses in the A fibers. These included the rustling of leaves, the chirp of tree and field crickets, and, in one instance, ultrasonic components in the wingbeat sounds made by another moth. Occasionally, the A fibers discharged regularly as if detecting a rhythmic sound, though none was audible to the observers and its source (if any) remains a mystery. There is no evidence that these identified and unidentified sounds are important in the life of a moth, yet it must be said that a moth can detect them, and a careful study of moth behavior in their presence would be of value.

Several families of moths lack ears and show no response to ultrasonic stimuli. Some of these, such as the sphinx or hawk moths and the larger saturniid moths, are probably too much of a mouthful for the average bat, and might find no survival advantage in a warning device. Others are of the same size and general habits as the noctuids and might be expected to suffer attacks by bats. Included in this group are some common pests such as the tent caterpillar. It will be interesting to learn whether these forms owe their success in survival to some structural or behavioral countermeasure that compensates for the lack of a tympanic organ.

In spite of these unanswered questions, we believe that some progress has been made in putting together the sensory information received by an animal, and relating this to what the animal does. That this has been possible in moths is only because of the small number of channels through which acoustic information reaches the nervous system in these insects. Further examples of this favorable situation have been described in other insects, and still others are waiting to be explored.

REFERENCES

GRIFFIN, DONALD R., 1958 *Listening in the dark*. Yale University Press, New Haven.

GRIFFIN, D. R., F. A. WEBSTER, and C. R. MICHAEL, 1960 The echolocation of flying insects by bats. *Animal Behaviour*, vol. 8, pp. 141–154.

ROEDER, K. D., 1959 A physiological approach to the relation between prey and predator. In: *Studies in Invertebrate Morphology*, Smithsonian Misc. Coll., vol. 137, pp. 287–306.

ROEDER, K. D., and A. E. TREAT, 1957 Ultrasonic reception by the tympanic organ of noctuid moths. *Journ. Exp. Zool.*, vol. 134, pp. 127–158.

ROEDER, K. D., and A. E. TREAT, 1961 The detection of bat cries by moths. In: *Sensory Communication*, ed. by W. Rosenblith. M. I. T. Technology Press, Cambridge, Mass.

ROEDER, K. D., and A. E. TREAT, 1960 The acoustic detection of bats by moths. Proc. XI Internat. Entomol. Congr.

SCHALLER, F., and C. TIMM, 1950 Das Hörvermögen der Nachtschmetterlinge. *Zeitschr. Vergl. Physiol.*, vol. 32, pp. 468–481.

TREAT, A. E., 1955 The response to sound of certain Lepidoptera. *Ann. Entomol. Soc. America*, vol. 48, pp. 272–284.

TREAT, A. E., and K. D. ROEDER, 1959 A nervous element of unknown function in the tympanic organs of moths. *Journ. Insect Physiol.*, vol. 3, pp. 262–270.

section
six

LEARNING AND
MOTIVATION
Now that we have studied the genetics, physiology, and development of animal behavior (with an excursion into sensory processes, communication, and orientation), we turn to the psychologist's favorite topics: learning and motivation. It will be obvious to the student that many of the preceding readings have been concerned with these topics. It should be equally obvious, at this point, that learning and motivation ultimately depend on physiological processes and the genetic constitution of the individual. Therefore, although the subject matter appears in this section as a separate category, we are still dealing with the same basic problem—the determination of behavior.

An accepted generalization is that the learning ability of animals increases as we move up the phylogenetic scale. Yet psychologists have had great difficulty in devising tests that would categorize the learning ability of animals in other than a very crude fashion. The first two readings in this section illustrate attempts to solve this problem.

Readings 41, 42, and 43 concern learning in mollusks, planarians, and amphibia, respectively. Reading 44 considers the interference with learned responses by "unlearned" responses. In readings 45 and 46 some unusual reinforcers for learning are examined. The section ends with a critique of energy models of motivation, and a plea for the study of a greater number of animal species.

Suggestions for Further Reading:

BIRNEY, R. C., and R. C. TEEVAN, eds., *Reinforcement*. Princeton, N. J.: Van Nostrand, 1961.
HILGARD, E. R., and D. MARQUIS, *Conditioning and Learning* (2d ed.) Gregory Kimble, ed. New York: Appleton-Century-Crofts, 1960.
Physiological Mechanisms in Animal Behaviour. Cambridge University Press, 1950, Part IV.

429

J. M. WARREN

39   Oddity Learning Set in a Cat*

> This reading and the following one are concerned with comparisons of learn-
> ing ability in different species. In reading 39, Warren reports an experiment on
> the ability of cats to solve the oddity problem; reading 40 concerns the ability
> of horses and raccoons to repeatedly reverse a learned response. Both problems
> meet with only limited success in providing criteria for distinguishing animal
> species in terms of learning ability.
>
> This reading is reprinted from the *Journal of Comparative and Physiological
> Psychology*, 1960, **53**, 433–434, with the permission of the author and the
> American Psychological Association.

Boyd and Warren (1957) found that cats
learned the oddity problem slowly and
did not generalize the oddity principle
when tested with stimuli which differed
markedly from those used in original training. The purpose of the present experiment
was to determine whether previous training
on three-choice discrimination and reversal
problems would facilitate acquisition and
generalization of the oddity principle by
cats.

Method

SUBJECTS

The five cats studied were approximately nine months old at the beginning
of the experiment. They had previously
served in investigations of transfer and retention in discrimination learning (Bramel
& Warren, in press; Warren & Kimball,
1959).

APPARATUS

The Wisconsin General Test Apparatus
has been described in detail by Harlow

* This research was supported by Grant
M-1364 from the National Institute of Mental
Health, United States Public Health Service.
The author is indebted to G. G. Ball for assist-
ance in collecting the data.

(1949). The stimuli were 51 double pairs
of wooden objects varying in multiple visual dimensions, and were presented on a
white test tray containing three food wells,
spaced 6 in. apart.

PROCEDURE

The Ss were tested on 48 trials per day
throughout the experiment unless the criterion of 20 correct responses in a block of
24 noncorrection trials was met in fewer
trials. The correct stimulus appeared in the
right, left, and center positions in a balanced irregular sequence in all stages of
the experiment.

*Three-choice discrimination and rever-
sal problems.* In these problems, one (A)
stimulus was presented with two identical
(B) stimuli on every trial, the A stimulus
being odd and correct until the cat attained
the criterion. Then the B stimulus became
odd and correct in the presence of two
identical A objects. A series of 20 such discrimination and subsequent reversal problems preceded oddity training.

Oddity training. In the true oddity
problem, the designation of the A and B
stimuli as odd and correct varies from trial
to trial in irregular sequence. The Ss were
trained on one problem under these conditions until they attained the criterion or
failed to do so in 40 days (1920 trials).

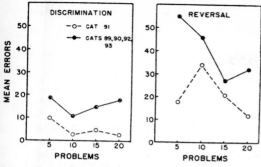

FIG. 1. Interproblem learning of three-choice discrimination and reversal problems.

After solution of the original oddity problem, 30 additional problems involving new and distinctively different sets of stimulus objects were presented and training continued to criterion on each.

Results

THREE-CHOICE DISCRIMINATION
AND REVERSAL

The results are presented in Figure 1, which shows mean total errors, including those made in the criterional series, as a function of successive blocks of 5 problems. Four cats made no appreciable gains in discrimination learning; their performance improved over the first 15 reversals, but deteriorated on the last problem block. Cat 91 was the only one which showed a marked reduction in errors on the discrimination problems, and it made fewer errors than the other cats throughout the reversal series.

ODDITY

Cats 89, 90, 92, and 93 were tested for 40 days without approaching the criterion. They averaged 61% and 51% errors on Days 1 to 5 and Days 36 to 40, respectively; "learning" consisted of the formation of strong stimulus preferences.

The fifth S, 91, reached criterion on the first genuine oddity problem in 336 trials and made a total of 147 errors. Its performance on the series of generalization

problems is shown in Figure 2, a plot of total errors against successive blocks of 5 problems; errors on the original problem are indicated on the ordinate to facilitate comparison. This figure indicates that Cat 91 showed a marked reduction in errors over the first 10 generalization problems and learned the last 20 test problems very quickly. Mean total errors on Problems 11 to 30 was 4.5, which means that the criterion was attained in the minimum number of trials on almost all problems in this set.

Discussion

The results obtained from Cat 91 demonstrate that, under favorable conditions, a cat can solve an oddity problem quite quickly and can generalize the principle very effectively. Differences in procedure preclude detailed interspecies comparisons, but this cat's terminal level of performance may be reasonably characterized as falling within the range of individual differences among rhesus monkeys (Meyer & Harlow, 1949), and as exceeding the attainments of other infraprimate animals tested on oddity (Pastore, 1954; Wodinsky & Bitterman, 1953).

The four cats which failed to solve the oddity problem differed markedly from

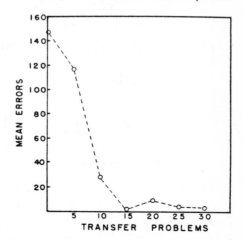

FIG. 2. Oddity learning-set curve for Cat 91.

91 in performance on the three-choice discrimination and reversal problems. Unlike the successful cat, the failures made more errors on both discrimination and reversal with three stimuli than they had made on comparable tasks with two objects as naive animals (Warren & Kimball, 1959). The fact that the only cat to master oddity was also superior in discrimination learning suggests a relationship between the processes involved in discrimination and multiple-sign learning in cats, such as that which has been shown in monkeys (Moon & Harlow, 1955).

Summary

Five young cats were trained on 20 three-choice discrimination and reversal problems before being trained on an oddity problem. Only the S which was most successful on the discrimination and reversal series solved the oddity problem. It formed a learning set for efficient solution of oddity problems over a series of 30 transfer problems. Its final performance approximated that of rhesus monkeys and exceeded that of any infraprimate species on which data have been reported.

REFERENCES

BOYD, B. O., and J. M. WARREN Solution of oddity problems by cats. *J. comp. physiol. Psychol.*, 1957, **50**, 258–260.

BRAMEL, D., and J. M. WARREN Retention of discrimination habits by cats. *J. genet. Psychol.*, in press.

HARLOW, H. F. The formation of learning sets. *Psychol. Rev.*, 1949, **56**, 51–65.

MEYER, D. R., and H. F. HARLOW The development of transfer of response to patterning by monkeys. *J. comp. physiol. Psychol.*, 1949, **42**, 454–462.

MOON, L. E., and H. F. HARLOW Analysis of oddity learning by monkeys. *J. comp. physiol. Psychol.*, 1955, **48**, 188–194.

PASTORE, N. Discrimination learning in the canary. *J. comp. physiol. Psychol.*, 1954, **47**, 389–390.

WARREN, J. M., and H. KIMBALL Transfer relations in discrimination learning by cats. *J. comp. physiol. Psychol.*, 1959, **52**, 336–338.

WODINSKY, J., and M. E. BITTERMAN The solution of oddity-problems by the rat. *Amer. J. Psychol.*, 1953, **66**, 137–140.

J. M. WARREN and HELEN B. WARREN

40   Reversal Learning by Horse and Raccoon*†

See introduction to reading 39.

Reprinted from *The Journal of Genetic Psychology*, 1962, **100**, 215–220, by permission of the authors and The Journal Press.

A. The Problem

When rats (Dufort, Guttman and Kimble, 1954) and cats (Cronholm, Warren and Hara, 1960) are tested on serial reversals of the same discrimination habit, they show a progressive reduction in the

* This research was supported by Research Grants NSF-G3278 from the National Science Foundation, and M-1364 from the National Institute of Mental Health, U. S. Public Health Service.

† The authors are grateful for Kim Firestone's assistance in testing the horses.

number of errors per reversal. The purpose of the present experiment was to investigate the performance of two less frequently studied species, raccoon and horse, on similar series of discrimination reversals.

B. Method

1. SUBJECTS

The single raccoon studied, aged one year at the time of testing, had been hand fed during infancy and was quite tame and well adapted to the laboratory. He had previously served in an experiment on *umweg* learning in a closed field maze (Warren and Warren, 1959). During this experiment he had continuous access to water and dry dog food in his living cage and received pork kidney, a highly preferred food, as a reward for correct responses during the test sessions.

Two horses were not laboratory subjects; to emphasize this fact we refer to them by their names, Pancho and Rag Mop. They lived in and were tested at a riding stable, and throughout the experiment were ridden during the morning by students. The horses were tested in the early afternoon, approximately seven hours after their morning feeding.

2. APPARATUS

The raccoon was tested in the Wisconsin General Test Apparatus (Harlow, 1949). A black object was always presented on the right, and a white object on the left, on a grey tray containing two food wells 12 inches apart, so that both brightness and positional cues were constant and relevant.

The horses, tested in a large paddock, were released at the entrance gate and required to choose between two boxes, 40 feet from the entrance and 20 feet from one another. The box on the right was black and the one on the left white, so that brightness and spatial cues were combined

in the same fashion for the horses as for the raccoon. It was impossible for humans, and presumably horses, to tell which of the boxes, 30 inches deep, contained hay until approached within one or two feet.

3. PROCEDURE

On the first training trial neither stimulus was rewarded. S was required on subsequent trials to choose the initially nonpreferred stimulus and training was continued until the criterion of 11 correct out of 12 responses, with the last eight all correct, was attained. Upon completion of the preliminary discrimination, S was required to select the previously incorrect stimulus. Thereafter, the two stimuli became alternately correct and incorrect as the criterion was satisfied. The animals were trained to criterion on one problem per day with minimal intervals between trials. The raccoon completed 20 reversals; circumstances beyond our control prevented training the individual horses on more than six and nine reversals. The noncorrection method was used throughout.

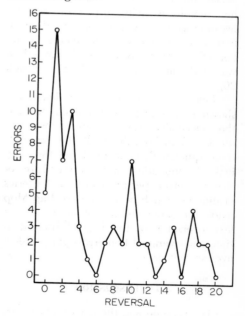

FIG. 1. Reversal learning by a raccoon.

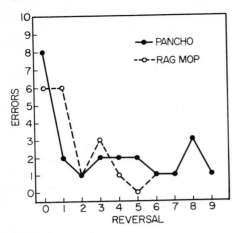

FIG. 2. Reversal learning by two horses.

C. Results

The results for the raccoon are presented in Figure 1, which shows that this S made a striking improvement in performance over the series of reversal tasks. This animal never on subsequent reversals made as many errors as on the first reversal. Indeed, on only four occasions did he commit as many errors on reversal learning as in solving the original discrimination (Reversal 0). The average number of errors on Reversals 1 through 4 was 8.75, and on Reversals 17 through 20, 2.25.

Learning curves for the two horses are shown in Figure 2. Both animals learned the successive reversal problems very quickly; Pancho solved all the reversals more quickly than he mastered the original discrimination, and averaged fewer than two errors per reversal over the series of nine on which he was tested. Rag Mop made the same number of errors on the first reversal as on the original discrimination, and averaged two errors per problem over six reversals.

D. Discussion

The raccoon and the horses all showed a rapid reduction in the number of errors

made in learning successive reversals of a positional discrimination. Qualitatively similar results have been obtained in comparable experiments with cats (Cronholm, Warren and Hara, 1960), human imbeciles (House and Zeaman, 1959) and rats (Dufort, Guttman and Kimble, 1954). Within this series of mammals, proficiency in inter-reversal learning is not related to capacity for solving more complex problems. Rats and imbeciles approach the limit of one error per reversal most rapidly, cats and raccoons most slowly. Yet imbeciles (House and Zeaman, 1958) do not form learning sets for non-spatial visual discriminations, and rats (Koronakos and Arnold, 1957) form such sets far less efficiently than either cats (Warren and Baron, 1956) or raccoons (Shell and Riopelle, 1957).

The serial reversal task, however, does clearly differentiate between higher vertebrates, and fish and invertebrates. Chickens (Warren, Brookshire, Ball and Reynolds, 1960), in addition to the mammals just listed, show a marked reduction in errors on consecutive habit reversals. The results obtained from several species of fish (Adkins and Fields, 1957; Bitterman, Wodinsky and Candland, 1958; Warren, 1960), crabs (Datta, Milstein and Bitterman, 1960) and sowbugs (Thompson, 1957) have been consistently negative. In fact, in some studies a progressive *deterioration* in performance has been observed (e.g., Adkins and Fields).

The findings just discussed clearly support the supposition that major stages in the evolution of the nervous system are correlated with the emergence of new capacities for solving complex problems, rather than with increases in the rate of simple learning.

E. Summary

A raccoon and two horses were tested on serial reversals of a positional discrimination. A rapid decline in the number of errors made on consecutive reversals was observed in all three animals. Improvement in the rate of interreversal learning on simple discriminations does not correlate with taxonomic status or ability to solve more complex problems within the series of mammals studied. However, all mammals tested on this task "learn to learn," but fish and invertebrates do not.

REFERENCES

1. ADKINS, R. J., and P. E. FIELDS: Conditioning young steelhead trout to colored lights. *U. Wash. Sch. Fish. Tech. Rep.*, 1957, No. 33.
2. BITTERMAN, M. E., J. WODINSKY, and D. K. CANDLAND: Some comparative psychology. *Amer. J. Psychol.*, 1958, **71**, 94–110.
3. CRONHOLM, J. N., J. M. WARREN, and K. HARA: Distribution of training and reversal learning by cats. *J. Genet. Psychol.*, 1960, **96**, 105–113.
4. DATTA, L., S. MILSTEIN, and M. E. BITTERMAN: Habit-reversal in the crab. *J. Comp. Physiol. Psychol.*, 1960, **53**, 275–278.
5. DUFORT, R. H., N. GUTTMAN, and G. A. KIMBLE: One-trial discrimination reversal in the white rat. *J. Comp. Physiol. Psychol.*, 1954, **47**, 248–249.
6. HARLOW, H. F.: The formation of learning sets. *Psychol. Rev.*, 1949, **56**, 51–65.
7. HOUSE, B. J., and D. ZEAMAN: Reward and non-reward in the discrimination learning of imbeciles. *J. Comp. Physiol. Psychol.*, 1958, **51**, 614–618.
8. HOUSE, B. J., and D. ZEAMAN: Position discrimination and reversals in low-grade retardates. *J. Comp. Physiol. Psychol.*, 1959, **52**, 564–565.
9. KORONAKOS, C., and W. J. ARNOLD: The formation of learning sets in rats. *J. Comp. Physiol. Psychol.*, 1957, **50**, 11–14.
10. SHELL, W. F., and A. J. RIOPELLE: Multiple discrimination learning in raccoons. *J. Comp. Physiol. Psychol.*, 1957, **50**, 585–587.
11. THOMPSON, R.: Successive reversals of a position habit in an invertebrate. *Science*, 1957, **126**, 163–164.
12. WARREN, J. M.: Reversal learning by paradise fish (*Macropodus opercularis*). *J. Comp. Physiol. Psychol.*, 1960, **53**, 376–378.
13. WARREN, J. M., and A. BARON: The formation of learning sets by cats. *J. Comp. Physiol. Psychol.*, 1956, **49**, 227–231.
14. WARREN, J. M., and H. B. WARREN: Interspecies differences in learning by carnivores? *Percep. & Motor Skills*, 1959, **9**, 346.
15. WARREN, J. M., K. H. BROOKSHIRE, G. G. BALL, and D. V. REYNOLDS: Reversal learning by white leghorn chicks. *J. Comp. Physiol. Psychol.*, 1960, **53**, 371–375.

P. B. D E W S

41 Some Observations on an Operant in the Octopus

Reading 31 surveyed the sensory and motor capacities of *Octopus*. In the following reading, three octopuses were presented with an operant conditioning problem; *i.e.*, they had to learn to perform a certain act in order to secure a reinforcement. Two of the three subjects successfully solved the problem.

The section on "Procedure" reports that the "responses were shaped." "Shaping" a response consists of reinforcing successive approximations of the desired response until, finally, the appropriate response is performed.

The abbreviation *crf* stands for continuous reinforcement; it means that each successful response is reinforced.

Reprinted from the *Journal of the Experimental Analysis of Behavior,* 1959,
2, 57–63, by permission of the author and the Society for the Experimental
Analysis of Behavior. Three tables have been omitted.

Operant behavior has been successfully demonstrated in all species of mammals and birds for which a serious attempt has been made. Comparatively little attention has been paid to invertebrate species. This paper reports preliminary exploration of the behavior of the octopus (*O. vulgaris.* Lamark) to see whether components of its behavior could be found which fulfill the definitive requirements necessary to identify them as operants. The octopus has the advantage over most invertebrate species in that it has well-developed motor behavior of a nature which makes the selection of an arbitrary, objectively recorded response quite easy. In addition, Young and Boycott (1955) describe behavior in the octopus which is almost certainly operant in nature, i.e., not elicited, but maintained by its consequences. One reason for interest in this problem is that the octopus belongs to a phylum (Molusca) which has evolved independently of the pathway which leads to the vertebrates since Cambrian times (some 500 million years ago). If the phenomena of operant behavior are to be found in the octopus as well as in the vertebrate species studied, then these phenomena probably are of very general biological significance.

Three octopuses have been studied. All three were trained to pull a lever which led to the delivery of food. In two, reasonably consistent lever-pulling behavior was maintained until extinction; only partial success was obtained with the third octopus.

Method

Subjects were three octopuses (*O. vulgaris*), each weighing 500 grams, designated for identification purposes Albert, Bertram, and Charles. Each lived in its own tank of circulating sea water from which it was never removed during the experiments. The tanks of Albert and Charles were 4 feet 6 inches long by 2 feet 6 inches wide, and contained a depth of about 2 feet 6 inches of sea water. The tank of Bertram was 6 feet long and 2 feet 3 inches wide, and contained a depth of 2 feet 6 inches of sea water. At one end of each tank at the bottom were two or three bricks, which the octopus arranged to make a house. The undisturbed octopus spent almost all its time sitting in its house, "looking" out with one eye.

The lever was ¼-inch brass rod which entered the water vertically and reached to within about 3 inches of the bottom. It was pivoted at a board which was rested across the top of the tank during an experiment. The pivot permitted the lever to be moved in only a single plane; but movement in either direction in that plane activated a light precision switch.* Operation of the switch led to illumination of a lamp which in definitive experiments was arranged to shine vertically into the water from above at the end of the tank opposite to that of the "house" of the octopus (the "far" end of the tank). The lever was arranged about the middle of the tank, somewhat nearer the far end. Only one lever and light assembly was used, the whole being moved from tank to tank for experiments on the various octopuses.

The response was movement of the lever so that the lamp lighted. Reinforcement was delivery of a small piece of fish about one-tenth of a filleted 3-inch sardine. The fish was on a nylon line with a small glass sinker.

Procedure

The animals were deprived of food a day, and then responses were shaped as follows:

1) Taking the fish from the line when presented close by, moving up and down, in the beam of the light.

* "Acro" switch.

2) Swimming to the far end of the tank and taking the fish when presented in the beam of the light.

3) Approach to the lever.

4) Finally operation of the lever.

A similar shaping procedure was followed for all three octopuses. The following representative account gives in detail the sequence used with Bertram; the sequences used in the other two animals did not differ in any important particulars.

Day 1 No food. Previous to this the octopus had been fed with "several" small crabs per day.

Day 2 Took pieces of fish from line when presented 10-20 centimeters away in light beam.

Day 3 Octopus took total of nine pieces of fish over 5-hour period, starting each time from "house." First piece was presented 20 centimeters away, but remaining eight presented about middle of tank (i.e., about 80 centimeters away).

Initially, animal took fish only when it had been presented about 15 minutes, but last three were taken in 2-5 minutes.

Day 4 Eight pieces of fish taken over 6 hours. First three taken from positions intermediate between middle and far end of tank, remaining five from far end. Animal started from house each time. Last four were taken within 1 minute of presentation.

Day 5 Took five pieces of fish, each with 1 minute of presentation, from far end of tank on each of four occasions through day (total, 20 pieces of fish).

Day 6 Took 10 pieces of fish in single session; required to return to house between presentations.

Day 7 Lever introduced. Octopus ignored lever except to avoid touching it when swimming by.

Day 8 Like Day 7.

Day 9 Small piece of rubber tubing put around lower end of lever, to provide what was hoped would be more attractive surface for octopus tentacles.

Also attached to lower end of lever, by short piece of thread, was a small maltese cross. The stream of water responsible for circulation and aeration of water in the tank was directed towards the lever, causing the cross to dance and twirl. These additions to the lever were adequate to cause the octopus to approach the lever, whereupon a piece of fish was presented. After a few such approaches, it was possible to require that the lever be encircled by two or more tentacles before the fish was presented. On two occasions, obtained fish while still having tentacle around lever; pulled lever at this time and was promptly given second piece of fish. Encircled lever with tentacles (and was given fish) 22 times during period of 1 hour; on three of these occasions, actually operated the lever.

Day 10 et sec. Required to operate lever before fish was presented. When the lever was operated and the light came on, the light was then kept on by manual switch and the fish introduced at far end of tank. When the octopus came over and took the fish, the light was kept on a few more seconds. When the fish line was released—free of fish—by octopus, a stop watch was started and the time to the next lever operation noted. This cycle was continued until the animal had had 20 pieces of fish, or until more than 10 minutes elapsed between release of line and operation of lever. The octopus was given the opportunity of obtaining these 20 pieces of fish (two filleted sardines total) at each of two sessions, one in the morning and the other some 3-4 hours later in the afternoon. This was the only food obtainable by the octopus during the experiments.

Results

All three octopuses obtained 40 reinforcements on several consecutive days without the latency between release of the fish line and operation of the lever exceeding 10 minutes on any occasion.

An attempt was made to reinforce lever-pulling by Albert intermittently on a small fixed-ratio schedule — two, then three . . . . The first 10 reinforcements on this day were given on the *crf* procedure above described. The next 10 were given at every other lever-pull; each time the lever was operated the lamp lighted in the usual way and was kept lit until the octopus released the lever and moved to the far end of the tank. At this time, either the light was extinguished and timing to the next lever-pull started (following odd-numbered responses), or food was presented in the usual way. The animal completed 20 more lever-pulls under this procedure without any latency rising to 10 minutes. In the afternoon session, after reinforcement of the initial response, the ratio was raised to 3:1. Under this procedure, the animal obtained five more reinforcements (i.e., 15 lever-pulls), but the latencies progressively rose and, after the 16th response, reached 10 minutes, the arbitrary cut-off point. On Day 6, only a few responses (4) were not reinforced, and 19 reinforcements were obtained before a latency of 10 minutes occurred. *Crf* was reintroduced, and over the next 6 days . . . the animal made 260 consecutive responses each within 10 minutes of release of the fish line. On the 13th day, extinction was instituted; the lamp lit on a response and remained on until the octopus came to the far end of the tank; but it was then turned off without presentation of fish. In the a.m. session of Day 13, 20 responses were made without occurrence of a latency of more than 10 minutes; but in the afternoon session, only 13 were made before a 10-minute pause. On the 14th day, 15 and 9 responses were made before a 10-minute pause in the morning or afternoon sessions, respectively. Since this animal had made 260 consecutive responses without a latency exceeding 10 minutes when on *crf*, the repeated occur-

rences of these long latencies when reinforcement of the response was discontinued are evidences of operant extinction.

On Days 14 through 17, Bertram made 120 consecutive responses; the mean latency fell to less than 30 seconds on Days 16 and 17 . . . . Reinforcement was then discontinued; 79 responses were made on Days 17 (p.m.), 18, and 19, until a latency of 10 minutes occurred. On Day 20, no response occurred in 20 minutes, again giving clear evidence of operant extinction. There was some "spontaneous recovery" on Day 21, but a performance of 20 consecutive responses without more than a 10-minute latency was not achieved.

Charles was more capricious and effective, and sustained control was not achieved. The best series was achieved on Days 9 and 10, when 80 consecutive responses were made without a latency in excess of 10 minutes. The behavior of this animal, however, differed from that of the other two in a number of interesting respects.

1) Whereas Albert and Bertram gently operated the lever while free-floating, Charles anchored several tentacles on the side of the tank and others around the lever and applied great force. The lever was bent a number of times, and on the 11th day was broken, leading to a premature termination of the experiment.

2) The light, suspended a little above the level of the water, was not the subject of much "attention" by Albert or Bertram; but Charles repeatedly encircled the lamp with tentacles and applied considerable force, tending to carry the light into the tank. This behavior is obviously incompatible with lever-pulling behavior.

3) Charles had a high tendency to direct jets of water out of the tank; specifically, they were in the direction of the experimenter. The animal spent much time with eyes above the surface of the water, directing a jet of water at any individual who approached the tank. This behavior interfered materially with the smooth conduct of the experiments, and is, again,

clearly incompatible with lever-pulling.

The activities described in 2 and 3 above became progressively more predominant as the experiments proceeded; and on Days 20 and 21 they had become so predominant as to lead to cessation of lever-pulling behavior before 20 reinforcements had been obtained. The variables responsible for the maintenance and strengthening of the lamp-pulling and squirting behavior in this animal were not apparent.

Discussion

The behavior of lever-pulling in these experiments showed the following characteristics of an operant:

1) It was found possible to differentiate the response by deliberate shaping.

2) The occurrence of the response was maintained by its consequences (the presentation of fish).

3) The tendency of the response to occur fell when it was no longer reinforced.

The attempt to establish the response as a free operant, permitting continuous observation of its frequency of occurrence, was not successful. At least two factors contributed to this failure:

1) Once an octopus has taken firm grip of an object, it has a high tendency to retain a firm grip. In its natural environment, the train of events following seizure of an object has probably usually only one of two conclusions: either the eating of the object, or its release to pursue another object. In these experiments, once an octopus had operated the lever, it tended to maintain the lever in the operated state, and could only be dislodged by the provision of an alternative object (light beam and dangling fish). It was further necessary to make sure these objects were presented too far from the lever for the octopus to be able to reach them while still retaining possession of the lever. These measures were effective in obtaining a discontinuous response, but only at the expense of severely reducing the possibility (and significance) of obtaining a "rate-of-occurrence" measure of the operant.

2) Only relatively short sequences of crf were presented before the attempt was made to introduce a fixed-ratio schedule of reinforcement.

Conclusion

The "law of effect" appears to operate in the octopus as in vertebrates. In view of the wide phylogenetic separation of these types of animals, these findings add to the evidence of the very general biological applicability of this law.

Acknowledgment

This work was carried out at the Stazione Zoologica, Naples, Italy. I wish to thank the director, Dr. P. Dohrn, and his staff for their hospitality and help, and in particular, Mr. M. J. Wells for lessons on the handling of octopuses. The cost of the apparatus used in this work was defrayed by a Grant from the National Institutes of Health (M-2094).

REFERENCE

BOYCOTT, B. B., and J. Z. YOUNG A memory system in *Octopus vulgaris* Lamark. *Proc. Roy. Soc. Lond. B.* 143: 449, 1955.

JAMES V. McCONNELL

42 Memory Transfer through Cannibalism in Planarians*

At what point in the evolutionary development of animals does learning first appear? Because there is no universally agreed upon definition of learning, a definitive answer cannot be given. However, James V. McConnell and his colleagues have demonstrated that planarians, at least, are capable of associating a given response with a given stimulus. In this reading, McConnell reviews his experimental program and summarizes some fascinating experiments on the effects of regeneration and cannibalism on retention of a learned response in planarians.

McConnell is the editor of the delightful *Worm Runners' Digest,* an Informal Journal of Comparative Psychology published by the Planaria Research Group of the University of Michigan in Ann Arbor.

The following article is reprinted from the *Journal of Neuropsychiatry,* 1962, 3, 542–548, with the permission of the author and the publisher.

Suggestion for further reading: Jacobson, A. L., "Learning in Flatworms and Annelids," *Psychological Bulletin,* 1963, **60,** 74–94.

The research that I am going to outline today had its start several years ago, and I trust you will allow me to give you a few of the pertinent background details, if only to convince you that our work is more serious than it sometimes sounds, and of sufficient scope at least to approach respectability.† It was in 1953, when I was a graduate student at the University of Texas, that a fellow student, Robert Thompson, suggested to me that we attempt to condition a planarian, or common flatworm. Having avoided the rigors of introductory Zoology up to that point, my only prior experience with worms had been at the business end of a fishing pole. I soon dis-

* *Acknowledgments:* Much of the research reported in this paper was supported by grants from the National Institute of Mental Health and from the Atomic Energy Commission.

† For an excellent survey of the history of worm running, see the paper by Allan L. Jacobson (15).

covered, however, that fishing worms are round, while planarians are flat. Planarians are also usually less than an inch in length, and rather interesting in their own right.

Flatworms occupy a unique niche on the phylogenetic scale, being the lowest organisms to possess bilateral symmetry, a rude form of encephalization, and a human, synaptic-type nervous system. According to some psychological theories—the ones that postulate that learning is a matter of reshuffling connections among neurons—the planarian should be the lowest organism to be able to demonstrate "true" learning. As far as we knew in 1953, no one had ever demonstrated unequivocally that these organisms could indeed be trained. Since then, of course, we have discovered the usual obscure reference that antedates our work by 30 years—it appears in Dutch and was published in a little-read European journal(1)—but I am not at all sure that even this knowledge would have

TABLE 42-2

Mean turns, contractions, and combined
responses on the first 15 and last
15 test trials for group SC
(shock control)

RESPONSE	FIRST 15 TEST TRIALS	LAST 15 TEST TRIALS	DIFF.[a]
Turns	5.4	4.2	−1.2
Contractions	0.2	0.4	0.2
Combined	5.6	4.6	−1.0

a None of the differences is significant at the
.05 level of confidence.

deterred us. At any rate, Thompson and I
set out in 1953 to attempt classical conditioning in planarians.

Imagine a trough gouged out of plastic,
12 inches in length, semi-circular in cross-
section, and filled with pond water. At
either end are brass electrodes attached to
a power source. Above the trough are two
electric light bulbs. Back and forth in the
trough crawls a single flatworm, and in
front of the apparatus sits the experimenter, his eye on the worm, his hands on
two switches. When the worm is gliding
smoothly in a straight line on the bottom
of the trough, the experimenter turns on
the lights for 3 seconds. After the light has
been on for two of the three seconds, the

experimenter adds one second of electric
shock, which passes through the water and
causes the worm to contract. The experimenter records the behavior of the worm
during the two-second period after the light
has come on but before the shock has
started. If the animal gives a noticeable
turning movement or a contraction prior
to the onset of the shock, this is scored as
a "correct" or "conditioned" response.(2)

From this brief description of the experimental paradigm, many of you will
recognize that Thompson and I were attempting to establish a form of Pavlovian
conditioning in our experimental animals
(Group E), and according to our data, we
were successful. Planarians occasionally
give a mild and presumably innate response
to the onset of the light even when it has
not been previously paired with shock, so
we ran a control group that received just
trials of photic (light) stimulation (Group
LC); we also ran a control group that
received just shock, occasionally interspers-
ing a test trial of light alone (Group SC).
All animals were given 150 trials. Over
that period of time, as Tables 42–1 and
42–2 show, the experimental animals,
which received light paired with shock,
showed a significant increase in respon-
sivity, while the control groups showed
either no change at all or a significant
decline.

Hence Thompson and I concluded that
we had accomplished what we set out to

TABLE 42-1

Mean turns, contractions, and combined
responses on the first 50 and last 50
trials for groups E (experimental)
and LC (light control)

GROUP	RESPONSE	FIRST 50 TRIALS	LAST 50 TRIALS	DIFF.	p
E	Turns	12.6	16.6	4.0	.01
	Contractions	1.2	5.0	3.8	.01
	Combined	13.8	21.6	7.8	.01
LC	Turns	11.7	7.6	−4.1	.01
	Contractions	0.6	2.1	1.5	
	Combined	12.3	9.7	−2.6	

accomplish—namely, we had proven that worms could be conditioned (3).

Those of you who have ever chopped up a planarian in a Zoology course will know that these animals have enormous powers of regeneration. A large specimen may be cut into perhaps 50 pieces, each of which will eventually regenerate into a complete organism. It was while we were running that first experiment that Thompson and I wondered aloud, feeling rather foolish as we did so, what would happen if we conditioned a flatworm, then cut it in two and let both halves regenerate. Which half would retain the memory? As it happened, we never got around to performing that experiment at Texas, for Thompson received his doctorate soon after we finished our first study and went on to Louisiana State University and bigger and better things—namely, rats. When I went to the University of Michigan in 1956, however, I was faced with the difficult problem that in the academic world, one must publish or perish. The only thing I knew much about was flatworms, so I talked two bright young students, Allan Jacobson and Daniel Kimble, into performing the obvious experiment on learning and regeneration.

Kimble, Jacobson and I did the following. We took our experimental animals and trained them to a criterion of 23 responses out of any block of 25 trials. When they had reached this criterion, we assumed that

they were properly conditioned and immediately cut them in half across the middle. Head and tail sections were then put in individual bowls and allowed about 4 weeks to regenerate. At the end of this period, these experimental animals (Group E) were re-trained to the same criterion and savings scores calculated. We also ran a group of worms which were cut, allowed to regenerate, and then were conditioned for the first time—this to tell us if cutting and subsequent regeneration in any way sensitized the animals to conditioning (Group RC). Another control group was conditioned, then allowed to rest uncut for a month before being retested (Group TC)—this to tell us how much forgetting we could expect in our experimental animals had we not cut them in half.

In all honesty I must admit that we did not obtain the results we had expected. We

TABLE 42-4

Number of trials to criterion for group RC (regeneration control)

S	HEAD	TAIL
RC1	134	150
RC2	188	179
RC3	276	85
RC4	395	300
RC5	250	325
M	248.6	207.8

TABLE 42-3

Number of trials to criterion for group E (experimental)

S	ORIGINAL TRAINING	RETEST HEAD	RETEST TAIL
E1	99	50	51
E2	191	37	24
E3	97	48	72
E4	83	35	44
E5	200	30	25
M	134	40	43.2

TABLE 42-5

Number of trials for group TC (time control)

S	ORIGINAL TRAINING	RETEST
TC1	123	24
TC2	153	25
TC3	195	62
TC4	131	43
TC5	325	45
M	185.4	39.8

had assumed that the regenerated heads would show fairly complete retention of the response for, after all, the head section retained the primitive brain and "everybody knows" that the brain is where memories are located. And, as Tables 42–3, 42–4, and 42–5 indicate, the heads did show just as much retention as did the uncut control animals. We had also hoped, in our heart of hearts, that perhaps the tails would show a slight but perhaps significant retention of some kind, merely because we thought this would be an interesting finding. We were astounded, then, to discover that the tails not only showed as much retention as did the heads, but in many cases did much better than the heads and showed absolutely no forgetting whatsoever. Obviously memory, in the flatworm, was being stored throughout the animal's body, and as additional proof of this we found that if we cut the worm into three or even more pieces, each section typically showed clear-cut retention of the conditioned response (4).

It was at this time that we first postulated our theory that conditioning caused some chemical change throughout the worm's body, and it was also about then that Reeva Jacobson came along to help us test what seemed at the time to be rather an odd hypothesis. She took planarians, cut off their tails, and conditioned the heads

TABLE 42-6

Number of trials to criterion for totally regenerated animals

S	ORIGINAL TRAINING	RETEST AFTER TOTAL REGENERATION
1	200	166
2	325	143
3	300	220
4	327	51
5	75	62
6	381	94
mean	268	122.7
SD	102	60

before any regeneration could take place. Then she let her animals grow new tails. She next removed these new tails and let them grow new heads, ending up with apparently completely reformed organisms. These total regenerates, as we called them, were then tested for any "savings" of the original conditioning. By now we knew what to expect from planarians, and so we weren't too surprised when Reeva's regenerated flatworms showed a significant retention of what the original organism had learned. True, as Table 42–6 suggests, these total regenerates did not demonstrate the complete retention that our original animals had shown, but they did remember enough so that our hypothesis seemed vindicated (5).

By now, worms were in the *Zeitgeist*. Edward Ernhart, working with Carl Sherrick at Washington University, demonstrated not only that flatworms could learn a two-unit T-maze, but also that this maze habit was retained by their animals following cutting and regeneration. Again, the tails remembered at least as much as did the heads (6). Ernhart is perhaps most famous, however, for a more recent study of his. If one takes a flatworm and splits the head straight down the middle, time and time again, the two halves will not heal together but will each regenerate into a complete head. One ends up, then, with a two-headed worm. Ernhart compared the length of time it took two-headed animals to be conditioned with the length of time it took one-headed (or normal) animals to reach the same criterion and found that he had validated an old aphorism—two heads are indeed better than one (7).

Roy John and William Corning, working at the University of Rochester, became quite interested in the chemical theory of learning about this time, and undertook one of the most spectacular pieces of research yet to come from any worm laboratory. John reasoned that learning in flatworms had to be mediated, at least in part, by some molecular change within the organism's cells. Since Hydén had found changes in RNA in nerve cells as a result of experience (8), John believed that RNA might be implicated in learning and retention in planarians. So he and Corning conditioned a number of flatworms, cut them in half, and let them regenerate in a weak solution of ribonuclease, which breaks up RNA. When they compared their experimental animals with a number of controls, they found evidence that the experimental heads were relatively unaffected by the ribonuclease, while the tails showed complete forgetting. The tails could be retrained, but it took approximately as long the second time as it had the first (9).

Ralph Gerard, the noted neurophysiologist, interprets the data as follows: There are probably two distinct but related physiological mechanisms for learning in planarians. The first such mechanism is the familiar one of neural interconnections which are reshuffled in the brain due to the animal's experiences — the so-called circuit-diagram model, if I may be permitted the analogy. Structural changes in the neural pathways in the brain would presumably not be altered by ribonuclease, which accounts for the fact that the Rochester head-regenerates showed no real forgetting. The second type of memory mechanism, however, involves a change in the coding of the RNA molecules in the cells throughout the worm's body. Presumably whenever the animal learns, the RNA is altered appropriately so that when regeneration takes place, the altered RNA builds the memory into the regenerated animal right from the start. If the RNA were destroyed by the ribonuclease, it is likely that the DNA in the cells would replace the lost RNA, but this replacement RNA would not carry the changed code since the DNA was presumably unaffected by the learning (10).

If all of this sounds rather complex, you must forgive me. I am not at all sure that at this early date we have more than the vaguest notion just how learning could affect RNA nor how, much less why, this altered RNA might build the memory into

the regenerating tissue. The important thing to remember is that John's hunch that RNA might be involved in memory seems to have been substantiated.

Before further discussing RNA and memory, I should like to detail, briefly, some other research that Roy John and Bill Corning, at Rochester, and my own group of worm runners at the University of Michigan and at the Britannica Center in Palo Alto, have been pursuing jointly. In 1957, when we got our first results on retention of learning following regeneration, and came up with our chemical hypothesis, it seemed to us that we might be able to transfer a memory from a trained animal to an untrained animal if we could somehow get the right chemicals out of the first worm and into the second. We spent several years trying to test this admittedly wild notion without much success. First we tried grafting the head of a trained animal onto the tail of an untrained planarian, but this never worked very well. If one reads introductory zoology texts, one often gets the notion that this little operation is most easy to perform. Sadly enough, the best average on record is three successes out of 150 attempts(11) and we simply did not have 150 trained heads to waste. We tried grinding the trained worms up and injecting the pieces into untrained animals, but we never could master the injection techniques. It was only some time after we began this work that it occurred to us that we could let the animals do the transferring for us. For, under the proper conditions, one worm will eat another. And since planarians have but the most rudimentary of digestive tracts, there seemed an excellent chance that the tissue from the food worm would pass into the body of the cannibal relatively unchanged.

So, with Barbara Humphries as our chief experimenter, we conditioned a number of worms, chopped them into small pieces and hand-fed the pieces to untrained cannibals. We also took the precaution of feeding a number of untrained worms to untrained cannibals for a control or comparison group. Our first pilot study gave us such unbelievable results that we immediately instituted several changes in our procedure and repeated the study not once, but four times. And each time the results were quite significant—and still rather unbelievable. I should mention before going any further that the chief procedural change we made was the institution of a "blind" running technique which helped guard against experimenter bias. Under this blind procedure, the person actually training the worms never knows anything about the animals he runs—we follow an elaborate coding system in which each animal's code letter is changed daily. The experimenter then doesn't know which ani-

mal is in which group, nor even which animal is which from day to day. Thus, as far as we could tell, we could not have unconsciously tampered with the data.

The results of this work, as Table 42–7 shows, were somewhat startling. In all five studies, it was clear that the cannibals which had fed on trained worms gave approximately half again as many conditioned responses during the first days of training as did the cannibals which had fed on untrained worms. In our studies, the differences between the two groups tended to disappear after the first few days as the control animals approached criterion. The experimental animals were presumably so close to criterion right from the start that the slope of their learning curve was much less than that of the controls (12) (13).

I would also like to mention a couple of fortunate mistakes we made which do not prove anything but which are interesting evidence in their own right. One time our elaborate coding system broke down and a control animal was fed a piece of conditioned worm. For several days prior to this feeding, the control animal had been responding at an average of 2 or 3 times out of any 25 trials. Immediately following this inadvertent meal of conditioned tissue, the animal performed at criterion level, giving 23 responses out of the next 25 trials. Then there was one group of cannibals which we accidentally fed animals that had been given a number of conditioning trials, but which were not even close to criterion when we cut them up. The cannibals which ate these trained but not-yet-conditioned worms showed absolutely no transfer effect at all.

Now, if we had been the only ones to have obtained such results, our findings might be dismissed as the achievement of crackpots. Luckily for us, Corning, Karpick, and John instituted their own program of cannibalism shortly after we did and so far have run two large and very well controlled studies, both using the blind technique, and have obtained results which are essentially identical to ours (14).

TABLE 42–7

Number of responses in first 25 training trials for cannibals fed conditioned planarians (experimentals) and for cannibals fed unconditioned planarians (controls)

NUMBER OF RESPONSES IN FIRST 25 TRIALS	
EXPERIMENTALS	CONTROLS
4	1
6	1
7	3
8	4
8	4
8	4
9	5
10	5
10	5
10	6
11	6
12	6
13	6
14	7
14	7
15	10
15	10
15	11
15	11
17	16
18	22
19	
mean 11.73	7.14

And, as if this were not enough, our work has just been replicated by a high school student. Let me quote briefly from the Washington *Post* of 25 March, 1962. "A 17-year-old girl's rather startling answer to a rather startling question—'Is Knowledge Edible?'—brought her one of the two top prizes in a Northern Virginia Science Fair yesterday. Tentatively, Ruth Ann Ziegler's answer is 'yes.'

"What Miss Ziegler found was that a worm who eats an educated worm learns things twice as fast as his brother who eats an uneducated worm. Hence her title, 'Is Knowledge Edible?'

"By electrical shocks she taught flatworms to respond to light. An ordinary flatworm needs about 260 shocks before he responds without one. He is then 'conditioned.'

"Experiments taught Miss Ziegler that a worm fed the head of an unconditioned worm needs an average of 264 shocks. A worm fed an unconditioned tail needs 269.

"But a worm fed a conditioned tail takes only 168 shocks and a worm fed a conditioned head a mere 140 shocks.

"This experiment was part of Miss Ziegler's effort to see if conditioned learning is affected by chemicals and, if it is, if it can be passed on through regeneration and ingestion. It's apparently 'yes' all the way."

Frankly, we are not quite sure where all of this work leaves us—except that we are most definitely out on a limb of some kind. At the moment, a number of laboratories around the country are starting investigations into the biochemistry of learning, using planarians as their tools. Specifically, several of us are attempting to extract RNA, DNA and other biochemicals from conditioned worms to feed to untrained cannibals. If we can show, for example, that RNA and only RNA causes the memory transfer, we can surely hope to determine the subtle molecular differences between "trained" and "untrained" RNA. If this could be done, we would be one step closer to cracking the problem of the molecular properties of memory—perhaps a giant step closer at that, particularly if it turns out that teaching the animals different sorts of habits causes different sorts of changes in the RNA molecules. But perhaps that is too much to hope for at the present.

Now, in conclusion, let me attempt to tie all of this research together. We have shown that planarians are capable of learning, that this learning survives cutting and regeneration, that the memory storage mechanism has a biochemical component (probably RNA) which is widely distributed throughout the animal's body, and that learning seems to be transferrable from one animal to another via cannibalistic ingestion. If memory in higher organisms is also mediated via biochemical changes, and if these changes are specific to the habits learned, we might eventually discover a substance (probably RNA with a deliberately modified structure) which would facilitate learning if it were incorporated into animal or human bodies. If so, the research we have been doing with our lowly flatworms may have practical consequences we never dreamed of when we began our work some nine years ago.

REFERENCES

1. Van Oye, P.: *Natuurwetenschappelijk Tijdschrift*, **2**: 1–9, 1920.
2. McConnell, James V., P. R. Cornwell, and Margaret L. Clay: *Amer. J. Psychol.*, **73**: 618–622, 1960.
3. Thompson, Robert, and James V. McConnell: *J. Comp. Physiol. Psychol.*, **48**: 65–68, 1955.
4. McConnell, James V., A. L. Jacobson, and D. P. Kimble: *J. Comp. Physiol. Psychol.*, **52**: 1–5, 1959.
5. McConnell, James V., Reeva Jacobson, and D. M. Maynard: *Amer. Psychologist*, **14**: 410, 1959, (abstract).
6. Ernhart, E. N., and C. Sherrick, Jr.: "Retention of a maze habit following regeneration in planaria *(D. maculata),*" Paper read at Midwestern Psychological Association, St. Louis, May 1959.

7. ERNHART, E. N.: *Worm Runner's Digest*, 2: 92–94, 1960.
8. HYDEN, HOLGAR: In: Seymour M. Farber and Roger H. L. Wilson (eds.), *Control of the Mind*, McGraw-Hill, New York, 1961.
9. CORNING, W. C., and E. R. JOHN: *Science*, 134: 1363–1365, 1961.
10. GERARD, RALPH: Personal Communication, 1961.
11. KENK, ROMAN: *J. Exp. Zool.*, 87: 55–69, 1941.
12. HUMPHRIES, BARBARA M., and REEVA JACOBSON: *Worm Runner's Digest*, 3: 165–169, 1961.
13. MCCONNELL, JAMES V., REEVA JACOBSON, and BARBARA M. HUMPHRIES: *Worm Runner's Digest*, 3: 41–47, 1961.
14. CORNING, W. C., R. KARPICK, and E. R. JOHN: Personal communication from E. R. John, 1961.
15. JACOBSON, ALLAN L.: "Learning in Flatworms and Annelids," *Psychol. Bull.*, 1963, 60: 74–94.

L I N C O L N   P.   B R O W E R   and
J A N E   V A N   Z A N D T   B R O W E R

43   Investigations into Mimicry

The mechanisms by which one species avoids the predation of another species are of interest to many biologists (reading 38). Mimicry is one example of such an adaptive mechanism. In the following reading, Brower and Brower describe a form of mimicry that depends on the learning ability of the predator for its success. In this case, toads are the predators studied. Most psychologists would suspect that toads would prove to be very slow learners; yet Brower and Brower demonstrate that toads are capable of learning a visual discrimination in very few trials. The implication is clear: If we wish to establish a valid classification of the learning abilities of animals, we must present problems that have meaning in terms of the natural history of the species studied.

Reprinted from *Natural History*, 1962, **71**, 8–19, by permission of the authors and The American Museum of Natural History. Several photographs have been omitted.

Just one hundred years ago, the great English naturalist H. W. Bates published a classical paper interpreting some of the observations he had made on mimicry in tropical American butterflies, which was based on eleven years of research in the Amazon Valley He presented his report to the Linnaean Society of London, and within a short time, mimicry became a key support of the theory of evolution by natural selection, which Charles Darwin and Alfred Russel Wallace had outlined to the society three years earlier, in 1858.

Bates had returned to England from South America with vast collections consisting of individuals of nearly 15,000 species, no less than 8,000 of which were then new to science. Contemplating the facts he had gathered, Bates saw that his observations contained unique evidence in support of Darwin's and Wallace's new theory. His own hypothesis concerned mimetic analogies, which were, in the naturalist's own words, "resemblances in external appearance, shapes, and colours between members of widely distinct families. . . ."

His idea of mimicry was based particularly on the tropical butterflies of the family Heliconiidae. In South America he had noticed that among the myriad insects these common butterflies with brilliant coloration and slow, conspicuous flight were never eaten by the abundant birds and lizards of the jungle. Surprisingly, other butterflies of a second, quite unrelated family appeared superficially identical to the Heliconiids. To explain this curious relationship, Bates proposed that the common Heliconiids were distasteful to insect-eacting vertebrate predators. Upon trying one, Bates postulated, a bird would find it unpleasant and would reject it. The bird would then remember this bad experience, and when encountering the butterfly's bright color pattern again would refuse the insect on sight. Now, if a palatable species looked like a common, distasteful one, the predator would mistake the palatable butterfly for the unpalatable insect. Thus, a palatable butterfly could, by deception, escape being eaten. Such a deceptor is called the mimic, and the distasteful species it resembles is termed the model. Bates also discovered that the mimic is much rarer than the model. This is reasonable because, in learning what is good to eat, birds would most often attack the common model, and so learn quickly that its color pattern was associated with an unpleasant taste. Mimicry would thus be effective.

The question of whether or not vertebrate predators, and especially birds, really do eat butterflies became a subject of controversy among naturalists, because neither ornithologists nor entomologists had recorded many observations of birds attacking these insects in nature. Two camps developed. One stated flatly that birds never eat butterflies, that any similarities in appearance of unrelated butterfly species are due to chance, and that mimicry is a figment of man's imagination. The proponents of mimicry countered this argument by gathering extensive observations, particularly in the Tropics, where some kinds of birds feed heavily on butterflies during certain seasons of the year. These men also found that model butterflies they had

caught in their nets often bore V-shaped notches in their wings or V-shaped scars where the powdery scales normally covering the wings had been removed. It was soon discovered that birds sometimes chased and snapped at other individuals belonging to the model butterflies' species, but then let them go. And when these butterflies were caught, it became clear immediately that the torn or rubbed areas on the wings were caused by the birds' beaks. The beak marks, besides showing that birds do attack butterflies, also provided indirect evidence that the models were unpalatable: they were tried but then rejected. Moreover, recent experiments by H.B.D. Kettlewell, in England, have shown conclusively that birds prey heavily on species of moths that had rarely been seen to be eaten by birds. Similarly, in the past two years we have observed a flock of red-winged blackbirds, *Agelaius phoeniceus* (Linné), catching and devouring many large swallowtail butterflies in a swamp in south central Florida. These findings that birds do eat Lepidoptera in nature point to the danger of drawing false conclusions based on insufficient observations.

Shortly after the turn of the century, some observers attempted to perform experiments with caged predators, including birds, lizards, and monkeys, to which model butterflies were offered. Almost invariably, the brightly colored models proved to be unpalatable. Without doubt, the greatest co-ordinator of these observational studies of mimicry was Sir Edward Poulton, for many years Hope Professor at Oxford University in England. It was Poulton who, while lecturing in 1909 to the Entomological Society of America, drew attention to three relatively simple instances of mimicry among North American butterflies, one of which will be described below, and pointed out the opportunities for research they offered. For in spite of a vast literature about observational studies, actual experimental evidence for the existence of mimicry was strikingly inadequate, as

A. E. Emerson, the famous American ecologist, emphasized as recently as 1949.

As though the lack of conclusive experimental evidence for mimicry were not enough of a problem, the very origin of mimicry puzzled scientists at first. While Bates' hypothesis offered an explanation of the incredible resemblances between a number of insects, considerable time passed before the mechanisms of the early evolution of mimicry began to be understood. As mentioned previously, a mimic appears superficially to resemble its model, but in fact the two are not closely related. When a mimic butterfly is examined in detail, the careful observer can see that in characteristics such as the number and the arrangement of wing veins, the structure of the legs, or the sexual organs, it is like other members of its own family and not like the model butterfly at all. How, then, does it happen that in color pattern alone the mimic is altered so as to differ radically from its relatives and resemble the model? This can be explained by reference to a well-known example of mimicry in the North American butterflies. The familiar monarch and viceroy frequent summer gardens throughout the eastern United States, and related pairs of butterflies occur in Florida and in the Southwest. The monarch, *Danaus plexippus* (Linné), is the model, and it is known from experimental studies to be distasteful to some birds, such as the Florida scrub jay, *Aphelocoma coerulescens coerulescens* (Bosc). The viceroy, *Limenitis archippus archippus* (Cramer), is the palatable mimic. Both model and mimic are orange in ground color with black and white markings, and look remarkably alike. However, the viceroy's non-mimicking relatives are all basically blue-black in color. They include several species of *Limenitis* from the Northeast, the Rocky Mountain states, and the Far West. Because of the prevalence of blue-black coloration among the viceroy's relatives, it is considered the ancestral shade of the viceroy. The problem, then, is to account for a change in the viceroy

from its probable original dark color to its present orange, mimetic coloration, which resembles the monarch's.

The study of heredity has disclosed that spontaneous, heritable changes called mutations occur in the germ plasm of all living things. These mutations may result in visible differences in characteristics, such as the color pattern of a butterfly's wing. Knowing this, one can start with the presumably dark viceroys, and reconstruct the manner in which their orange coloration has theoretically evolved. Suppose among the dark ancestral viceroys a few slightly orange individuals arose through mutation. These, along with the commoner, blue-black ones, would both make up the viceroy population. Now, if an experienced predator that had learned to avoid orange-colored monarchs were to come upon these viceroys, it would be more likely to eat the blue-black form of the viceroy than it would the pale orange one, because even a hint of orange would remind the predator of the distasteful monarch. Thus, more of the new, orange variant viceroys would survive to produce offspring than would the blue-black form, even though the sum total of individuals of both forms would be the same in each new generation. If we extend this situation by imagining not just one mutation for pale orange, but rather a series of small color and pattern changes occurring at intervals during a very long period of time, it can be seen that through the agency of discriminating predators, the color variant of the viceroy most like the unpalatable model would tend always to prevail. In this way, apparently, the present, orange viceroy, so like the monarch, has gradually evolved.

Butterflies belonging to the insect order Lepidoptera were the subject of Bates' classical theory. There are numerous other instances of striking resemblances between different kinds of insects. For example, many bees (Hymenoptera), noxious because of their stings, are models for harmless flies (Diptera) that look, act, and even sound very much like bees.

While conducting our research program in south central Florida at the Archbold Biological Station, we became interested in two instances of mimicry involving bees and their fly mimics. The first concerns the bumblebee, *Bombus americanorum* (Fabricius), which is mimicked by a robberfly, *Mallophora bomboides* (Wiedemann). The two insects are seen together quite frequently in fields where blooming plants of the pea family are found. Like the bee, the robberfly has a black and light color pattern, a plump, fuzzy body, and hairy legs. On the third pair of legs it even has two patches of light hairs that simulate the pollen baskets of the bumblebee. The second model-mimic pair that we studied is the honeybee, *Apis mellifera* Linné, and the dronefly, *Eristalis vinetorum* (Fabricius). The dronefly has a narrow, black marking along the middle of its back that creates the impression of the honeybee's "wasp-waist." The dronefly also has beelike yellow and black rings girdling its abdomen. The buzzing of the dronefly, as well as its habit of feeding along with honeybees at certain composite flowers, make it a very convincing mimic of the honeybee to the human observer.

We wanted to know if this similarity is also confusing to insect-eating predators. Are the bee models really noxious? Is it the sting that makes them so? And what will happen when a predator that has encountered a bee is then given a harmless fly mimic? In order to test the effectiveness of mimicry of the bumblebee and of the honeybee, we carried out laboratory experiments in which caged toads, *Bufo terrestris* (Bonnaterre), were used as predators. Known as the southern toad, this animal was a particularly good subject because it is a common insect eater in the southeastern United States and is abundant in the vicinity of the Archbold Biological Station, where we caught them for our experiments. The toads were taken to the laboratory and were confined singly in cubic cages twelve inches on a side. The bottom and back of each cage was made of plywood, the two sides and front of gray plastic screening, and the top was a removable piece of glass that allowed access to the inside. Cardboard partitions separated the cages so that the toads could not see one another, thus precluding the possibility that the behavior of one might influence another visually. Each cage was equipped with a three-quarter-inch-deep water dish.

In preparation for each day's test, which was conducted in the evening when the toads were naturally active, bumblebees and robberflies or honeybees and droneflies were collected in fields near the Archbold Station. They were stored in a cold room until needed, and then were anesthetized lightly with carbon dioxide so they could be handled easily and prepared for presentation to the toads. In addition to the models and mimics, we also needed edible insects that we knew were acceptable to toads. By presenting these insects to the toads, we could make certain that the animals were hungry enough to eat palatable insect food, even if they should reject a model or mimic. For the bumblebee-robberfly experiments we used large dragonflies, *Pachydiplax longipennis* (Burmeister), as edible insects, and for the honeybee-dronefly tests we gave the toads beetle larvae, called mealworms, *Tenebrio molitor* Linné, which have approximately the same bulk as the models and mimics.

After trying many different methods of presenting the insects to the toads, we finally settled upon a technique that proved very satisfactory. Toads will eat food only if it moves. To standardize the motion of the insects, each was strung with a fine needle and 50-gauge, gray cotton thread so that it could be suspended and moved in front of a toad, to be seized or rejected. The animal had thirty seconds to eat each food item lowered into its cage. If the food was not eaten, the thread was pulled up, withdrawing the insect. During an experiment, model, mimic, and edible insects were presented in such an order that the toad could not learn to anticipate what was coming next. A sample random sequence for two successive days in the bumblebee experiment was as follows: edible, model; mimic, edible/mimic, edible; model, edible.

The experiments on the bumblebee-robberfly complex were conducted with six toads. Of these, three were experimental animals and three were control animals. The experimental toads were given ten live bumblebees and ten dragonflies, singly, at the rate of four insects a day. At first, each readily seized a bumblebee, but in so doing was severely stung on the tongue and roof of the mouth. The toad reacted by making violent movements with its tongue, by blinking, by listing toward the side of the injury, by puffing up the body, and by ducking the head, which produced a generally flattened appearance. After one or two such experiences, the three experimental toads learned that bumblebees were noxious and they would not strike at the others that were offered. They consistently ate the dragonflies, however, showing that they could distinguish between noxious and edible insects. The crucial part of the experiment was the substitution of robberfly mimics for bumblebees. Would the toads eat the flies, or would they confuse them with the bumblebees and reject them? Of the thirty robberflies that were presented to the three experimental toads, only one robberfly (3 per cent) was eaten.

Meanwhile, the three control toads were playing a key role in the experiments. They were used to determine the actual edibility of the robberfly mimic. These toads were never exposed to the sting of a bumblebee. They were offered only robberflies and dragonflies. What were their reactions to the mimic? Two of the three ate the robberfly readily every time it was presented. The third toad was bumped in the face by the first robberfly it was given. This experience seemingly affected the toad, since it subsequently rejected all mimics, although, like the other two controls, it ate all the dragonflies. To summarize, then, of the fifty-one robberflies presented to the control toads, thirty-four (67 per cent) were eaten.

One further aspect of mimicry remained to be tested. Was the sting really the source of the bumblebee's noxiousness? It is quite easy—with the aid of a dissecting microscope and fine watchmaker's forceps—to remove a bee's stinging mechanism. First the bee is anesthetized with carbon dioxide. Then it is placed on its back on the stage of the microscope. The abdomen is pressed carefully with the forefinger, which causes the sharp point of the stinger to protrude. This is grasped with the forceps, and the whole stinging apparatus and the sac containing the liquid poison is pulled out. Thirty-six bumblebees were prepared in this way and were then presented to the three control toads. Twenty-four of the harmless bumblebees were eaten by the two toads that had eaten robberflies. The third toad, which had been bumped by the robberfly, rejected the twelve operated bumblebees presented to it. These results told us two things: first, that the sting was the source of noxiousness in bumblebees, and second, that a toad that refused robberflies would also reject bumblebees. This indicated that toads fail to distinguish between bumblebee models and robberfly mimics.

If we now look at the results of this experiment as a whole, we can reach several conclusions that answer the initial questions we set out to test. The experimental toads showed us that live bumblebees were highly noxious to them and that toads, after being stung, could learn to reject bumblebees on sight. When the robberfly mimic was offered instead of a bee, the toads also refused the mimic. However, two control toads that never experienced bumblebees ate robberflies readily. Therefore, we concluded that the rejection of the robberfly by the experimental toads could be attributed to mimicry. These toads apparently learned that the bumblebee's color pattern was associated with the noxious sting and confused the robberfly's coloration with that of the bumblebee. Mimicry was thus shown to be effective.

A second experiment was performed with honeybee models and their dronefly mimics. A large number of toads served as caged predators. We wanted to be able to compare the reactions of toads that ate mimics freely at the beginning of the experiment with the same toads' reactions to mimics after experiencing the model. In order to do this, it was necessary for each toad to pass a qualification test before being allowed to participate in the experiment; each had to begin by eating mimics as well as the edible mealworms. Of the sixty-seven toads that were brought in from the wild and tested, forty-four qualified. The other twenty-three did not, because they failed to eat mealworms or droneflies, or both. Fourteen of this group ate their mealworms but refused the first dronefly, and some also exhibited a reaction of rejection to the droneflies by ducking and puffing up. Without further experiments it is not possible to say conclusively why the toads rejected the initial mimics. However, their behavior suggested strongly that these animals were already agents in mimicry: that the toads had had experience with honeybees before being caught, and when they were confronted with mimics in the laboratory, they confused the two. This is possibly a valid conclusion, because all fourteen of the toads ate the mealworms, which shows that they were discriminating between the food items offered, and were not simply rejecting everything.

In addition to the qualification test to select only those toads that would initially eat the mimics, a second precaution was taken to insure that only visual mimicry was involved in the investigation. All the droneflies were killed by deep-freezing before they were presented to the toads. In this way, we eliminated the possibility that auditory mimicry, caused by the similarity of the buzz of the dronefly mimic and the honeybee model, might influence

TABLE 43–1

Two typical toads' reactions in honeybee-dronefly tests.

SUCCESSIVE INSECTS PRESENTED	EXPERIMENTAL TOAD (LIVE HONEYBEES WITH STINGING APPARATUS INTACT)	CONTROL TOAD (DEAD HONEYBEES WITH STINGING APPARATUS REMOVED)
First Day		
Mealworm	Eaten	Eaten
Dronefly	Eaten	Eaten
Dronefly	Eaten	Eaten
Mealworm	Eaten	Eaten
Honeybee	Eaten (Stung)	Eaten
Mealworm	Eaten	Eaten
Mealworm	Eaten	Eaten
Honeybee	Rejected	Eaten
Second Day		
Honeybee	Eaten (Stung)	Eaten
Mealworm	Eaten	Eaten
Mealworm	Eaten	Eaten
Honeybee	Rejected	Eaten
Honeybee	Rejected	Eaten
Mealworm	Eaten	Eaten
Dronefly	(Rejected)	(Eaten)
Mealworm	Eaten	Eaten

the toads' reactions. To begin the experiment, the forty-four qualified toads were divided into two groups: half were designated as experimental subjects, and the others as controls. The experimental animals were given a series of five live honeybees and five mealworms. The control toads were given five dead honeybees from which the stinging apparatus had been removed, and five mealworms. These bees had also been killed by deep-freezing to eliminate their buzzing, which in itself might have caused the controls to reject them. The order in which the insects were presented to all the toads in both groups and the reactions of a typical control toad and a typical experimental toad are shown in Table 43–1, upper left.

The experiments showed that the live

honeybees did indeed sting the experimental toads, although apparently not as severely as the larger bumblebees had stung the toads in the other tests. A few of the toads ate the live honeybees without evident discomfort, but most, after receiving two or three stings, rejected the honeybees on sight. The control toads, for the most part, readily ate their frozen bees from which the stinging mechanism had been removed. This shows that the sting of the honeybee, perhaps reinforced by its buzzing, accounts for its rejection as food by the experimental toads. Both groups of toads continued to eat mealworms throughout the experiment. This indicates that the experimental toads that rejected the bees actually had learned to tell the difference between the two. In the final test, both the controls and the experimentals were given a last dronefly mimic, followed by a final mealworm. All forty-four toads ate the mealworm, which indicates that they accepted insect food readily to the end of the experiment. The vital question is: did more control toads than experimental toads eat the last dronefly mimic? The results are summarized in Table 43–2, which shows that there was a striking difference between the reactions of the two groups of toads. Nearly all (86 per cent) of the control toads ate the final dronefly, whereas less than half (41 per cent) of the experimental toads ate their last dronefly. We can conclude that the experience of the experimental toads with live honeybees greatly reduced the likelihood that they would eat the dronefly mimics. To a large degree the noxious model did protect the mimic from being eaten. The experiment, therefore, offered strong evidence in favor of Bates' theory. The final, essential support, so long overlooked by naturalists, depended again upon the control toads. By eating the droneflies at the beginning and end of the experiment, they proved that the dronefly was palatable, and was thus a true, visual, Batesian mimic.

It is interesting to compare the results

TABLE 43-2

Numbers of experimental toads (fed intact, live honeybees) and control toads (fed dead honeybees, with stinging apparatus removed) eating and rejecting a final dronefly mimic.

	EXPERIMENTAL TOADS	CONTROL TOADS	TOTAL
Ate Final Mimic	9 (41%)	19 (86%)	28
Rejected Final Mimic	13 (59%)	3 (14%)	16
Totals	22 (100%)	22 (100%)	44

of the honeybee-dronefly experiments with those of the bumblebee-robberfly tests. Were the two models equally noxious? Were the mimics in each instance protected to the same extent from being eaten by the toads? The results showed that the three experimental toads attacked a total of nine out of fifty-one bumblebees (18 per cent), whereas in the experiments with honeybees, the twenty-two experimental toads seized seventy-seven out of one hundred and ten (70 per cent). This indicated that the bumblebee is more noxious to toads than is the honeybee, because fewer trials were needed to teach the toads to reject the former on sight. This is undoubtedly attributable, in part, to the bumblebees' being larger and possessing more toxic substance than do honeybees. In addition, bumblebees can inject the poisonous fluid into an attacker repeatedly, while honeybees can sting only once. Was this difference also reflected in the percentage of mimics eaten by the experimental toads in the two experiments? The results indicated that it was: only two out of a total of thirty robberflies (7 per cent) were attacked; however, nine out of twenty-two droneflies (41 per cent) were seized. These results fit one part of the mimicry theory very nicely. Students of natural selection have reasoned that the more noxious the model, the more protected the mimic would be from predation. The bumblebee and honeybee appear to exemplify, for the first time, a situation in which two levels of noxiousness do confer differing degrees of immunity to attack by toads.

These experiments are only the beginning of a vast amount of basic biological research necessary to understand more fully the evolution of mimicry. One particularly interesting but as yet unsolved problem concerns the possibility of an additional reason for the mimicry of the bumblebee by the robberfly. These flies are commonly known as bee killers because they prey on Hymenoptera by preference, although if bees are scarce, the flies will eat large beetles, bugs, and grasshoppers. In the course of our field research, we kept records of the kinds of prey that robberflies were seen to attack, and found that the bumblebee was the favorite food of *Mallophora bomboides*, the robberfly that resembles the bumblebee. The manner in which the robberfly seized its prey was precise and swift. It would perch on a stalk in a vertical position about one to three feet from the ground. As a bumblebee rose from feeding at a nearby blossom, the fly rapidly flew to the bee from above and behind it and grasped the dorsum with its long hairy legs. Then the robberfly immediately drew the bumblebee toward its body, inserted its mouthparts into the bee's thorax, and injected a substance that paralyzed the bee almost instantaneously. The fly then returned to a stalk, often the same one from which it had begun the attack, and, in a vertical position once more, proceeded to digest the prey externally by pumping its digestive juices into the bee. This caused the soft tissues of the bee to liquefy, and the fly sucked in the resulting fluid. The feeding process took approximately five to ten minutes to

complete. Afterward, the empty exoskeleton of the bumblebee might be left adhering to the plant stem.

We have suggested that the mimicry of the bumblebee by the robberfly may facilitate the mimic's exploitation of its model as food. This means that bumblebees would tend to defend themselves more successfully against those forms of the robberfly that least resemble it. On the other hand, those robberflies that closely imitate the bumblebees would tend not to be noticed until it was too late for a bee to defend itself or to escape. This would favor the survival of robberflies that look like bumblebees, and thus would bring about the evolution of mimicry. Experiments to test this idea have not yet been conducted. A possible procedure would be to confine the insects in a room-size screen cage. Thus, one could observe large numbers of a robberfly species that closely mimics the bumblebees actually attacking them. Then, robberflies of a species that does *not* resemble bumblebees could be introduced into a similar cage with bumblebees. The relative success of both robberfly species in attacking bumblebees could then be compared. Batesian mimicry, which was described in the toad experiments, and the suggested aggressive mimicry, both favor the enhancement of the resemblance between the mimic and the model. There is no reason why the two selective forces could not work together and be cumulative in their effect.

Further experiments on the degree of protection afforded the mimic by a very noxious model in comparison to one less so, the duration of memory of the predators, and their discriminatory ability are a few of the important points to be studied in the laboratory and in the natural environments of the animals. Complicated and fascinating groups of tropical insects, and even Bates' classical butterflies, still remain to be investigated.

KELLER BRELAND
and MARIAN BRELAND

44   The Misbehavior of Organisms

Techniques of animal training have been known for centuries. The development of principles of operant conditioning, however, formalized and simplified these techniques. Keller and Marian Breland, of Animal Behavior Enterprises in Hot Springs, Arkansas, have demonstrated that the principles of operant conditioning can be used to train a variety of animals for commercial purposes. In the following reading, however, they report a peculiar "breakdown" of learned behavior, which they have repeatedly observed in their animals.

American Psychologist, 1961, **16**, 681–684. Reprinted by permission of the authors and the American Psychological Association.

There seems to be a continuing realization by psychologists that perhaps the white rat cannot reveal everything there is to know about behavior. Among the voices raised on this topic, Beach (1950) has emphasized the necessity of widening the range of species subjected to experimental techniques and conditions. However, psychologists as a whole do not seem to be heeding these admonitions, as Whalen (1961) has pointed out.

Perhaps this reluctance is due in part to some dark precognition of what they might find in such investigations, for the ethologists Lorenz (1950, p. 233) and Tinbergen (1951, p. 6) have warned that if psychologists are to understand and predict the behavior of organisms, it is essential that they become thoroughly familiar with the instinctive behavior patterns of each new species they essay to study. Of course, the Watsonian or neobehavioristically oriented experimenter is apt to consider "instinct" an ugly word. He tends to class it with Hebb's (1960) other "seditious notions" which were discarded in the behavioristic revolution, and he may have some premonition that he will encounter this bete noir in extending the range of species and situations studied.

We can assure him that his apprehensions are well grounded. In our attempt to extend a behavioristically oriented approach to the engineering control of animal behavior by operant conditioning techniques, we have fought a running battle with the seditious notion of instinct.[*] It might be of some interest to the psychologist to know how the battle is going and to learn something about the nature of the adversary he is likely to meet if and when he tackles new species in new learning situations.

Our first report (Breland & Breland, 1951) in the *American Psychologist*, concerning our experiences in controlling animal behavior, was wholly affirmative and optimistic, saying in essence that the principles derived from the laboratory could be applied to the extensive control of behavior under nonlaboratory conditions throughout a considerable segment of the phylogenetic scale.

When we began this work, it was our aim to see if the science would work be-

[*] In view of the fact that instinctive behaviors may be common to many zoological species, we consider *species specific* to be a sanitized misnomer, and prefer the possibly septic adjective *instinctive*.

yond the laboratory, to determine if animal psychology could stand on its own feet as an engineering discipline. These aims have been realized. We have controlled a wide range of animal behavior and have made use of the great popular appeal of animals to make it an economically feasible project. Conditioned behavior has been exhibited at various municipal zoos and museums of natural history and has been used for department store displays, for fair and trade convention exhibits, for entertainment at tourist attractions, on television shows, and in the production of television commercials. Thirty-eight species, totaling over 6,000 individual animals, have been conditioned, and we have dared to tackle such unlikely subjects as reindeer, cockatoos, raccoons, porpoises, and whales.

Emboldened by this consistent reinforcement, we have ventured further and further from the security of the Skinner box. However, in this cavalier extrapolation, we have run afoul of a persistent pattern of discomforting failures. These failures, although disconcertingly frequent and seemingly diverse, fall into a very interesting pattern. They all represent breakdowns of conditioned operant behavior. From a great number of such experiences, we have selected, more or less at random, the following examples.

The first instance of our discomfiture might be entitled, What Makes Sammy Dance? In the exhibit in which this occurred, the casual observer sees a grown bantam chicken emerge from a retaining compartment when the door automatically opens. The chicken walks over about 3 feet, pulls a rubber loop on a small box which starts a repeated auditory stimulus pattern (a four-note tune). The chicken then steps up onto an 18-inch, slightly raised disc, thereby closing a timer switch, and scratches vigorously, round and round, over the disc for 15 seconds, at the rate of about two scratches per second until the automatic feeder fires in the retaining compartment. The chicken goes into the compartment to eat, thereby automatically

shutting the door. The popular interpretation of this behavior pattern is that the chicken has turned on the "juke box" and "dances."

The development of this behavioral exhibit was wholly unplanned. In the attempt to create quite another type of demonstration which required a chicken simply to stand on a platform for 12-15 seconds, we found that over 50% developed a very strong and pronounced scratch pattern, which tended to increase in persistence as the time interval was lengthened. (Another 25% or so developed other behaviors — pecking at spots, etc.) However, we were able to change our plans so as to make use of the scratch pattern, and the result was the "dancing chicken" exhibit described above.

In this exhibit the only real contingency for reinforcement is that the chicken must depress the platform for 15 seconds. In the course of a performing day (about 3 hours for each chicken) a chicken may turn out over 10,000 unnecessary, virtually identical responses. Operant behaviorists would probably have little hesitancy in labeling this an example of Skinnerian "superstition" (Skinner, 1948) or "mediating" behavior, and we list it first to whet their explanatory appetite.

However, a second instance involving a raccoon does not fit so neatly into this paradigm. The response concerned the manipulation of money by the raccoon (who has "hands" rather similar to those of the primates). The contingency for reinforcement was picking up the coins and depositing them in a 5-inch metal box.

Raccoons condition readily, have good appetites, and this one was quite tame and an eager subject. We anticipated no trouble. Conditioning him to pick up the first coin was simple. We started out by reinforcing him for picking up a single coin. Then the metal container was introduced, with the requirement that he drop the coin into the container. Here we ran into the first bit of difficulty: he seemed to have a great deal of trouble letting go of the coin.

He would rub it up against the inside of the container, pull it back out, and clutch it firmly for several seconds. However, he would finally turn it loose and receive his food reinforcement. Then the final contingency: we put him on a ratio of 2, requiring that he pick up both coins and put them in the container.

Now the raccoon really had problems (and so did we). Not only could he not let go of the coins, but he spent seconds, even minutes, rubbing them together (in a most miserly fashion), and dipping them into the container. He carried on this behavior to such an extent that the practical application we had in mind—a display featuring a raccoon putting money in a piggy bank—simply was not feasible. The rubbing behavior became worse and worse as time went on, in spite of nonreinforcement.

For the third instance, we return to the gallinaceous birds. The observer sees a hopper full of oval plastic capsules which contain small toys, charms, and the like. When the S_D (a light) is presented to the chicken, she pulls a rubber loop which releases one of these capsules onto a slide, about 16 inches long, inclined at about 30 degrees. The capsule rolls down the slide and comes to rest near the end. Here one or two sharp, straight pecks by the chicken will knock it forward off the slide and out to the observer, and the chicken is then reinforced by an automatic feeder. This is all very well—most chickens are able to master these contingencies in short order. The loop pulling presents no problems; she then has only to peck the capsule off the slide to get her reinforcement.

However, a good 20% of all chickens tried on this set of contingencies fail to make the grade. After they have pecked a few capsules off the slide, they begin to grab at the capsules and drag them backwards into the cage. Here they pound them up and down on the floor of the cage. Of course, this results in no reinforcement for the chicken, and yet some chickens will pull in over half of all the capsules presented to them.

Almost always this problem behavior does not appear until after the capsules begin to move down the slide. Conditioning is begun with stationary capsules placed by the experimenter. When the pecking behavior becomes strong enough, so that the chicken is knocking them off the slide and getting reinforced consistently, the loop pulling is conditioned to the light. The capsules then come rolling down the slide to the chicken. Here most chickens, who before did not have this tendency, will start grabbing and shaking.

The fourth incident also concerns a chicken. Here the observer sees a chicken in a cage about 4 feet long which is placed alongside a miniature baseball field. The reason for the cage is the interesting part. At one end of the cage is an automatic electric feed hopper. At the other is an opening through which the chicken can reach and pull a loop on a bat. If she pulls the loop hard enough the bat (solenoid operated) will swing, knocking a small baseball up the playing field. If it gets past the miniature toy players on the field and hits the back fence, the chicken is automatically reinforced with food at the other end of the cage. If it does not go far enough, or hits one of the players, she tries again. This results in behavior on an irregular ratio. When the feeder sounds, she then runs down the length of the cage and eats.

Our problems began when we tried to remove the cage for photography. Chickens that had been well conditioned in this behavior became wildly excited when the ball started to move. They would jump up on the playing field, chase the ball all over the field, even knock it off on the floor and chase it around, pecking it in every direction, although they had never had access to the ball before. This behavior was so persistent and so disruptive, in spite of the fact that it was never reinforced, that we had to reinstate the cage.

The last instance we shall relate in detail is one of the most annoying and baffling for a good behaviorist. Here a pig was conditioned to pick up large wooden coins and deposit them in a large "piggy bank." The coins were placed several feet from the bank and the pig required to carry them to the bank and deposit them, usually four or five coins for one reinforcement. (Of course, we started out with one coin, near the bank.)

Pigs condition very rapidly, they have no trouble taking ratios, they have ravenous appetites (naturally), and in many ways are among the most tractable animals we have worked with. However, this particular problem behavior developed in pig after pig, usually after a period of weeks or months, getting worse every day. At first the pig would eagerly pick up one dollar, carry it to the bank, run back, get another, carry it rapidly and neatly, and so on, until the ratio was complete. Thereafter, over a period of weeks the behavior would become slower and slower. He might run over eagerly for each dollar, but on the way back, instead of carrying the dollar and depositing it simply and cleanly, he would repeatedly drop it, root it, drop it again, root it along the way, pick it up, toss it up in the air, drop it, root it some more, and so on.

We thought this behavior might simply be the dilly-dallying of an animal on a low drive. However, the behavior persisted and gained in strength in spite of a severely increased drive—he finally went through the ratios so slowly that he did not get enough to eat in the course of a day. Finally it would take the pig about 10 minutes to transport four coins a distance of about 6 feet. This problem behavior developed repeatedly in successive pigs.

There have also been other instances: hamsters that stopped working in a glass case after four or five reinforcements, porpoises and whales that swallow their manipulanda (balls and inner tubes), cats that will not leave the area of the feeder, rabbits that will not go to the feeder, the great difficulty in many species of conditioning vocalization with food reinforcement, problems in conditioning a kick in a cow, the

failure to get appreciably increased effort out of the ungulates with increased drive, and so on. These we shall not dwell on in detail, nor shall we discuss how they might be overcome.

These egregious failures came as a rather considerable shock to us, for there was nothing in our background in behaviorism to prepare us for such gross inabilities to predict and control the behavior of animals with which we had been working for years.

The examples listed we feel represent a clear and utter failure of conditioning theory. They are far from what one would normally expect on the basis of the theory alone. Furthermore, they are definite, observable; the diagnosis of theory failure does not depend on subtle statistical interpretations or on semantic legerdemain— the animal simply does not do what he has been conditioned to do.

It seems perfectly clear that, with the possible exception of the dancing chicken, which could conceivably, as we have said, be explained in terms of Skinner's superstition paradigm, the other instances do not fit the behavioristic way of thinking. Here we have animals, after having been conditioned to a specific learned response, gradually drifting into behaviors that are entirely different from those which were conditioned. Moreover, it can easily be seen that these particular behaviors to which the animals drift are clear-cut examples of instinctive behaviors having to do with the natural food getting behaviors of the particular species.

The dancing chicken is exhibiting the gallinaceous birds' scratch pattern that in nature often precedes ingestion. The chicken that hammers capsules is obviously exhibiting instinctive behavior having to do with breaking open of seed pods or the killing of insects, grubs, etc. The raccoon is demonstrating so-called "washing behavior." The rubbing and washing response may result, for example, in the removal of the exoskeleton of a crayfish. The pig is rooting or shaking—behaviors which are strongly built into this species and are connected with the food getting repertoire.

These patterns to which the animals drift require greater physical output and therefore are a violation of the so-called "law of least effort." And most damaging of all, they stretch out the time required for reinforcement when nothing in the experimental setup requires them to do so. They have only to do the little tidbit of behavior to which they were conditioned —for example, pick up the coin and put it in the container—to get reinforced immediately. Instead, they drag the process out for a matter of minutes when there is nothing in the contingency which forces them to do this. Moreover, increasing the drive merely intensifies this effect.

It seems obvious that these animals are trapped by strong instinctive behaviors, and clearly we have here a demonstration of the prepotency of such behavior patterns over those which have been conditioned.

We have termed this phenomenon "instinctive drift." The general principle seems to be that wherever an animal has strong instinctive behaviors in the area of the conditioned response, after continued running the organism will drift toward the instinctive behavior to the detriment of the conditioned behavior and even to the delay or preclusion of the reinforcement. In a very boiled-down, simplified form, it might be stated as "learned behavior drifts toward instinctive behavior."

All this, of course, is not to disparage the use of conditioning techniques, but is intended as a demonstration that there are definite weaknesses in the philosophy underlying these techniques. The pointing out of such weaknesses should make possible a worthwhile revision in behavior theory.

The notion of instinct has now become one of our basic concepts in an effort to make sense of the welter of observations which confront us. When behaviorism tossed out instinct, it is our feeling that some of its power of prediction and control were lost with it. From the foregoing examples, it appears that although it was easy to banish the Instinctivists from the science during the Behavioristic Revolution, it was not possible to banish instinct so easily.

And if, as Hebb suggests, it is advisable to reconsider those things that behaviorism explicitly threw out, perhaps it might likewise be advisable to examine what they tacitly brought it—the hidden assumptions which led most disastrously to these breakdowns in the theory.

Three of the most important of these tacit assumptions seem to us to be: that the animal comes to the laboratory as a virtual *tabula rasa,* that species differences are insignificant, and that all responses are about equally conditionable to all stimuli.

It is obvious, we feel, from the foregoing account, that these assumptions are no longer tenable. After 14 years of continuous conditioning and observation of thousands of animals, it is our reluctant conclusion that the behavior of any species cannot be adequately understood, predicted, or controlled without knowledge of its instinctive patterns, evolutionary history, and ecological niche.

In spite of our early successes with the application of behavioristically oriented conditioning theory, we readily admit now that ethological facts and attitudes in recent years have done more to advance our practical control of animal behavior than recent reports from American "learning labs."

Moreover, as we have recently discovered, if one begins with evolution and instinct as the basic format for the science, a very illuminating viewpoint can be developed which leads naturally to a drastically revised and simplified conceptual framework of startling explanatory power (to be reported elsewhere).

It is hoped that this playback on the theory will be behavioral technology's partial repayment to the academic science whose impeccable empiricism we have used so extensively.

REFERENCES

BEACH, F. A. The snark was a boojum. *Amer. Psychologist,* 1950, **5,** 115–124.

BRELAND, K., and M. BRELAND A field of applied animal psychology. *Amer. Psychologist,* 1951, **6,** 202–204.

HEBB, D. O. The American revolution. *Amer. Psychologist,* 1960, **15,** 735–745.

LORENZ, K. Innate behaviour patterns. In:

Symposia of the Society for Experimental Biology. No. 4. *Physiological mechanisms in animal behaviour.* New York: Academic Press, 1950.

SKINNER, B. F. Superstition in the pigeon. *J. exp. Psychol.,* 1948, **38,** 168–172.

TINBERGEN, N. *The study of instinct.* Oxford: Clarendon, 1951.

WHALEN, R. E. Comparative psychology. *Amer. Psychologist,* 1961, **16,** 84.

T R A V I S   I.   T H O M P S O N †

45 Visual Reinforcement in Fighting Cocks*

Recent experimentation has shown that a variety of different stimuli may act as reinforcers for learning. The following experiment demonstrates that a fighting cock will perform an operant response for visual reinforcement.

FR 25 stands for a *fixed ratio* where every twenty-fifth response is reinforced.

Journal of the Experimental Analysis of Behavior, 1964, **7,** 45–49. Reprinted with the permission of the author and the Society for the Experimental Analysis of Behavior.

ABSTRACT Fighting cocks were conditioned to emit a key-pecking response on a fixed ratio reinforcement schedule leading to the visual image of another fighting cock. In addition, the relative reinforcing properties of the visual reinforcer were compared with food and water reinforcers in a three-choice, non-reversible option situation. The relative reinforcing effects of mirror presentation and another rooster visually presented through a window, were compared. The mirror maintained a relatively lower response output.

▶ The analysis of unlearned agonistic behavior (Verplanck, 1957) has been primarily carried out using observational methods

* This research was supported by grants MY-1604 from the National Institute of Mental Health and NsG 189-61 from National Aeronautics and Space Administration, to the University of Maryland.

† National Science Foundation Postdoctoral Fellow 41088.

in controlled "natural" environments. Much of this research has been concerned with the characteristics of the stimulus sufficient to evoke agonistic display (Aronson, 1957; Crane, 1949; Tinbergen, 1957). Frequently this complex stimulus is a male member of the same species or a replica of a male introduced by the experimenter, intruding into an established territory (Baerends and Baerends, 1950; Forselius, 1957; Picciolo, 1961; Tinbergen and Van Iersel, 1947). While the domestic rooster does not exhibit territoriality, *per se,* a species-specific agonistic display pattern, directed toward other roosters has been observed (Guhl, 1953). In fighting cocks, this threatening display is elicited by the visual image of another rooster. Such threat behavior very rapidly leads to attack, with resulting injury and frequently to the death of one of the adversaries.

The present research makes use of the visual image of a rooster, not as a releasing stimulus (Tinbergen, 1951), but rather as a positively reinforcing stimulus for an operant response. The purpose of this experiment was to establish the positive reinforcing effects of the visual image of one fighting cock for the operant behavior of another. In addition, the reinforcing effects of this visual stimulus were compared with food and water reinforcers.

Method

SUBJECTS

Two sexually mature Red Gavillan roosters obtained from a nearby farm served. The subjects (Ss) had been maintained in common flocks with hens and roosters until the time of purchase, when they were transferred to individual cages. During the two weeks prior to the experiment, the Ss (A and B) received *ad libitum* food and water, and had free access to pigeon grit.

APPARATUS

A chamber, 24 by 36 by 24 in. inside dimensions, equipped with three pigeon keys, a pellet feeder and a solenoid valve-operated water dispensing device, served as the experimental living space. The response keys and two receptacles to receive food pellets (D and G 45 mg) and tap water were located along one wall. A conical receptacle 1½ in. deep and 2 in. in diameter was filled with water, and drained at a constant rate (15 sec per reinforcement). Visual stimuli were presented through a window 12 in. square cut into the left wall of the chamber. Red, blue and green lights were located behind the keys so the translucent key disc could be illuminated. A 25-watt lamp showing through a grating in the ceiling served as a general house light. An exhaust blower provided continuous ventilation and helped maintain a relatively constant temperature in the chamber.

PROCEDURE

Bird A was placed in the test chamber for a period of 61 days, following the two weeks pre-experimental period. The S received all of its food, water and social stimulation in the experimental situation. Since there was adequate time to obtain sufficient quantities of all three reinforcers, no effort was made to maintain constant body weight.

Initially, a mirror was presented to the S in the experimental chamber by turning off a lamp behind a one-way glass window for 10 sec. Responses on the appropriate key would be followed by water reinforcement, three 45-mg food pellets, or mirror presentation. All three key lights were illuminated before a response occurred on any key. As soon as a response was emitted on one key, the other two key lights turned off, and further responses on those keys had no effect until the response requirement on the first-pecked key was completed. Upon completion of the response requirement (a fixed number of responses) on that key, a reinforcer was presented and all three key lights turned on again, providing the opportunity for S to select the reinforcer for which it would work. This procedure has been described by Findley (1962) as a three choice non-reversible option situation. The number of pecks required to procure a reinforcer on the three keys was gradually increased to 75 over a period of 25 days. In order to specify that the mirror presentation was the reinforcing stimulus, a piece of transparent plate glass replaced the one-way glass for five days at the end of this period.

Subsequently, another cage containing rooster B was placed adjacent to the experimental cubicle. Vision between the experimental and adjacent stimulus cage was effected by rotating a screen, when the S completed the response requirement on the appropriate key. The S in the outer cage had no control over the screen, but acted as a reinforcing stimulus for the experi-

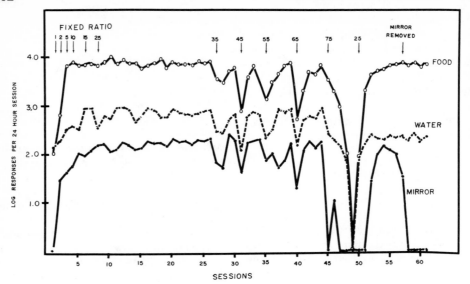

FIG. 1. The logarithms of the numbers of responses for food, water and social reinforcement during the first 61 days of the study. The ratio size is indicated by the numbers along the top of the figure.

mental S. Throughout this phase of the experiment, the reinforcing stimulus bird had *ad libitum* food, water and pigeon grit.

Upon completion of this series of procedures using Bird A as subject, Bird B was placed in the chamber and a similar series of manipulations was performed. While there were differences in number of sessions required to reach various levels of performance, the general sequence of procedures was alike for the two birds.

Results

The logarithms of the numbers of responses emitted on each of the three keys over the first 61 days of the study are presented in Fig. 1. The rate of acquisition of the ratio behavior leading to the three reinforcers reveals the general propensity of the S to work for these stimuli. Food reinforced behavior reached the highest stable baseline level after three, 24-hr sessions, water reinforced responding following six sessions and mirror-reinforced behavior after 10 sessions. Baseline performance for food at FR 25 was approximately

100 times that for the "social" reinforcer, and 10 times the total number of water responses per session.

As the ratio was changed by increments of 10 above FR 25, a decrease in response output was followed by a return to the previous daily output. Successive increments in the FR resulted in increasingly larger decreases in total daily response output on the three keys, followed by longer recovery times to the pre-increase levels of performance.

Increasing the ratio to FR 75 produced a marked reduction in responding for the mirror reinforcer, with lesser decrements in food and water output. After three more days at FR 75, responding on all three keys had ceased. The ratio was reduced to 25 after three successive days with no indication of a return of mirror responding. Both food and water responding rapidly stabilized at near the pre-increase level, but behavior for the mirror reinforcer was returned more gradually. Replacement of the one-way mirror with transparent glass resulted in a reduction in mirror responses to 35 on the first day, with no mirror responses for four succeeding days. Cessation of responding on the "mirror" key indicates that the mirror presentation was responsible for maintaining this operant rather than illumination changes associated with the mirror presentation.

At this point the lucite screen and the second bird were introduced. Responding on the three keys was re-established, substituting the visually presented S for the mirror image. The ratio was increased from FR 1 to FR 5 during the first 24-hr session.

Over the next 10 days, the ratio was gradually increased to FR 25. The characteristic ratio performance (Ferster and Skinner, 1957) began to deteriorate at ratio values above FR 25, so the behavior was allowed to stabilize at this level. The course of acquisition of responding for the three reinforcers was very much like that seen using the mirror as the visual stimulus and is, therefore, not reproduced graphically. Responding on the "social" key stabilized at values closer to the total output for

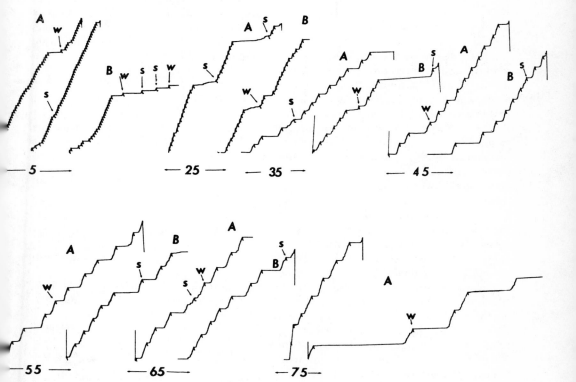

FIG. 2. Sample cumulative records for Birds A and B at fixed ratio values of 5, 25, 35, 45, 55, 65 and 75. All reinforcements were food except those indicated by an arrow and the letters W(water) and S(social).

water reinforcement (food $\cong$ 10,000, water $\cong$ 700, social $\cong$ 500).

Figure 2 presents sample cumulative records for both Ss (A and B) for food, water and social reinforcers. In general, when an S began to work for a food reinforcer, the ratio was completed in a characteristic, positively-accelerated scallop, and a brief post-reinforcement pause.

Ratio performance for water and visual reinforcement was at an overall lower rate and tended to be more erratic. Responses on the "social" key differed somewhat from water behavior in that they occurred in irregularly-spaced short bursts, interspersed with periods of more characteristic ratio behavior. Furthermore, as the size of the ratio increased, the magnitude of such variability increased, finally associated with total disruption at FR 75.

Discussion

The visual image of a fighting cock almost invariably precedes aversive consequences for another rooster in the "natural" environment. The present data indicate that this same stimulus can act as a positive reinforcer for a key-pecking operant in another rooster. The number of responses maintained by this reinforcer was found to vary with the amount of work required to obtain food, water and visual reinforcement.

The relative biological significance of the three reinforcers in this situation is suggested by the order in which the three operants were acquired, the order by which responding was diminished by increasing the work requirement and the order in which responding reappeared upon lowering the ratio size. The stability of the behavior emitted for the three reinforcers over a range of work requirements from FR 5 to FR 65 indicates the constancy of the relationship of these reinforcers and the reliability of the procedure.

The possibility that a first response on the visual reinforcement key was "acci-dental", and then followed by responses reinforced by reinstatement of the opportunity to respond for food or water reinforcement, seems highly unlikely. During the four-day period when the mirror was removed, but the illumination changes continued as previously, no responses were emitted on the visual reinforcement key (Fig. 1, days 58–61). On day 82 the lamp illuminating the "visual" key burned out, unnoticed by the experimenter for 18 hr. No responses were recorded on this key during this period despite the fact that responses would have been reinforced as usual. When the lamp was replaced, the S began responding within 5 min, re-establishing the prior FR 25 performance almost immediately.

Thus, responding on the "visual" key appears to be a function of the appropriate discriminative stimulus (key illumination) and reinforcing consequences (mirror presentation), not generalization from one key to another or chaining of responding on the "visual" key leading to food or water.

REFERENCES

ARONSON, L. R. Reproductive and parental behavior. In: M. E. BROWN (Ed.), *The physiology of fishes.* New York: Academic Press, Inc., 1957.

BAERENDS, G. P., and J. BAERENDS VAN ROON An introduction to the study of the ethology of Cichlid fishes. *Behaviour,* 1950, No. 1, 1–243.

CRANE, J. The comparative biology of Salticid spiders at Rancho Grande, Venezuela, IV. An analysis of display. *Zoologica,* 1949, **34**, 159–214.

FERSTER, C. B., and B. F. SKINNER *Schedules of reinforcement.* New York: Appleton-Century-Crofts, 1957.

FINDLEY, J. An experimental outline for building and exploring multi-operant behavior repertoires. *J. exp. Anal. Behav.,* 1962, **5**, 113–166.

FORSELIUS, S. Studies of Anabantid fishes, I. A qualitative description of the reproductive behavior in territorial species investigated under laboratory conditions with special regard to the genus *Colisa*. An introduction. *Zool. Bidrag.*, 1957, **32**, 93–302.

GUHL, A. M.   Ch. 17 in: E. S. E. HAFEZ (Ed.), "The Behavior of Chickens" *The behaviour of domestic animals*. Baltimore: Williams and Wilkins, 1962.

PICCIOLO, A. R.   *Sexual and nest discrimination by species of Colisa and Trichogaster.* Unpublished doctoral dissertation, University of Maryland, 1961.

TINBERGEN, N.   *The study of instinct.* London: Oxford University Press, 1951.

TINBERGEN, N.   The function of territory. *Bird Study*, 1957, **4**, 14–27.

TINBERGEN, N., and J. J. VAN IERSEL   Displacement reactions in the Three-spined Stickleback. *Behaviour*, 1947, **1**, 56–63.

VERPLANCK, W. S.   A glossary of some terms used in the objective science of behavior. *Psychol. Rev.*, 1957, **64**, 1–42.

R O B E R T   A.   B U T L E R
and   J E R O M E   H.   W O O L P Y

46   Visual Attention in the Rhesus Monkey[*]

Reading 45 showed that a visual image of another male chicken could act as a reinforcer for the fighting cock. In the following experiment, part of a continuing series by Robert A. Butler and his colleagues, a similar technique is used to study the visual preferences of rhesus monkeys.

Reprinted from the *Journal of Comparative and Physiological Psychology*, 1963, **56**, 324–328, by permission of the authors and the American Psychological Association.

ABSTRACT   Monkeys' viewing behavior to various 2-dimensional displays provided by slides and motion pictures was studied by a paired-comparison testing technique. The number of times and the total duration of time that S viewed each display in a 2-window cubicle were recorded automatically. Monkeys spent more time ($p < .01$) viewing motion pictures that were (a) in focus, (b) brightly illuminated, (c) moving at normal rather than slower rates, (d) in color, and (e) spatially oriented in the proper manner. They watched automatically changing slides more than stationary slides ($p < .01$). The duration of individual viewing responses contributed more to total viewing time than did the number of viewing responses.

▶ During the last decade a large number of experiments have been carried out in the general area of exploratory behavior. These studies were designed to show that rewards other than food, water, sex, and escape from pain, can effectively influence behavior; several reviews of the researches appear in the literature (Butler, 1960; Lana, 1960; Welker, 1961; White, 1959).

The experiments to be reported here utilized the rhesus monkey's propensity to explore the surrounding environment visually. The purpose of the study was to elucidate those stimulus characteristics which can effectively maintain visual attentiveness. A paired-comparison technique was used with projected slides and motion pictures serving as visual incentives.[†]

Method

SUBJECTS

A total of 14 adult rhesus monkeys participated in this study. Originally, the

[*] This research was supported through a grant from the National Science Foundation.

[†] The authors express their appreciation to Peter Donshik for his assistance in testing Ss.

experimental group consisted of 12 animals. Two were dropped because they failed to respond persistently in the test situation. They were replaced by two other animals recently freed from another experiment. All animals had been Ss in previous investigations which employed visual incentives as reinforcers.

APPARATUS

During testing Ss were housed in a metal box which was 2 ft. wide, 2 ft. long, and 2 ft. high, and supported by a stand 3 ft. high. Lucite windows, 3 in. wide and ½ in. high, were located on opposite walls of the box. In order for S to look out of either window, it had to put its head into a relatively small cubicle. One side of each cubicle was formed by a compartment housing two exciter lamps arranged vertically and spaced approximately 1 in. apart. The other side was formed by a compartment housing two photomultiplier vacuum tubes arranged horizontally and in close proximity. The inside face of each compartment was composed of a glass filter which filtered most of the light emanating from the lamps and vacuum tubes, passing only wave lengths in the violet region. A metal plate

covered the top of the cubicle. The bottom of the cubicle was left open so that S could sit close to the window while viewing the outside environment. The bottom edge of the window was 12 in. above the floor of the box.

The S when positioning its head to look out of a window interrupted the light beam emanating from the exciter lamps. This increased the positive voltage from the photomultiplier (RCA931A) to the amplifier tube (6201), which in turn activated a relay, thereby closing the circuit. An impulse counter registered the number of times that the circuit was closed. The length of time that it was held closed was cumulated on a running time meter. The sensitivity of the mechanism was set so that any time S's head was within 1½ in. of the window, the relay was activated, thus closing the circuit. And, the circuit remained closed as long as S stayed near the window. When S withdrew its head a distance greater than 1½ in. from the window, the circuit was opened and the running time meter automatically stopped. The circuitry for each window mechanism was separate from that of the other; hence, S's viewing behavior at each window was recorded on separate impulse

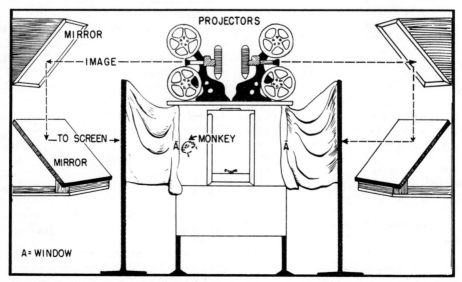

FIG. 1. Diagrammatic sketch of the test situation.

TABLE 46-1

A list of conditions presented to the monkeys

EXPERIMENTAL CONDITIONS	VISUAL INCENTIVES[a]	TESTS NO.	TESTS DURATION (MIN.)
1. Stationary slide vs. lighted screen	CS-1	2	5
2. Stationary slide vs. changing slides	CS-1 & CS-2	2	5
3. Motion picture vs. slides	MP-1 & CS-2	2	5
4. Speed of motion:			
a. 24 F/sec. vs. 12 F/sec.	MP-2	4	10
b. 22 F/sec. vs. 16 F/sec.	MP-3	4	10
5. Clarity of display (varied focal distance)			
a. 85 in. (in focus) vs. 42 in. (out of focus)	MP-4	4	10
b-1. 85 in. vs. 42 in.	MP-5	2	10
b-2. 85 in. vs. 62 in.	MP-5	2	10
b-3. 62 in. vs. 42 in.	MP-5	2	10
6. Brightness of display			
a-1. 100 v. vs. 50 v.	MP-4	4	10
a-2. 117 v. vs. 40 v.	MP-4	2	10
b. 117 v. vs. 40 v.	MP-6	2	10
7. Presence of color in display			
a. Color vs. black and white	MP-7	4	10
b. Color vs. black and white	MP-8	2	10
8. Spatial orientation of display			
a. Rightside up vs. upside down	MP-4	4	10
b. Rightside up vs. upside down	MP-7	2	10

a CS-1 = stationary colored slide of monkeys; CS-2 = colored slides of various animals changing every 10 sec. MP-1 = motion picture showing behavior of laboratory rhesus monkeys; MP-2 = "Zoo Babies"; MP-3 = "Hoppy, the Bunny"; MP-4 = "Social Behavior of the Rhesus Monkey"; MP-5 = "Flipper, the Seal"; MP-6 = "Spotty, the Fawn"; MP-7 = "The Monkey and the Organ Grinder"; MP-8 = "Playground Safety."

counters and running time meters. The sensitivity of the amplifiers was set so that S could not close the circuit, and activate the recording instruments, merely by placing its hands or arms up to either window. There is little question but that when the circuit was closed, S was looking out of the window. Indeed, before the apparatus was used for formal experimentation, an observer watched the window from outside the box while several different Ss were being adapted to the test situation. Each time that the recording mechanism was activated, S had its eyes practically "glued" to the window.

Figure 1 shows a diagram of the test room. Two 35mm. slide projectors (Revere 888 and Viewlex), as well as two 16mm. motion picture projectors (Bell and Howell, Diplomate and Filmosound) were available for use. An image from either a slide or motion picture was projected horizontally upon a mirror which was attached to the wall of the test room. The projected image was reflected off the first mirror onto a second one and off that onto a 12-× 13½-in. translucent screen. Each screen was supported by a wooden stand which was placed 2 ft. in front of a window. The S, from the window, could look directly upon the screen. Heavy, black cloth was fastened from the top and sides of the test box to the top and sides of the stand supporting the screen. Hence, S could see little other than that which was being projected upon the screen.

Throughout a test session, the projection equipment was operating continuously. However, the projectors were wired so that the projection lamp was turned on *only* when S positioned its head close to a window and hence closed that particular circuit.

Listed in Table 46–1 are the various experimental conditions, the visual incentives employed in each, and the number and length of the test sessions. Each experimental condition comprised two visual incentives which differed from one another in one or more ways. A particular visual incentive was associated equally often with each of the two windows. The order of presentation of experimental conditions did not always follow the numerical listing of the conditions as represented in Table 46–1. Most of the experimental conditions that essentially constituted replications, i.e., the "b" group of conditions, were carried out after all the "a" group of conditions had been completed. The length of a test session was governed by the visual incentives employed. When slides were presented, the conditions where the slide changed automatically every 10 sec. necessitated a short test session since the slide holder for the automatic projector could only accommodate 36 slides. Hence, a 5 min. test session was given for Condition No. 1, 2, and 3. Ten minute tests were employed when motion pictures were used as visual incentives since the running time for many of these films was not much longer than 10 min.

Whether a condition consisted of 2 or 4 test sessions depended upon the particular situation. Only 2 test sessions were given in the conditions using slides because by the end of the second session, either Ss as a group showed no consistent preference for either visual incentive or they all clearly preferred viewing the same incentive. In either event, further testing would not have contributed directly to the aim of this experiment. Two tests were frequently given

when motion pictures were used. In these instances, the tests represented essentially a replication of one of the experimental conditions using a different film for the visual incentives. In some repeat tests, the variable under investigation was manipulated so that the apparent difference between the two incentives was made smaller. Except for Condition No. 4a and 4b the motion picture projectors were run at 16 F/sec. A variac, inserted between each projector lamp and its respective ac source, was used to compensate for any differences in apparent brightness between the visual incentives as judged by the two Es. Usually little or no compensation was necessary. Since this technique of using mirrors inverted the projected images, the motors of the motion picture projectors had to be run in reverse and the films threaded from the bottom to the top reel in order for the images to appear rightside up. With the exception of MP-1 and MP-4, the motion pictures were produced by Coronet Films. All were filmed at 24 F/sec.

TESTING PROCEDURE

The S was placed in the test box located in a sound-deadened room. The overhead lights were turned off, leaving the room dark, and the projectors were turned on. When S made its first response to a window a stop watch was activated marking the beginning of the test session. Usually S, after looking out one window, would immediately go to the other window. It was rare indeed when as much as 1 min. elapsed between the initial response to one window and the initial response to the other. The number of responses and cumulative time that S spent viewing the incentives were registered separately for each window and recorded at 1 min. intervals. At the end of the session E entered the room, turned off the projector and removed S from the test box. In order for the visual incentives to be available for projection throughout the entire test session, it was necessary that S respond relatively soon after being placed in the test box. Ten of the original 12 Ss almost always responded to one of the windows within a few seconds after the projectors were turned on. The remaining two monkeys frequently failed to respond for several minutes and were replaced by two others that readily responded in the test situation.

Results

Table 46–2 summarizes the results. All tests of significance were carried out using the Wilcoxon matched-pairs, signed-ranks test. Significant differences between incentives ($p < .01$) were found for one or more indices of responsiveness in all but three series of tests. Since lack of significance between incentives appears to be the exception in these test series, a brief comment on these particular situations seems warranted. In Condition No. 1 where Ss could view either a projected photograph of another monkey or a blank screen there was no indication that, with further testing, significant differences would ever be expressed. This, however, was not the case for Condition No. 8b. It had just been shown in Condition No. 8a that it made a difference whether the motion picture was projected rightside up or upside down. As seen in Table 46–2, Ss spent more time viewing the rightside up image (differences were significant beyond the .05 level) and the mean duration of responses was longer when viewing the properly oriented scene. The Es were reasonably confident, in view of the comparable data from the a and b test series, that spatial orientation can play an effective role in the incentive value of a visual display. Hence, no further testing time was devoted to this situation.

The third condition where no significant differences between incentives were found was No. 6b. Here, the lamp intensities for the highest and lowest illumination levels were set as far apart as possible with the constraint being that Es could still perceive moving forms under the lowest illumination level although the details were

TABLE 46–2

Mean value for each response index

CONDITION		RESPONSE INDEX[a]		
		R	TT	MDR
1:	Slide	13.7	19.8	1.5
	Screen	18.0	24.0	1.2
2:	Chge	22.9	61.8[b]	3.1[b]
	Stat	16.1	24.6	1.9
3:	MP-1	25.8	95.4[b]	5.4[b]
	Chge	17.5	26.4	1.9
4a:	24 F/sec	36.0	109.2[b]	3.6[b]
	12 F/sec	30.5	63.6	2.5
4b:	22 F/sec	32.3[b]	99.0[b]	3.5
	16 F/sec	25.5	63.6	3.0
5a:	In-focus	18.4	63.0[b]	4.8[b]
	Out-of-focus	18.6	32.4	1.8
5b-1:	In-focus	24.5	80.4[b]	3.5[b]
	Out-of-focus	22.8	28.0	1.3
5b-2:	In-focus	27.4	82.8[b]	3.5[b]
	Out-of-focus	23.8	33.6	1.6
5b-3:	In-focus	24.7	45.6[b]	1.9[b]
	Out-of-focus	23.2	30.6	1.3
6a-1:	Bright	17.6	83.4[b]	4.8[b]
	Dim	18.5	49.8	3.0
6a-2:	Bright	39.4	145.8[b]	3.6[b]
	Dim	36.4	68.4	2.0
6b:	Bright	31.8	81.0	2.7
	Dim	27.6	57.0	2.2
7a:	Color	23.4	117.0[b]	5.5[b]
	Black and white	21.3	87.6	4.4
7b:	Color	32.2	127.2[b]	4.4[b]
	Black and white	31.8	90.0	2.5
8a:	Rightside up	42.1[b]	164.4[b]	4.1[b]
	Upside down	32.2	87.0	2.8
8b:	Rightside up	37.6	122.4	3.7
	Upside down	34.3	93.0	2.8

a R = response frequency; TT = total time, in seconds, spent viewing an incentive; MDR = mean duration of responses in seconds.

b Signifies that the difference between incentives was significant ($p < .01$) for that particular index of responsiveness. The letter b is attached to that entry of the pair which has the larger value.

indistinguishable. The reason why the intensity differences were not the same as those used in Condition No. 6a-1 was that we wanted to compare three different brightness levels in a way similar to that for focal distances (Condition No. 5b-1, 2, and 3). However, since no significant differences were obtained between any of the response indices when the two extremes of intensity were used (117 v. vs. 42 v.) no further testing was done under Condition No. 6b. It was suspected that the particular film ("Spotty, the Fawn") for some reason was not effective in maintaining Ss' interest. Mean duration of responses was brief (2.7 sec.) even when the film was being shown in full illumination. The Ss were then retested with the film on social behavior serving as the visual incentives (Condition 6a-2). The outcome of the retest clearly demonstrated that differences in brightness can influence the monkey's responsiveness to visual incentives. The Ss spent more than twice as much time viewing the brighter of the two projected images.

It is apparent from Table 46-2 that the duration of the individual responses contributed much more to the total viewing time than did the number of responses for nearly all conditions.

Discussion

What appeared to be happening in this type of testing situation was that a monkey, enclosed in a box which has two windows, each providing a different view, repeatedly sampled the view at each window. Perhaps, when S was sitting in the middle of the test box, it was not aware of which window led to the "preferred" view. But the rhesus monkey has a strong propensity to explore visually, and as soon as S went to either window the stimulus characteristics of the display were instrumental in governing how long he remained at the window. We suggest that duration of a response is an expression of visual attention.

For a visual display to maintain the attention of monkeys, it appears that stimulus change is of prime importance. When the same stimuli were displayed throughout a test session, Ss spent little time viewing them (Condition No. 1). It is of interest that a photograph of another monkey elicited no more viewing behavior than did a homogeneously illuminated screen. This finding has been obtained previously using a somewhat different experimental procedure (Butler, 1961). Yet a static visual display can be effective in arousing S's interest if it is changed frequently. This suggests that S may attend to a photograph even though this type of display is not an especially compelling one. But it may be that the stimulus change which was effective was that of light to dark to light, which occurred every 10 sec. when one slide was being replaced by another. Certainly changes in the illumination level can reinforce responses in a variety of species (Welker, 1961).

Whatever may be the explanation of the preference for periodically changing stimuli that consisted of photographs of animals, the incentive value of this type of display was almost insignificant when compared to that provided by continuously changing stimuli depicting movements of animals (see Condition No. 3). And within the domain of movement, rate affected the incentive value of the display. Our data showed that Ss spent more time viewing the motion picture that was projected at the faster velocity. In these test series, however, rate of movement was confounded with the apparent "naturalness" of movement. The faster of the two velocities of projection in both test situations was nearer to the filmed velocity and unfortunately we did not project a film at a velocity which exceeded that employed in the filming of the events.

It is not stimulus change per se afforded by a view of a motion picture that is responsible for the display's enhanced incentive value. This point is clearly illustrated by the tests where images were projected in and out of focus. The Ss did not remain long at the window when the figure-ground relations of the display were indistinct, even though stimuli in these situations were continuously changing. Probably, the images projected under conditions of low illumination were not effective in maintaining visual attention for the same reason; viz, the figure-ground relations were blurred.

Once one appreciates the significance of the fact that rhesus monkeys will do something in order to view two dimensional displays and also that Ss do not respond to the displays indiscriminately, the data from Condition No. 1 through 6 are what one might expect. They show, in essence, that Ss prefer to view clearly perceptible figures in motion. That these are watched for longer intervals when the scenes are in color emphasizes the variety stimulus events that can influence visual attention. And the fact that viewing behavior is increased when the images are projected in the proper orientation lends

credence to the possibility that Ss are responding to the projected images as being representative of real objects.

REFERENCES

BUTLER, R. A. Acquired drives and the curiosity-investigative motives. In: R. H. WATERS, D. A. RETHLINGSHAFER, and W. E. CALDWELL (Eds.), *Principles of comparative psychology*. New York: McGraw-Hill, 1960. Pp. 154–173.

BUTLER, R. A. The responsiveness of rhesus monkeys to motion pictures. *J. genet. Psychol.*, 1961, 98, 239–245.

LANA, R. E. Manipulation-exploration drives and the drive reduction hypothesis. *J. genet. Psychol.*, 1960, 63, 3–27.

WELKER, W. I. An analysis of exploratory and play behavior in animals. In: D. W. FISKE and S. R. MADDI (Eds.), *Functions of varied experience*. Homewood, Ill.: Dorsey, 1961. Pp. 175–226.

WHITE, R. W. Motivation reconsidered: The concept of competence. *Psychol. Rev.*, 1959, 66, 297–333.

R. A. HINDE

47 Energy Models of Motivation

In this article, Robert A. Hinde (co-author of reading 5) reviews four different models of motivation, all of which use the concept of energy to explain behavior. He compares several different aspects of these models and then questions whether an energy concept is necessary to explain behavior. See reading 2 for details of Tinbergen's hierarchical system.

Reprinted from *Symposium of the Society for Experimental Biology. No. XIV. Models and Analogues in Biology*, 1960, 119–213, with the permission of the author and the Company of Biologists Limited.

Introduction

The problem of motivation is central to the understanding of behaviour. Why, in the absence of learning and fatigue, does the response to a constant stimulus change

from time to time? To what is the apparent spontaneity of behaviour due? This paper is concerned with one type of model which has been developed to help answer such questions—namely that in which changes in the organism's activity are ascribed to changes in the quantity or distribution of an entity comparable to physical, chemical or electrical energy.

Such models have been developed by theoreticians with widely differing backgrounds, interests and aims, and the frameworks of ideas built round them diverge in many respects; but in each case the energy treatment of motivation is a central theme (cf. Carthy, 1951; Kennedy, 1954). They have had a great influence on psychological thought, and although they are unlikely to continue to be useful, it is instructive to examine their nature, their achievements and their limitations.

The Models

The four models or theories to be discussed here are those of Freud, McDougall, Lorenz and Tinbergen. They are only four of many in which energy concepts are used, but in them the energy analogy is made explicit in terms of a mechanical model, instead of being merely implied by a 'drive' variable which is supposed to energize behaviour. The models were designed to account for many features of behaviour in addition to the phenomena of motivation, and here it will be necessary to extract only those aspects relevant to the present theme.

In the psycho-analytic model (Freud, 1932, 1940) the id is pictured as a chaos of instinctive energies which are supposed to originate from some source of stimulation within the body. Their control is in the hands of the ego, which permits, postpones or denies their satisfaction. In this the ego may be dominated by the super-ego. The energy with which Freud was particularly concerned—the sexual energy or libido—is supposed not to require immediate discharge. It can be postponed, repressed, sublimated, and so on. The source of this energy lies in different erogenous zones as the individual develops, being successively oral, anal and phallic, and it is in relation to these changes that the individual develops his responses to the external world. The instinctual energy is supposed to undergo various vicissitudes, discussions of

which often imply that it can be stored, or that it can flow like a fluid. It may become attached to objects represented by mental structures or processes (libidinal cathexes) and later withdrawn from them in a manner that Freud (1940) likened to protoplasmic pseudopodia: it has also been compared with an electric charge. Thus some of the characteristics of the energy depend on its quantitative distribution.

McDougall (1913) envisaged energy liberated on the afferent side of the nervous system, and held back by 'sluice gates.' If the stimuli necessary to open the gates are not forthcoming, the energy 'bubbles over' among the motor mechanisms to produce appetitive behaviour. On receipt of appropriate stimuli, one of the gates opens, and the afferent channels of this instinct become the principal outlet for all available free energy. Later (1923) he used a rather more complex analogy in which each instinct was pictured as a chamber in which gas is constantly liberated. The gas can escape via pipes leading to the executive organs when the appropriate lock(s) is opened. The gas is supposed to drive the motor mechanisms, just as an electric motor is driven by electrical energy.

The models of Lorenz and Tinbergen have much in common with McDougall's. Lorenz's 'reaction specific energy' was earlier (1937) thought of as a gas constantly being pumped into a container, and later (e.g. 1950) as a liquid in a reservoir. In the latter case it is supposed that the reservoir can discharge through a spring-loaded valve at the bottom. The valve is opened in part by the hydrostatic pressure in the reservoir, and in part by a weight on a scale pan which represents the external stimulus. As the reservoir discharges, the hydrostatic pressure on the valve decreases, and thus a greater weight is necessary to open the valve again.

Tinbergen (1951) pictured a heirarchy of nervous centres, each of which has the properties of a Lorenzian reservoir. Each centre can be loaded with 'motivational impulses' from a superordinated centre and/or other sources. Until the appropriate stimulus is given the outflow is blocked and the animal can show only appetitive behaviour: when the block is removed the impulses can flow into the subordinate centre or be discharged in action.

It is important to emphasize again that the theories of these authors have little in common except for the energy model of motivation—they were devised for different purposes, and the more recent authors have been at pains to emphasize their differences from the earlier ones. For instance, for McDougall the most important feature of instinct was the 'conative-affective core', while for Lorenz it was the stereotyped motor pattern. Furthermore, the models differ greatly in the precision with which they are defined. The Freudian model is a loose one: its flexibility is perhaps necessary in view of the great range of behavioural and mental phenomena it comprehends, but makes it very difficult to test. The other models are more tightly defined, but differ, as we shall see, in their supposed relations to the nervous system.

In spite of such differences, all these models share the idea of a substance, capable of energizing behaviour, held back in a container and subsequently released in action.° In the discussion which follows, I shall be little concerned with the other details of the models, or with the ways in which the theories based on them differ. Furthermore, I shall disregard the niceties of terminology, lumping instinctual energy, psychophysical energy, action specific energy and motivational impulses together as, for present purposes, basically similar concepts.

Reality Status of the Models

Until recently, students of the more complex types of behaviour could get little

° It will be clear that in some respects the postulated entity has the properties of a material substance, rather than energy. However it is on the 'energy' properties of flowing and 'doing work' that the models primarily depend.

help from physiology, and had to fashion their concepts without reference to the properties of the nervous system. Many, indeed, advocated this course from preference, either on grounds of expediency, suggesting that knowledge of the nervous system was still too primitive and might be misleading, or on principle, claiming that physiology and behaviour were distinct levels of discourse. At present the models and theories used in attempts to understand, explain or predict behaviour range from those whose nature is such that physiological data are irrelevant (Skinner, 1938) to those which consist of a forthright attempt to describe psychological data in physiological terms (Hebb, 1947, 1955). The former type may be applicable over a wide range of phenomena, but only at a limited range of analytical levels: the latter may point the way to analysis at lower levels, but their expectancy of life depends on their compatibility with the phenomena found there.

The originators of all the models discussed here regard them as having some relation to structures in the nervous system, but vary in the emphasis which they lay on this. Tinbergen, although freely emphasizing the hypothetical status of his model, clearly regards his 'centres' as neural structures, and his 'motivational impulses' as related to nerve impulses. He speaks of his hierarchical scheme as a 'graphic picture of the nervous mechanisms involved'. McDougall likewise regards the relationship between model and nervous system as a close one, for he localizes the 'sluice gates' in the optic thalamus. Lorenz, on the other hand, usually treated his model in an 'as if' fashion—he did not suggest that we should look for reservoirs in the body. He did, however, bring forward physiological evidence in its support —quoting, for instance, Sherrington's work (1906) on spinal contrast, and von Holst's (1936) work on endogenous rhythms in fishes; and he sometimes uses such terms as 'central nervous impulse flow' as a synonym for 'reaction specific energy'. His use of physiological evidence was, however, *post hoc*—the model was based on behavioural data and the physiological evidence came later.

Freud's model developed from physiology, in particular from a sensory-excitation-motor-discharge picture of nervous function, and its basic postulates are almost a direct translation of such ideas into psychological terms—excitation into mental energy, the discharges of excitation into pleasure, and so on (Peters, 1958). However, Freudian theory developed far beyond these primitive notions, and then bore little or no relation to physiology, even though the instincts were supposed to have an ultimately physiological source.

Thus two of these models (Tinbergen and McDougall) had explicitly physiological implications; that of Lorenz was usually used in an 'as if' fashion; and Freud's, although it had physiological roots, became divorced from any supposed structures or functions in the nervous system. However, as we shall see, all have been influenced by the covert introduction of existence postulates concerning the explanatory concepts used.

The Relation of Behavioural Energy to Physical Energy

In these theories the concept of energy, earlier acquired by the physical sciences from everyday observation of behaviour, is reclaimed for use in its original context. In accounting for the organism's changing responsiveness, the theorist is concerned with its capacity for doing work and an energy concept seems an obvious choice. The use of such a concept, however, brings with it the temptation of ascribing to the behavioural energy the various properties of physical energy. Thus it may be said to flow from point to point, or to exist in more than one form (bound or free, in Freudian theory). It is of fundamental importance to the theorist to recognize that such properties are additional postulates in the behaviour theory: because

behavioural energy is postulated to account for the activity of organisms, it *need* share no other properties with the energy postulated to account for the movement of matter. The distinction is particularly important in that students of behaviour, while using a concept of behavioural energy to explain the behaviour of the whole animal, may simultaneously be concerned in establishing bridgeheads with physiologists, who use energy in a manner closely similar to the physicists.

Freud ascribed many of the properties of physical energy to mental energy, which was stored, flowed, discharged, and so on, but he did recognize the importance of distinguishing between them. Thus he wrote (1940) 'We have no data which enable us to come nearer to a knowledge of it [mental energy] by analogy with other forms of energy'. The use of the phrase 'other forms' is revealing, and finds an echo in the work of the psychoanalyst Colby (1955), who discussed this question in detail and elaborated an even more complex energy model. Colby regards mental energy as a postulated form of energy in addition to mechanical, thermal, electrical and chemical, and states that it '*does not disobey*' the principles formulated for other forms of energy, though conversion into these other forms is not 'yet' possible. It appears that for him psychic energy would be expected to obey the Laws of Thermodynamics but for the fact that organisms are open systems. Colby, however, is clearly ambivalent on this issue, for elsewhere he emphasizes that psychic energy is not mechanical, thermal, chemical or electric, and writes 'Perhaps we have no right to speak of energy at all'. Another analyst (Kubie, 1947), with a highly sophisticated attitude to energy concepts, draws a sharp distinction between psychic and physical energies, although he does invest them with similar properties:

'It is therefore scientifically necessary to keep clearly in mind the fact that the psychodynamics dealt with in psychoanalysis refer to something which is loosely analogous to, but still very far from, the exacter field of thermodynamics. These psychodynamics deal with an effort to estimate *(a)* the sources of energy, *(b)* the kinds of quantities of energy, *(c)* the transformations of energy, one into another, and *(d)* the distributions of energy. But the "energy" referred to here means not what is intended by the physicist, but *simply apparent intensities of feelings and impulses, or in psychoanalytic terms "the libido".*

McDougall was less reserved than Freud on this issue, and clearly regarded his 'psycho-physical energy' as a form of physical energy. 'We are naturally inclined to suppose that it is a case of conversion of potential energy, stored in the tissues in chemical form, into the free or active form, kinetic or electric or what not; and probably this view is correct.' He further suggested that there is a positive correlation between the flow of energy and the 'felt strength' of the impulse.

With Lorenz and Tinbergen this question was concealed. Lorenz's reaction specific energy, pictured as a liquid, was clearly only distantly related to physical energy. Since the model was primarily an 'as if' one, the question of conversion to physical energy did not arise. Tinbergen's motivational impulses, although supposedly related to physical energy exchanges in the nervous system, were not regarded as physical energy sums themselves. In spite of this, a number of properties of physical energy came to be ascribed to them—thus they could be 'discharged in action,' 'stored,' 'released,' 'flow,' 'spark over' and so on (Hinde, 1956). This has undoubtedly influenced the course of research (see below).

Thus although, in the four schemes at present under consideration, the relation between behavioural energy and physical energy was not particularly close, some properties of the latter insinuated themselves almost unnoticed into the behavioural theories. Physical and behavioural energy have in fact often been confused in theories of motivation: for instance, Brown

(1953) uses as evidence for an energizing function of drives the 'marked disproportionality between the energy content of a stimulus and the energy expended in response'.

The transposition of properties from physical to behavioural energy could be helpful, suggesting new questions which open further avenues of research or coordinating previously unrelated facts. However, their presence is a danger, and likely to lead to sterile endeavour, if their nature is not recognized, and if they are introduced not as stated postulates but as known properties of physical energy which are therefore without further thought ascribed to a hypothetical behavioural energy. Some examples of confusions which have arisen in this way are discussed below.

Number of Forms of Energy Postulated

An important issue in these models is the number of forms of energy postulated. The behaviour of an organism is diverse: is a different form of energy to be postulated for each type of behaviour, or is there only one form producing behaviour differing according to the structure within which it acts?

Freud, in an early model, postulated two basic types of energy—sexual energy (libido) and energy pertaining to the self-preservative instinct.[†] Later, sexual and self-preservative were grouped together as 'Life' instincts, in contrast to the 'Death'

† If the difference between the energies of the sexual and self-preservative instincts is one of kind, then the dichotomy is distasteful to biologists, for there is no reason for supposing that different examples of sexual (in a broad sense) behaviour on the one hand, and self-preservative behaviour on the other, classified together on functional grounds, have anything causally in common. Lloyd Morgan (1912) made a similar dichotomy in his top level instincts of self-preservation and race maintenance, which also involves a confusion of functional and causal categories.

instincts, which become manifest when directed outwards as the instinct of destruction.‡ Within each major group of instincts are recognized component instincts differing in their source, aim, object and in their quantitative distribution: but it is not always clear whether these differences are thought to lie in the nature of the energy, or in the structure within which the energy acts. Sometimes Freud stated that the instincts differ primarily because of the differing quantities of excitation accompanying them (Freud, 1915), but later he often implied differences of quality in the energy itself (Freud, 1924). Colby (1955), who, as we have seen, associated the concept of behavioural energy closely with physical energy, emphasized that all energy must be neutral, its 'aim', etc. being acquired only when it acts through a structure.

McDougall is ambivalent on the number of sources of energy, stating the possibilities on the one hand that the instincts each have their own energy, and on the other that they all draw on a common supply: he inclines towards the second view.

Lorenz is concerned primarily with limited sequences of behaviour, and not with a synthesizing model of the behaviour of the whole organism. It was therefore sufficient for him to talk about action specific energy. From his earlier writings it was not clear whether the specificity of this energy was supposed to be due to its nature or to the structure within which it acts, but later, because of the occurrence of displacement activities (see below), he concluded that the specificity was due to the structure. Furthermore, Lorenz did not suppose that the reservoirs for functionally related activities were fed from a common source: he (1937) emphatically

‡ There remains, by implication, a third type of energy—Ego—which may oppose both sexual and destructive instincts. Freud thought of the Ego as deriving energy from the Id, but there are divergent views on this. Indeed there are numerous variants on this theme—some psychoanalysts, for example, postulate a neutral energy.

opposed McDougall's view of superordinated instincts which employ motor mechanisms as means to an end, regarding such instincts merely as functional categories. Rather Lorenz emphasized the individuality of each type of response, and ascribes to the external situation the integration of discrete responses into functional units.

Tinbergen's scheme differs from that of Lorenz in this matter, for the motivational impulses were supposed to descend the hierarchical system of nervous centres: each such system constituted an 'instinct'. The impulses were thus general at least to all the activities of one hierarchical system, and, since he regarded (1952) 'sparking over' from one system to another as possible, perhaps to all. Since Tinbergen suggests that each activity is supplied by motivational impulses both from the superordinated centre and from its own specific source, his scheme combines features from those of McDougall and Lorenz.

The importance of this question for energy theorists is emphasized by Thorpe (1956). Most behaviour is directive in the sense that variable means are used to a constant end. If all behaviour depends on one type of energy, then the directiveness must be a consequence of the structure in which the energy acts: since the motor patterns used to achieve a certain goal may be diverse, this seems to demand a fantastic complexity of structure. Thorpe therefore prefers to think of there being an element of directiveness in the drive itself—and thus prefers Lorenz's model, in which the energy is specific to the action, to Tinbergen's scheme, in which the motivational impulses flow down a hierarchical scheme containing a limited number of channels.

Utility and Level of Applicability of Energy Models

These energy models of motivation were developed with a minimum of reference to physiological data—they were intended for the understanding or prediction of behaviour from behavioural data.

It is therefore on this level that, in the first instance, they must be assessed. It has been said that it does not help to ascribe feeding behaviour to a feeding drive, or to feeding specific energy, any more than it helps to postulate a locomotive force to explain the progress of a railway engine. This type of criticism is based on a misunderstanding. Although the mere postulation of a locomotive force may be of little use, there is a level—that of classical dynamics—in which the language of forces and so on helps a great deal in predicting the behaviour of railway engines. We can say, for instance, what will happen if the engine meets a stationary truck on the line (see also McDougall, 1923).

In a similar way, energy models have been surprisingly successful. The Freudian energy model not only accounts for the more general properties of motivated behaviour, such as its apparent spontaneity and persistence, but also for the manner in which instincts can change their aim (displacement in the psychoanalytical, not the ethological, sense) and the way in which component instincts can replace each other. Similarly, Lorenz's reservoir analogy and Tinbergen's hierarchy comprehend the relation between the threshold of stimulation necessary to elicit a response and the time since it was last released; the occurrence of appetitive behaviour, responses to normally inadequate stimuli, and ultimately vacuum activities (i.e. responses in the absence of the appropriate stimuli) if the releasing stimuli are withhheld; the variations in intensity at which instinctive activities appear; the initial 'warming up' phase and the after-response shown by many responses, and many other aspects of changing responsiveness. Further, differences between the characteristics of response patterns can be related in an 'as if' fashion to differences in the dimensions of the reservoir. These models are thus of value in illustrating diverse properties of behaviour in a simple manner, and can be used for explanation and exposition. In addition, the analytical study of behaviour forms

only a first stage in its understanding—the products of the analysis must be re-synthesized so that the relations between them can be understood: for this such models can be an invaluable aid.

However, we have seen that some of the models purport to go further than this —they are not just 'as if' models of the mechanisms underlying the behaviour, but representations of those mechanisms themselves. They must thus be assessed also by their compatibility with our knowledge of the nervous system. Indeed even the 'as if' models must ultimately be assessed in this way, for only if the model is close to the original will the question it poses be relevant, and only then will it continue to be of service as analysis of the original proceeds. To take an example from physics, the ray theory of light, used originally for explanations of shadow-casting, etc., suggested questions (e.g. 'What is it that travels?') which paved the way for the corpuscular and wave theories. Although the latter is essential in some contexts (such as the explanation of diffraction), the ray theory retains its usefulness, for a treatment of shadow-casting in terms of the wave theory would be unnecessarily clumsy. Further, the two theories remain compatible with, and translatable into, each other (Toulmin, 1953). For similar reasons, it is important to assess these energy models of motivation not only at the behavioural level, but also in terms of their compatibility with lower ones. Although a model must not resemble the original too closely, or it will lose just those properties of simplicity and manipulability which makes it useful, it must approximate to it, or the questions it suggests will be irrelevant.

Difficulties and Dangers

In the following paragraphs we shall consider some of the difficulties and dangers inherent in the use of an energy model of motivation. These arise in part from misunderstandings of the nature of the model, and in part from incompatibilities between the properties of the model and those of the original.

(i) CONFUSION BETWEEN BEHAVIOURAL ENERGY AND PHYSICAL ENERGY

We have already seen that behavioural energy, postulated to account for changes in activity, need share no properties with physical energy. Not only is there no necessary reason why it should be treated as an entity with any of the properties of physical energy, but the question of its convertibility into physical energy is a dangerous red herring. The way in which the properties of the model may be confused with those of the original have been discussed for Freudian theory by Meehl & McCorquodale (1948). Concepts like libido or super-ego may be introduced initially as intervening variables without material properties, but such properties have a way of creeping into discussion without being made explicit. Thus Meehl & McCorquodale point out that libido may be introduced as a term for the 'set of sexual needs' or 'basic strivings,' but subsequently puzzling phenomena are explained in terms of properties of libido, such that it flows, is dammed up, converted, regresses to earlier channels, and so on. Such properties are introduced surreptitiously as occasion demands, and involve a transition from admissible intervening variables, which carry no existence postulates, to hypothetical constructs which require the existence of decidedly improbable entities and processes.

Such difficulties are especially likely to occur when a model which purports to be close to the original, like that of Tinbergen, develops out of an 'as if' model, like that of Lorenz. This case has been discussed elsewhere (Hinde, 1956). To quote but one example, ethologists have called behaviour patterns which appear out of their functional context 'displacement activities'. These activities usually appear when there is reason to think that one or more types of motivation are strong, but unable to find expression in action: instead, the animal shows a displacement activity, which seems to be irrelevant. Thus when a chaffinch has conflicting tendencies to approach and avoid a food dish, it may show preening behaviour. Such irrelevant activities were explained on the energy model by supposing that the thwarted energy 'sparked over' into the displacement activity—sparking over being a property of (electrical) energy which was imputed to the behavioural energy. This idea hindered an analytical study of the causal factors underlying displacement behaviour. Thus it has recently become apparent that many displacement activities are not so causally irrelevant as they appear to be, for those factors which elicit the behaviour in its normal function context are also present when it appears as a displacement activity. For example, some displacement activities appear to be due to autonomic activity aroused as a consequence of fear-provoking stimuli or other aspects of the situation. The displacement activity may consist of the automatic response itself (e.g. feather postures in birds) or of a somatic response to stimuli consequent upon autonomic activity (Andrew, 1956; Morris, 1956). In other cases the displacement behaviour consists of a response to factors continuously present, which was previously inhibited through the greater priority of the incompatible behaviour patterns which are in conflict (van Iersel & Bol, 1958; Rowell, 1959). Of course it remains possible that the intensity of the apparently irrelevant behaviour is influenced by factors not specific to it, including those associated with the conflicting tendencies (see also Hinde, 1959).

Similarly in psychoanalytical theory we find not only that within one category of instincts (e.g. sexual) the constitutent instincts can change their aim, but also that 'they can replace one another—the energy of one instinct passing over to another' (Freud, 1940). Explanations of this type may be useful at a descriptive level, but are misleading as analysis proceeds.

(II) THE DISTINCTION BETWEEN THE ACCUMULATION AND RELEASE OF ENERGY

In all energy models, the energy is supposed to build up and subsequently to be released in action. McDougall, Lorenz and Tinbergen, all of whom were influenced by Wallace Craig, compare the releasing stimulus to a key which opens a lock. This apparent dichotomy between releasing and motivating effects is a property of the model, and may not be relevant to the mechanisms underlying behaviour. Although many factors appear to have both a motivating and a releasing effect on the responses they affect—they appear both to cause an increase in responsiveness, and to elicit the response—this does not necessarily imply that two distinct processes are at work. For example, if a given input increased the probability of a certain pattern of neural firing, it might appear in behaviour both that the responsiveness was increased and that the behaviour was elicited.

This sort of difficulty is the more likely to arise, the more precisely the model is portrayed. Thus McDougall, who did not work out his model in such detail as Lorenz and Tinbergen, implied that motivation and release were in fact one process when he wrote 'The evoking of the instinctive action, the opening of the door of the instinct on perception of its specific object, increases the urgency of the appetite'.

(III) IMPLICATIONS ABOUT THE CESSATION OF ACTIVITY

In all these theories, the cessation of activity is ascribed to the discharge of energy—the behavioural energy flows away as a consequence of performance. Influenced by the analogy with physical energy, Freud held that the main function of the nervous system is to reduce excitation to the lowest possible level. McDougall, Lorenz and Tinbergen imply a similar view, and the two latter emphasize that it is the performance of more or less stereotyped motor patterns which involve the discharge of the energy.§

This view of the cessation of activities comes naturally from models in which the properties of physical energy are imputed to behavioural energy. It is, however, also supported by another type of argument, also involving a *non sequitur*. Much behaviour is related to an increase in stimulation. Therefore, it might be argued, all activity is due to an increase in stimulation, and cessation of activity is related to a decrease. On an energy model, stimulation may increase the energy, and thus decrease in activity is related to a decrease in energy.

Such a view is incompatible with the data now available on two grounds. First, cessation of activity may be due to the animal encountering a 'goal' stimulus situation, and not to the performance of an activity. If this goal stimulus situation is encountered abnormally early, the behaviour which normally leads to it may not appear at all. McDougall recognized this, and indeed defined his instincts in terms of the goals which brought about a cessation of activity. This, however, made it necessary for him to be rather inconsistent about his energy model. While the energy was supposed to drive the motor mechanisms, it was apparently not consumed in action, but could flow back to other reservoirs or to the general source. The more precisely described Lorenz/Tinbergen models, on the

§ In doing so they did not imply that behavioural energy is converted into physical energy—thus Tinbergen (1952) suggests that even sleep is an activity, in which, presumably, behavioural energy is discharged.

The view that a fall in responsiveness is normally due to the performance of a stereotyped activity is not a necessary consequence of the use of energy models—Freud and McDougall did not suggest that energy could be discharged only in this way—but their use makes such errors more likely. Lorenz and Tinbergen were apparently also influenced by over-generalizing from the observation that performance of some stereotyped activities leads to a fall in responsiveness, to the conclusion that all falls in responsiveness are due to such activities.

other hand, do not allow for reduction in activity by consummatory stimuli: reduction in responsiveness occurs only through the discharge of energy in action. These models are misleading because they are too simple—energy flow is supposed to control not only what happens between stimulus and response, but also the drop in responsiveness when the response is given. In practice, these may be due to quite different aspects of the mechanisms underlying behaviour: for instance the energy model leaves no room for inhibition (Kennedy, 1954). Further, even if the cessation of activity is in some sense due to the performance, many different processes may be involved: the mechanism is not a unitary one, as the energy model implies (see below).

Secondly, if activity is due to the accumulation of energy and cessation to its discharge, the organisms should come to rest when the energy level is minimal. In fact, much behaviour serves the function of bringing the animal into conditions of increased stimulation. This has been shown dramatically with humans subjected to acute sensory deprivation—the experimental conditions are intolerable in spite of the considerable financial reward offered (Bexton, Heron and Scott, 1954). Energy theories are in difficulty over accounting for such 'reactions to deficit' (Lashley, 1938).

(IV) UNITARY NATURE OF EXPLANATION

In these energy models, each type of behaviour is related to the flow of energy. Increase in strength of the behaviour is due to an increased flow of energy, decrease to a diminished flow. The strength of behaviour is thus related to a single mechanism. It is, however, apparent that changes in responsiveness to a constant stimulus may be due to many different processes in the nervous system and in the body as a whole —for instance, the changes consequent upon performance may affect one response or many, may or may not be specific to the stimulus, and may have recovery periods varying from seconds to months. Energy

models, by lumping together diverse processes which affect the strength of behaviour, can lead to an over-simplification of the mechanisms underlying it, and distract attention from the complexities of the behaviour itself. Similarly, energy models are in difficulty with the almost cyclic short-term waxing and waning of such activities as the response of chaffinches to owls, the song of many birds, and so on.

Kubie (1947) has emphasized this point with reference to the psychoanalytic model. Changes in behaviour are referred to quantitative changes in energy distribution, but in fact so many variables are involved (repression, displacement, substitution, etc.) that it is not justifiable to make easy guesses about what varied to produce a given state. Similar difficulties in relation to other models have been discussed by Hinde (1959).

Precht (1952) has elaborated the Lorenzian model to allow for some complication of this sort. Analysing the changes in strength of the hunting behaviour of spiders, he distinguishes between 'drive' which depends on deprivation, and 'excitatory level', which is a function of non-release of the eating pattern. The distinction is an important one, but it may be doubted whether the elaborate hydraulic system which he produced is really an aid to further analysis.

Tinbergen's model translated the Lorenzian reservoir into nervous 'centres'. Changes in response strength are ascribed to the loading of these centres. Now for many types of behaviour it is indeed possible to identify loci in the diencephalon whose ablation leads to the disappearance of the behaviour, whose stimulation leads to its elicitation, and where hormones or solutions produce appropriate effects on behaviour. There is, however, no evidence that 'energy' is accumulated in such centres, nor that response strength depends solely on their state. Indeed the strength of any response depends on many structures, neural and non-neural, and there is no character by character correspondence between such postulated centres and any structure in the brain.

Although the greatest attraction of these energy models is their simplicity—a relatively simple mechanical model accounting for diverse properties of behaviour —there is a danger in this, for one property of the model may correspond to more than one character of the original. This difficulty has in fact arisen in many behaviour systems irrespective of whether they use an energy model of motivation. Thus a single drive variable is sometimes used not only with reference to changes in responsiveness to a constant stimulus, but also to spontaneity, temporal persistence of the effects of the stimuli, after-responses (i.e. the persistence of activities after the stimulus is removed), the temporal grouping of functionally related activities, and so on. As discussed elsewhere (Hinde, 1959), there is no *a priori* reason why these diverse characters of behaviour should depend on a single feature of the underlying mechanism: an over-simple model may hinder analysis.

(v) INDEPENDENCE OF ACTIVITIES

Another difficulty which arises from the use of energy models, though by no means peculiar to them, is due to the emphasis laid on the independence of different activities. Lorenz & Tinbergen (1938) write 'If ever we may say that only part of an organism is involved in a reaction, it may confidently be said of instinctive action'. Activities are interpreted as due to energies acting in specific structures, and not as responses of the organisms as a whole. Both types of attitude carry disadvantages, but an over-emphasis on the independence of activities leads to a neglect of, for instance, sensory, metabolic or temperamental factors which affect many activities.

Is an Energy Concept Necessary?

We have seen that these energy models will account for diverse properties of behaviour, but that they meet with serious difficulties when the behaviour is analysed more closely. They have also been strangely sterile in leading to bridgeheads with physiology. These shortcomings of energy models have been emphasized by a number of other writers (e.g. Kubie, 1947; Deutsch, 1953; Bowlby, 1958). Energy concepts are useful in descriptions of changes in behaviour, but are they necessary? Colby states that 'a dynamic psychology must conceive of psychic activities as the product of forces, and forces involve energy sums. It is thus quite necessary that metapsychology have some sort of energy theory'. Is this really so?

Kubie (1947) has pointed out that psychological phenomena are the product of an interplay of diverse factors. A rearrangement of these factors can alter the pattern of behaviour without any change in hypothetical stores of energy. Such a view is in harmony with the known facts about the functioning of the nervous system. The central nervous system is not normally inert, having to be prodded into activity by specific stimuli external to it. Rather it is in a state of continuous activity—a state supported primarily by the non-specific effects of stimuli acting through the brain-stem reticular system. Factors such as stimuli and hormones which affect specific patterns of behaviour are to be thought of as controlling this activity, of increasing the probability of one pattern rather than another. Changes in strength or threshold can thus be thought of as changes in the probability of one pattern of activity rather than another, and not as changes in the level of energy in a specific neural mechanism. This involves some return to a 'telephone exchange' theory of behaviour, but with emphasis on the non-specific input necessary to keep the switch mechanism active, and with switches which are not all-or-none, but determine the probability of one pattern rather than another. Furthermore, switching does not depend solely on external stimuli—i.e. we are not concerned with a purely reflexological model. This is not the place to pursue this view further: it suffices to say that it seems possible and preferable to formulate behaviour theories in which concepts of energy, and of drives which energize behaviour, have no role.

Summary

1. Phenomena of motivation have often been explained in terms of an energy model.

2. The energy models used by Freud, McDougall, Lorenz and Tinbergen are outlined briefly.

3. The extent to which these models are considered by their authors to correspond with structures in the nervous system is discussed.

4. The relation between physical energy and the postulated behavioural energies are examined.

5. The number of forms of energy postulated by each author is discussed.

6. These models have had considerable success in discussions of the behaviour of the whole animal.

7. They have, however, certain grave disadvantages. In particular, these arise from a confusion between the properties of physical and behavioural energy, and from attempts to explain multiple processes in terms of simple unitary mechanisms.

8. It seems doubtful whether an energy concept is in fact necessary at all.

Acknowledgments

I am grateful to Drs. J. W. L. Beament, John Bowlby, Charles Kaufman and W. H. Thorpe for their comments on the manuscript.

REFERENCES

ANDREW, R. J., 1956 Some remarks on conflict situations, with special reference to *Emberiza* spp. *Brit. J. Anim. Behav.* 4, 41–45.

BEXTON, W. H., W. HERON, and T. H. SCOTT, 1954 Effects of decreased variation in the sensory environment. *Canad. J. Psychol.* 8, 70–76.

BOWLBY, J., 1958 The nature of the child's tie to his mother. *Internat. J. Psychoanalysis*, 39.

BROWN, J. S., 1953 Problems presented by the concept of acquired drives. In: *Current Theory and Research in Motivation*, a symposium. Univ. of Nebraska.

CARTHY, J. D., 1951 Instinct. *New Biology*, 10, 95–105.

COLBY, K. M., 1955 *Energy and Structure in Psychoanalysis*. New York: Ronald Press Co.

DEUTSCH, J. A., 1953 A new type of behaviour theory. *Brit. J. Psychol.* 44, 304–317.

FREUD, S., 1915 Instincts and their vicissitudes. *Collected Papers*, Vol. IV.

FREUD, S., 1923 *The Ego and the Id*. London: Hogarth Press, 1947.

FREUD, S., 1924 The economic problem in masochism. *Collected Papers*, Vol. II, XXII.

FREUD, S., 1932 *New Introductory Lectures on Psychoanalysis*. London: Hogarth Press, 1946.

FREUD, S., 1940 *An Outline of Psychoanalysis*. New York. London: Hogarth Press, 1949.

HEBB, D. O., 1947 *The Organization of Behaviour*. New York: Wiley.

HEBB, D. O., 1955 Drives and the C.N.S. (Conceptual Nervous System). *Psych. Rev.* 62, 243–254.

HINDE, R. A., 1956 Ethological models and the concept of drive. *Brit. J. Philos. Sci.* 6, 321–331.

HINDE, R. A., 1959 Unitary drives. *Anim. Behav.* 7, 130–141.

HINDE, R. A., 1960 (In press.)

HOLST, E. VON, 1936 Versuche zur Theorie der relativen Koordination. *Pflüg. Arch. ges. Physiol.* 237, 93–121.

IERSEL, J. J. A. VAN, and A. C. BOL, 1958 Preening of two tern species. A study on displacement. *Behaviour* 13, 1–89.

KENNEDY, J. S., 1954 Is modern ethology objective? *Brit. J. Anim. Behav.* 2, 12–19.

KUBIE, L. S., 1947 The fallacious use of quantitative concepts in dynamic psychology. *Psychoanalytic Quart.* 16, 507–518.

LASHLEY, K. S., 1938 Experimental analysis of instinctive behaviour. *Psychol. Rev.* 45, 445–471.

LLOYD MORGAN, C., 1912 *Instinct and Experience*. London: Methuen.

LORENZ, K., 1937 Über die Bildung des Instinktbegriffes. *Naturwiss* 25, 289–300, 307–318, 324–331.

LORENZ, K., 1950   The comparative method in studying innate behaviour patterns. *Sym. Soc. Exp. Biol.* IV, 221–268.

LORENZ, K., and N. TINBERGEN, 1938   Taxis und Instinkthandlung in der Eirollbewegung der Graugans. *Z. Tierpsychol.* **2**, 1–29. Translated in: C. H. SCHILLER, 1957. *Instinctive Behaviour.* London: Methuen.

McDOUGALL, W., 1913   The sources and direction of psychophysical energy. *Amer. J. Insanity.* Not consulted. Quoted in McDOUGALL, 1923.

McDOUGALL, W., 1923   *An Outline of Psychology.* London: Methuen.

MEEHL, P. E., and K. McCORQUODALE, 1948   On a distinction between hypothetical constructs and intervening variables. *Psych. Rev.* **55**, 95–107.

MORRIS, D., 1956   The feather postures of birds and the problem of the origin of social signals. *Behaviour* **9**, 75–113.

PETERS, R. S., 1958   *The Concept of Motivation.* London: Routledge and Kegan Paul.

PRECHT, H., 1952   Über das angeborene Verhalten von Tieren. Versuche an Springspinnen. *Z. Tierpsychol.* **9**, 207–230.

ROWELL, C. H. F., 1959   The occurrence of grooming in the behaviour of Chaffinches in approach-avoidance conflict situations, and its bearing on the concept of "displacement activity." *Ph.D. Thesis.* Cambridge.

SHERRINGTON, C. S., 1906   *Integrative Action of the Nervous System.* New York: Scribner.

SKINNER, B. F., 1938   *The Behavior of Organisms.* New York: Appleton Century.

THORPE, W. H., 1956   *Learning and Instinct in Animals.* London: Methuen.

TINBERGEN, N., 1951   *The Study of Instinct.* Oxford.

TINBERGEN, N., 1952   Derived activities: their causation, biological significance, origin and emancipation during evolution. *Quart. Rev. Biol.* **27**, 1–32.

TOULMIN, S. E., 1953   *The Philosophy of Science.* London: Hutchinson.

M. E. BITTERMAN

48   Toward a Comparative Psychology of Learning*

M. E. Bitterman is a noted learning theorist whose early work was devoted almost exclusively to studies of the laboratory rat. Recently, however, Bitterman has changed the emphasis of his work and, in this connection, undertaken studies on a greater variety of species. In this reading, he states the goals of his new research and reviews some of the problems he has encountered in studying learning in lower animals.

Reprinted from *The American Psychologist*, 1960, **15**, 704–712, with the permission of the author and the American Psychological Association.

In the early years of this century, when the experimental study of animal intelligence was just getting under way, many different species were brought into the laboratory. From the very beginning, to be sure, there was some preference for the higher animals, but, on the whole, early interest ranged rather widely up and down the

* This paper is adapted from an address to the Eastern Psychological Association at its 1959 meeting. The research described has been supported by Grant M-2857 from the National Institute of Mental Health and Contract Nonr-2829(00) with the Office of Naval Research. Reproduction of this paper in whole or in part is permitted for the purposes of the United States Government.

phylogenetic scale. Before long, however, the scope of research narrowed. Attention became fixed on a small number of mammalian forms, which were chosen primarily for reasons of convenience, and treated as representative of animals in general, with the cheap and docile rat easily leading all the rest.

A set of curves which nicely illustrates this trend was published some years ago by Beach (1950). Based on a count of papers appearing between 1911 and 1948 in the *Journal of Comparative and Physiological Psychology* and its forerunners, the *Journal of Comparative Psychology* and the *Journal of Animal Behavior,* the curves show how interest in the rat mounted rapidly, while interest in the submammalian forms declined. In the thirties, a stable pattern emerged, about 60% of the papers dealing with the rat, about 30% with mammals other than the rat, and about 10% with the lower forms (the submammalian vertebrates and the invertebrates). If we make the computations required to bring these curves up to date, we find no significant change in the state of affairs decried by Beach a decade ago. Please note that Beach's curves are based on all papers published in a single journal. If we count only the papers on learning, and look at a broader sample of journals, the effect becomes even more striking. About 90% of our work on animal learning has been done with the rat.

Of course, specialization has its advantages, and, if the process of learning were essentially the same in all animals, it would be rather improvident of us to diffuse our efforts over the phylogenetic scale; but the only way to find out whether the process of learning *is* essentially the same in all animals is to make some careful studies at widely separated points in the scale. We have not made such studies. It is our willingness to *assume* that the process of learning is essentially the same in all animals which has been responsible in large measure for our concentration on the rat.

The assumption comes to us from Dar-

win, who was interested in psychological as well as in structural continuity. For Darwin, novelty was incompatible with continuity, and his purpose was to demonstrate that any seemingly unique property which made its appearance in the animal series really was not unique at all—that some hint or promise of it always could be discovered at an earlier point in the series. On the basis of the only evidence available to him —the tall tales of naturalists and zookeepers—Darwin decided that phylogenetic differences in intelligence were differences "of degree and not of kind." Not even in the intelligence of man could Darwin find anything new. Capacities which *seemed* peculiar to man, he explained, could be traced to man's use of language, which itself—"half-art and half-instinct"—clearly bore "the stamp of its gradual evolution" (1871, pp. 105-106). Darwin's formula for bridging the gap between man and the infrahuman animals has a contemporary flavor; it finds wide use even today.

The early comparative psychologists were not entirely convinced by Darwin's arguments. Critical of his anecdotal evidence, and proud of their own new methods, they were determined to have a look for themselves; but their skepticism did not last long. Observing a variety of animals in problem boxes, mazes, and discriminative situations of one sort or another, they were more impressed by the similarities in behavior than by the differences, and quickly succumbed to the Darwinian view. Thorndike, himself, showed the way. At the outset, his contempt for certain features of Darwin's position was undisguised —"man was no more an animal with language," he wrote, "than an elephant was a cow with a proboscis" (1898, p. 87)—but, prepared though he was to find important phylogenetic differences in mode of learning, he found none. His very earliest observations led him to the "working hypothesis" that the process of learning was essentially the same throughout the phylogenetic series. All animals, for Thorndike, were "systems of connections subject to change by the law of exercise and effect" (1911, p. 280), differing only in the particular connections formed and in the ease of connection. The influential Watson took the same position, although he rejected the law of effect and tried to get along with exercise alone—"in passing from the unicellular organisms to man," said Watson, "no new principle is needed" (1914, p. 318) —and gradually Thorndike's working hypothesis became transformed into an article of faith. The transformation is reflected in Beach's curves. As a working hypothesis, the proposition that learning is essentially the same in all animals led to the study of many animals. As an article of faith, it led, by the principle of least effort, to concentration on one.

Specific illustrations of the contemporary faith are not hard to find. Dollard and Miller base their account of human personality and psychotherapy on the assumption that, as they put it, "any general phenomena of learning found in rats will also be found in people" (1950, p. 63). They admit that "people may display additional phenomena not found in rats," but at no point in their book can one find any indication that they take the possibility very seriously. What they refer to as "the higher mental processes" of man they explain in terms of mediating responses, primarily linguistic in character, to which the general laws of stimulus-response connection are assumed to apply.

Another interesting example of the contemporary faith was provided by Skinner a few years ago, when, in an address to the Eastern Psychological Association, he attempted to justify his disregard of the standard statistical procedures. Those procedures are necessitated, he said, only by the fact of individual differences, and they lose all point when individual differences are eliminated "in advance of measurement." To demonstrate the extent to which his own method eliminates irrelevant sources of variability, he presented, among others, the curves shown in Figure 1. The curves were made by three animals trained

FIG. 1. Cumulative-frequency curves for pigeon, rat, and monkey (not necessarily in that order) trained on a multiple fixed-interval-fixed-ratio schedule of reinforcement. (From SKINNER, 1956.)

in three different laboratories on a multiple fixed-interval-fixed-ratio schedule of reinforcement—one by a pigeon, one by a rat, and one by a monkey. "Pigeon, rat, monkey, which is which?" Skinner asked, and he answered:

It doesn't matter. Of course, these three species have behavioral repertoires which are as different as their anatomies. But once you have allowed for differences in the ways in which they make contact with the environment, and in the ways in which they act upon the environment, what remains of their behavior shows astonishingly similar properties. Mice, cats, dogs, and human children could have added other curves to this figure. And when organisms which differ as widely as this nevertheless show similar properties of behavior, differences between the same species may be viewed more hopefully. Difficult problems of idiosyncrasy or individuality will always arise as products of biological and cultural processes, but it is the very business of the experimental analysis of behavior to devise techniques which reduce their effects except when they are explicitly under investigation (1956, pp. 230–231).

The function of these curves, the context suggests, was not to demonstrate that the process of learning is essentially the same in pigeon, rat, and monkey; that was assumed. The function of the curves was to demonstrate the power of the method, which was found in the fact that it *reveals* the essential similarity of the three animals despite substantial sensory and motor "idiosyncrasies."

Whatever Skinner's purpose, his curves do, of course, show some interesting similarities in the learned behavior of quite different animals, and evidence of the same sort has been accumulating since the turn of the century. A comparable set of curves dating back to the years between 1901 and 1904 is shown in Figure 2. Like those of Skinner, they represent the work of three independent investigators working with three different animals—a monkey, a rat, and a bird (in this case, a sparrow). The apparatus employed was the Hampton Court maze, as popular in its time as Skinner's box is today. "Monkey, rat, sparrow, which is which?" it was asked at the turn

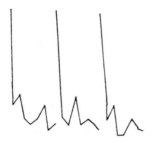

FIG. 2. Relative-error curves for sparrow, rat, and monkey (not necessarily in that order) trained in a Hampton Court maze. (After SMALL, 1901; KINNAMAN, 1902; and PORTER, 1904.)

of the century, although the question went to the nature of phylogenetic differences rather than to the power of the maze method, and the answer came: "It doesn't matter." That answer is no more warranted now than it was 50 or 60 years ago. Attractive as the Darwinian hypothesis may seem, it should not be accepted on the basis of superficial resemblances of this sort. The resemblances may, in fact, be more than superficial, but we shall never know until our level of inquiry becomes more than superficial.

Our skepticism must, of course, be based to a considerable extent on some guesswork about the significance of phylogenetic differences in brain development. Thorndike, too, was interested in brain development, but he was inclined to attribute to it a purely quantitative significance; he

early speculated that brain development meant merely the capacity for a greater number of connections and greater efficiency of connection. Even in recent years this kind of thinking has been common—for example, Miller (1951) has suggested that brain development may have no more significance than the addition of banks of keys to an automatic calculator—but brain development is more than an increase in the mass of brain tissue. New structures, such as the cortex, have appeared, which suggest the possibility of new functions. It is interesting to note, by the way, that the acceptance of the Darwinian hypothesis was accompanied by a growing disregard for the facts of brain structure. After giving up their inquiry into animal consciousness, the early comparative psychologists were at some pains to establish that there still remained to them an area of investigation different from that of the zoologists, and that their methods and findings were as important as those of the zoologists. If some primitive experiments with a maze or a problem box suggested that the process of learning was the same in monkey and sparrow, why then perhaps the difference in brain development had no fundamental significance. That was the attitude which Watson expressed when, speaking of man's frontal lobes, he said that "simply because we have the tissue" it does not necessarily "have a life and death significance" (1914, p. 320). To be sure, we must agree with Watson in principle. If extensive and detailed investigation at a number of widely separated points in the phylogenetic scale reveals no fundamental difference in the mode of learning, we must sooner or later conclude that differences in brain structure have no relevance for mode of learning; but we should not be quite as easily persuaded as Watson.

Of course, not everyone *has* been as easily persuaded. From time to time, skeptical voices have decried the facile acceptance of Darwin's hypothesis and have urged the development of a systematic comparative psychology, but they have not often been able to propose a reasonable way of going about it. One of the most respected advocates of comparative research was Yerkes (1917), whose approach was that of the mental tester. Yerkes' idea was to develop a standardized situation appropriate to the sensory-motor capacities of a variety of species, and to order the species on the basis of their performance in it. This seems to be the common conception of comparative psychology even today. For example, following the lead of Harlow (1949), a number of investigators recently have been comparing raccoons, children, chimpanzees, and monkeys of varying description in terms of their rates of improvement in long series of discriminative problems. No wonder there has been little enthusiasm for comparative psychology so conceived. When I mention to someone that I am making comparative studies of learning, his first question is apt to be, not "How are you going about it?" but "How do you know that your measures are comparable?" He assumes automatically that I am comparing the animals in terms of certain absolute measures of performance from which I propose to infer differences in ability, and he wonders, then, how I can ever be sure that differences in performance *are* due to differences in ability rather than to sensory, or to motor, or to motivational differences. I sometimes find difficulty in convincing such a person that there is another kind of comparative research.

Suppose that I introduce a target into the living tank of a fish and reward the animal with a pellet of food for pushing against it.† The measure of performance is latency of response—the number of seconds which elapse between the introduction of the target and the animal's response to it—and I plot a curve showing change in latency over a series of reinforced trials. After the latency of response has fallen to a stable level, I terminate reinforcement and plot the progressive increase in latency

† For methodological details, see Longo and Bitterman (1959).

which ensues. This procedure is directly analogous to one which has been used rather widely with the rat, and the results obtained—the acquisition and extinction curves—are quite similar to those for the rat. The absolute latencies may be very different in the two animals, but the *relation* between latency and trials is very much the same under conditions of consistent reinforcement and nonreinforcement, and it is the relation in which I am interested. In the past 50 or 60 years, we have begun to work out many such relations for the rat, and our theory of learning in the rat represents an effort to find order and meaning in those relations. I am interested now in the extent to which similar relations are to be found for the fish, because I am interested ultimately in determining whether a single theory will fit both animals.

Here, then, is the plan: Taking the much-studied rat as a point of departure, I select for comparison another animal—a fish—which is different enough from the rat to provide a marked phylogenetic contrast, yet similar enough to be studied under analogous conditions. The two animals are not to be compared in terms of their absolute scores in some standard apparatus. Work with the fish, like work with the rat, is to be directed at the discovery of functional relations. Its goal is a theory of the fish with which to compare the theory of the rat (Bitterman, Wodinsky, and Candland, 1958).

This conception of the comparative psychology of learning (as an attempt to determine whether learning in different animals may be understood in terms of the same set of laws or whether different laws are required) is not a new one. It was implied in the writings of Thorndike, and in the work of a small number of subsequent investigators, such as Schneirla (1946), who continued to take the comparative problem seriously. It was stated quite clearly by Hull (1945), although he himself did not give much weight to the possibility that different laws might operate at the different phylogenetic levels. As yet, however, there has been no explicit attempt to deal with a methodological difficulty which has seemed to stand between this conception and fruitful research—a difficulty similar to that by which the mental-test strategy is utterly defeated.

To the extent that functional relations of the same kind appear in fish and rat no one is troubled. The principle of parsimony leads us all to assume—though perhaps incorrectly—that the same process of learning is operating in the two forms. Suppose, however, that different functional relations appear. We may not be as ready then to infer that the underlying processes of learning are different. We may wonder, and with good reason, whether some peripheral factor—sensory, or motor, or motivational—is responsible for the discrepancy, and we may despair of ever being able to control such variables in comparative experiments. How should we hope to find a situation whose sensory and motor demands upon our fish are equivalent to those of the runway of the bar pressing apparatus upon the rat? How should we hope to produce in our fish levels of motivation comparable to those which commonly prevail in experiments with the rat? Fortunately, the problem is not an insoluble one. While the prospects for *control by equation* are slim indeed, there is available a perfectly suitable alternative, which we may speak of as *control by systematic variation*.

Consider, for example, the paradoxical relation between consistency of reinforcement and resistance to extinction which has been established in a variety of experiments with the rat, and suppose that a like effect fails to appear in an analogous experiment with fish—that a partially reinforced group of fish extinguishes *more* rapidly than a consistently reinforced group. Are we led at once to the conclusion that different processes of learning operate in fish and rat? Certainly not. We must consider carefully the possibility that the relation between consistency of reinforcement and resistance to extinction is influenced by certain contextual variables,

such as drive level or effortfulness of response, and that in our experiment with the fish we have permitted one of these variables to take on a value well beyond the range prevailing in experiments with the rat. Interactive interpretations of this kind can be tested without great difficulty. It does not matter that we are unable to equate such variables as drive level in fish and rat; we know how to manipulate them and that is enough. If, working with *either* animal, we find the same relation between consistency of reinforcement and resistance to extinction at diverse levels of drive, the possibility that a difference *between* animals may be explained in terms of drive level is ruled out, and other interactive hypotheses can be tested in like manner. It may be well to note that the example which I have chosen is more than hypothetical. The initial resistance to extinction of *Tilapia macrocephala* (the fish with which my colleagues and I have been working) *is* greater after consistent than after partial reinforcement, and the outcome is the same with spaced or with massed trials, after relatively small or relatively large amounts of training, and at different levels of drive (Longo and Bitterman, 1960; Wodinsky and Bitterman, 1959, 1960). My main concern here, however, is with general strategy.

Given the decision to study some simple animal (such as the fish) under conditions analogous to those which have been used for the study of learning in the rat, with functional relations to provide the basis for comparing the two forms, there remains the question of where to begin. Intuitively, there seem to be many points at which the learning of fish and rat might be compared with profit, and my only verbalizable guiding principle has been to begin with conditions whose effects at the level of the rat have resisted analysis in terms of our simplest constructs. Contemporary learning theory seems to me to underestimate the rat, but I have developed a certain sentimental attachment to it, and the idea has occurred to me that a more comfortable place might be found for it at some earlier place in the animal series. That is, the rat phenomena which embarrass the theory simply may not appear in some more primitive form. Consider again the paradoxical effect of partial reinforcement on resistance to extinction in the rat, which once it seemed possible to explain in terms of stimulus generalization. The neo-Guthrians have attempted to bolster the failing generalization principle with a rather dubious habituation principle, but even the two principles together cannot deal adequately with all of the data. Suppose, however, that partially reinforced fish showed the paradoxical effect when and only when they could be expected to do so on the basis of these simple principles. We might then be willing to conclude that contemporary S-R theory is appropriate at the level of the fish, although new processes of learning came into operation at the level of the rat. As it happens, the paradoxical effect does not appear in our fish even where these simple principles suggest that it should; but I am only half serious, of course, about the possibility of finding an exemplary S-R creature in the lower reaches of the phylogentic scale. I do, however, have considerable confidence in the notion that the mammalian phenomena which confound the theory are less likely to appear in more primitive species than are those which have suggested its basic postulates, and I have chosen to begin with the former because I am interested in maximizing the probability that functional differences will be discovered if they do in fact exist.

If the much-studied rat is to provide a phylogenetic frame of reference for comparative work with other animals, the choice of starting point also must depend on the structure of existing literature on the rat. Despite the volume of that literature, it is not exactly rich in well-defined functional relations, probably because so much of our past effort has been devoted to a search for crucial experiments designed to resolve certain very broad theo-

retical problems which arose out of the very earliest work on animal intelligence. I certainly do not regret this effort. The problems are real ones, and we have gained much insight into them. It is significant, I think, that nothing much in the way of well-defined functional relations has been forthcoming even from those who have rejected the traditional questions and advocated a vacant empiricism; in the hands of the Skinnerians, for example, batteries of expensive automatic equipment have yielded little more than an idiosyncratic assortment of kymograph tracings scarcely capable of quantitative analysis. Theoretical concern may not lead of necessity to the plotting of functional relations, but certainly it must not be thought to constitute an inevitable bar. The position is easier to defend that a mature investigator does not take the trouble to make systematic measurements unless they promise to clarify some larger problem. In any event, the theoretical concern which I am here attempting to delineate encourages the discovery of functional relations—both in new animals and in old. I must note that my interest in comparative work with new animals has not made it possible for me to give up work with the rat. My original notion—that I would study only the new animals and compare the functional relations obtained with those already available in the literature for the rat—proved far too simple. Sometimes an experiment with the fish gives rise to questions about the rat for which there are no adequate answers in the literature, and I may be too interested in those answers to be content to wait until somebody else happens to supply them.

Exploratory work with new animals is not for the impatient; the ratio of achievement to effort, at least in the beginning, is rather small, which should not be surprising in the light of the history of research on the rat. One must learn how to keep each new animal in the laboratory, how to motivate it, and something about its perceptual and motor capacities, before the quest for an appropriate set of experimental conditions even can be begun. The difficulties are many, and failure much more common than success.

In our work with the fish, as it happens, my colleagues and I have progressed at a quite satisfactory rate. We have succeeded in developing a set of efficient, objective techniques, well suited to a variety of species, which permit us to attack the problems of learning in fish on a broad front. One of these techniques, which has been mentioned already, and to which we have given most of our attention thus far, involves the presentation of a target at which the animal is trained to strike for food reward. After some preliminary work with a crude, mechanical system (Haralson and Bitterman, 1950), we developed a more sensitive and reliable electronic one (Longo and Bitterman, 1959). The present target is a disk of metal mounted on a light rod which is inserted into the needle holder of a crystal phonograph cartridge, and the amplified output of the cartridge is used to operate a set of relays which record and reward response. A single-target apparatus may be used either in Thorndikian or in Skinnerian fashion. That is, one may measure the latency of response in discrete trials, each trial beginning with the introduction of the target and terminating with its removal; or one may measure rate of response to a continuously available target. With two targets introduced simultaneously, choice may be measured, as in the T maze or jumping apparatus. More recently, we have developed two additional techniques, one for the study of escape and avoidance, which is so closely patterned after Warner's shuttle box as to require no further description here, and one for the study of classical conditioning (Horner, Longo, and Bitterman, 1960a, 1960b). In our classical conditioning situation, the US is brief shock, and a paddle inserted into the water detects the generalized response which the CS soon begins to elicit. Again a phonograph cartridge plays an important role, its amplified and integrated output driving a counter which

provides an objective measure of response-magnitude. The scope of comparative research made possible by these three techniques is considerable, but they came, it must be emphasized, only after several years of trial which yielded very little in the way of useful data. Our work with other animals often has progressed at a much less satisfactory rate, and in some cases we have made almost no progress at all.

An invertebrate to which we have devoted a good deal of fruitless effort is the Bermuda land crab, *Gecarcinus lateralis,* which is quite easy to keep in the laboratory. It lives at 78° F. on some moist sand in a small fish tank, and it does nicely on half a peanut, some lettuce, a bit of raw carrot, and piece of eggshell once each week. It even does nicely for months on no food at all, which was a source of some disappointment to us, since we had been led to believe that its appetite was good. Failing at first to elicit consistent interest in food under our experimental conditions, we turned to escape. We tried light and heat which did not prove suitable, and then shock, which proved quite disorienting, often causing the animal to drop most of its limbs. At last, after some months of fruitless effort, we hit upon immersion in distilled water, which (probably because of its interference with salt regulation) seemed to produce a rather sustained effort to escape.

The uppermost drawing in Figure 3 illustrates the earliest form of the apparatus which we then proceeded to develop, an adaptation of a long, narrow fish tank that we happened to have on hand. We painted one end black, the other end white, and made a clear plastic starting compartment for the center, with two yoked guillotine doors that were raised simultaneously to permit choice. A coarse wire mesh ramp at one end led up out of the water to the home cage of the animal, also equipped with a guillotine door. The other end offered no escape from the water, but a dummy cage was set there for visual bal-

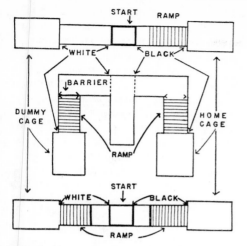

FIG. 3. Apparatus for the study of learning in the crab.

ance. In this situation, our crabs rapidly developed a preference for the positive side, whereupon we constructed the more elaborate apparatus sketched in the central portion of Figure 3. There was a stem leading to a T-shaped choice-point, and there were ramps on both sides, each of which could be blocked off by a barrier which was not visible from the choice-point. In this apparatus, the crabs did not learn at all; they would remain for long periods in the stem, scrabbling ineffectively at the front wall. When we removed the stem and installed a starting compartment of the earlier kind, performance improved, but the elbows still seemed to make for considerable confusion. At last, we removed the end-sections of the apparatus, returning to the original linear pattern, and the animals regained their earlier efficiency. Several months were lost in making the circle. The new apparatus, sketched in the lower portion of Figure 3, does, of course, have features that the earliest did not. There are two ramps, with a guillotine door before each. Both doors are down to begin with, and the door on the correct side is raised only after the subject has made a correct choice.

Under these conditions, it was possible

for us to complete our first formal study of learning in the crab—an experiment on habit reversal (Datta, Milstein, and Bitterman, 1960). In the course of that work, however, we had occasion to become dissatisfied with our technique. Clearly, we were able to achieve considerable control over the behavior of our animals, but the relatively low accuracy of our control group (which was not reversed) suggested the possibility that a higher level of drive should be sought. Now we are using dilute solutions of acetic acid in place of the distilled water. The acid strikingly improves both speed and accuracy of performance, but the animals do not survive many experimental sessions. Perhaps we shall be able to find a concentration strong enough to motivate the animals satisfactorily yet weak enough that it will not impair their health, or perhaps we shall be able to find a buffering procedure to promote post-experimental recovery from the effects of immersion in strong solutions. So the search for a suitable motivating technique continues.

Another arthropod with which we have been working recently is the blowfly, *Phormia regina*. Our interest in this animal was stimulated by the physiological investigations of V. G. Dethier (for example, Dethier and Bodenstein, 1958), who taught us how to breed it and how to keep it in the laboratory. We have studied the fly in a simple runway and in a number of choice-situations, such as that shown in Figure 4. The work is done with harnessed individuals. The subject is anesthetized with CO_2, and a leash of light thread with

FIG. 4. Apparatus for the study of learning in the fly.

a loop in its distal end is fixed to the dorsal surface with a bit of wax. The operation does not impair flying ability, but flight is limited in the experimental situation by a length of wire threaded through the loop at the end of the leash. In the apparatus sketched in Figure 4, the wire is curved, permitting the animal to alight only on one or the other of the two targets, one of which is baited with sugar solution. After innumerable variations of method and procedure, our efforts to develop situations

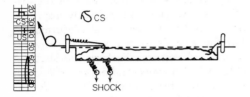

FIG. 5. Apparatus for the study of learning in the earthworm.

suitable for systematic studies of learning in the blowfly seem finally to be meeting with a certain degree of success.

An animal with which we have had no success whatsoever as yet is the earthworm. For a long time I have been wanting to make a systematic study of the process of classical conditioning in a really primitive animal, and for the kind of work I have in mind it is not enough merely to look at the animal and try to decide whether or not it twitches when the CS is presented; an objective measure of response-magnitude is required. A few years ago, I came upon a paper by Galambos (1939) which seemed to meet the need. Galambos was interested in the movement of the earthworm, not in its learning, but his work led me to explore the possibility of a Bechterevian apparatus for the worm, the most recent version of which is shown in Figure 5. The animal lies in a narrow, covered trough, in the floor of which two electrodes are set, two loops of linen thread having been sewn previously into the dorsal musculature— one anteriorly and one posteriorly. A thread runs from the posterior loop to a

fixed post, and another thread runs from the anterior loop to a spring which is attached to a second post. The spring is weak enough to permit withdrawal in response to shock, but strong enough to encourage return to the basal position when shock terminates. A third thread runs from the anterior loop to a kymograph on which response is recorded, as shown in the tracing. In this situation, brief shock elicits a response that looks very much like the flexion which shock to the limb elicits in the dog, and a neutral stimulus paired with shock may elicit a weak copy of the same response. Usually, however, the CR is a much more subtle affair which, though clearly visible to the naked eye, may fail entirely to activate the recording pen. After a good deal of time and effort devoted to the development of this apparatus, I have decided reluctantly that it should be abandoned in favor of an electronic technique which promises greater sensitivity.

Having emphasized the difficulties and disappointments which seem to be inherent in this exploratory work with relatively unfamiliar animals, I must note that it affords a rather special kind of enjoyment —a kind of enjoyment that I began to taste as an undergraduate in Schneirla's laboratory, but that I found only rarely in my subsequent work, which was more in accord with the spirit of the times. For many years, the field of animal learning has been dominated by a controversial, deductive spirit. Most of us have acted as though we knew all about the learning process, and as though the only purpose of our experiments was to demonstrate the validity of our convictions. The controversy was fun, of course, and to some extent even productive—we managed certainly to accumulate a considerable amount of data on learning in the rat—but in my recent dealings with fish, and fly, and crab, and worm, I have come again to a kind of research that is at once more satisfying and more productive. Its function is inquiry, not proof. When I ask about the effects of partial reinforcement on resistance to extinction in the fish, or about the course of habit reversal in the crab, I have not the slightest notion what the answer will be; I can only wait eagerly for the outcome of my experiments. I am not suggesting, of course, that the same attitude cannot be taken in work with the rat. I am suggesting only that it comes more readily in work with the primitive animals, which are so far removed phylogenetically from those which have been taken as models by the various parties to the controversy—the lower mammals, on the one hand, and, on the other, man. Broadening the phylogenetic base of our work will facilitate the broadening of our outlook, and perhaps one day we shall be able to approach even the higher forms in the same spirit of discovery.

REFERENCES

BEACH, F. A.   The snark was a boojum. *Amer. Psychologist*, 1950, **5**, 115–124.

BITTERMAN, M. E., J. WODINSKY, and D. K. CANDLAND   Some comparative psychology. *Amer. J. Psychol.*, 1958, **71**, 94–110.

DARWIN, C.   *The descent of man and selection in relation to sex.* Vol. 1. London: Murray, 1871.

DATTA, L. G., S. MILSTEIN, and M. E. BITTERMAN   Habit reversal in the crab. *J. comp. physiol. Psychol.*, 1960, **53**, 275–278.

DETHIER, V. G., and D. BODENSTEIN   Hunger in the blowfly. *Z. Tierpsychol.*, 1958, **15**, 129–140.

DOLLARD, J., and N. E. MILLER   *Personality and psychotherapy.* New York: McGraw-Hill, 1950.

GALAMBOS, R.   Potentials from the body wall of the earthworm. *J. gen. Psychol.*, 1939, **20**, 339–348.

HARALSON, J. V., and M. E. BITTERMAN   A lever-depression apparatus for the study of learning in fish. *Amer. J. Psychol.*, 1950, **63**, 250–256.

HARLOW, H. F.   The formation of learning sets. *Psychol. Rev.*, 1949, **56**, 51–65.

HORNER, J. L., N. LONGO, and M. E. BITTERMAN   A classical conditioning technique for small aquatic animals. *Amer. J. Psychol.*, 1960, **73**, in press. (a)

HORNER, J. L., N. LONGO, and M. E. BITTERMAN   A shuttlebox for the fish and a control-circuit of general applicability. *Amer. J. Psychol.*, 1960, **73**, in press. (b)

HULL, C. L.   The place of innate individual and species differences in a natural-science theory of behavior. *Psychol. Rev.*, 1945, **52**, 55–60.

KINNAMAN, A. J.   Mental life of two *Macacus rhesus* monkeys in captivity. *Amer. J. Psychol.*, 1902, **13**, 173–218.

LONGO, N., and M. E. BITTERMAN   Improved apparatus for the study of learning in the fish. *Amer. J. Psychol.*, 1959, **72**, 616–620.

LONGO, N., and M. E. BITTERMAN   The effect of partial reinforcement with spaced practice on resistance to extinction in the fish. *J. comp. physiol. Psychol.*, 1960, **53**, 169–172.

MILLER, N. E.   Comments on multiple-process conceptions of learning. *Psychol. Rev.*, 1951, **58**, 375–381.

PORTER, J. P.   A preliminary study of the psychology of the English sparrow. *Amer. J. Psychol.*, 1904, **15**, 313–346.

SCHNEIRLA, T. C.   Ant learning as a problem in comparative psychology. In: P. L. HARRIMAN (Ed.), *Twentieth century psychology.* New York: Philosophical Library, 1946. Pp. 276–305.

SKINNER, B. F.   A case history in scientific method. *Amer. Psychologist*, 1956, **11**, 221–233.

SMALL, W. S.   Experimental study of the mental processes of the rat. *Amer. J. Psychol.*, 1901, **12**, 313–346.

THORNDIKE, E. L.   Animal intelligence: An experimental study of the associative processes in animals. *Psychol. Rev., Monogr. Suppl.*, 1898, **2** (4, Whole No. 8).

THORNDIKE, E. L.   *Animal intelligence.* New York: Macmillan, 1911.

WATSON, J. B.   *Behavior: An introduction to comparative psychology.* New York: Holt, 1914.

WODINSKY, J., and M. E. BITTERMAN   Partial reinforcement in the fish. *Amer. J. Psychol.*, 1959, **72**, 184–199.

WODINSKY, J., and M. E. BITTERMAN   Resistance to extinction in the fish after extensive training with partial reinforcement. *Amer. J. Psychol.*, 1960, **73**, 429–434.

YERKES, R. M.   Methods of exhibiting reactive tendencies characteristic of ontogenetic and phylogenetic stages. *J. anim. Behav.*, 1917, **7**, 11–28.

section
seven

SOCIAL BEHAVIOR, ETHOLOGY, AND EVOLUTION

Although previous readings in this book have touched upon social behavior, ethology, and evolution, these topics are of primary concern in the readings that follow. There are good reasons for grouping the three topics in one section.

Social behavior may be defined as the behavior of an animal, or a group of animals, in response to others of the same, or different, species. The social aspects of an animal's behavior are obviously of great importance in determining biological adaptiveness. Consequently, ethologists have concentrated much of their research on the study of the social behavior of animals. The readings included in this section present several good examples of such ethological research. The method generally used is a combination of careful observation of the animal in its natural setting and field experiments, which frequently utilize models. Emphasis is placed on the evolutionary antecedents and the biological adaptiveness of the behavior.

Suggestions for Further Reading:

ALLEE, W. C., *The Social Life of Animals.* Boston: Beacon Press, 1958.

CALHOUN, J. B., *The Ecology and Sociology of the Norway Rat.* (U. S. Public Health Service Publication No. 1008) Washington, D. C.: Government Printing Office, 1963.

ETKIN, W., *Social Behavior and Organization among Vertebrates.* Chicago: University of Chicago Press, 1964.

KLOPFER, P. H., *Behavioral Aspects of Ecology.* Englewood Cliffs, N. J.: Prentice-Hall, 1962.

PORTMANN, A., *Animals as Social Beings.* New York: Viking, 1961.

TINBERGEN, N., *Social Behaviour in Animals.* London: Methuen, 1953.

495

J. P. SCOTT

49 The Analysis of Social Organization in Animals*

In this reading, J. P. Scott outlines a system for the classification of social behavior in animals and lists some of the ways in which it may be used. Peck-orders, territoriality, and related concepts are briefly discussed.

Reprinted from *Ecology*, 1956, **37**, 213–221, with permission of the author and the publisher.

Introduction

Following Darwin's emphasis on the principle of adaptation in organic evolution, biologists became strongly interested in the study of individual animal behavior. Adaptation could only be inferred from fossils, but could be observed directly in living forms. Up till 1900 a great many biologists concentrated their efforts in this field, which was at that time almost as popular as comparative anatomy and embryology. Shortly afterwards two discoveries were made which strongly influenced this type of research. One was the rediscovery of Mendelian heredity, and a great many workers who were interested in general evolutionary problems shifted their attention to genetics. The other was the establishment of general laws of learning following Pavlov's studies of conditioned reflexes, and those workers with psychological interests tended to elaborate these findings with studies of behavior in the rat.

About 1920 a new era in behavioral research began with the description of social organization in birds. Elliot Howard (1920) wrote on the significance of song and territory in birds and Schjelderup-

* This paper was originally delivered, September 7, 1954, at Gainesville, Florida, as part of a program on "Social Organization of Animals" given in honor of Dr. W. C. Allee.

Ebbe (1922) discovered the existence of social dominance in chickens. Shortly afterward Allee approached the problem from a more general viewpoint with his review on animal aggregations (1927) and later book by the same title (1931). Since that time a large body of information has been accumulating around the problem of social organization, and this paper will briefly describe some general methods and the kinds of results to be expected from its study.

The study of the social organization of a species may be delimited by the natural units of social organization, which are usually species populations and their subgroups. It differs from a general ecological study in which the unit of organization is the animal and plant community, which may be composed of many different sorts of animal and plant populations. It also differs from psychological analysis in which the unit of organization is the individual and where the primary interest lies in internal organization. So defined, the analysis of social organization occupies an intermediate position between the sciences of ecology and psychology, and overlaps with both at many points.

At the present time we have only a few definite standard techniques for the study of social behavior and organization (Scott, 1950). However, there are certain general methods which have achieved wide use and which can be recommended to anyone working in the field. The analysis of social organization in any animal should begin with a thorough descriptive study in which the seasonal and daily cycles of behavior are thoroughly surveyed. An essential part of this study is the identification of individuals, since without this information the details of social organization can only be surmised. Descriptive study should also include a study of the development of social behavior and organization from birth to maturity, since behavior and organization change with age. This systematic descriptive information naturally leads to certain hypotheses which can be studied experimentally, and it is found that many types of factors can affect social organization. These may be described as ecological, psychological, physiological, and genetic; and appropriate techniques used for the examination of each.

Classification of General Behavior Patterns and Their Comparative Study

In relating genetic factors to social organization it has been found that each species has certain characteristic ways of adapting to the environment and that these "patterns of behavior" in part determine the nature of social organization which can be developed in the species. As a guide to the study of characteristic patterns of behavior the author has developed a general scheme of classification. This scheme is intended to include the kinds of behavior generally recognized by students of animal behavior rather than to conflict with them, and has been found useful in making general descriptive studies of the type described above (Scott 1945, 1950a). It was developed originally by attempting to classify the behavior patterns described in several species of animals by other authors, as in Allen's (1911-1914) study of the blackbird and Dean's (1896) study of the river dogfish.

The chief rule for any good scheme of

classification is that it should be natural and conform to discontinuity which exists in nature and which can be recognized by independent observers. The scheme of classification should be logical, and one which includes all related phenomena. Terms in common usage may be employed, provided their meanings are clear and describe the observed phenomenon correctly, but they should not be redefined with new meanings as this leads to great confusion. Finally, terms should be descriptive and not imply some theoretical interpretation of the facts.

These rules for classification and terminology conform to general usage in biological science. In addition, the author feels that one should be conservative about forming new terms inasmuch as they add to the labor of acquiring a scientific vocabulary, but that one should not hesitate to form new ones where necessary. Those which are useful will stand the test of time and those which are not useful will tend to be discarded.

The following classification includes all the major patterns of social and semi-social adaptation which have so far been described.

Contactual Behavior. This may be defined as simply maintaining bodily contact and, as Allee (1931) has shown, the formation of simple aggregations through behavior of this sort occurs very widely throughout the animal kingdom. The adaptive significance of the behavior may vary a great deal. A group of mammals may huddle together for warmth whereas a group of Paramecia may form because the bodies of their fellows afford protection against unfavorable chemical conditions. This extremely simple type of social behavior affords a possible basis for the evolution of higher types of behavior.

Ingestive Behavior. This may be defined as behavior concerned with the taking of solids and liquids into the digestive tract and is found very widely although not universally throughout the animal kingdom. It may have an important social significance in animals which feed their young, and becomes highly social in the nursing behavior of mammals.

Eliminative Behavior. This is defined as behavior associated with the elimination of urine and feces from the body. Special behavior is rarely seen in aquatic animals but highly elaborate patterns may be developed in terrestrial species which build nests or lairs. In such forms as wolves and the prong-horned antelope, it may acquire considerable social significance.

Sexual Behavior. This may be defined as behavior connected with the fertilization process and includes the usual courtship and copulation behavior of animals. It occurs very widely though not universally in the animal kingdom and is undoubtedly one of the most primitive forms of social behavior.

Epimeletic Behavior. (Gr. *epimeleteon,* care-giving). This may be defined as the giving of care or attention. It has been called maternal behavior but is also found in males in animals like the ostrich which incubates the eggs, and in many other animals where there is biparental care of the young. It could be called parental behavior except for the fact that in many species it is done by animals other than the parents as, for example, the mutual grooming of adult primates, and the care of the young by worker females in the social insects. This behavior includes what has been called by the more specific terms of attentive behavior and nurturance.

Et-epimeletic Behavior (Gr. *aeteo,* beg, + epimeletic). This is defined as calling and signaling for care and attention and is very widely found in animals which give some care to the young. The behavior may be vocal, as in infant mammals, or simply be some sort of movement, as in the larvae of bees and ants. This behavior could be called infantile except that it also occurs in adult animals. In most cases it is used as a substitute for direct adaptation by an individual which is itself helpless or unable to adapt.

Agonistic Behavior (Gr. *agonistikos,* combative). This is defined as any behavior associated with conflict or fighting between two individuals. The term fighting behavior was originally used, but it was found that patterns of behavior involving escape or passivity were very closely related and could not be included under the narrow term of fighting. This type of behavior occurs principally in the arthropod and vertebrate phyla.

Allelomimetic Behavior (Gr. *allelo,* mutual, + *mimetikos,* imitative). This is defined as any behavior in which animals do the same thing with some degree of mutual stimulation and consequent coordination. It is seen developed to a high degree in schools of fishes, flocks of birds and herds of mammals. It could be called imitative behavior except that to most people this implies some degree of learning, which is not necessarily involved, and the idea of a model and a mimic rather than mutual stimulation. Such behavior in birds has been described as mimesis by Armstrong (1952) and as contagious or infectious behavior by other authors. The two latter terms appear to be somewhat undesirable in that they suggest that the behavior is transmitted in the manner of a disease.

Investigative Behavior. This may be defined as sensory inspection of the environment. This has been called exploratory behavior in the rat, where the animal actively explores the environment with nose and whiskers. However, in an animal with highly developed eyes, such behavior may consist merely of glancing around without movement of the whole body. The more general term of investigation appears preferable.

When the above classification is used to organize descriptive data the result is a detailed list of activities under each category which gives the characteristic ways in which a species responds in relation to major behavioral functions (Scott 1950a). Many of these exist in playful or immature forms as well as adult patterns.

It is also possible that patterns of behavior grouped in the above or similar categories may reflect an underlying nervous organization. For example, the behavior of an inexperienced male mouse of the C57 Black strain attacked by a superior fighter follows a regular and predictable sequence (Scott and Fredericson 1951). He first fights back, and when this is not successful he attempts to escape. If he fails in this he adopts a defensive posture, and if cornered he may lie on his back with feet in the air. We may eventually come to think of "systems of behavior" organized around a particular function, but general evidence still needs to be obtained on the point.

The categories may also be used to check the completeness of a descriptive study, leading to the discovery of behavior which has passed unnoticed. Sometimes a major category of behavior is almost or entirely absent, and this affords an opportunity for characterizing the social life of the species.

For example, allelomimetic behavior is highly developed in the sheep and almost entirely absent in the mouse, which results in two very different types of social organization (Scott 1945a).

Species differences can also be found within a category of behavior. For example, the agonistic behavior of sheep and goats consists largely of butting. Sheep back off and run together head on, but goats typically rear up and butt with a sideways thrust of the head. A scheme of classification can be used as a systematic framework for such comparative studies of species differences in behavior, as well as making it easier to do a complete descriptive job. A high standard of scholarship requires such a complete systematic method, which has too often been missing in past studies of comparative behavior.

Comparative studies lead to the conclusion that the presence or absence of a given type of social behavior affects the type of social organization developed by the species. Stated more specifically, the presence of a given behavior pattern defines the types of social relationships which may be developed from it.

Social Relationships

Social organization may be analyzed in terms of social relationships. Such a relationship is defined as regular and repeatable behavior between two or more individuals, and it in turn may be described in terms of the patterns of behavior exhibited by the individuals taking part. The classical example of a social relationship is the peck order in hens in which one individual regularly threatens or pecks the other which just as regularly dodges or submits to pecking. Social behavior is not identical with social organization. In the case of two strange hens, behavior at first consists of unorganized fighting, and it is only after several encounters that behavior is organized through learning and habit formation into a regular dominance-subordination relationship. Even in the social insects, where heredity seems to play a relatively stronger role, social organization is not automatic. Experience in early life determines the species with which social relationships are formed by larvae taken by slave-raiding ants. Social behavior may therefore be considered an important but not the sole determiner of social relationships, and this should be kept in mind in making analyses of the two phenomena.

A great many types of social relationships are theoretically possible if all types of social behavior are considered. The number of possible combinations of behavior patterns in a species which shows all of the 9 types of behavior classified above may be theoretically calculated as follows. There are 9 possible combinations where both members of the relationship exhibit the same type of behavior and 36 possible combinations where the individuals exhibit unlike behavior, making a total of 45

(Scott 1953). Some of these combinations are frequently seen, such as the dominance order in which behavior of both individuals is agonistic. Some of them may be commonly overlooked as, for example, the combination of sexual and agonistic behavior exhibited by male and female rodents when the female is not in heat, and many of them are yet to be described. It is possible, of course, that certain ones are only theoretical and do not occur in nature. Some of them which have been widely observed are described below, using the names commonly applied to them.

Simple Aggregations. In this type of relationship the behavior of both animals is contactual. As Allee has shown, such relationships exist very widely in the animal kingdom, but their occurrence is apt to be irregular and nonspecific because of their dependency on environmental conditions.

Dominance - Subordination Relationships. In this type of relationship the behavior of both individuals may be described as agonistic. That of one individual consists of a threat or actual fighting while the other individual remains passive or attempts to escape. Evidence gathered by Allee (1950) and his students and summarized by Collias (1944) shows that this type of relationship is widespread in the vertebrates and occurs in at least some arthropods. It does not occur in many of the lower animals which are incapable of fighting.

Leader-Follower Relationships. The behavior of both individuals may be classed as allelomimetic, but there is an unequal degree of stimulation so that one tends to lead and the other follow. This has been described in sheep (Scott 1945), deer (Darling 1937) and ducks (Allee *et al.* 1947) and deserves more extensive study. It should not be confused with cases in which a dominant animal drives a group before him, as in the case of a stag and does in the rutting season.

Sexual Relationships. The behavior of both individuals is sexual. Although sex behavior has been extensively described in many species, very few analytic studies of the resulting social relationships have been made. Dominance and sexual relationships may be interdependent in both chickens (Guhl and Warren 1946) and chimpanzees (Nowlis 1942).

Care-Dependency Relationships. In this case the behavior of one individual is epimeletic while the behavior of the other individual may be one of several different types. An infant animal may exhibit et-epimeletic behavior, as when a young lamb is separated from the flock, or it may exhibit ingestive behavior in the process of nursing. In animals like dogs which regularly clean the young, the latter may exhibit eliminative behavior. This type of relationship has been widely described but subjected to very little experimental analysis in animals.

Mutual Care. In this case the behavior of both individuals is epimeletic, and an example is seen in the mutual grooming of primates. In spite of its theoretical importance for considerations of basic human sociology, such relationships have been little studied in animals.

Trophallaxis. This is a complex relationship described by Wheeler (1923) in the social insects. Both individuals may exhibit investigative behavior, and one usually exhibits epimeletic behavior in providing food from the crop while the other ingests the food. On subsequent occasions the roles may be reversed.

Mutual Defense. This is another complex relationship in which the members exhibit both agonistic and allelomimetic behavior. It has been described in such animals as muskoxen, wolves, baboons and many kinds of birds in reaction to hawks, but has not been subjected to extensive analysis.

It would appear from the above presentation that the complete analysis of the social organization of a species can be an extremely complex affair, and that the simple description of the dominance-subordination relationships does not give the whole story by any means. However, the task is not hopeless since in any actual case the number of important relationships turns out to be relatively small.

Biological Classification of Social Relationships

As described above, analysis of the social organization of an animal species consists of a systematic description of the basic patterns of behavior and their organization into social relationships. If an animal gave the same responses to all individuals the relationships would be simple to describe and a low degree of social organization would result. As indicated above, the behavior of individuals is frequently unlike and the concept of differentiation (Tinbergen 1953) becomes a useful one. Behavior may be differentiated by biological factors such as age and sex on the one hand and by psychological factors involving learning on the other. As Carpenter (1934) has pointed out, there are three biologically determined types of individuals in mammals: males, females and young. When these are combined in all like and unlike combinations, a total of six basic relationships can be established. These are essentially super-categories under which those relationships mentioned in the previous section may be grouped. For example, male-male relationships can include dominance-subordination and mutual care relationships as well as many others. This general scheme can be applied to other animals as well as primates and is particularly useful in studying groups of wild animals where it is difficult to distinguish individuals except by age and sex.

In the case of the social insects which have biologically differentiated castes, the scheme may be amplified to include greater numbers of basic relationships. A similar extension must be made when social relationships are developed between two different species, as commonly occurs in domestication (Scott 1953).

Analysis of Specific Social Relationships

So far, the anaylsis of social organization has been considered in terms of behavior of the whole organism and relationships between organisms. It is also possible to investigate the internal processes which in part determine behavior and through it influence social organization. Since the methods used are well known to physiologists and psychologists, the scope of such investigations will be described only briefly here.

One basic field of study is the analysis of the complex network of physiological factors which is associated with any major pattern of behavior (Scott and Fredericson 1951). Available information of this sort tends to be scattered and unequal. The physiology of sexual and ingestive behavior has been widely studied, but our knowledge of agonistic behavior comes largely from the domestic cat. The physiology of certain types of behavior, such as investigative and allelomimetic, is almost completely unknown.

A related field of investigation is concerned with the physiological genetics of social behavior and social relationships. As Collias has shown (1943), dominance-subordination relationships may in part be determined by such physiological factors as weight and hormones, which in turn may depend on the genetic differentiation of sex. Further genetic variability in physiological factors affecting social behavior introduces an individual specificity into social relationships. Those of the genetic variant will fall into the usual broad categories but will also show certain unique and specific differences.

In animals which are capable of learning, social behavior becomes differentiated on the basis of mutual adaptation and habit formation as well as on the basis of biological differences. As shown by Ginsburg and Allee (1942) the formation of a dominance order is at least in part related to the psychological principles of learning. Once such a relationship is formed and firmly established by habit, it may be extremely difficult to upset it by altering biological factors, as shown by Beeman and Allee (1945). Among the higher animals it is probable that all social relationships are affected by the psychological processes of problem solving (or adaptation) and habit formation. Neglect of these factors in favor of an assumption of purely genetic or instinctive determination of behavior may lead to serious errors of interpretation (Lehrman 1953).

As with physiological factors, psychological processes tend to introduce specificity into social relationships. In a study of social organization of sheep it was found that any given lamb had a general leader-follower relationship toward all adults in its tendency to follow them, although this tendency was strongest with regard to the mother. Its care-dependency relationships, on the other hand, were extremely specific and developed only with its own mother (Scott 1945).

In any species which has the psychological capacity to discriminate between individuals, such specific relationships will be expected to occur. It likewise follows that unless the scientific observer develops a similar ability to identify individuals, specific social relationships will pass unnoticed, and with them a large part of social organization. There is a vast difference between the observation that hens tend to peck each other (a general relationship) and the knowledge that within each pair there is one which always pecks and one which always dodges (a peck order consisting of a group of specific relationships).

If social relationships were entirely determined by biological factors it would be expected that all female-female relationships in a given species would be the same except as affected by chance genetic vari-

ability. Such is obviously not the case in the peck-order studies, and it is probable that a similar specificity will be found in many other types of social relationships when studied in detail. The general analytic method is to identify all individuals in the social group and then bring them together in pairs in a situation which will elicit the kind of behavior being studied (agonistic, sexual, etc.). A well-designed experiment includes results on all possible combinations of pairs, observed in an order which controls factors such as fatigue, habit formation, etc. The total possible number of combinations in a group is given by the formula

$$\frac{n(n-1)}{2}$$

(Carpenter 1940), so that such a study becomes very lengthy if n (the total number of individuals in the group) is large. The study should be supplemented with observations on the whole group, as it is possible that pairs may react differently when in the presence of others.

Many models for this type of study may be found in the literature (Collias 1951), particularly those done with dominance-subordination relationships, and the methods need not be described in greater detail here. Guhl (1953) has written an excellent summary of methods used for the study of specific dominance and sexual relationships in the domestic fowl. As indicated above, there is a need for the extension of these methods to the study of other sorts of social relationships in order to obtain a more complete picture of social organization.

The importance of specificity in social relationships is likewise apparent when analysis is made from a developmental viewpoint, and this has led to the concept of socialization.

Socialization

Experiments which modify the social environment have tended to bring out the general principles of socialization. Any highly social animal that has been so far studied has behavioral mechanisms whereby, early in development, an individual forms positive social relationships with its own kind and usually with particular individuals of its kind. At the same time, other behavioral mechanisms operate to prevent such relationships being formed with other species and, to a lesser extent, with other groups of its own kind. Raising an individual with any other species including human beings usually produces an individual which is socialized to the strange species. Essential patterns of social behavior remain unaltered and are given in response to the strange species to the extent that such behavior is compatible.

The process of socialization has been shown to take place within limited periods of time by Lorenz (1935) in birds and also in such mammals as the sheep (Collias 1953) and dog (Scott and Marston 1950). Lorenz has been chiefly concerned with the positive mechanisms to which he has given the general term "imprinting," but, in the case of the mammals mentioned, some information is also present regarding the negative mechanisms which normally prevent social attachment to other species. In the dog and wolf, for example, agonistic behavior may be elicited by strangers at a very early age, effectively preventing positive contact as the animal grows older (Scott 1953a).

These effects have led to the concept of critical periods in the process of socialization (Scott and Marston 1950). There are points in development where it is very easy to change the individuals to which an animal becomes socialized, and other points later or earlier in development when this is difficult or impossible. A study of the process of socialization thus forms an important part of the developmental analysis of social organization.

An excellent review of experiments on the general effects of modifying early experience has been made by Beach and Jaynes (1954). As applied to the problem of social organization the most useful techniques may be outlined as follows. The first step is a detailed descriptive study of development, paying particular attention to social behavior patterns and changes in sensory, motor and psychological capacities. We have attempted to set up a model outline for this type of study in the case of two species of mammals, the dog and mouse (Scott and Marston 1950; Williams and Scott 1953).

A developmental study may be supplemented by two sorts of simple experimental procedures. One is to take male and female individuals at birth or hatching and have them reared by another species, human or otherwise. This method has produced brilliant results in the hands of Lorenz (1935), and may be extended further to the rearing of individuals in semi-isolation (Thompson and Heron 1954). The other is to castrate male and female individuals as early as possible in development, which gives some indication of the importance of hormonal changes and sexual behavior in social development.

Observations on the time of development of various capacities and patterns of behavior require experimental verification. On the basis of present evidence, the development of many species falls into natural periods based on beginnings or changes of important social relationships. This gives a basis for the experimental analysis of the factor of time in early social experience. Modification of social experience may be begun at different points in development and continued for appropriate periods. Controls for physiological and structural changes, genetic differences, random environmental factors and the psychological factors of learning are important in the design of these experiments (King and Gurney 1954).

Social Organization between Groups

Most of the work on analysis of social organization has been done within groups, and correctly so. The most frequent aspects of social life in animals appear to be concerned with what are called by the human social psychologists "face-to-face contacts in small groups." However, some organization between groups apparently does exist, as reported in Carpenter's (1934, 1940) studies of howling monkeys and gibbons. Likewise, the territorial organization of passerine birds during the breeding season may be considered as organization between small family groups. Obviously, such organization is most likely to occur under natural conditions, and its existence is one of the possibilities which should be looked for in field studies.

The evidence for the existence of territoriality in small mammals has been summarized by Blair (1953), who finds that instances of defense of definite boundaries are relatively rare. As with birds, group territorial defense in mammals may be described simply in terms of a general dominance-subordination relationship, in which the group or individuals within the group tend to be dominant over the individual trespassing on the territory (Murie 1944; King 1955). However, in the case of howling monkeys Carpenter (1934) reports that groups maintain regular daily contacts with each other by howling at dawn, and this is possibly also the case in birds such as quail which vocalize regularly. The "wars" between colonies of ants appear to involve a general relationship in which all strange individuals are attacked.

The relationship between separate social groups is a problem of considerable theoretical interest and should be investigated wherever possible. Analysis should include the means by which new groups are formed, and the fate of isolated individuals as well as territoriality. King (1955) has found a definite group territorial system in prairie dogs, with a tendency for adults to move out and colonize new areas after raising the young, which are left to occupy the old territory. Carpenter's (1940, 1934) studies of the gibbon and howling monkey are excellent models for the analysis of this and other aspects of social organization.

Conclusion

It will be seen from the foregoing outline that the complete analysis of the social organization of even a single species is an enormous task. It is not likely that the job will ever be entirely completed, though such a point is being approached in such favorite objects of study as the chicken, mouse, stickleback, honeybee, army ant and termite. The task must be divided into sections, and emphasis placed upon important points of fact and theory.

Collecting observations on behavior patterns and their organization into basic biologically determined social relationships can often be done with a study of a year or two. Much material is already available in publications written for other purposes, particularly in natural history and ecological life history studies. A great deal of information on European species is contained in studies of comparative behavior patterns done by the "ethologists," although they have frequently concerned themselves with the nature of stimulation ("releasers") rather than social organization. The systematic classification of material from these sources often saves a great deal of time as well as providing confirmatory evidence for original study.

The analysis of socialization and specific social relationships is more complicated and time-consuming, and is difficult to do except in a laboratory or seminatural environments, although it has been shown that social dominance does exist under natural conditions (J. W. Scott 1942). Indeed, the more basic the analysis, the slower it becomes, and a division of labor among scientists is necessary when physiological and genetic factors are studied. This brings up the problem of coordination of effort.

The study of the social organization of behavior tends to unify knowledge. Behavior is usually defined as activity of an entire organism and thus is affected by factors customarily divided up in all the conventional subdivisions of zoology and psychology. When behavior is considered in relation to social organization the subject matter is widened still further to include certain aspects of general social science. It is obviously impossible for anyone to have a thorough and complete knowledge of all these fields, but the specialist in any one of them should at least have a general knowledge of the others and their relation to his own. The ecologist, as a last surviving type of general biologist, should have a particular advantage in this respect. Meetings such as this one, in which the speakers have training in such diverse fields as genetics, psychology, and ecology, can do much to promote the interchange of ideas and mutual comprehension.

A final word may be said concerning the necessity of maintaining a high standard of scientific work. As stated in the beginning of this article, we still have very few specific standardized techniques for the analysis of social organization, and to insist upon the enforcement of standards prematurely would do much to discourage new and creative lines of research. The harm that can be done by publishing inconclusive pilot experiments or generalizing from superficial descriptions based on study of a few individuals is equally great. We can and should insist on general standards of thoroughness and repeatability, on controls for the wide variety of genetic, physiological, developmental, psychological, ecological, and social factors known to affect behavior, and on the necessity for final experimental verification of any theory.

The resulting well-established facts and theories of social organization in animals have widespread significance. Such information has great practical importance in wildlife management and in the care of animals under domestication. For example, if it is planned to recolonize a vacant territory with social animals, the new individuals must have been socialized toward each other or otherwise the group will disintegrate and fail to survive.

A knowledge of social organization is an essential part of understanding the general ecology of the species. Populations of animals do not exist in nature as randomly distributed individuals but as socially organized groups. Enough has been said in the foregoing article to indicate that an immense amount of information is still to be gathered about the social organization of animals, and even some of our common and familiar species are far from completely understood.

Finally, the collection of knowledge regarding social organization in animals and the resulting generalizations which will be made should prove to be of great help in understanding certain human problems. A great many problems of human maladjustment can be attributed to interference with the process of socialization, whose study should be one of the primary concerns of child psychology. A more thorough knowledge of animal societies should contribute greatly to our understanding of the biological and psychological bases of human social organization.

Summary

An attempt has been made in this article to present a systematic general outline for the analysis of social organization in animals. Methods include systematic description of the important behavior patterns of the species based on studies of the daily and seasonal cycles of behavior and upon the development of behavior in the individual from birth until maturity and old age. These basic patterns of behavior determine to a large extent the general types of social relationships which are possible in the species.

Further analysis of specific social relationships depends upon identification of every individual in the social group and should be verified by experimental combinations of every possible pair.

Study of the process of socialization should include a systematic descriptive study of changes in the basic behavioral capacities: sensory, motor, psychological, and patterns of social behavior, with particular reference to relative timing and its consequences. Some remarks are made concerning general application of the method, and the significance of the results.

REFERENCES

ALLEE, W. C., 1927 Animal aggregations. *Quart. Rev. Biol.*, **2**: 367–398.

ALLEE, W. C., 1931 *Animal aggregations. A study in general sociology.* Chicago: Univ. Chicago Press.

ALLEE, W. C., 1950 Extrapolation in comparative sociology. *Scientia*, **43**: 135–142.

ALLEE, W. C., M. N. ALLEE, F. RITCHEY, and E. W. CASTLE, 1947 Leadership in a flock of White Pekin ducks. *Ecology*, **28**: 310–15.

ALLEN, A. A., 1911–14 The red-winged blackbird: a study in the ecology of a cat-tail marsh. *Abs. Proc. Linnean Soc. N. Y.*, No. 24–25.

ARMSTRONG, E. A., 1952 Behavior is contagious, too. *Animal Kingdom*, **55**: 88–91.

BEACH, F. A., and J. JAYNES, 1954 Effects of early experience upon the behavior of animals. *Psych. Bull.*, **51**: 239–263.

BEEMAN, E. A., and W. C. ALLEE, 1945 Some effects of thiamin on the winning of social contacts in mice. *Physiol. Zool.*, **18**: 195–221.

BLAIR, W. F., 1953 Population dynamics of rodents and other small mammals. *Rec. Ad. Genetics*, **5**: 1–41.

CARPENTER, C. R., 1934 A field study of the behavior and social relations of howling monkeys. *Comp. Psych. Monogr.* No. 48, **10**(2): 1–168.

CARPENTER, C. R., 1940 A field study of the behavior and social relations of the gibbon (*Hylobates Lar*). *Comp. Psych. Monogr.* No. 84, **16**(5): 1–212.

COLLIAS, N., 1943 Statistical analysis of factors which make for success in initial encounters between hens. *Amer. Nat.*, **77**: 519–538.

COLLIAS, N., 1944 Aggressive behavior among vertebrate animals. *Physiol. Zool.*, **17**: 83–123.

COLLIAS, N., 1951 Social life and the individual among vertebrate animals. *Ann. N. Y. Acad. Sci.*, **51**: 1074–1092.

COLLIAS, N., 1953 Some factors in maternal rejection in sheep and goats. *Bull. Ecol. Soc. Amer.*, **34**: 78.

DARLING, F. F., 1937 *A herd of red deer.* London: Oxford Univ. Press.

DEAN, B., 1896 The early development of Amia. *Quart. J. Mic. Sci.*, **38**: 413–444.

GINSBURG, B., and W. C. ALLEE, 1942 Some effects of conditioning on social dominance and subordination in inbred strains of mice. *Physiol. Zool.*, **15**: 485–506.

GUHL, A. M., 1953 Social behavior of the domestic fowl. *Kansas State College Ag. Exp. Sta. Technical Bull.* No. 73.

GUHL, A. M., and D. C. WARREN, 1946 Number of offspring sired by cockerels related to social dominance in chickens. *Poultry Sci.*, **25**: 460–472.

HOWARD, H. E., 1920 *Territory in bird life.* London: Murray.

KING, J. A., 1955 Social behavior, social organization and population dynamics in a black-tailed prairiedog town in the Black Hills of South Dakota. *Contr. Lab. Vert. Biol., Univ. Mich.*, No. 67, 123 pp.

KING, J. A., and N. L. GURNEY, 1954 Effect of early social experience on adult aggressive behavior in C57BL/10 mice. *J. Comp. and Physiol. Psych.*, **47**: 326–330.

LEHRMAN, D. S., 1953 A critique of Konrad Lorenz's theory of instinctive behavior. *Quart. Rev. Biol.*, **28**: 337–363.

LORENZ, K., 1935 Der Kumpan in der Umwelt des Vogels. *Journal für Ornithologie*, **83**: 137–213, 289–413. For English summary see: The companion in the bird's world. *Auk*, **54**: 245–273, 1937.

MURIE, A., 1944 *The wolves of Mt. McKinley.* U.S.D.I. Fauna Series No. 5.

NOWLIS, V., 1942 Sexual status and degree of hunger in chimpanzee competitive interaction. *J. Comp. Psych.*, **34**: 185–194.

SCHJELDERUP-EBBE, T., 1922 Beiträge zur Sozial-psychologie des Haushuhns. *Zeit. Psych.*, **88**: 225–252.

SCOTT, J. P., 1945 Social behavior, organization and leadership in a small flock of domestic sheep. *Comp. Psych. Monograph* No. 96, **18**(4): 1–29.

SCOTT, J. P., 1945a Group formation determined by social behavior; a comparative study of two mammalian societies. *Sociometry*, **8**: 42–52.

SCOTT, J. P., 1950 (Ed.) Methodology and techniques for the study of animal societies. *Ann. N. Y. Acad. Sci.*, **51**: 1001–1122.

SCOTT, J. P., 1950a   The social behavior of dogs and wolves: an illustration of socio-biological systematics. *Ann. N. Y. Acad. Sci.*, **51**: 1009–1021.

SCOTT, J. P., 1953   Implications of infrahuman social behavior for problems of human relations. In: *Group relations at the crossroads*, M. SHERIF and W. A. WILSON, eds. New York: Harper.

SCOTT, J. P., 1953a   The process of socialization in higher animals. In: *Interrelations between the social environment and psychiatric disorders*. New York: Milbank Memorial Fund.

SCOTT, J. P., and M. MARSTON, 1950   Critical periods affecting the development of normal and mal-adjustive social behavior of puppies. *Jour. Genet. Psych.*, **77**: 25–60.

SCOTT, J. P., and E. FREDERICSON, 1951   The causes of fighting in mice and rats. *Physiol. Zool.*, **24**: 273–309.

SCOTT, J. W., 1942   Mating behavior of the sage grouse. *Auk*, **59**: 477–498.

THOMPSON, W. R., and W. HERON, 1954   The effects of early restriction on activity in dogs. *J. Comp. and Physiol. Psych.*, **47**: 77–82.

TINBERGEN, N., 1953   *Social behaviour in animals*. New York: John Wiley.

WHEELER, W. M., 1923   *Social life among the insects*. New York: Harcourt, Brace.

WILLIAMS, E., and J. P. SCOTT, 1953   The development of social behavior patterns in the mouse, in relation to natural periods. *Behaviour*, **6**: 35–64.

J O H N   A.   K I N G

50   Intra- and Interspecific Conflict of *Mus* and *Peromyscus**

In this interesting article, John A. King (author of reading 22) reports on the aggressive behavior of two genera of mice. In this case, a laboratory experiment leads to hypotheses about what occurs under natural conditions.

Reprinted from *Ecology*, 1957, 38, 355–357, with the permission of the author and the publisher.

The occasions in which house mice (*Mus musculus*) and native American mice, particularly *Peromyscus*, come into contact are numerous. Not only do the two genera meet in man-made buildings located near the native habitat of *Peromyscus*, but also in the field where *Mus* are occasionally found associated with *Peromyscus* far from human habitation. Despite the frequent association of these two genera, little is known about their interactions. Do they compete for food or shelter? Is *Mus* able to replace *Peromyscus*? If so, is this accom-

* This study was supported by Grant MH-123 of the National Institute of Mental Health, U. S. Public Health Service.

plished by overt aggression, by greater reproductive potential, or by better utilization of the available resources? The history of introduced animals is filled with their success in replacing native species by one or all of these methods. For example, the introduced gray squirrel (*Sciurus carolinensis*) appears to be successfully replacing the common squirrel (*S. vulgaris*) throughout many regions in England (Shorten 1953). On the other hand, intraspecific conflicts are often intense while individuals of another species may live in the same environment without conflict.

The purpose of the present experiment is to examine the aggressive behavior of

Peromyscus and *Mus,* both in relation to other members of the same species and in relation to each other.

Methods

The animals in this experiment were sixteen male *Peromyscus maniculatus bairdii* and sixteen male *Mus musculus,* of the C57BL/10 inbred strain. The *Peromyscus* were descendants of a stock received from Dr. W. Prychodko, who obtained them from the Laboratory of Vertebrate Biology, University of Michigan. This stock of *Peromyscus* had been bred in the laboratory for seven years prior to the experiment. The *Mus* are an inbred strain maintained at the R. B. Jackson Memorial Laboratory (Snell 1952). Although the C57BL/10 strain has been derived from domestic mice, they are similar to wild *Mus musculus* (Calhoun 1956), and may successfully live as feral commensals, even breeding with wild *Mus.* They are known to be aggressive (Bauer 1956) but perhaps not more so than wild *Mus musculus* (Southwick 1955). Usually domesticated forms are less aggressive than their wild progenitors (Richter 1954).

Individuals of both genera were weaned at 30 days of age and caged individually until they were tested when mature at 6 to 10 months of age.

The tests were given in wooden boxes 6 × 6 × 12 inches similar to the cages used for housing the mice. A removable partition separated the combatants until the test began. One measure of aggressiveness was the number of encounters which resulted in a fight. Another measure of aggression was the fighting response latency (Fredericson 1949) which was taken as the elapsed time from the moment when the partition was removed until the first vigorous fight began. The frequency of running away, squeaking, nosing, grooming, and attacking preceding a fight was also recorded.

Procedure 1 consisted of giving eight mice of each species a series of five daily trials with seven other individuals of the same species in a round-robin fashion. Each trial lasted for a period of five minutes or until the mice began to fight, when the mice were separated in order to prevent dominance. This procedure tested for intraspecific aggression.

Procedure 2 consisted of taking the mice used in *Procedure 1* after mouse had fought every other individual of the same species and placing it with a mouse of the other species for two trials. Each mouse had two encounters with four individuals of the other species. The trials were five minutes in duration like those of *Procedure 1.* On the day following the individual tests, all the mice were placed in a large observation box 30 × 30 × 39 inches with wood shavings on the floor, activity wheel, food rack, water bottle, elevated nest box and ramp leading to the nest box. This procedure tested for interspecific aggression.

Procedure 3 employed eight different mice of each species in a series of five daily trials with individuals of the other species. Each trial lasted five minutes or until the mice began to fight. This procedure was essentially like *Procedure 2* except that the mice used in this procedure had not previously encountered any other mice, either of the same species or a different species.

Results

Intraspecific aggression. Since each animal had an opportunity to fight five times with the seven other individuals of its genus, there were 35 opportunities to fight in all. Of these 35 opportunities, the *Peromyscus* fought an average of 11.2 times, while the *Mus* fought an average of 34 times. There was no overlapping in these frequencies. The individual *Peromyscus* which fought most frequently had 17 fights, while the least frequent fighter among the *Mus* fought 31 times.

The fighting response latencies of *Peromyscus* were significantly slower when tested by the Chi-square technique; significance was calculated from the number of pairs that fought before or after the two minute median ($x^2 = 10.28$; $P < .01$). The mean of fighting response latencies for *Peromyscus* was 4.01 min. while the mean for Mus was 0.84 min. The mean response latency of only those pairs of *Peromyscus* which fought is still considerably slower (3.63 min) than that of the *Mus*. This indicates that *Peromyscus* are less ready to engage in combat than the *Mus*.

The most significant difference in the prefight behavior of the two genera was in the frequency of nosing and grooming each other. *Peromyscus* engaged in both activities more frequently (noses: $t = 3.56$; $P < .01$; grooms: $t = 3.67$; $P < .01$) than *Mus*. Although the frequency of prefight behavior depends largely on the amount of time the mice have before fighting (response latency), these behavioral activities perhaps distinguish the aggressive characteristics better than any other measure. The frequent nosing and grooming behavior elicited by *Peromyscus* often suggested dominance without a fight. When the male *Peromyscus* approached and nosed each other, one usually began to groom the other. Any attempt of one individual to reciprocate the grooming led to vigorous grooming, from which either a fight developed or one member submitted to being groomed. The passive mouse then usually curled in a corner or sometimes rolled over on its back and allowed the active groomer free access to any part of its body. When the active mouse stopped grooming, it explored the cage and returned at intervals to resume grooming. The passive mouse rarely left the corner where he had been groomed. These differences in activity and grooming strongly suggest that dominance may be established without overt fighting in *Permoyscus* in contrast to *Mus*, which rarely establish dominance without fighting vigorously.

Interspecific aggression. After the intraspecific patterns of aggression had been established by the round-robin pairings,

the same individuals were paired with four members of the other genus for two trials. *Mus* attacked *Peromyscus* on the average of 20 times per trial or 40 times for each pair. None of the *Peromyscus* attacked *Mus*. The intraspecific patterns of behavior for each genus were maintained in the interspecific fighting situation. On the first encounter the *Peromyscus* usually started to groom the *Mus*, while the *Mus* soon began to attack the *Peromyscus*. In only one encounter of one pair did the *Peromyscus* attempt to fight back. All other pairings were typified by the frequent attacks of *Mus* upon *Peromyscus*. The latter assumed a defense posture, attempted to hide, ran away, or leaped wildly about the cage.

After the last test the *Peromyscus-Mus* pairs were left together for two hours. One *Peromyscus* was killed and two others were badly bitten by the *Mus* in this time.

Since the interspecific patterns of aggression established by the mice could have resulted from the previous intra-specific experience, eight additional mice of each species were brought together in pairs for five successive 5-minute trials (*Procedure 3*). These mice had been isolated since they were weaned at 30 days of age and had experienced no previous aggression.

The lack of previous aggression experience appeared to inhibit the aggressive responses of both species during the first two or three trials. During these first trials most *Peromyscus* leaped wildly about the cage while the *Mus* carefully explored the cage. Only one pair had more than three contacts during the first two trials. Occasionally the *Peromyscus* jumped upon *Mus* as the former leaped about wildly. This type of treatment tended to intimidate the *Mus* and they squeaked and ran away. By the fourth and fifth trials, however, the *Mus* began to attack the *Peromyscus*. The mean number of attacks by *Mus* was 16.0 per mouse, while *Peromyscus* attacked *Mus* a mean of 2.5 per mouse. Most of the *Peromyscus* attacks were accomplished by one mouse. A Mann-Whitney U test indicates that *Mus* attacked *Peromyscus* significantly

($P < .02$) more times than *Peromyscus* attacked *Mus*.

When all the mice of both species were placed together in the large observation box the *Mus* immediately began to attack each other and the *Peromyscus*. Since the *Peromyscus* quickly escaped from the *Mus* in the large box, only other *Mus* resisted the attacks of each other. The *Mus* did not discriminate in their fights with other individuals. After the first four minutes, the intensive fighting subsided and the *Mus* assumed a defense posture on approach of another *Mus*. Sporadic outbreaks of fighting still occurred at intervals as the aggressive individuals continued to attack and stir the entire group into fighting. Other than the sporadic fighting, the defensive attitude persisted in the *Mus-Peromyscus* relationships. When a *Mus* approached a *Peromyscus* the latter assumed the defense posture and no fight followed. During the fighting among the *Mus, the Peromyscus* tended to huddle together in a corner and to keep out of the way. At the end of the 45-minute observation period, most *Peromyscus* were huddled together in a corner; most *Mus* were grooming and licking their wounds, while two *Mus* kept making rounds attacking the defensive *Mus* from time to time.

The mice were kept together for three days. During that time the two genera made some adjustment to each other and they were occasionlly observed huddled together. Fighting was not observed, although there were occasional disputes with a mild attack, chase, defense posture and squeaks among both genera.

The *Mus* were removed on the third day and only the *Peromyscus* were left. One of them became aggressive by the fourth day and actively chased the others. None of the other *Peromyscus* approached him.

Discussion

The greater aggressiveness displayed by *Mus* than *Peromyscus* under laboratory conditions suggests that whenever the two genera come into contact under natural conditions the *Peromyscus* may be attacked by the *Mus* and driven from the immediate region. However, it may well be that the two genera will occur in the same area under favorable conditions because *Peromyscus* does not resist the attacks of *Mus* and can easily escape the latter. Under unfavorable conditions, such as a high population density or a severe shortage of food or shelter, it is likely that *Peromyscus* are replaced by *Mus*. The type of interspecific competition need not result from the better utilization of environmental resources by *Mus* nor from their higher reproductive potential. Instead, the competition may take the form of overt attacks by *Mus* on *Peromyscus* as both genera are forced into more frequent contacts during population peaks.

The testing procedure demonstrated how the patterns of intraspecific aggression affected interspecific relationships. Different patterns of aggression were not displayed intraspecifically and interspecifically. Rather, the behavior a mouse showed toward its species-member was duplicated in its behavior toward a different species. *Peromyscus* tended to groom and huddle together, while *Mus* fought with each other. Consequently, when placed together, the aggressiveness of *Mus* was maintained and the initial attempts of *Peromyscus* to groom were replaced by escape behavior. When both genera were placed together in the large cage, the behavior patterns of each genus increased the frequency of intraspecific contacts. The *Mus* fought among themselves and the *Peromyscus* huddled together. This maintenance of specific patterns of behavior illustrates that the behavior of each species tends to result in intraspecific associations rather than interspecific associations among animals occupying similar ecological niches.

Summary

The aggressive behavior of 16 *Peromyscus maniculatus bairdii* and the C57BL/10 inbred strain of 16 *Mus musculus* was measured in individual combats with members of the same species and members of the other species. The *Mus* were more aggressive than *Peromyscus* in both intraspecific and interspecific combats. Patterns of aggressive behavior characteristic for each species tend to be maintained when both species encounter each other. The great aggressiveness of *Mus* suggests that they are capable of driving *Peromyscus* out of natural situations whenever the two species frequently encounter each other.

REFERENCES

BAUER, F. J., 1956 Genetic and experiential factors affecting social reactions in male mice. *J. Comp. Physiol. Psychol.*, 49: 359–364.

CALHOUN, J. B., 1956 A comparative study of the social behavior of two inbred strains of house mice. *Ecol. Monogr.*, 26: 81–103.

FREDERICSON, E., 1949 Response latency and habit strength in relationship to spontaneous fighting in C57 black mice. *Anat. Rec.*, 105: 29 (Abstract).

RICHTER, C. P., 1954 The effects of domestication and selection on the behavior of the Norway rat. *J. Nat. Cancer Instit.*, 15: 727–738.

SHORTEN, M., 1953 Notes on the distribution of the grey squirrel (*Sciurus carolinensis*) and the red squirrel (*Sciurus vulgaris leucourus*) in England and Wales from 1945 to 1952. *J. Anim. Ecol.*, 22: 134–140.

SNELL, G. D., 1952 Standardized nomenclature for inbred strains of mice. *Cancer Res.*, 12: 602–613.

SOUTHWICK, C. H., 1955 Regulatory mechanisms of house mouse populations: Social behavior affecting litter survival. *Ecology*, 36: 627–634.

WILLIAM C. DILGER

51 Excerpts from: The Comparative Ethology of the African Parrot Genus *Agapornis*

Several sections of the original article have been omitted in this reading. These sections covered the general biology and physical description of lovebirds, the behavior of their young in the nest, their maintenance activities, and their locomotion. Reprinted here are the "Introduction," sections on "Agonistic Behavior" and "Reproductive Behavior," and the "Summary."

In order to follow the species comparisons made in the article, it is necessary to keep the taxonomy of the genus in mind. The following chart lists the species mentioned by Dilger and some of their important characteristics.

"Primitive"

Solitary nesters
Sexual dichromatism

Agapornis cana

Agapornis taranta

Agapornis pullaria

Agapornis swinderniana: (Not studied by Dilger)

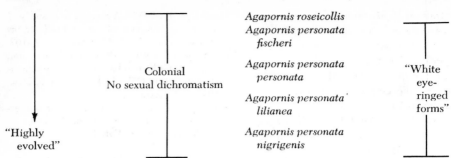

"Highly evolved"

Colonial
No sexual dichromatism

Agapornis roseicollis
Agapornis personata fischeri

Agapornis personata personata

Agapornis personata lilianea

Agapornis personata nigrigenis

"White eye-ringed forms"

Note the conclusions about the evolution of behavior patterns that Dilger, an ornithologist, is able to draw as a result of his careful study of the biology and taxonomy of the genus.

Readings 2 and 5 provide definitions for the ethological terms used in this reading.

Reprinted from *Zeitschrift für Tierpsychologie*, 1960, **17**, 649–685, with the permission of the author and the publisher: Paul Parey, Berlin and Hamburg. Several figures have been omitted.

Introduction

The genus *Agapornis* is composed of several closely related and allopatric species which readily breed and hybridize in captivity. Moreover, they demonstrate a fairly consistent trend from a relatively "primitive" form *(cana)* to the most "highly evolved" one *(p. nigrigenis)*. In addition, many behavior patterns show both quantitative and qualitative differences, greatly facilitating studies of the evolution of species-typical behavior.

All of the described species are being studied, with the exception of *swinderniana* which has not yet been obtained. The minimum number of individuals studied was about fifteen *(p. lilianae)* and the maximum about forty (both *roseicollis* and hybrids between *roseicollis* and *p. fischeri*). These birds were observed both in indoor breeding cages in which one pair at a time was observed and in large outdoor flight cages in which several pairs at a time were observed. Several small, specially designed, cages were also used to obtain photographic records of certain behavior patterns (see Dilger, 1958, for a complete description of these).

All of the behavior of each species was first carefully described and then evaluations were made of the function, survival value, causation, and evolution of each behavior pattern. The methods used were those commonly employed by ethologists and described, for instance, by Tinbergen (1959).

At first, observations were recorded directly in notebooks but later by speaking into a small tape recorder and then transcribing these notes into notebooks. This enabled uninterrupted observations to be made and was a vastly superior method. Hundreds of feet of motion picture film were taken with the aid of a Bell and Howell time and motion camera. This technique permitted the study of behavior exactly as it occurred in time and space, being especially valuable in studying the exact interactions of two or more individuals.

All species were fed a diet consisting of French's Parakeet Seed (a mixture of red and white mullet and canary seed), French's Conditioning Food (a diet supplement containing a variety of small seeds, dried milk products, and other ingredients including several vitamins), cuttle bone, quartz gravel, and fresh water. All but the small-billed *cana* and *pullaria* relish sunflower seeds as well.

AGONISTIC BEHAVIOR

Basically, plumage sleeking and movements (or intention movements for locomoting or biting) oriented toward another are indicative of a tendency to attack and, conversely, plumage fluffing and movements (or intention movements) away from another are indicative of a tendency to escape. A conflict of the attack and escape drives is recognized by a combination of these actions (ambivalent behavior) either alternately or simultaneously. These ambivalent patterns certainly serve a signal function judging from overt responses but only a few seem to have become ritualized into displays.

The white eye-ringed forms and *roseicollis* are especially social in their behavior and they, particularly, have developed much inhibition with regard to biting one another. The biological advantage of such inhibition is readily apparent when one regards the large, powerful, and sharply hooked bills characteristic of these species.

Bill-fencing. This seems to be a highly ritualized activity consisting of lowering the bill and making a thrust at the opponent's toes. The attacked bird responds by attempting to parry this thrust with its bill and also tries to make a counter-thrust of its own which the other bird attempts to parry in turn. This behavior may be quite prolonged and the birds keep their bills very close, and the "fight" may take place through considerable vertical distance from as high as they can reach down to perch level. The action may be prolonged or quite brief, may be very rapid or somewhat slower, although the speed does not vary nearly as much as does the duration. Birds with apparently strong and well-matched motivations may fence for several minutes and the action may cover many inches of perching space as they advance and retreat. More commonly, however, Bill-fencing is merely a "token" fight in which a few quick parries and thrusts are made, apparently without any serious attempts to actually bite toes. Even in the rare prolonged and vigorous encounters between adults it is rare for a toe to be actually nipped although sometimes one gets the impression that the contestants are evidently trying very hard to do so.

There is strong inhibition associated with biting, or attempting to bite, an opponent anywhere but the toes even though many opportunities to do so present themselves during the course of a bout Bill-fencing.

Nestlings have only occasionally been observed to fight with each other, but newly fledged birds do so fairly often. These birds have, from the very first, a strong tendency to nip toes and do not ordinarily attempt to bite anywhere else. They also attempt to Bill-fence but are not very adept, and in encounters with each other, and particularly with adults, often get severely nipped. Usually no visible damage is done, occasionally blood is drawn, and very rarely is a distal phalange snipped off. As these young birds become older they become more skillful at Bill-fencing, until finally it is rare for them to be bitten. The decrease in actual nipping seems to be due not only to increased skill in Bill-fencing but also in learning to avoid situations that may lead to a fight.

The increased skill in Bill-fencing may be facilitated by the negative reinforcement associated with getting a painful nip. It appears that Bill-fencing is an example of a highly stereotyped activity with both learned and not-learned elements interacting to perfect the definitive pattern.

When a bird is grasped by a toe, it characteristically utters a loud series of rather high-pitched, plaintive squeals which result in its quick release.

It is common for one bird of a mated pair to get the other to move by administering a gentle pinch (or an intention movement to do so) to the nearest toe of the other. This does not ordinarily result in Bill-fencing but merely in the "attacked" bird unhurriedly moving along. This may be repeated until the "attacker" has

FIG. 1. An adult male *Agapornis cana* performing the Aggressive Walk.

achieved the desired amount of movement in the "attacked."

The bill color contrast strongly with the face color in all species except *cana*. It is also perhaps of interest to remark that the biting ability of recently fledged young seems greatly reduced although their bills are fully developed and hard. It is not clear whether this is merely due to a lack of exercise of the great masseter muscles or is a special adaptation serving to protect them from serious damage while effective Bill-fencing is being learned.

Actual biting attacks in *cana, pullaria,* and *taranta* seem to be less inhibited in action. They also have more displays associated with attack and escape than have *roseicollis* and the white eye-ringed forms.

Aggressive Walk. Cana, pullaria, and *taranta* have a peculiar walk when attempting to supplant an opponent while on foot. This consists of long, rapid strides toward the opponent, the body being held at a shallow angle with the perch but the head carried horizontally (Fig. 1). If the opponent does not at least make intention movements to move away the attacker will, as it approaches, show sings of increasing fear, expressed by ruffling first the feather

of the crown, then the back and scapulars, and finally, particularly in *cana,* the entire plumage including the wings and tail. Gaping, clearly an intention movement to bite, is often employed here (Fig. 2). Gaping and rufflings are also employed as defensive threats by a bird prevented from escape either because of physical restrictions of the environment (e.g., cornered in a nest box) or because of a strong conflicting motivation, the expression of which is incompatible with the motor patterns of fleeing. . . .

The extreme ruffling and fluffing of the entire plumage as an indication of thwarted escape is best developed in *cana* in which it has by far the lowest threshold of response. It is seen in *taranta* much less frequently and here it evidently has a much higher threshold. The same seems to be true for *pullaria*. In *roseicollis* and the white eye-ringed forms, this behavior has a very high threshold and has never been seen in its extreme form. The only plumage erections encountered in these birds are general fluffings of the entire plumage in submissive birds or in birds prevented from fleeing because of a conflicting drive, particularly incubation. The wings and tail are not involved.

Females of *cana,* in particular, are typ-

FIG. 2. An adult male *Agapornis cana* supplanting another male and adopting the ruffling and gaping associated with fear conflicting with aggression.

ically aggressive near their nest sites, threatening all conspecifics in the vicinity. These, when entering the nest hole, even mildly threaten their own mates by spreading the tail as they disappear head first into the cavity . . . Males, when entering the cavity, may do the same to their females although here the response is not unvarying. Strange birds, under similar circumstances, are threatened with the entire body being ruffled (see also under nest defence behavior).

Carpal-flashing. This aggressive display is apparently peculiar to *taranta* males. It consists of the carpal areas being quickly exposed by flicking them out from the body with little disturbance of the normal resting position of the wing tips. This display is oriented frontally at the opponent and, seen from the latter's point of view, it appears as two quick and simultaneous flashes of black against a green background. . . . This serves to stop the advance of another or even causes it to retreat. It has not been seen in those species in which it might also be expected to occur, the other species with black wing-linings (*cana* and *pullaria*). It is possible that it does occur in these two species but has a particularly high threshold. However, *pullaria* males have what is a homologous display which involves holding the carpals out stiffly and is used both in sexual and agonostic situations.

Mobbing. Mobbing behavior is highly developed in *roseicollis* and the white eye-ringed forms but absent, or at least very much reduced, in the others. The division is again coincident with the division between the social and relatively non-social species.

When *cana, taranta,* and *pullaria* are confronted with a predator, such as a dog or a man, they utter a series of "alarm" calls which are rather high pitched, differing for each species. They show relatively little evidence of attack, judging from their overt behavior, but merely utter these calls and remain where they are or flee. On the other hand *roseicollis* and the white eye-

ringed forms, under similar circumstances, utter a rapid series of high-pitched squeaks and, at the same time, beat their wings rapidly with the body held quite erect. Mobbing behavior indicative of only relatively mild stimulation consists of the squeaks only, which are given slower and lower in pitch. As the stimulation becomes stronger the birds utter faster and higher pitched squeaks until the wing beat component also comes in. If the predator does nothing, the mobbing gradually wanes, but if the predator continues to approach the mobbing becomes stronger and the birds may flee to a new vantage point where the mobbing is continued; squeaking as they fly. On one occasion, when I entered a large *roseicollis* flight-cage to retrieve an injured bird, the mobbing birds actually approached me *en masse* and made many intention movements to fly at me although none actually attacked. The noise and visual effect of a whole flock mobbing at the same time creates a considerable disturbance and might well act as a strong deterrent to many predators. This sort of behavior probably would not be nearly as effective if only two or three birds were engaged, and this may be the reason it has evolved so strongly in the more social species.

Alert Posture. [Omitted figure] shows the characteristic alert posture in *Agapornis.* It is much like the mobbing stance and may lead to mobbing if the stimulus causing the "alert" is close enough and precisely located by the birds.

Nest Cavity Defence. Nest cavity defence behavior is well developed in *cana,* poorly developed in *taranta,* suspected but unknown in *pullaria,* and apparently non-existent in *roseicollis* and the white eye-ringed forms. The increase in mobbing activity and the coincident increase in nest complexity through this same series may compensate for the lack of nest cavity defence in the latter two species.

Both sexes of *cana* take part in the nest cavity defence. Well-grown young also take part when they are available. The behavior is most complete in the adult female. When disturbed in the nest cavity the feathers of the entire body are ruffled, the wings and tail partly spread, and a rapid series of harsh buzzing notes are uttered. If the intruder persists in its approach, the bird suddenly and simultaneously compresses the plumage; utters a sharp, high-pitched *"yip"*; and lunges at the intruder. The effect of this is quite startling and it is difficult to hold a hand near, even though the bird does not actually bite. Biting will occur, however, in all species if the bird is grasped.

If the male and/or young are present in the nest they will take part in the ruffling and buzzing but will not lunge or *yip.*

The threshold for this behavior is very high in *taranta.* Much greater stimulation is necessary for its release and even when it does occur the wings and tail are not spread nor is a lunge or *yip* given. Ruffling the body plumage and a series of harsh rasping sounds are all that occur. The males and juvenals of *taranta* have never been noticed to take part.

When a female *cana* and a nest of well-grown young exhibit their nest cavity defence behavior, the beginnings and ends of the displays are abrupt and perfectly coordinated. This makes it easy to time both the duration of such activity and the lag between stimulation and the onset of the buzzing. On several occasions we pre-sented a female *cana* and her nestlings with a regularly repeated and standardized stim. ulus. We timed the lag between the presentation of the stimulus and the onset of vocalizations, the duration of the vocalizations, and then waited twenty seconds after the cessation of vocalizations before presenting the next stimulus. In this way we obtained data over periods up to two hours. We found that the time lag between the stimulations and the vocalizations was from zero to twenty seconds. The duration of the vocalizations fell off rapidly with repeated stimulation until they remained about thirty seconds in length even after prolonged periods of repeated stimulation (Fig. 3). The extinction of this response is apparently difficult to achieve. This is probably of considerable survival value as it would be disadvantageous to have this response wane entirely in the presence of repeated attempts at predation while trapped in the nest cavity. The nest itself offers no defence whatsoever (as it would in the white eye-ringed forms) and the bill of *cana* is small compared to those of the others.

The buzzing of *cana* and the rasping of *taranta* in nest defence are very similar to sounds uttered when being handled. Somewhat similar nest defence displays are given by the Budgerigar (*Melopsittacus undulatus*) and the Blossom-headed Parrakeet (*Psittacula cyanocephala*).

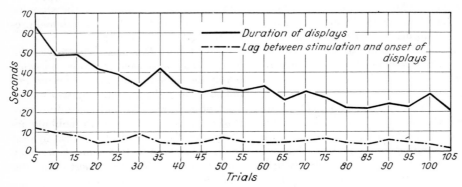

FIG. 3. Graph showing the waning of the nest defence display of *Agapornis cana* upon repeated stimulation and also the lapse in time between the stimulations and the onset of the displays (see text for explanation). The data are plotted from a succession of five-trial means.

The white eye-ringed forms and *rosei-collis,* when disturbed in the nest, merely cower with the head lying flat on the substrate (sometimes they try to wedge themselves head first into a corner) or they flee out the entrance hole.

REPRODUCTIVE BEHAVIOR

Pair Formation.—Little precise information is available on pair formation. We know that these birds all form pair bonds very quickly and ordinarily remain paired until one of the partners dies. Pair bonds may be broken by removing the birds from one another's sight and hearing for several weeks. We also know that birds still in juvenal plumage will form pair bonds which are usually heterosexual but are sometimes homosexual. These latter bonds seem to break up spontaneously in time. Adults, if given a choice, will ordinarily only form heterosexual pair bonds. Adult *roseicollis* and the white eye-ringed forms (all sexually non-dichromatic) easily form homosexual bonds if potential mates of the opposite sex are not available. The sexually dichromatic species have never been observed to form such homosexual attachments. However, two male *pullaria* were once seen to form a temporary and rather loose bond but this species is not as strikingly dichromatic as are *cana* and *taranta* and this, in some way, may have contributed to the formation of the bond. On the other hand, the homosexual pairs of *rosei-collis* and the white eye-ringed forms seem to be as difficult to disrupt as are normal heterosexual pairs. As might be expected, one member of these latter homosexual pairs (regardless of the sex involved) always assumes the male sexual role and the other the female sexual role. This, once established, remains absolutely consistent. A homosexual male pair will not, however, inspect a nest site nor demonstrate any interest in nest material. A homosexual female pair will occupy the same nest cavity and both birds will collect, carry, and utilize nest material and both will simultaneously lay eggs and incubate.

The exact mechanisms of pair formation are obscure. If a group of unpaired adults are liberated into a large flight cage they will form a rather well-knit flock (especially the more social forms). They tend to perform their various maintenance activities in concert. Each bird seems to attempt to interact socially with a number of others, however. This consists of attempts to preen others, to sit closely with others and so forth. Soon it becomes apparent that certain of these combinations seem to be more fortunate than others and the two birds tend to seek each other's company in preference to other birds. This bond becomes progressively stronger until in just a few hours the pair bonds seem to have become firmly established. It is not clear which sex takes the initiative. Cinat-Thompson (1926) found that female Budgerigars *(Melopsittacus undulatus)* choose males to which they are most attracted on the basis of color pattern and voice. It may be that in *Agapornis* the males "test" a variety of females by attempting to preen them, sit with them, and so forth until they find one which accepts their presence most easily. Aside from these activities, the most important "pair cementing" activity seems to be courtship feeding (see below for description and discussion).

Nest-building. Interest is shown in possible nest sites soon after adults form their pair bonds or soon after juvenal pairs attain their adult plumage. The female in particular investigates entrance holes and soon chooses a cavity within which to build her nest. The male remains close to the female throughout these activities but his interest seems to be in her and not particularly in the nest site.

The nesting of *pullaria* is somewhat different. As far as is known this species chooses hard, earthy, aboreal ant nests as nest sites. These are burrowed into; the tunnel usually turning to one side before the chamber is excavated. Sometimes the tunnel turns upward so that the chamber lies over the tunnel (Prestwich, 1957;

Perry, 1959; Serle, 1957). Probably the female does the excavating (Hampe, 1937). However, the evidence is somewhat contradictory. Pitman in Moreau (1948) says that both sexes excavate and Prestwich (1957) says, "the task of excavating falls mainly to the female. The males show great enthusiasm but are more of a hindrance than any real help." Perry (1959) says on page 120 that ". . . the pair succeeded in making a tunnel right through the ant mound!" On page 121, however, Perry says, . . . "the female was busy excavating into the cork slab. This went on for several days until a deep tunnel had been made and the hen eventually disappeared altogether." Based on the evidence for *pullaria* and on what we know of male activity in the other species, it is probably safe to say that the male, although closely attentive to the female, does little or no excavating.

Agapornis, cana, taranta, and *pullaria* are rather solitary nesters in the wild. This is borne out by our observations on our captive birds which show little social cohesiveness when several pairs are attempting to nest in the same outdoor flight cage; indeed, these birds engage in much interpair aggression under such conditions. On the other hand *roseicollis* and the white eye-ringed forms tend to be quite colonial in their nesting. The nest-box tends to be defended by the resident pair in all species but often strangers are allowed to sit on it. The entrance hole itself, however, is always defended. Most of the defence is carried out by the male; apparently because the female is simply not available much of the time as a result of incubation and brooding. Both sexes will threaten or attack intruders regardless of sex in *roseicollis* and the white eye-ringed forms. On the other hand, the sexually dichromatic

FIG. 4. An adult female *Agapornis taranta* tucking nest material (sunflower seed hulls) in her feathers; (top) in her rump, (left) in her flank, and (right) in the side of her neck. Note that she has many missing feathers which have been used to augment the nest material, and the extensive ruffling of the entire plumage. This method of tucking is typical for *cana* females as well.

cana and *taranta* have a tendency for males to defend against other males and females against females. The females of these species are particularly aggressive toward strange females and vigorous fights sometimes occur, especially during the time nest sites are being selected. Males of these species are typically far more tolerant of intrusion.

Normally, only females of all species prepare and carry nesting material, which consists of pieces of bark, leaves, plant

FIG. 5. (Top) An adult female *Agapornis roseicollis* about to tuck a strip of nest material in her rump feathers. Note that only the rump feathers are ruffled to receive this material, and the uniformity of the strips cut, judging from where she has been cutting. (Bottom) Nest of *Agapornis roseicollis*. Note the rather deep cup made possible by the long strips of nest material.

stems, wood fibers, paper, etc. In addition to such materials, females of the white eye-ringed forms also utilize twigs, chewing them from larger branches or picking them up from the ground. Females of *cana*, *taranta*, and *pullaria* bite off very small pieces of nesting material and carry them, many pieces at a time, thrust amidst the feathers of the entire body. The entire plumage is ruffled as if to receive such material every time a piece is being placed in the feathers. The feathers are compressed again during each bout of cutting the next piece. Fig. 4 (3 parts) shows a female *taranta* tucking small pieces of material (sunflower seed hulls) and also shows the characteristic appearance of the plumage of *taranta* females while nest-building. *A. taranta* has the unique habit of also utilizing its own feathers as nest material. These are obtained while the bird is in the nest and it is not clear whether she actually plucks herself or whether the feathers fall out naturally. If they are plucked, the male may help as her head also ordinarily shows much feather loss. We have never seen males of *cana*, *taranta*, or *pullaria* cut or carry nesting material. However, Perry (1959) observed a male *pullaria* carrying nest material in the feathers of his back. These species do not carry very much material and its very nature precludes the possibility of building any sort of structure. Instead, the material serves as a soft pad lining the shallow saucer-shaped scrape in the detritus at the bottom of the cavity. . . . In the wild, *pullaria*, at least, may sometimes carry no nesting material (Serle, 1957).

Agapornis roseicollis females also tuck material amidst the feathers but only those of the lower back and rump are utilized, and only these are erected during bouts of tucking. Moreover, the pieces of material cut by *roseicollis* are much larger and take the form of strips having quite uniform characteristics relative to length, width, and straightness. Several pieces are tucked before the bird flies off to the nest. Fig. 5 (top) shows a female *roseicollis* about to

tuck a strip of nest material. The nature of this material (long strips) permits a structure of sorts to be built within the cavity. They typically fashion a rather deep cup in which the eggs are deposited (Fig. 5, bottom).

The white eye-ringed forms carry nest material only in their bills. Hampe (1936), however, had a young male *p. fischeri* which often stuck nesting material in the feathers of its rump. These forms, as mentioned above, carry twigs as well as strips of paper, bark, or leaves which they have cut. This latter material seems more variable in its characteristics than it is in *roseicollis* and is probably a reflection of the fact that it no longer has to be transported in the feathers. The ability to carry twigs as well as other material allows these birds to build rather elaborate nests consisting of a completely roofed chamber in which the eggs are deposited and a narrow tunnel leading up to the cavity entrance. . . . Moreau (1948) states that such a nest is a structure, ". . . that could hardly exist unless it were supported below and on all sides." This is definitely not the case. The material is carefully positioned and interwoven in such a way that the entire nest can be removed from the nesting cavity without its losing its shape or identity in any way. The highly developed motor patterns employed by these birds, which result in such an elaborate structure, are being studied at the present time in our laboratory by Mrs. William Keeton, and this information along with facts concerning the evolution of nest building in the genus will be the subject of a forthcoming paper.

We do agree with Moreau (1948), however, that the carrying of material thrust amidst the feathers represents a primitive condition for the genus. We also agree with him in doubting the explanation put forward by others that this method of carrying serves to free the bill for climbing into awkwardly situated nest entrances. White eye-ringed birds all climb well with the aid of the bill even though they may be carrying nest material at the same time.

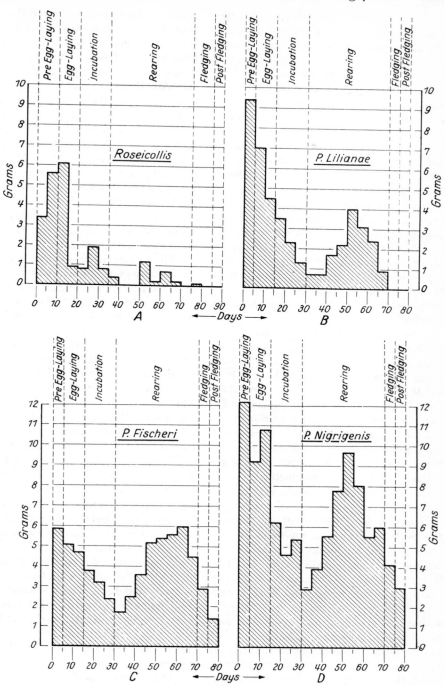

FIG. 6. Graph showing the nest material utilization (in grams) by a) *Agapornis roseicollis:* 2 females, 2 cycles; b) *A. p. lilianae:* 1 female, 1 cycle; c) *A. p. fischeri:* 2 females, 11 cycles; and d) *A. p. nigrigenis:* 1 female, 7 cycles. Successive five-day means were plotted.

Males of *roseicollis* and the white eye-ringed forms have been seen to occasionally cut nesting material and carry it about. It is exceedingly rare, however, for them to carry material into the nest. Interestingly enough, male nest material cutting and carrying is only done in connection with heterosexual pairs. Homosexual male pairs show no interest in nest material. This observation, coupled with observations on normal pairs, leads us to conclude that such activity in males is largely, if not entirely, the result of mimesis afforded by the nest material preparation by the female. We know that mimetic behavior between members of a pair is particularly strong. Homosexual pairs of males are not stimulated to respond to nest material if adjacent females are active in nest building although such activity is clearly "contagious" (both visually and auditorily) among adjacent females.

The preparation and utilization of nesting material in all of these species does not seem to be as dependent upon a specific phase of the reproductive cycle as it is in many birds (e. g., Benoit, 1956:234). Paired females of all species (unknown for *pullaria*) prepare and carry nesting material throughout the year in the presence of nesting material and a nest site. This activity occurs regardless of the stage of reproduction (or non-reproduction). However, the amount of such activity, as reflected in the amount of nest material utilized, varies markedly with the stage of the cycle in the white eye-ringed forms. Details of this for *roseicollis, p. fischeri, p. lilianae,* and *p. nigrigenis* are given in Fig. 6. It may be seen that two peaks of activity occur; one just before and during egg-laying and the other during the period the young are developing in the nest. The least activity occurs during incubation and during the period between nestings. The tendency to carry nest material is strong during incubation but the female is mostly unavailable to engage in such activities. When she does make an occasional brief appearance, in order to defecate or to eat or drink, she ordinarily performs a strong bout of comfort movements and then takes a few moments to engage in a brief but intense bout of nest material cutting and makes at least one trip into the nest with material. However, during the period between nestings, the female, who now has plenty of time, cuts and carries steadily but in a rather desultory fashion. It is apparent that the drive for nest building is high throughout the reproductive period and that the peaks of activity are the result of superimposed conflicting activities which inhibit nest-building. Nest-building activity does not seem to be so markedly divided into peaks in *cana* and appears to be somewhat intermediate in *roseicollis.*

The placement of material is governed by a complex of stimuli which have not been worked out thoroughly in every case. This will be a part of the forthcoming paper by Keeton. In brief, it may be mentioned that (aside from constructing the nest itself) cracks of light; splinters of wood, twigs, etc. behind which softer material can be wedged; and fresh feces all prompt the deposition of nesting material. The response to fresh feces functions during the nestling stage as a nest sanitation measure. However, experimentation determined that this response is present during egglaying and incubation. During the nestling stage the amount of nest material deposited varies directly with the amount of feces deposited. However, a few days before the young fledge, their feces gradually take on the drier characteristics of adult feces and here the nest material deposition drops markedly. We have added and subtracted to the amount of feces deposited in nests and have always obtained a corresponding adjustment in the amount of nest material carried. Foreign objects in the nest, including dead young, are not carried out but are covered with nesting material.

Older young of the white eye-ringed forms do not tend to remain in the nest chamber, but eventually spend most of their time clustered near the entrance hole.

Sexual Behavior. Males of all species come into sexual condition before the females. We do not know what stimulates the males but they seem at least relatively independent of varying day lengths, judging from the breeding success we have observed under varying light conditions. Males perform a variety of courtship activities ("courtship" being used in the sense of Morris, 1956) and at first the females respond overtly with "indifference", active avoidance, or aggression. As time goes on, however, females clearly gradually begin to have a stronger and stronger tendency to behave sexually; until finally the time arrives when they will permit copulation. One function, therefore, of male sexual displays is to stimulate females until their physiological condition will permit them to exhibit sexual behavior (long term arousal). This is in contrast to the similar male activities which serve as stimuli for short term arousal (permitting copulations to occur) after females are in sexual condition. Long term arousal may take anywhere from a few days to two or three weeks. Short term arousals usually take place in a few seconds to several minutes. The speed of the long term arousal seems to be dependent upon the persistence of the male's sexual activities and upon other environmental conditions such as availability of nest sites, nesting material, interference from other birds and so on. Short term arousal seems to be dependent not only upon the sexual activity of the male but largely upon conflicting tendencies in the female (feeding, resting, comfort activities, etc.) and, primarily, upon nest-building which occupies a large part of her time. Male sexual behavior remains strong throughout nest-building, egg-laying , and into incubation, but wanes markedly during late incubation and remains weak until the next reproductive cycle (which may overlap with rearing young). Males of all species have essentially the same activities comprising their sexual behavior. In order to fully understand these activities it must be realized that the two strongest tendencies ordinarily present in a "courting" male are to avoid the female (fear) and to approach her (sex or "mating" in Morris's, 1956, terms). Thus, a male *Agapornis,* particularly of *roseicollis* and the white eye-ringed forms, has the typical conflict of FaM according to Morris's system where "f" refers to flee, "a" to attack, and "m" to mate. The female, on the other hand, has the typical conflict that can be expressed as fAm (in other words, little tendency to flee, considerable tendency to attack, and little tendency to behave sexually). Of course, for copulation to occur both must eventually achieve the situation symbolized as faM, and the sexual activities of the male function to achieve this state. The following is a description of these sexual activities with comments on their differences, similarities, functions, causations, and evolution.

Switch-sidling. This activity is clearly the result of conflicting tendencies to approach and not to approach (or even flee from) the female. The male sidles along the perch toward or away from the female, repeatedly turning around as he does so. When sidling toward the female, the male typically turns away from her. Causally, this seems to be very much like the "pivoting" described for various small birds (e. g., the Zebra Finch, *Poephila guttata,* Morris, 1954). Weaker tendencies to Switch-sidle cause the omission of the turning component, or they are expressed merely as intention movements to turn while sidling. The speed, direction, and duration of Switch-sidling depends primarily upon signals from the female. If she gives the slightest sign of becoming less aggressive and/or more apt to behave sexually (e. g., slight fluffing of the plumage, particularly of the face and/or a slight leaning forward), the male will sidle toward her more rapidly. If the female signals that she is more aggressive (e.g., any plumage sleeking, especially the face; and/or becoming more erect on the perch) the male will sidle away more rapidly. How far the male travels away from her depends largely upon when she signals a more amenable attitude. If she doesn't do so the male will not continue sidling away indefinitely but will usually fly over her and land on her other side. The female may sometimes respond more strongly by attacking or, more rarely, fleeing.

Carpals Held. Only *pullaria* males utilize this display and it consists of the bird, with sleeked plumage, raising the carpals out from the body and then, standing rather erect, moving about stiffly, and orienting frontally to the female. This is strangely reminiscent of the Aggressive Upright used by gulls and is probably homologous to the Carpal Flash of *taranta* males. The tail is also spread during high intensity bouts and this display seems to be caused by fear conflicting with sexual or aggressive motivation.

Head-bobbing. This has been derived from the Head-bobbing associated with courtship feeding (see below). The movements consist of repeated bobbing of the head and vary somewhat from species to species, tending to be more numerous and faster in *cana, taranta,* and *pullaria* and fewer and slower (more exaggerated) in the white eye-ringed forms. They are intermediate in these respects in *roseicollis.* In *roseicollis* and the white eye-ringed forms, the males, during high intensity courtship bouts (characterized by extreme persistence despite repeated thwartings and rapid transition from one display to another) perform many Head-bobbings but

will not feed the female even if she should proffer her bill. This is why we believe that this movement is at least partially ritualized. This particular use of Head-bobbing has not been seen in *cana, taranta,* or *pullaria.* Head-bobbing may occur during Switch-sidling and seems independent of the distance from the female. Figs. 7 and 8 show the differences in form of this movement in *cana, roseicollis,* and the white eye-ringed forms.

Displacement Scratching. This is a particularly interesting display because it nicely demonstrates the evolution of a display from its non-signal precursor (head-scratching). All species will, upon being thwarted, scratch the head with a foot. In *cana, taranta,* and *pullaria,* this movement is indistinguishable from ordinary head-scratching. In *roseicollis,* the scratching movements are faster and often directed at the bill, rather than at the head plumage; they also occur much more frequently than in *cana, taranta,* and *pullaria.* In the white eye-ringed forms, the movement is still faster and most often directed at the bill; here it occurs most frequently of all. A scratching bout may consist of several scratchings in both *roseicollis* and the white eye-ringed forms. In addition to these changes throughout the evolutionary series, the foot employed shows differences from species to species. Originally, the leg nearest the female is the one employed; probably because this leg is already lifted as an intention movement to mount and

FIG. 7. The forms of the head-bobbing associated with courtship feeding in a) *Agapornis cana,* b) in *A. roseicollis,* and c) in *A. p. fischeri.* Note the various amounts of feather ruffling and amplitudes of the movements; also note the differences in body position.

FIG. 8. (Left) Copulation in *Agapornis roseicollis*. Note the ruffled wrists and tilted head with ruffled cheeks and throat. This is typical of *personata* females as well. (Right) Copulation in *Agapornis taranta*. Note the sleeked wrists and untilted head devoid of any ruffling. This is typical of *cana* and *pullaria* as well. The open mouth (squeaking) is species-typical for *taranta* females only.

may, therefore, be an example of what Lind (1959) has termed an activation of an instinct caused by transitional action. The leg nearest the female seems to always be employed by *cana, taranta,* and *pullaria*. However, in *roseicollis* the ratio of employment of the near foot to the far foot is 3:2. In *p. fischeri* and *p. personata* this ratio is 7:6, and in *lilianae* and *nigrigenis* this ratio is very close to 1:1. Displacement Scratching in these latter five forms seems to have approached neurophysiological emancipation. We do not yet have precise figures on the frequency of occurence of scratchings directed at the bill as opposed to those directed at the cheek. However, frequently when a bird scratches its cheek it will immediately afterward flick its head; this is apparently a movement having the function of rearranging disturbed feathers. Consequently, those scratchings directed at the cheek should be more often followed by head flicks than those directed at the bill. The percentages of the time Displacement Scratchings are followed by head flicks for various species are as follows: *roseicollis* (8%), *p. fischeri* (2%), *p. personata* (3%), and even lower in *p. nigrigenis* and *p. lilianae*. Our data for *cana,*

taranta, and *pullaria* are too meager for confident evaluation but subjective observation makes it quite clear that the percentages would be much higher than for *roseicollis*. Frequently only intention movements for Displacement Scratching are given. These frequently occur when the external situation, responsible for the thwarting, resolves before the scratching can be completed, or if the male apparently has a rather low sexual motivation when thwarted.

Tail-wagging. This comfort movement, described above, is frequently employed as a displacement activity by *roseicollis* and the white eye-ringed forms. However, it is not seen when the male is exhibiting low intensity courtship behavior as is Displacement Scratching. It is as if Tail-wagging, being unritualized, is more effective as a displacement activity than is the highly ritualized Displacement Scratching, especially during very strong thwartings.

Displacement Preening. Apparently, only *cana* normally demonstrates highly ritualized Displacement Preening. Immediately upon being thwarted, during a bout of precopulatory activity, the male makes rapid, small amplitude, sideways jerks of the head. The true nature of these movements may be seen when the thwarting is especialy strong. Here, the sideways movements have greater amplitude and the bill then frequently briefly probes the feathers of the sides of the upper breast. Interestingly, one male *roseicollis* was seen to do this two or three times, although this display is apparently extinct in all but *cana*.

"Pseudofemale" Soliciting. The performance of this activity described below is so common during the precopulatory bouts of *roseicollis* and the white eye-ringed forms that it must be regarded as a normal activity. It may be given merely as an intention movement, or the complete act may be performed. It is not usually maintained for more than a second or two at the most and always occurs in situations characterized by the thwarting of a strong tendency to behave sexually (mounting the female). However, it seems to have little or no value in alleviating the "uncomfortable" conditions of thwarting as it is ordinarily sandwiched between intense Displacement Scratching and/or Tail-waggings. The female, under such circumstances, usually makes at least intention movements to mount the male and sometimes does so briefly. Such male soliciting is always facilitated by his back being toward her.

It is, of course, well known that most, if not all, the motor patterns associated with sexual behavior in vertebrates are available for performance in both sexes. The dependence of the sexual motor patterns, exhibited by *roseicollis* and the white eye-ringed forms, on what the partner is doing becomes especially apparent when the situation is somewhat aberrant. For example, sometimes a bout of precopulatory activity will take place on the top of a nest box, a platform seven and a half inches square. Under this circumstance, as the male sidles after the female and she sidles away, a circular chase around the box top results;

both birds then alternately adopt the sexual motor patterns of the other (attempting to mount and soliciting). It is as if the very tight, circular course taken by the birds confuses them as to who is following whom!

Such "pseudomale" and "pseudofemale" behavior has never been seen in the sexually dichromatic species.

Squeak-twittering. This, the only vocalization associated with male precopulatory behavior, has an interesting history. Basically, it is composed of a long series of repetitive notes. In *cana*, this vocalization is made up of a great variety of notes, relatively low in pitch and not at all musical or rhythmical. It is uttered most often after the female has gone into the nest box or has otherwise become absent during a bout of precopulatory behavior. In this context it seems to be associated with a certain amount of thwarting. The same is true for *taranta;* although here the vocalizations are somewhat harsher and more rhythmical.

In *roseicollis,* Squeak-twittering is higher in pitch, less variable in frequency, and distinctly rhythmical. These conditions are even further pronounced in the white eye-ringed forms. In the former as well as the latter, this vocalization is nearly always associated with Displacement Scratching, which suggests that Squeak-twittering may also be associated with thwarting.

Supplanting. Supplanting attacks on nearby birds increase markedly as the intensity of male precopulatory behavior rises. I would have expected males to be increasingly "oblivious" to other outside influences as their preoccupation with precopulatory behavior increased. It seems, however, that in the face of repeated thwartings during precopulatory behavior, the males become increasingly aggressive but are unable to direct this to their females and redirect, instead, to nearby birds. Our data for *roseicollis* and the white eye-ringed forms indicate that such supplanting attacks are most frequently followed by mountings or attempts to mount.

Copulation. This is the least variable and terminal appetitive activity of a successful bout of "precopulatory" behavior. The male mounts the female by stepping up on her back; not by flying up and landing on her as is done by many birds. The female may solicit copulation by crouching with the body held nearly horizontally, wings raised (but not much extended), and the head and tail raised. The feet also assume a wide stance on the perch and the feathers around the cloaca are parted. In very strongly soliciting females the head and tail may even be raised beyond the vertical. In these cases the plumage is also fluffed more than usual. A weak tendency to solicit is characterized by a slight wing raising. As the tendency becomes stronger the wings are raised even more (they are never quivered), and finally the head and tail become involved along with the crouch. No vocalizations are associated with female solicitation. The female will often solicit in response to a varying amount of male precopulatory behavior, but more often she does not actually solicit until the male makes an intention movement to mount. Rarely, a female will solicit without any immediate prior activity on the part of the male. In these cases the male simply mounts without any preliminary display.

As soon as the male mounts, he grasps the female's flank feathers in his feet, lowers his tail to one side of hers, and makes cloacal contact with a twisting, thrusting motion. Copulation consists of a series of these movements repeated with rhythmical regularity (about two per second). This activity may last from a few seconds to as long as over six minutes. After every dozen or so thrustings the male changes sides (places his tail on the other side of the female's) very quickly; so quickly that the normal rhythm is scarcely broken. Dismountings before sperm emission are usually initiated by the female. She may

threaten the male with Gaping over her shoulder or simply leave, either sidling or flying off (simply sidling away ordinarily does not dislodge the male unless she also threatens). In the few cases where the male has been seen to dismount on his own accord, it has been to supplant another bird which has approached too closely. In these cases the female usually remains in the copulatory posture, and the male immediately returns and resumes. After a prolonged copulation, the female remains in the copulatory posture for a few seconds after the male dismounts. Her cloaca then appears swollen, wet, and reddened if there has been sperm emmission; if not, the cloaca retains its normal appearance.

Males do not hold on with the bill during copulation but will occasionally use the closed bill as a crutch for support during mounting or once in a while during copulation. Males often flap the wings as if to aid in their balance. Females may also do this, but not so commonly.

Females of the sexually non-dichromatic species hold the head tilted sideways with the cheeks and throat ruffled during copulation. The feathers of the wrists are commonly ruffled also. These are the features most visible to the male during copulation (Fig. 8, left). It is as if males of these species have to be constantly reminded as to the sex of their partners and the females have thus evolved a compensatory "diethism" in the absence of sexual dichromatism. If such females abandon the cheek ruffling and head tilt during copulation, the male usually dismounts at once and resumes precopulatory activities.

Females of *cana, taranta,* and *pullaria* do not hold the head tilted to one side nor are the cheeks, throat, and wrists ruffled (Fig. 8, right). A monotonous series of rapid squeaks is uttered constantly by *taranta* females during copulation; these are the only females which vocalize in this context. This vocalization sounds somewhat like Squeak-twittering in males but is more regular in frequency and may have an appeasement function. The males of the dichromatic species are not typically as afraid of their mates as are the others. There seems to be less conflict between attack and/or escape with sex.

If sperm emission occurs, there are no more precopulatory activities for some time (ordinarily a half hour to an hour or more elapses before the next such bout). Ordinarily, many incomplete copulations occur throughout the day. However, no copulations under about two and a half minutes in length seem to result in sperm emission.

There are no postcopulatory displays by either sex in any species of *Agapornis*. The females do not even engage in bouts of plumage ruffling and shaking, preening, and so forth. Ordinarily, both birds remain quite still for some time after the male dismounts.

Changes in Precopulatory Activities in Time. As a pair (particularly among the white eye-ringed forms and *roseicollis*) has progressively more breeding experience, the procopulatory displays change markedly. All of the components remain in their species-typical forms but their frequencies undergo alteration; Switch-sidling becomes less "intense" and Squeak-twittering eventually almost disappears in some cases. Displacement Scratching becomes less frequent in response to typically fewer thwartings. It is as if the birds gradually get to "know" each other better and their interactions become smoother because of increased sensitivity to each other's individual response variations. For reliable quantitative comparisons between species it is therefore necessary to compare birds having similar amounts of breeding experience.

Courtship-feeding. This is a particularly interesting activity since, like nest material preparation, transportation, and utilization, it apparently is influenced by successive physiological causal factors, as well as having several functions. First of all, courtship feeding occurs throughout the year. Hence, it seems to be another one of the many activities between mated pairs and probably serves, along with these, to constantly reinforce the pair bond and to ameliorate any inhibitions there may be for close bodily contact between the birds.

Birds may often be seen to engage in other activities during courtship feeding (for example, various stretching movements of the wings and legs). Once, a pair of Budgerigars were seen to engage in courtship feeding during copulation!

Courtship feeding, however, becomes much more frequent in occurrence with the onset of reproductive activities, and may actually be one of the activities which tend to stimulate the female reproductively. This behavior continues throughout the period of sexual activity and gradually grades into behavior characterized by the male feeding the female while she is incubating and brooding young. Feeding the female while she is incubating probably provides an important proportion of her nourishment as she typically briefly emerges from the nest cavity only three or four times a day. Later, when the young are being raised, this behavior not only helps to nourish the female but enables the female to provide the very young nestlings with well processed food since it has been partly digested by both parents. When the young become older, both parents feed them directly and now they receive essentially undigested, whole hulled seeds. At this time courtship feeding is relatively infrequent and the male continues to feed the young until they are several days out of the nest. The frequency of courtship feeding again increases. The head-bobbing component of courtship feeding differs from species to species (Fig. 7), but these differences are most exaggerated in *roseicollis* and the white eye-ringed forms during the sexual phase of the cycle and may, therefore, reflect the presence of sexual motivation superimposed on courtship feeding. More likely, however, these special feather adjustments may reflect the typical fear of these males toward their females and indicate a degree of submissiveness during sexual activities.

One of the reasons I believe that courtship-feeding is not prompted by sexual motivation is the fact that it frequently immediately follows a successful copulation but clearly sexual activities never do so.

All of the activities thought of as precopulatory may sometimes be associated with courtship feeding during the sexual phase of the cycle. It may be that courtship feeding has its own unique responsible internal state which can be somehow linked to other drives which may lower or raise the threshold of its performance.

Only the male feeds the female in *roseicollis* and the white eye-ringed forms. . . . Much plumage fluffing and ruffling is done by these females, indicating their submissiveness. In *cana* and *taranta* the female frequently feeds the male; more often in *cana*. . . . No plumage ruffling occurs here. It appears that, during the evolution of this genus, there has been an increasing tendency to relegate courtship feeding to a strictly unilateral activity with the male doing the feeding. This may have been possible because of the increasing stimulatory value, through the series (toward colonialism) of other birds outside the pair which would perhaps compensate for any possible reductions of stimulation associated with a lack of reciprocity in courtship feeding.

Recognition of Young. After many attempts to achieve the rearing of young by foster parents by swapping egg clutches, we found that none of the species normally having red-downed young would feed newly hatched white-downed young and *vice versa*. However, the pairs among which we made the swappings had all raised many prior broods of their own. We then attempted to get *roseicollis* (red-downed young) to raise white-downed young by giving such eggs to a pair which had never bred before. In this we were com-

pletely successful. Moreover, when we gave this pair red-downed young of the same age as the white-downed young they were rearing, they refused to feed the former. Young of different species which are well-feathered appear much more unlike each other than they do at hatching, yet these birds may be placed in nests of other species and raised with no difficulty.

At the present time we are concentrating on greater comparative quantification of the behavior of these birds and have begun to investigate the effects of early experience and genetics on the development of species-typical behavior.

Summary

The comparative ethology of the parrot genus *Agapornis* is described and discussed (development of the young, maintenance activities, agonistic behavior, and reproductive behavior). It is apparent that there is a fairly uniform evolutionary trend in the genus represented by the living forms from *cana* through to *personata nigrigenis*. This trend involves the gradual loss and acquisition of various behavioral and morphological characters. Certain of these trends sometimes tend to reverse themselves. Certain of the more important trends are listed below:

1) loss of sexual dichromatism, *pullaria* being intermediate in this regard.
2) development of increasing colonialism, *roseicollis* probably representing an intermediate condition.
3) early loss of both nest defence displays and ritualized displacement preening.
4) increasing ritualization of displacement scratching and, finally, the appearance of unritualized tail-wagging as a displacement activity.
5) gradual loss of carrying nest material in the feathers and the acquisition of carrying such material in the bill.
6) increase in size of strips of nest material and, finally, the utilization of twigs.

7) increase in complexity of nests from a simple pad (cana, taranta, and pullaria) to a well-formed cup (roseicollis) to an elaborate substantial structure featuring a roofed nest chamber and tunnel connecting it to the outside entrance (personata).

8) loss of reciprocal courtship feeding and the ritualization of the head-bobbing component as a precopulatory display.

9) blue rumps develop (pullaria), become strongly developed (roseicollis and swinderniana), begin to be lost (p. fischeri and p. personata), and are lost (p. lilianae and p. nigrigenis).

10) development of increasing exaggeration of head color and pattern.

11) gradual development of more predictable sexually-specific behavior relative to attack, escape, and sex (coincident with gradual loss of sexual dichromatism).

Some features are species-specific and must have developed after the ancestral population had severed its genic connections with the rest of the genus. Some of these are: 1) pale bills in cana and again in roseicollis, 2) Carpal Flashing in taranta males, 3) squeaking in copulating taranta females, 4) burrowing into tree ant nests by pullaria, 5) developing black bill in swinderniana, 6) use of feathers as nest material by taranta, 7) development of white, naked skin around eyes in personata, and 8) carrying nest material in bill by personata.

Sleeping upside down must have been ancestral to both Agapornis and Loriculus. It is still retained by Loriculus but spottily by Agapornis (strong in pullaria, and weak in taranta).

In the less social species, particularly in cana, agonistic behavior has become associated with rather elaborate threat and appeasement displays but little inhibition in actual fighting if the displays fail in their function. The results of such fighting, though rare, are disastrous. On the other hand, the more social species have little

ritualization associated with threat but the fighting itself has become highly ritualized (Bill-fencing). Here, the ritualized fighting and inhibition associated with biting serves to prevent damage to contestants; a distinct advantage among birds having many contacts with others of their kind.

The development of highly ritualized displays from non-signal precursors is readily apparent in this genus. It is also apparent that there are not a large number of displays associated with sexual or agonistic behavior. This suggests that display extinction must be as normal as display evolution and that there must be very strong competition among existing displays from the standpoint of their value as signals prompting certain responses in the recipient. The selective pressure molding precopulatory displays, for instance, probably initially stem from the inherent response capabilities of the recipient. Those activities capable of achieving quicker and/or more profound effects are probably selected for over others, all else being equal. The loss of highly ritualized displacement preening in all but cana, the development of highly ritualized displacement scratching in roseicollis through to personata, and the appearance of displacement tail-wagging in these latter birds probably represent such a struggle for display survival. It is interesting, in connection with this, that an "extinct" display will sometimes appear rarely in an individual of a species normally no longer exhibiting this behavior. For instance, the Displacement Preening of cana has been seen in its highly ritualized form one or twice in a male roseicollis.

The head has obviously become exceptionally important in the behavioral interactions of these birds and much activity and special color patterns are associated with this (courtship-feeding, Bill-fencing, reciprocal preening, strongly contrasting bill colors, and the development of conspicuous eye-rings).

Preliminary investigations on hybrids (the subject of a forthcoming paper) and on birds variously deprived of certain early experiences lead to the conclusion that many, if not all, species-typical patterns are dependent upon an intricate complex of both learned and not-learned methods of acquiring such behavior. This subject is being explored further at present. The individual development of Bill-fencing, nest building, and recognition of newly hatched young are cases in point.

Acknowledgments

I wish to express my appreciation to the R. T. French Co. and to the National Science Foundation (N.S.F. G-5518) for financial aid. Many people were of assistance during the course of the study and in criticising the manuscript but I would like to particularly thank Mr. and Mrs. Alan Brockway, Mr. and Mrs. Robert Ficken, Dr. Robert Goodwin, Miss Helen Hays, Mrs. William Keeton, and Miss Jane Seligson. Drs. Daniel Lehrman, Konrad Lorenz, and Niko Tinbergen helped me with many useful and stimulating discussions. Mr. David Allen was especially helpful with photographic matters. I wish also to thank Prof. O. Koehler for preparing the German Summary. I hasten to add that none of these people are responsible for any errors of omission or of commission which may have occurred.

REFERENCES

ADLERSPARRE, A., 1938 Dimorphismus des Jugendkleides und Nestbau bei *Agapornis*. *J. Ornith.* 86, 248.

BENOIT, J., 1956 Etats physiologiques et instincts de reproduction chez les oiseaux. In: *L'Instinct dans le comportement des animaux et de l'homme*. Paris.

CINAT-THOMPSON, H., 1926 Die geschlechtliche Zuchtwahl beim Wellensittich *(Melopsittacus undulatus* Shaw). *Biol. Zentralbl.* 46, 543.

DILGER, W., 1958 Studies in *Agapornis*. *Avic. Mag.* 64, 91.

HAMPE, H., 1937 The nesting habits of *Agapornis pullaria*. *Avic. Mag.* 2, 148.

HAMPE, H., 1957 Die Unzertrennlichen. Pfungstadt.

LIND, H., 1959 The activation of an instinct caused by a "transitional action." *Behaviour* 14, 123.

MOREAU, R., 1948 Aspects of evolution in the parrot genus *Agapornis*. *Ibis* 90, 206, 449.

MORRIS, D., 1954 The reproductive behaviour of the Zebra Finch *(Poephila guttata)*, with special reference to pseudofemale behaviour and displacement activities. *Behaviour* 6, 271.

MORRIS, D., 1956 The function and causation of courtship ceremonies. In: *L'Instinct dans le comportement des animaux et de l'homme*. Paris.

NEUNZIG, R., 1926 Zur Systematik und Biologie der Gattung *Agapornis*. *Verh. Ornith. Ges. Bayern* 17, 112.

PERRY, J., 1959 Breeding the Red-faced Lovebird *(Agapornis pullaria)* in South Africa. *Avic. Mag.* 65, 119.

PETERS, J., 1937 *Check-list of Birds of the World, Vol. 3*. Cambridge.

PRESTWICH, A., 1957 Breeding the Red-faced Lovebird *Agapornis pullaria*. *Avic. Mag.* 63, 1.

SERLE, W., 1957 A contribution to the ornithology of the eastern region of Nigeria. *Ibis* 99, 371.

TINBERGEN, N., 1959 Comparative studies of the behaviour of gulls (Laridae): a progress report. *Behaviour* 15, 1.

WILLIAM C. DILGER

52

Changes in Nest-Material Carrying Behavior of F₁ Hybrids between *Agapornis roseicollis* and *A. personata fischeri* during Three Years

The following reading is an example of a frequently used method of scientific communication: the published abstract of a paper read at a scientific meeting. Because the lovebird species, described by Dilger in the previous reading, can crossbreed, experiments in behavior genetics are possible. An experiment of this kind is described briefly in this abstract.

Reprinted from *American Zoologist,* 1961, 1, p. 350, by permission of the author and the publisher.

The nest-material carrying of the same 6 female hybrids was studied from its onset to the end of the three-year period. Carrying in the bill *(fischeri)* and in the feathers of the back *(roseicollis)* are the two methods employed by the parental species.

The hybrids begin by spending much time attempting to carry by tucking, a method never successful for them. They manage to carry a small amount to the nest in their bills (6%). The next two months is marked by an improvement of the bill carrying method (to 41%). At this time the two methods are in strong conflict. The remainder of the time is associated with a slow but steady (about 10% a year) improvement in carrying in the bill and a coincident drop in behaviors associated with tucking. At the end of the period, over 73% are carried in the bill. Possible reasons are discussed. (Supported by grant G-14205 from the N.S.F.)

NIKO TINBERGEN

53   The Shell Menace

Niko Tinbergen (co-author of reading 5) has devoted many years to ethological studies of several animal species. In the following reading, he describes a series of experiments concerned with the black-headed gull's removal of empty eggshells from its nest. Note the use of models to determine which aspects of the shell result in its removal. The use of such models is a frequent technique in ethological research.

Reprinted from *Natural History,* 1963, **72**, 28–35, by permission of the author and the American Museum of Natural History. Several photographs have been omitted.

Suggestion for further reading: Tinbergen, N., *The Herring Gull's World.* New York: Basic Books, 1961.

When a chick is about to hatch, it cracks the shell near the obtuse end. Then, by rhythmic stretching movements (for which chicks have a muscle that degenerates after hatching) it lifts off a small "lid" and half-rolls, half-crawls out of the shell.

In some species, such as gallinaceous birds and ducks, the parents rarely if ever pay any attention to the empty egg shells; they lead the young away as soon as they are dry, leaving nest and shells behind. Most other birds dispose of the shells in one way or another. Hawks are reported to eat them, as a general rule; grebes take them in their bills and "drown" them some distance from the nest. Most birds fly away with each shell and drop it a good distance from the nest, although not at any particular place. Black-headed Gulls (the Old World cousins of Bonaparte's Gull) do this regularly, and while there is variability in the time, few if any fail to remove a shell within two hours after hatching; sometimes they do it within a matter of minutes.

One could hardly imagine a more trivial response, for it takes no more than, at most, thirty seconds of a bird's time each year—between three and ten seconds for each of its three eggs. Yet, as biologists, we have gradually become convinced that very few such regular occurrences are really insignificant. When my friends and I began to look more closely at egg shell removal, we began to suspect that it must in some way be a very useful response. The argument was indirect. We had noticed that several predators, such as Carrion Crows, Herring Gulls, and even neighboring Black-headed Gulls, were often quick to seize an egg or a newly hatched chick, in spite of the fact that their khaki coloring and dark blotching make them difficult to detect. It is not for nothing, therefore, that broods are rarely left unguarded. Parent gulls take turns at the nest and the "on duty" bird seldom leaves before having been relieved by its partner. When a gull flies away from the nest to dispose of the egg shell, and so leaves the brood unguarded for something between three and ten seconds, even

this short absence can be heavily penalized when a crow dashes down for a "grab and fly" robbery. So when, despite this threat, all members of the species take the risk, we must suspect that there are advantages that outweigh the disadvantage, or the habit would have been eliminated by natural selection. Therefore, we speculated, there must be something that penalizes the broods that have "untidy" parents.

As to the nature of the penalty, there were several possibilities. An empty egg shell might slip over an unhatched egg, and so trap the chick inside. This has actually been observed in birds that lay eggs with strong shells. The sharp edge of the broken shell might injure the chick. This, too, has been reported—by poultry breeders, for instance. Another possibility was that three shells left in the nest might interfere with the parents' efficiency in brooding the chicks. After all, a gull has only three brood spots—one for each egg or chick. Neither of these three possibilities seemed probable in our species, which has extremely thin shells that are easily crushed. Nor did we think much of the possibility that the moist, organic material that is sometimes left in the shell could be a breeding ground for pathogenic bacteria; the shells usually dry quickly. We were rather inclined to think of a fifth possibility: the shell, by being white inside and thus, at least to us, very conspicuous, might attract the attention of predators—such as crows and Herring Gulls, which hunt by sight—by helping to reveal the otherwise camouflaged brood. The gulls will remove not only egg shells but many other objects from their nests (such as mussel shells, bits of paper, leaves, and even bottle tops), which seemed to support this theory. Even more suggestive was the fact, reported by my co-workers Dr. and Mrs. Cullen, that while many species of gulls and terns remove their egg shells, the Sandwich Tern and the Kittiwake lack the response—and these two species are exactly those members of the group that have no camouflaged broods. The eggs of Sandwich Terns, although blotched, are very con-

	CROW	H. GULL	OTHERS	+TOTAL TAKEN / −NOT TAKEN	
WHITE	+14	+19	+10	+43	−26
NATURAL	+ 8	+ 1	+ 4	+13	−55

FIG. 1. White eggs proved to be more subject to predation than did those naturally camouflaged. Plus and minus signs indicate numbers of each taken or left.

spicuous, and the down of a Kittiwake chick is almost uniformly silvery-white.

When, in 1959, some of our guest workers were keen to tackle this problem with me, we decided to study it systematically in the large gulleries near Ravenglass, which is situated on a sandy peninsula on the Irish Sea coast of Cumberland, England. This was the beginning of a three-year study, in which I was joined at one time or another by Dr. G. J. Broekhuysen of Capetown, Miss C. Feekes of Utrecht, J. C. W. Houghton of Leeds, H. Kruuk of Utrecht, Miss M. Paillette of Paris, Dr. E. Szulc of Warsaw, and Dr. R. Stamm of Basel.

Two questions were posed. First, does or does not an egg shell, if left in or near the nest, expose the brood to increased predation? Second, how does a gull "recognize" an empty egg shell and how does it distinguish that shell from intact eggs, chicks, and nest material, none of which we ever observed a gull to carry?

We worked on the assumption that the egg shell would make the brood more conspicuous. Although this is so, at least to human eyes, in no species with allegedly camouflaged broods had it ever been put to the test with respect to the species' natural predators.

We laid out, singly and scattered over an open dune valley, equal numbers of natural-colored gulls' eggs and gulls' eggs

that we had painted white. From an observation blind erected on a dune top we observed which predators would take them, and which of the two types of egg they would take most often. The area was regularly patrolled by several Herring Gulls and by Carrion Crows, which found and ate a number of the eggs. Each test was broken off when roughly half the eggs had been discovered. After a few weeks the results became clear: although both types of eggs were taken, both the gulls and the crows found more white than natural-colored eggs (Figure 1). Not surprisingly, the crows, members of a tribe known for intelligence and keen sight, were better at finding eggs than were gulls. Also, the crows were extremely helpful to us, for unlike the gulls they did not stop looking for eggs when they were satiated, but continued to take and bury them, returning to such caches weeks after.

Later we repeated this experiment with painted hens' eggs. Half of them were uniformly khaki—a color that matched the base color of the gulls' eggs; the other half had irregular dotting added on the base color. Again, the uniformly colored eggs were taken in larger numbers than were the dotted eggs. The eggs, therefore, derive some protection from their coloration. However, since many of the natural eggs were found, the camouflage cannot be called very effective. Without the efficient manner in which Black-headed Gulls attack marauding crows, few gull eggs would survive.

Our next step was to test whether the presence of an empty egg shell next to a natural-colored gull's egg would endanger such an egg. Here we used a trick that I feel I must justify. We had seen that even a natural-colored egg could be found with relative ease. In the natural situation (that is, in the gulleries themselves) crows that entered the colony spent much of their time dodging the violent attacks of the gulls, while in our test area they were free of such attacks and could, as a result, look down continuously. We further realized that the prey, which in the natural situation would be betrayed by the egg shells, could be either eggs or chicks. Chicks are much better camouflaged than are eggs; moreover, they crouch in cover when the parents sound the alarm. So we decided to make things more difficult for the crows. All the eggs we laid out in the dune valley were covered with a few straws of marram

grass, which improved the camouflage most strikingly (in fact, some plovers use this trick themselves). Half the eggs were single; empty egg shells were placed at some 10 cm. distance from each of the other half. We weighted the situation a little against the expected results by covering the eggs that had an egg shell next to them slightly better than we did the single eggs. Thus, the single eggs were a little easier to find. In spite of this, our predators—again Carrion Crows and Herring Gulls—found 65 per cent of the eggs accompanied by the extra shell, and only 22 per cent of the single eggs.

Because some gulls move the shell no more, perhaps, than a couple of feet from the nest, we experimented with varying the distance between the egg and the shell. The result was clear-cut: the farther the shell from the egg, the less danger to the egg (Figure 2). In these tests we saw the crows alight near a shell, walk round for awhile, and then leave without having found the egg.

Could we now conclude the hypothesis

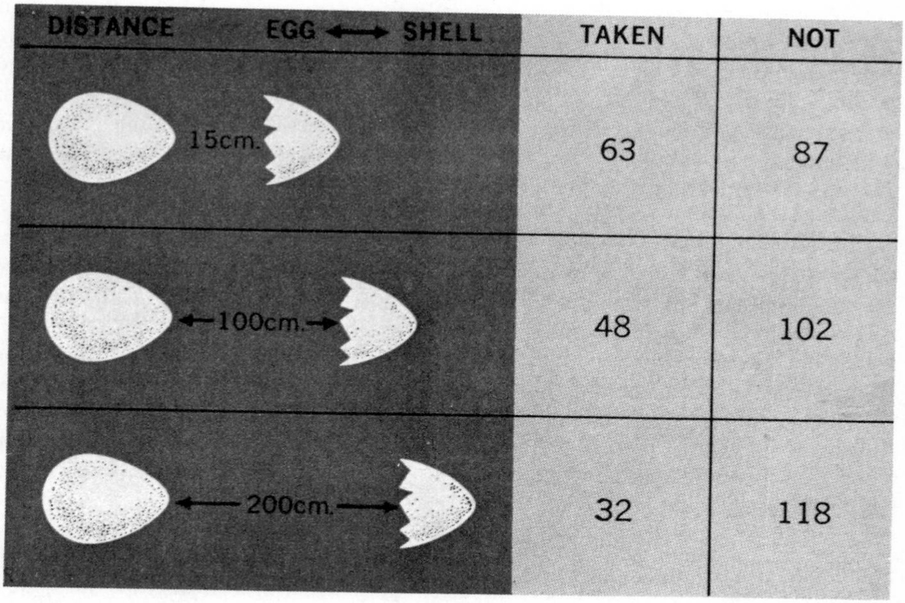

DISTANCE EGG ◄──► SHELL	TAKEN	NOT
15cm.	63	87
◄—100cm.—►	48	102
◄——200cm.——►	32	118

FIG. 2. Predation was much heavier on those eggs that were close to a broken shell. Chart shows varying distances between the two, and the numbers taken or not.

had been proved? In our opinion, not quite. We had shown that the presence of a shell endangered the egg, but as we had conducted our experiments outside the gullery, there had been no gulls to guard the eggs. In the gullery, however, removal of the egg shell, apart from making the brood less conspicuous, also involves abandoning the brood for a brief time, thus exposing it to predation. We were not entitled to judge the over-all effect of egg shell removal, because in our tests neither category of eggs was ever guarded by a gull, and the effects of continuous guarding were therefore not comparable with those of interrupted guarding. However, we have good reasons to suppose that the advantage of removing the egg shell outweighs the disadvantage. For one thing, gulls either sit on the nest or attack when a crow or a Herring Gull enters the gullery; for another, if they did not remove the shells at all, these would be attractants for days, whereas the danger caused by removal lasts only a few seconds. Whether or not any of the other advantages mentioned above will later prove to exist as well, our experiments have convincingly shown that, at least in the Black-headed Gull, egg shell removal can be considered a behavior component of camouflage, and part and parcel of the species' defense against predators.

We next wanted to find out the stimuli whereby the gulls recognize the egg shell. Although they remove a great variety of miscellaneous objects in addition to shells this does not mean that they respond with equal promptness to all objects. We presented the gulls with a variety of dummy shells, and compared their responses to them. First we determined the length of the season during which the gulls would remove egg shells we provided. At various times in the breeding season, from weeks before the eggs were laid until well after the chicks had hatched, we gave hundreds of gulls an egg shell each on the rim of their nests and checked, after a standard period of six hours, how many of them had removed the shell. We found that the first

responses, few and incomplete, appeared three weeks before the first egg was laid. After a gradual buildup, a high level of removal was reached while the eggs were being laid; this level was maintained throughout the incubation period (about twenty-four days), and it did not drop off until after the chicks had hatched. The level was so constant and so high that we knew we could test throughout the breeding season.

We could now begin to compare the different dummies. We made simple dummies that could easily be transported—rectangular strips of metal, 2 x 5 cm., and bent at right angles in the middle. Some of these we painted a light khaki; others dark khaki (equal to the color of eggs viewed from such a distance that the dots blurred); some white, some black, others bright red, yellow, or blue and others green. We marked a large number of nests and divided them into as many groups as we had models, with equal numbers of nests in each group. In one trial we gave each nest one dummy on its rim, with a different color for each group. After an hour we revisited all the nests and noted how many of each type of dummy had been removed. After having given the gulls a few hours rest, we repeated the test, continuing until each nest had received each color once. The different groups were presented with the dummies in a different order. After such a test we could directly compare the responses of all gulls to each model.

The results were rather surprising. The gulls did remove some of all the dummies, but some colors were removed much more consistently than others. It was clear that conspicuousness was no criterion. On the one hand, red, blue, and black were not carried away particularly often. On the other hand, both white and the khakis had a very high score, although white was extremely conspicuous and khaki was about the most cryptic color possible. Since we knew from other tests that the gulls had a good color sense, the only possible conclusion was that objects that had the same colors as real egg shells were most frequently removed, not those that were most conspicuous. The various green models (some of which were uniform, while others were dotted) had a very low score. This was particularly true of a shade of green that was very similar to that of young vegetation. The dotting made no difference, nor did contrast within one dummy (such as that offered by one that was khaki outside and white inside) raise the score.

These responses to color were obviously adaptive: strong responses to the natural main colors of the egg shell; a moderate response to objects of various bright colors that might occur in the natural situation (for instance, yellow, pink, and blue shells of snails and mussels are frequently kicked into the nest); and a low response to green. This latter reaction, we think, is adaptive, because the gulls showed little preference for particular shapes, and were quite willing to remove flat paper disks. Had they responded readily to green, they would probably also strip leaves from surrounding vegetation and so remove useful cover, in addition to leaving the nest unguarded far too often.

We tested various other properties of objects in much the same way. In some series we varied the shape of the models, in others the size, in others the distance between the egg shell and the nest. We found that the shape response was best to the real egg shell, second to halved ping-pong balls, third to the cylindrical rings, fourth to the "angles" we had used for our color tests, and fifth to the flat cardboard or metal strips.

Egg shells placed at various distances from the nest gave interesting results. As standard egg shells we used either real gulls' shells (gathered in masses at the end of each season and kept until the next year) or broken hens' eggs painted khaki.

The gulls' removal response fell off sharply with increased distance, just as did the predatory response of the crows. In this way we gradually acquired a rather good idea of the types of stimuli that to the gulls

characterized an egg shell to be removed.

We now turned our attention to two other aspects of behavior. As we had seen, the gulls carried away, with varying degrees of "enthusiasm," many different types of objects. In fact, one could say that any alien object tended to be removed—that is, any object not resembling an egg, a chick, or nest material. But we had not yet found out enough to be able to say what characteristics caused the birds to distinguish egg shells from each of these other things.

We knew that they would remove flat cardboard dummies, but nest material (mainly dry marram grass) is also practically flat and yet is not carried away. We decided to offer the gulls flat strips of different proportions. Four types of strips were made, all with a surface area of nine square centimeters, but ranging from squares of 3 x 3 cm. to rectangles of 18 x ½ cm. We found that those of 9 x 1 cm. were carried off most often, and that both the longer and squatter strips were carried less often. Why strips of 9 x 1 were carried more than strips of 4.5 x 2 we do not know, although we have some theories. The very long and thin strips of 18 x ½ cm. elicited interesting behavior. In only 66 out of 280 cases were they removed. Of those not removed, however, 46 per cent were built into the nest. We also made some direct observations from our blinds, and found that the matter was still more complex, for some of the gulls tried to eat the long strips. It is easy to be wise after the event, and we realized that the shape was not dissimilar to that of earthworms—the staple diet of this gull colony.

In order to discover how the gulls distinguished between shells and intact eggs we proceeded rather differently. When an egg is presented on a nest's rim, the gull usually retrieves it. The movement is characteristic: the bird stretches its neck, brings the bill down behind the egg, and rolls it into the nest, balancing it against the narrow underside of the bill. This response is not always prompt or complete; it can also misfire if the gull fails to balance the egg properly and loses it before it is rolled in. By direct observation one could notice even incipient responses that could not have been concluded from the position of the egg afterward. Similarly, an egg shell is not always completely removed, but incipient movements can be recognized: instead of bending the head over and beyond the object, the gull may nibble at the broken edge, or may pick it up only to drop it immediately. We wanted to observe all these responses, and therefore our next series of experiments involved watching individual birds from a blind.

In these tests the procedure is frankly anthropomorphic, as indeed it is in all the preceding tests. That is we first analyze the differences *we* see between an egg and an egg shell, and then try out the gulls' responses to each of these one by one. Now, an egg shell differs from an egg by weight, in having a broken contour when seen from the side, by being hollow, and by having a thin, ragged edge. Since the gull's response can be recognized by us before the egg is touched, the first response must be visual, and weight cannot influence the response at this stage. It was a further lucky circumstance for us that an empty, that is, blown, egg was retrieved as well as a normal one, showing that weight, too, had little, if any, effect on retrieving.

To test whether the broken contour had an effect on the gull, we compared the birds' responses to a true egg with those to an egg shell filled to the rim with plaster. This plaster-filled model did not offer a hollow space or a thin edge, since the plaster adhered exactly to the rim. Both models were always rolled in; no bird ever even nibbled at the rim of the plaster-filled egg. This meant that the broken contour was, to the gull, not a shell characteristic. When we filled egg shells with cotton wool — which fills the shell, but does not fit exactly to the rim, and so leaves a thin edge visible without, however, leaving a hollow space of any significance—the response was quite different: these models were nibbled at and removed. This meant that the hollowness

of the shell had very little effect. It looked as if the thin edge was the principal stimulus. To test this we offered blown eggs as controls, and for comparison similarly intact blown eggs on which was glued about one square centimeter of egg shell, which stood out at right angles from the egg's surface. This model had all the characteristics of a whole egg, but in addition offered a thin edge. No hollow was visible. In two out of every three tests this model was taken by the "flange" and removed; in the other tests it was rolled in. Often a bird alternated between the two responses, showing bits of each in turn. It seemed, therefore, that the thin edge was the main character by which egg shell was distinguished from egg.

This, however, raised a new problem. If the birds respond mainly to the thin edge, and not to hollowness, how does it happen that a newly hatched, wet chick, which has not yet fully left the shell, is not removed with the shell? While we do not yet know what characteristics of the chick might play a part, we found that the chick's weight has a profound effect. We gave the gulls egg shells in which pieces of lead that weighed as much as a chick were placed near the pointed end. Such eggs were always nibbled at, but as soon as they were lifted, the behavior simply ended. The bird might nibble again and again, but we never saw gulls remove such shells. This could not be because the bird saw the little piece of lead inside, for even a shell filled to the rim with cotton wool was carried off. The weight alone, therefore, is sufficient to stop a shell from being removed as long as the chick is not completely free. Probably the thin edge of such leaded shells was the reason none was ever rolled into the nest, as was the plaster-filled shell.

Once our interest in this behavior had been aroused, we began observations of egg shell removal patterns in other birds. It struck us that Ringed Plovers and Oystercatchers—which also nest on the peninsula and lay well-camouflaged eggs—removed their egg shells much more promptly than did the Black-headed Gulls. Of ten gulls we observed closely during the whole period of hatching, when there was no outside disturbance, two removed the shell one minute after hatching and one fifteen minutes after. The rest took from one to over three hours. Again we argued: if there is such a premium on removing the shell, why don't the birds do it more promptly, as the waders do? We believe we have found the solution. The Black-headed Gull is a colonial species. It is also a predator, and we found that some individual birds made it a practice to rob their neighbors whenever they could. They are not much attracted to fresh eggs and are, in fact, very inexpert at eating their contents. But pipped eggs and newly hatched chicks are often taken and swallowed whole. However, as soon as chicks are dry and fluffy, the robber gulls seem to lose interest in them. We think that this predation by "rogue" gulls is the environmental pressure that has prevented the parent gulls from removing the shells while the chick is vulnerable. Oystercatchers and Ringed Plovers, being solitary breeders, are not so delayed in shell removal because they do not have predatory neighbors.

Thus we gradually built up a picture of this seemingly insignificant activity. It certainly has survival value, and the analysis of the gulls' behavior revealed how beautifully adapted its control is to the needs. How do gulls acquire this efficiency? Is it "innate" response, or is it learned behavior? We believe that (as is usual with problems of development) the question is too simple.

We have found that on the one hand a gull in its first breeding season removes an egg shell, even if it is presented on the nest's rim before the first egg is laid. An egg presented to such an inexperienced bird is rolled in. It is true that we have so far tested only three such birds, but they responded as promptly and as completely as did more experienced birds.

On the other hand, we also have evidence of learning. We placed three plaster

eggs in each of a group of sixty nests. The eggs were painted pitch-black and were introduced into the nests before the birds had laid eggs of their own. Some of the birds deserted; others settled on the dummy eggs. Of the latter, some reacted by laying no eggs at all (a well-known effect of sitting on such dummies); others accepted the black eggs but added some eggs of their own. We removed the real eggs within half a day after they were laid, and were left with a group of fifty-six nests with black eggs. Similarly, we placed green eggs in a group of fifty-three nests. A control group of sixty pairs were left with their own eggs. The birds were allowed to incubate for, on the average, seventeen days. We then tested the responses of all birds to ring-shaped dummies (one of our earlier types) of the three colors involved: black, green, and khaki. We found that the birds that had sat on black eggs removed more black rings than either green or even khaki ones; the "green egg birds" removed more green than either of the other colors; and the controls carried more khaki than either green or black (Fig. 3). By changing the contents of the nest at the moment of the tests, we made sure that the birds had not been matching the color of the eggs in the nest with that of the ring—these birds had really learned the color of their eggs during incubation. They showed the same acquired preference in their egg-rolling response, and had transferred this experience to the egg shell removal response.

Even though we cannot claim to have done more than skim the surface of the problem, it is already clear that the control of egg shell removal is extremely complex, and beautifully adapted to the requirements. And yet it is only a minor part of the total set of devices by which these gulls defend themselves against predators. For one thing, there are other aspects to camouflage, such as the wonderfully adapted color glands that, in some unknown way, manage to lay down the pattern of blotching on the eggs; the protective color pat-

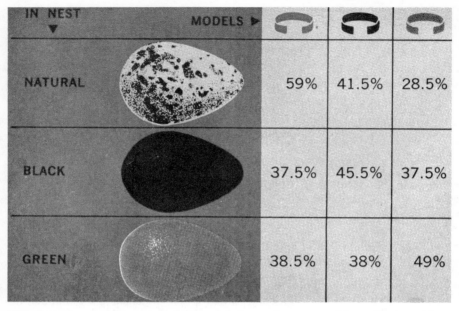

IN NEST ▼	MODELS ▶		
NATURAL	59%	41.5%	28.5%
BLACK	37.5%	45.5%	37.5%
GREEN	38.5%	38%	49%

FIG. 3. Percentage of egg shell dummies of three colors removed by gulls that had incubated eggs of the same colors, at the left, shows the effect of experience.

terns of the chicks and their ability to crouch in response to the alarm calls of the parents and even to hide under cover; the tendency of the adults to leave their nests at the slightest disturbance and thus, unlike camouflaged birds such as curlews and nightjars, to rely on the camouflage of the brood. But the protection of the brood does not depend on camouflage alone; I have already mentioned the massed attacks gulls make on crows.

Through our work on egg shell removal we have now become interested in the antipredator system of the Blackheaded Gull in all its aspects, and we begin to get indications that such things as synchronized laying, the characteristic pattern of nest-spacing, the seasonal and daily rhythms in the selection of the habitat, and several other traits of the gulls are related to defense against predators. And yet, losses through predation are heavy; thousands of young gulls fall victims to crows, Herring Gulls, hedgehogs, and foxes, to mention only the worst of the predators we have seen at work. Our observations on egg shell removal are but the first step in the unraveling of the highly complex relationships that apparently exist between these gulls and all their predators.

IRVEN DeVORE

54   Mother-Infant Relations in Free-Ranging Baboons*

There have been many studies in recent years concerned with primate behavior under natural conditions. Examples are George Schaller's work on the gorilla (*The Mountain Gorilla,* University of Chicago Press, 1963), observations of wild chimpanzees by Jane Goodale (*National Geographic,* 1963, **124,** 272–308) and Adrian Kortland (*Scientific American,* May 1962), and studies of the baboon by S. H. Washburn and Irven DeVore (*Scientific American,* June 1961). In the following reading, DeVore reviews the mother-infant relationship in wild baboons.

This article originally appeared as Chapter 10 of *Maternal Behavior in Mammals,* edited by Harriet L. Rheingold, Wiley, 1963. It is reprinted here with the permission of the author, the editor, and the publisher. Several figures have been omitted and the third footnote has been added by the author.

Suggestion for further reading: Southwick, C. H., ed., *Primate Social Behavior,* Princeton, N. J.: Van Nostrand, 1963.

The field observations on which this report is based were begun in Kenya in March, 1959. After a month of reconnaissance, systematic observations were begun in the Royal Nairobi National Park on April 1. Between April 1959, and January 1, 1960, I spent more than 800 hours in close observation of baboon troops—most of this time under optimum conditions. In July I was joined by S. L. Washburn, and for the next six months observations were divided between Nairobi Park and the Amboseli Reserve. . . . Altogether we spent more

* The field work on which this report is based was financed by a Ford Foundation grant for the study of the evolution of human behavior. The organization and presentation of the data for this report were supported by a National Science Foundation grant for the analysis of primate behavior while the author was a Fellow of the Miller Institute for Basic Research in Science, University of California, Berkeley. The support of these foundations, and the assistance of Dr. S. L. Washburn, who collaborated in the research, are gratefully acknowledged.

than 1200 hours in direct observation of baboons. Throughout the study, photographs were made daily with Leica M-3 cameras equipped with an assortment of lenses from 50 to 400 mm. During the early part of the study, observations were dictated into a "Dictaphone Dictet" portable tape recorder, and these tapes were transcribed each evening. Because many baboon social interactions are exceedingly complex, occurring rapidly and involving several individuals, some such recording device was considered essential for the accurate collection of behavioral data. When the "Dictet" failed, shorthand notes were taken by Nancy DeVore. These methods permit the observer to record complex behavioral events at the time they occur, and without shifting his eyes from the subjects to a note pad. At the close of the study we directed a professional photographer in taking 5000 feet of 16 mm color film (DeVore and Washburn, 1960; DeVore, 1962).

Descriptions of baboon social behav-

541

ior and ecology, including troop sizes, home range, diet, sexual behavior, and relations with other animals, have appeared elsewhere (Washburn and DeVore, 1961a; Washburn and DeVore, 1961b; DeVore and Washburn, 1963). Because so little was known about the behavior of free-ranging baboons at the time of the study, our aim was to describe the basic features of social life and ecology, and observations on mother-infant relations were only one part of a general program. All troops contain infants, however, and they occupy such an important position in the troop that many observations of infant behavior were recorded. Mother-infant relations described here are a composite of observations on infants in more than twenty-four baboon troops, but are based largely on observations of the nine troops in Nairobi Park, particularly the three troops in which every individual was known. The early life of only one identified infant was studied in detail. This infant, born about June 1, was a member of a troop which was observed continuously from June until mid-September, with additional observations at periodic intervals until late December. (Three additional infants were born in this same troop in early December.) In all, more than 2000 baboons were observed during the study. Age estimates were necessarily approximate; they were based on changes observed in juveniles over a 10-month period as well as on descriptions of the ontogeny of the closely related rhesus macaque.

Reactions of Nairobi Park baboons to humans vary from the very "tame" to the wild and completely unapproachable. The most rewarding observations were made on troops which had become accustomed to the proximity of persons in automobiles, but which were not so tame that the presence of humans disrupted their usual cycle of activities. We gathered most of these data while remaining inside a Land-Rover, staying within a few yards of the troop and moving with it throughout the day. This method permits the observer to keep every animal in the troop under close surveillance with a minimum of disturbance to the troop's normal activities. When these observations were compared with the observations made at a distance (through binoculars) both at Amboseli and in Nairobi Park, it was clear that the presence of human observers in an automobile made very little difference in the social behavior of these semitame troops.

Observations were made on both the "olive baboon" of the Nairobi highlands and the "yellow baboon" of the Kenya lowlands and coast. The former were studied primarily in the Royal Nairobi National Park, the latter in the Amboseli Reserve. Both types appear to be only local races of a very widespread genus (*Papio*) of the African savanna, occurring as far north as the Tibesti Plateau and living in savanna areas all the way to the Cape in the south. Field observations by Washburn in the Rhodesias and others in South Africa (Bolwig, 1959; Hall, 1960; Hall, 1961) indicate that the social behavior of these varieties is strikingly similar over a large area of Africa despite local variation in body size and coat color. Kummer's (1957) description of the behavior of hamadryas baboons shows a basic similarity between this species and the savanna varieties of *Papio*. Together with the macaques, their close relatives in Asia, the terrestrial monkeys of the Old World form a very widespread group with fundamental similarities in morphology, body chemistry, and behavior patterns.

Baboon Troops in Kenya

Although maternal care is the central subject of this chapter, the relations between mother and infant are enmeshed in a network of relationships which extends throughout the troop. A brief description of the social organization of a Kenya baboon troop will clarify the relationships described in the following discussion. Baboon troops vary in size from about 10 to 200; the average troop numbered 43 at Nairobi and 80 at Amboseli. Sexual dimorphism is especially marked in baboons: body size, canine teeth, and general robustness are all prominent in the male. As a result, adult males are completely dominant over other troop members. The pattern of dominance relationships among the adult males gives rise to a dominance hierarchy which is conservative and stable. Several of the older males may support each other in dominance interactions, forming a "central hierarchy" against the other adult males. The females and juveniles orient to these central hierarchy males, who, in turn, are the most active males in defending the troop and intervening in intratroop fights.

Dominance relations among adult female baboons are far less stable. Although some females are persistently dominant over others, stages in the reproductive cycle of each female create relative changes in her dominance status. An estrous female assumes a higher relative status when in consort with a male, and a female with a young infant is so protected by adult males that she is virtually immune from agonistic interactions. The remaining pregnant females form a comparatively stable hierarchy during the period of gestation. Although it is true that most social behavior is *ultimately* based on the dominance structure, one would be misled to think of daily life in a baboon troop as wholly or even largely aggressive and dominance oriented. Dominance status is recognized and seldom contested, and most of the day is spent in quiet feeding, resting, and grooming—activities which are only indirectly related to dominance status.

BIRTH PERIODICITY

Most of Kenya is subject to seasonal rainfall, with the majority of rain falling between October and May, and the heaviest falling between January and May. In both the Nairobi and Amboseli areas most baboons give birth at the onset of the rainy season. The plants on which baboons depend for food are most abundant in the period from December to May, and prob-

ably 80% of the young are born in the months of October, November, and December, that is, just before the food supply reaches its peak. How the baboon's reproductive cycle may be influenced by ecology is not yet known; even in the Nairobi and Amboseli areas some sexual activity occurs throughout the year, and an occasional infant may be born at any time.

Although most rhesus and Japanese macaque females give birth annually, baboon females apparently give birth only every 20 to 24 months. It was not possible to capture and examine females during the study, and this interval of about 2 years is based only on observational data. Estrous swelling and sexual activities do not begin in the female until her infant is about 12 to 15 months old. A gestation period of 6 months indicates that the minimum interval between births is 18 months. In areas where birth peaks are pronounced, this minimum interval may be extended by the effect of seasonal variations on the reproductive cycle.

For whatever reasons they occur, the concentration of births in the rainy season, and the interval of 2 years between infants for each female, have important consequences for the infant baboon. Because most infants are born within a brief period, in a troop of average size these infants will develop in a group of peers. Because of the 2-year interval in births, a newborn has relatively little contact with siblings. Orientation to a peer group, not to uterine kin, is the pattern of baboon life.

Stages of Infant Development

By a combination of physical and behavioral criteria, the development of young baboons can be divided into six ontogenetic periods, very comparable to the six periods described by Jay (1963) for langurs.

1. The newborn: birth to one month.
2. The infant—one: first to the fourth month.
3. The transition period (color change): fourth to the sixth month.

4. The infant—two: six month to one year.

5. The weaning period: eleventh to the fifteenth month.

6. The young juvenile: the second year of life.

The period of color change, when the infant changes from black to light brown, is the only stage marked by an obvious criterion. Other stages involve a somewhat arbitrary division of continuous growth and maturation. In addition, there is variation in the ontogenetic history of different infants, especially during the weaning period.

THE NEWBORN: BIRTH TO ONE MONTH

The newborn and the mother. Although several baboon infants were observed during the first day of life, and many more during the first week, the actual birth of an infant was never seen in the field. Gillman and Gilbert (1946) describe in some detail the birth of an infant in their laboratory colony of *Papio ursinus.* Labor lasted 7 hours and 23 minutes. In the final stages, the mother sat on the edge of a shelf in her cage, the perineum overhanging, and supported the infant's head when it appeared. As more of the body appeared, she pulled gently. Following birth the mother licked the infant clean and ate the placenta. Only 23 minutes after its head appeared, the infant was at the mother's breast.

The relation between mother and infant is constant and intense. The central nervous system of the newborn monkey is approximately the same as that of a 6-month-old human infant, and the monkey develops much faster. As a result, the newborn monkey can cling to its mother within a few hours of birth; when they sleep together at night, when the mother walks with the troop on its daily round, and when they rest during the day, the infant is always in its mother's arms or clinging to her body. A baboon troop travels 3 miles on most days, occasionally twice that far, and it would be impossible for the mother

to support the infant with her arm for even a small part of that distance. Because the mother must walk with the troop when it moves, the infant's ability at birth to cling to the hair on its mother's belly is essential for survival. During a long trek, the mother may clasp one hand to the infant on her belly once every 20 or 25 steps, but after the second day this is seldom seen. When the mother rests after a long walk, she usually holds the infant against her with one hand for the first few minutes, especially if she is sitting in a tree or above the ground, allowing the infant to relax its grip and rest.

For the first week or 10 days after birth the infant continues to receive its mother's undivided attention, including constant licking, grooming, and lip-smacking (a gesture of pacification). Grooming is the most important, time-consuming activity in baboon social life, and during the first few days of life, grooming by the mother is especially intensive. Every few minutes she explores the newborn infant's body, parts its fur with her fingers, licks and nuzzles it (Fig. 1). When the infant is not nursing,

FIG. 1. Mother grooming an infant 2 or 3 days after birth.

the mother turns it in every position for minute inspection. During these first days, the infant does not take its mouth from the mother's nipple for more than a few seconds at a time; it is completely dependent on its mother, who devotes her entire attention to the infant.

Vocalizations between mother and infant are very few—none, for example, comparable to the wailing of a human infant. Certain gestures by the mother begin early and are modified as the infant matures. Whenever the mother shifts her position she first presses the infant against her with a sweeping motion of her hand. When the infant is 3 weeks old, it frequently sits between the mother's legs without holding on. When the mother is ready to move, she grasps the infant, presses it to her belly, and stands up while still holding the infant against herself with one hand. Dropping her hand, she walks off without giving further support. The infant indicates that it is tired of riding by releasing the grip of its back legs and dangling by its arms beneath the mother. If the mother cannot stop, she scoops it back onto her belly with a sweep of her hand. If the troop is not moving away, however, the infant's action causes the mother to stop and sit with it in her arms for a few minutes. When the infant is still older, it often toddles on the ground under the mother as she walks slowly and eats. By this time the infant is taking almost all the initiative in grasping the mother's belly and riding, and only if the mother is suddenly startled does she clasp the infant to her as she runs farther away. Any of these actions may be accompanied by very soft cries or cooing sounds, usually by the infant. The mother makes almost no sound except that resulting from soft lip-smacking as she grooms her infant. Lip-smacking, initiated at birth by the mother, is one of the most frequent and important of all baboon gestures. For both sexes at all ages this gesture serves to reduce tension and promote tranquility in social interactions.

The newborn and other troop members.

The birth of an infant alters its mother's position in the troop entirely. During estrus the female is in consort with the males for short periods only, and during pregnancy she has relatively few contacts with adult males, but during lactation the mother is very closely associated with the adult males. As soon as her infant is born the mother moves to the heart of the troop to be near the oldest and most dominant males of the central hierarchy. Regardless of her former position in the female dominance hierarchy, the mother is now virtually immune from threat by other troop members because she enjoys the complete protection of the dominant males. The males themselves are intent upon protecting the new infant, a protection which necessarily includes the infant's mother. As each new infant is born its mother joins the other new mothers in the troop's center. By December there may be more than 20 mothers with newborn infants in a troop as large as 200. These mothers are a closely knit group, sitting beside adult males, grooming the males and each other when the troop rests, and walking close beside the males when the troop moves. The less dominant males walk at the edge of the troop, providing an extra zone of protection between the mothers in the troop's center and any predators which the troop may encounter (Washburn and DeVore, 1961a).

The birth of a new infant absorbs the attention of the entire troop. From the moment the birth is discovered, the mother is continuously surrounded by the other baboons, who walk beside her and sit as close as possible when she rests. Although they are very persistent, the mother resists all attempts to touch the infant, turning her back or walking away when pressed too closely. After a week or 10 days, older juveniles and females who sit beside the mother and groom her quietly for several minutes may be allowed to reach over and touch the infant lightly. Young juveniles and older infants sit near the mother and watch her newborn intently, but are seldom able to approach the mother because of the older troop members around her. The mother tolerates this interest in her infant very uneasily, and the infant never leaves her arms. Older juveniles or sub-adult females appear to be most highly motivated toward the newborn infant, and the moment a mother sits one or more of these females is likely to stop whatever she is doing and join the mother. The mother is approached with extreme gentleness, and, especially if the approaching female is subordinate to the mother in the female hierarchy, the hindquarters are lowered into a cringing form of "presenting."

The behavior of the other females around a new mother reflects their dominance status. During a rest period, a young female who begins grooming the mother is soon displaced by a more dominant, fully adult female, who then begins to groom the mother and to try to touch the infant. Since even females normally dominant over the mother usually approach with gestures of pacification and subordination, it is clear that the infant is a very great incentive for them. Occasionally a very dominant female may gently threaten the mother in order to touch the newborn.

Juvenile and young adult males express only perfunctory interest in the infant, but older males in the central hierarchy frequently come and touch the infant. These males are very straightforward, and the mother cringes when a male fondles her infant. (In baboons the direct approach of an adult male is very frightening to other troop members.) She does not try to avoid the males, however, and they often accompany their approach with vigorous lip-smacking. The degree of interest shown by adult males varies considerably. In the Nairobi Park troop observed over the longest period, one of the oldest males invariably joined a mother with a young infant during the daily rest periods. On several occasions the most dominant males carried young infants on their bellies, as long as 20 minutes in one instance. The older males, especially those in the central hierarchy, show much

more interest in infants than do young adult males. All the adult males of the troop, however, are sensitive to the slightest distress cries of a young infant and will viciously attack any human who comes between an infant and the troop. Since infants younger than 6 months are invariably near their mothers, who remove them from any danger, this protective attitude of the adult males is more clearly seen when the infants are older and may have wandered some distance from the mothers. Altmann (1960) found that adult male rhesus macaques also readily attacked him when he captured infant macaques on Santiago Island. These situations occur only when the troop is near human observers, but because of the adult males' generally protective attitude in the presence of predators, it is likely that this same attack would be launched against non-humans also.

It is scarcely possible to overemphasize the significance of the newborn baboon for the other troop members. Of the many behavior patterns which bind the members of a baboon troop together, the presence of young infants is of foremost importance. Grooming is the most frequent and obvious expression of "friendliness" and well-being, and the grooming clusters in a baboon troop are almost always formed around the mothers with the youngest infants. The protective presence of the adult males and the attraction of the infants combine to draw the other troop members toward the center of the troop.

The consequences of these behavior patterns of the other troop members are also very important for the mother and her infant. The protection afforded the mother while her infant is young is unique in baboon adult life and permits her to concentrate on the infant. The development of normal social patterns in the maturing infant depends heavily upon learning. The attractiveness of the young infant assures that it will always be surrounded by attentive troop members and that this learning will take place in a highly protected social environment.

THE INFANT—ONE:

FIRST TO THE FOURTH MONTH

Throughout the first month of life the infant rarely leaves its mother's arms. At the end of the first month the infant begins to acknowledge the constant attention of the other troop members, and its motor development now enables it to take a few steps away from the mother. During long rest periods, while the mothers of young infants sit in a cluster, their infants begin to tentatively approach each other. The moment the infants touch, each turns and runs back to its mother, so these first contacts last only a few seconds.

The female birth cycle has important consequences for the infant's socialization. In the first place, the young baboon has no sibling relationship as such. Its mother's previous offspring is 2 years old and has severed virtually all close ties with the mother. In addition, a birth peak assures that most infants will be part of a large group of approximately the same age. Throughout the first year, the infant becomes progressively more attached to this peer group and more independent of the mother. Finally, it is the infants of the previous year, now largely independent of their mothers, who play the major role in enticing the young infants from their mothers and initiating them to group play.

During the first month, the newborn attracts the attention of the older infants (infant-twos) and young juveniles, but they are unable to get near the infant. The interest of the adult females in the young infants begins to wane during the period from 1 to 4 months, and the older infants are able to move in closer to the mothers and to play very carefully with the young infants. This play is very brief; the young infant will not leave its mother for even 2 minutes until it is 9 weeks old, and it will leave then only if it is sitting beside an adult male.

Throughout these early months the mother becomes less and less disturbed by the overtures of the other troop members toward her infant. By 2 months of age the infant is often grasped by other females and clasped to the body, although the infant quickly struggles free and returns to its mother.

Another consequence of the infant's increasing muscular coordination and independence is its first attempts to ride the mother's back. Although there seems to be considerable individual variation, most infants ride briefly on the mother's back at 5 weeks. Until it is about 2 months old the infant continues to ride underneath the mother more often than on her back, and its position on her back is awkward and insecure. During these first attempts to ride the mother's back, the infant lies across it, at a 90 degree angle to her body. After the age of 2 months the infant often rides the mother's back in this crosswise fashion, but it shifts immediately to the mother's belly if it is frightened or if she is disturbed and runs. If the troop is suddenly startled, or an alarm call is heard, all the infants shift quickly to their mothers' bellies before the troop dashes away.

During this period the signals given by the mother become more elaborate. If the infant is sitting or standing beside the mother, the mother may indicate she is ready to walk away by a swift glance over her shoulder at the infant, by a slight lowering of her hindquarters, by a quick step directly away, or by some combination of these. Only if startled does the mother grab the infant and clasp it to herself. On several occasions an infant who had climbed 3 or 4 feet up into a low tree was called down when the mother wanted to move quickly away. To call the infant, the mother thrust her face toward it, staring intently and lip-smacking loudly. The infant responded by immediately climbing down into the mother's arms.

The 3-month-old infant is mature enough, both physically and socially, to remain away from the mother for longer periods of play and exploration. It still runs back to the mother constantly, but now the time intervals are reversed: the infant is away from the mother for several minutes at a time and in her arms for only a moment. Under ordinary circumstances this time away from the mother is spent tumbling with other black infants of the same age. The infant born in June, outside the birth peak, had no other baboons its own age with which to associate. It spent rest periods crawling all over the adults gathered near its mother. Most of the adult females tolerated or even encouraged the infant's attention, but adult females well below the mother in the hierarchy were very nervous when the infant climbed up on them, and brushed the infant off as quickly and quietly as possible. Adult males, even young adult males, allow black infants to crawl all over them with impunity. Infants of this age were seen climbing over a male's face, leaping repeatedly onto his shoulders from a nearby rock, and sitting upright on a male's back—liberties which no older baboon would dare take.

Interest in the young infant by both adult males and infant-twos reaches its peak in the period from 2½ to 4 months. The infant-twos wait outside the circle of grooming adults, taking every opportunity to draw the young infant a few feet away from the adults and into quiet play. The infant is still black, but is now wandering farther and farther away from the mother, and the older adult males watch it even more closely. Although the infant-twos and young juveniles tumble with the black infant, these adult males are sensitive to the young infant's every sudden move. Any sign of fear or frustration by the black infant causes an adult male to stare toward the play group, sometimes grunting softly, and the offending juvenile releases the infant immediately. . . . Should the black infant cry out, the adult males leap to their feet and the juveniles scatter in terror while the young infant returns to its mother.

THE TRANSITION PERIOD: FOURTH TO THE SIXTH MONTH

At about the fourth month, baboon infants begin to change from black to brown on the belly and on the sides of the face; by the end of the sixth month, they are predominantly brown and are called "infant-two" in this classification. It is also during this 2-month period that the infant adopts the sitting-up posture while riding the mother. . . . Although all the infants have adopted this jockey style of riding by the sixth month, they lie face down and clutch with both hands and feet when the mothers are forced to run.

Muscular coordination and emotional independence are developing rapidly at this age. Five- and six-month-old infants wander as far as 20 feet from their mothers when the troop is feeding quietly, but run back to the mother and ride her back whenever the entire troop moves to another feeding area. Under normal circumstances the infant takes all the initiative in coming to the mother to ride; the mother merely feeds with the troop, allowing the infant to ride or not as it wishes. But if something alarms the troop, the mother crouches in an easy position for the infant to mount, and looks rapidly around while she waits for the infant to reach her. If the mother sees the infant coming she often runs to meet it, crouching again and then dashing away as the infant leaps onto her back.

During the fifth and sixth months, the infant begins to taste solid foods, although these are probably still a negligible part of its diet. Although much more independent of its mother during the day, the 6-month-old infant draws close to the mother in the late afternoon, always riding her back when the troop moves down to the sleeping trees and sleeping in her arms at night. Interest in the infant by the adult females declines rapidly during this period, and by the time the infant is solid brown, is negligible. Jealous protection by the adult males continues unabated, however, and the older infants and young juveniles increase their efforts to entice the young infants into a play group.

THE INFANT—TWO:

SIXTH MONTH TO ONE YEAR

At the beginning of this period the young baboon is still very closely associated with its mother, but by the end, about 6 to 9 months later, the infant is virtually independent. Until it is 7½ months old, the infant rides on its mother's back for a large part of the day. By the end of the eighth month it spends much of the day away from the mother, but still rides its mother to the troop's sleeping trees in the evening and sleeps with her at night. Early in this period the infant tries many vegetable foods, often grasping the seed tassels of grasses as it sits astride its mother. Since the infant continues to take the mother's teats in its mouth, it is impossible to determine the end of her lactation period by observation, but judging by the mother's behavior and the infant's attention to solid foods, the infant is probably receiving little nourishment from the mother by the age of 10 months. If the mother stops to feed in one spot for very long, the infant climbs off her back and forages on its own, staying close by the mother's side during these feeding periods until it is 9 or 10 months old. If the infant finds a particularly choice morsel, this is often taken by the mother for her own consumption.

By its 8th month, the infant has little attraction for the adult females of the troop, and these sometimes threaten or even attack infants of this age. These attacks ordinarily consist of rolling the infant over and either holding it down or giving it a "token bite" on the back or at the nape of the neck. Although no infant is ever visibly wounded by such an attack, it always screeches in terror and its mother comes running to its defense. If the mother is considerably subordinate to the attacking female, her arrival has little effect, but her continued screeches bring an adult male

running and all involved scatter. Again it is the oldest males of the central hierarchy, who have been near the infants since birth, who are the most active males in breaking up such squabbles and protecting the infants. The mother continues to intercede for her infant until it is 2 years old, that is, until her next infant is born, but males usually protect infants well into the infants' 3rd year.

Orientation to peer group. As the tie between mother and infant weakens, the infants spend more and more time with their peer group, playing and resting together, and returning to their mothers only at dusk. This group of older infants stays very near the males of the central hierarchy during the day, even though their mothers are staying farther from the center of the troop now and may be separated from their infants by 30 yards. By the end of the 10th month the infant, who until now has depended largely upon its mother for both companionship and protection, looks to its peers for companionship and to the adult males for protection.

The infants play together as the troop walks along, groom each other (as well as their mothers and the adult males) when the troop rests, and join in much more energetic and elaborate play patterns than they did in previous weeks. Running, chasing, tumbling, nipping, and tailpulling may now last as long as 10 minutes without interruption. Along with this elaboration of social behavior the infants also extend the variety of types of play areas. Until the 8th or 9th month, play is usually confined to flat areas on the plain or under trees. Now the infants seek piles of rocks, low tree limbs, hanging vines, and stream beds, extending their play into a third dimension. Before this age, play is characteristically based on interpersonal contacts; now the physical environment is exploited as well. Young juvenile baboons are no longer kept away from the infants by the adults and frequently join the infant play groups. After a few moments, however, the rougher

FIG. 2. Female infant takes offered food by the side of beta male (alpha male in foreground and gamma male threatening in background).

play of the juveniles usually breaks up the infant play group and the infants withdraw again.

Orientation to adult males. Throughout this description of mother-infant relations in the baboon it has been repeatedly stressed that the relationship of the infant to the adult males is important at every stage of the infant's maturation. A relationship between an infant-two female and an adult male—observed over a 2-month period—illustrates how very close this relationship can become. When first seen, this infant had a disease of the face and scalp which grew steadily worse until the entire top of her skull was exposed. Apparently she was constantly hungry, with the result that she was as bold as an adult male in seeking access to favored feeding spots. When food was offered to the troop, she would run up to the food with the two most dominant males (who together formed the central hierarchy of this troop) and take food from beside them—utterly atypical behavior for a baboon. It soon became clear that she was able to take these liberties only because she enjoyed the complete protection of the older, "beta male," of the dominant pair. The sick infant was beta's constant companion, grooming him through the day, walking in his shadow when the troop moved, and sleeping beside him in the trees at night (Fig. 2). She even stayed beside him while he was in consort with an estrous female. This close association meant virtual ostracism from the other troop members, who rarely came near the infant except to try to threaten her away from her favored position by the adult male. In this respect she was treated much like a subordinate adult female who stays close to her consort during estrus.

When observations were begun on this troop, it contained two very emaciated adult females who disappeared within a few days. One of these females was apparently the sick infant's mother. That the infant was "adopted," not by another adult female, but by the oldest adult male in the troop, illustrates two important facets of the infant-two's relationships in the troop. By the age of 9 months, only an infant's mother, among the adult females, treats the infant in a protective and permissive manner. Instead, adult females begin to set limits on behavior which they will tolerate, and when these limits are exceeded, the infant is frequently rebuffed or chastised by a mild attack. Adult males, on the other hand, remain completely tolerant and protective. . . . Under these circumstances it is not surprising that an infant of this age became attached to an adult male rather than to another female. This example is a measure of the potential strength of the bond between adult males and infants. This male provided the constant care and protection ordinarily associated with maternal behavior. How frequently such behavior can occur could be checked experimentally. Zuckerman describes what appears to be a very similar relationship between an infant and an adult male hamadryas baboon in the London Zoo colony after the death of the infant's mother (1932, pp. 261-262). Itani (1959, printed in 1962) has described in detail a routinized form of paternal care in Japanese macaques during the birth season. A close tie between individual adult males and individual infants was commonly formed in 3 of the 18 troops being studied. It was rare in 7 more and absent in the remaining 8. Among the monkeys at Takasakiyama, 14 of the 18 dominant males exhibited this behavior. The evidence from baboons and Japanese macaques suggests that social bonds between adult males and infants are very strong in these terrestrial species, in striking contrast to the weak bonds between infants and adult males in more arboreal species (for example, langurs, Jay, 1963).

THE WEANING PERIOD: ELEVENTH TO THE FIFTEENTH MONTH

Shortly after the 9th or 10th month, on the average, the baboon infant undergoes the experience of rejection by the mother—rejection both from taking her nipple and from riding her back. There is wide variation in the time at which rejection occurs, and this period is influenced by many circumstances, including the size of the infant (about this time the infant becomes burdensome to carry) and the temperament of both the mother and her infant. But the most important single cause is the cessation of lactation, which is signaled by a concomitant resumption of turgescence in the mother's sexual skin. Since the female does not go through her normal cycles of sexual skin swelling during pregnancy or lactation, the end of lactation can be crudely estimated by records of the first postpartum swelling in the female. In their laboratory baboon colony, Gilbert and Gillman found that "In the majority of animals, amenorrhoea persists for at least five months; as long as ten months may elapse before the sex skin displays the first signs of renewed turgescence" (1951, p. 118).

The period during which the mother resumes her sexual skin swelling brings about another significant change in her social behavior. For more than a year she has not been receptive to adult males, but as her cycles resume and her swelling increases she becomes receptive, and the males begin to take a sexual interest in her again. Not only is most sexual behavior in baboons incompatible with infant care, but estrus in the female also increases her activity and her irritability. As her sexual skin swelling increases, the mother more actively repulses her infant's attempts to ride or nurse. During her first few monthly cycles these rejections by the mother seem to make the infant more anxious than ever to be in her arms, to hold her nipple in its mouth, and to ride her back to the sleeping trees. When the female is at the peak of her swelling (for about 1 week in a 35-day cycle) she is constantly with adult males and rarely near her infant, but as her swelling subsides she often accepts the infant again.

During these months of weaning it is the infant who takes the initiative in the mother-infant relationship. The infant follows the mother and grooms her often; the mother seems neutral toward her infant. When the mother forcefully rejects the infant, by brushing it off her back, holding it away from her breast, or by slapping and biting it, the infant gives a cry of fear and frustration which is heard at no other period in baboon life. Although part of this cry was indistinguishable (by the observer) from the distress cry which always brings an adult male to the scene, when given in this context the cry never attracts the attention of the other baboons. When a mother rejects her infant at dusk, the time of day when the infants ordinarily return to their mothers, the infant may go frantically from one adult to another, including the adult males, giving "frustration cries" before each adult. Even during this period the mother will always come to the aid of her infant if it is attacked by another female or juvenile, but if its cries are only from frustration, the mother ignores it.

Effect of mother's status on her infant. Most infants seem to pass through this weaning period rather smoothly, but some definitely do not. Even in the field it is possible to recognize individual differences in the personality of infants by the age of 6 months, and the weaning period emphasizes these differences. There seemed to be a high correlation between the amount of frustration and "insecurity" displayed by an infant and its mother's position in the female dominance hierarchy. Infants whose mothers were near the bottom of the hierarchy gave alarm cries more often and made more frequent demands on their mothers. These infants nursed and tried to ride their mothers' backs many weeks after their peers had ceased doing either. One especially "insecure" infant

succeeded in riding its mother's back at the age of more than a year, when it was too heavy to be carried any distance by her. . . .

In general, the year-old infant, even though it is away from the mother's side most of the day, shows that it is still very sensitive to her emotional states. Anything which upsets the mother, such as a serious fight among the females or the flight of the troop from danger, also upsets the infant; it runs to her and stays with her until the crisis is past. Because of this close bond, it is easy to understand that the infant of an especially subordinate female is subjected to repeated emotional shock when its mother must yield continuously before the threats of other females. In addition, mothers who bear the constant brunt of aggressive dominance by the other females seem to be more short-tempered and less responsive to their infants. These experiences of the infant are apparently compounded and intensified by the period of weaning and rejection, giving rise to the observable differences in behavior during this period. Hamburg (1963) has described some of the "endocrine responses to disruption of personally-crucial relationships" in human patients.[†]

By analogy, it is likely that the infants of dominant females are affected by the constant attitude of preeminence displayed by their mothers. In a brief field study it is impossible to link older infants and young juveniles to their mothers with certainty, but observations of an adult female consistently supporting a young juvenile in dominance interactions suggest the rem-

[†] In concluding the discussion he says: "Disruption of inter-individual bonds may have profound consequences in carbohydrate, protein, fat, electrolyte and water metabolism, and on crucial functions of the circulation. Such disruption is felt as deeply unpleasant, and an extraordinary variety of coping behavior patterns may be mobilized to restore acceptance, affection and mutual respect. Perhaps serious threat to a key relationship may be as much an emergency in psychophysiologic terms as threat of attack by a predator."

nants of the mother-infant bond. Through stereotyped interactions, in which a juvenile "enlists the support" of an adult female against a third troop member, it is possible for a juvenile to maintain temporary dominance over an otherwise superior animal. For this to be successful, however, the "mother" must herself be dominant over the third party. The dominance status of the mother thus determines the frequency of successful assertions of dominance by the juvenile. Workers at the Japan Monkey Centre, where the life history of many individual monkeys has been kept for nearly a decade, describe the effect of the mother's dominance status on her offspring. Only the infants of the most dominant females grow up in the troop's center. Here the infants apparently learn, from the adults around them, a domineering attitude toward peripheral troop members, and are more likely to adopt roles of leadership and dominance in adult life (Imanishi, 1960).‡

THE YOUNG JUVENILE:
THE SECOND YEAR OF LIFE

This period in the young baboon's development begins with the experience of

‡ Since the preparation of this paper, Koford (1963) has published an important, independent confirmation of the effect of the rhesus monkey mother's social rank on the rank of her male offspring. Although social rank generally conforms to the ages of the adult males, Koford found some notable exceptions "in which a subadult or newly adult 4- to 6-year-old male outranked older and larger males." In one band, for example, the ages of the males, in descending order of rank, were 8, 5, 4, 4, 8, 8, 7, 8, 7 and 6 years; in another band the ages were 10+, 6, 10+, 5, 6, 8, 8, 8, 7, and 7 years. All of these young, anomalously high-ranking males are the offspring of the most dominant females in the band. Although being born to a high-ranking mother clearly gives some males an advantage in the dominance hierarchy, it does not guarantee that the males can hold this high position. Koford also reports that two of these young, previously high-ranking males later joined new bands, where they assumed low rank.

weaning and ends with the birth of its mother's new infant. Most of this period is spent in the young juvenile play group, away from any adult when the troop is resting (the favorite play period for young baboons), and walking close to the males of the central hierarchy when the troop moves. By the 18th month the young juvenile is so seldom near its mother that it is impossible for an observer to associate the mothers and their offspring unless some crisis arises in the troop. A prolonged fight among the adults or a serious attack upon the juvenile will bring the mother to the juvenile's defense, but both these occurrences are rare. If danger threatens the troop, the juveniles flee to the adult males, not to their mothers. The young juveniles groom the adult males, their mothers, and each other with about equal frequency. The juvenile's mother, now pregnant again, is much more active in the female dominance hierarchy than she has been for many months.

By the time the juvenile is 2 years old its mother has given birth again, and any remaining emotional tie to the mother appears to be severed. It is possible that consistent pairings of adult males and estrous females, or of adult females with each other, are the carry-overs from earlier mother-infant relations, but this could not be proved during a brief field study. At 2 years of age the juvenile is with its peer group most of the day. Adult males continue to protect young juveniles, but the juveniles have now learned that they can no longer behave with impunity around adult males. In fact, the adult males are now protecting a new group of newborn infants from the juveniles' rough play.

Patterns of play. Constant peer-group play is the most characteristic activity of this age (2 to 3 years). The young juvenile begins to play at dawn, plays as the troop moves to a feeding place, plays frequently during the feeding periods, and plays almost constantly during rest periods. If a large troop remains in one spot very long, as many as four different play groups may form. Ranging from the cluster of black infants inside the circle formed by their mothers to a boisterous group of older juveniles at the troop's edge, these four play groups represent the infants born during the four preceding annual birth peaks. Harlow and Harlow (1962) have been able to distinguish the play of males from females at about 2 months of age in laboratory rhesus monkeys. This dichotomy is apparent in the play of baboons by the age of 2 years, even in the field. Juvenile male baboons play more roughly and longer; juvenile females groom more frequently and spend more time with the newborn infants in the troop.

Play is even more energetic at this age, but the play remains quiet. Any loud or prolonged noise from the juveniles brings a grunting threat from the adult males and play is interrupted. This same interference in juvenile play by the adult male has been recorded for howling monkeys (Carpenter, 1934), but in langurs (Jay, 1963) it is the adult females who thus interfere. In young juvenile baboons the play activity is cyclical: it becomes more and more vigorous until the females drop out. Juvenile males continue until one cries out; adults then break up the play and, after several minutes of quiet, play is resumed.

Demography and socialization. There are demographic variables in normal baboon troops which can considerably affect the socialization experience of the young infant and juvenile. One of the most obvious variables is group size. In a very small troop there may be only one or two infants born each year; in a large troop more than twenty. Play groups tend to build up to a size of at least six or eight individuals, and young infants without a peer group this large will start to play with older infants and young juveniles at an early age. The same is true for infants born outside the annual birth peak, no matter how large the troop. Because these infants are playing with older baboons, they are frightened or hurt more often. This means that adult males will intervene on behalf

of these infants much more often than would be necessary if they were playing only with infants of the same age. Whether this frequent contact with the adult male consoles or frightens the infant depends to some extent on the social position of its mother. The offspring of a dominant female is accustomed early in life to the superior position of its mother, and frequent contact with a dominant male would not appear to frighten it as much as it does the offspring of a subordinate female.

Discussion

The history of the maturation of the infant in a baboon troop during its first 30 months of life begins with the intensive mother-infant bond in a very protected social environment, and, through a series of increasing contacts with other baboons, extends outward to a widening circle of troop members. The close companionship and protection of the mother are supplanted by close ties with juvenile peers and by the protection of the adult males. By the time the infant is rejected by the mother it is capable of feeding on its own and is socially mature enough to fit into the pattern of troop life. At about 30 months of age its relations with the adult males shift—no longer the object of very tolerant protection it now enters a relationship of dominance-subordination. By this time it is well-developed enough to keep up easily with the troop on its own, and to sense and flee from danger. At this age it withdraws even more into its peer group and begins to pattern its behavior on the dominance-subordination relationships developing there. In this way the infant passes from the reflexive, dependent period of the neonate, through various combinations of affectional patterns, to a position of independence and individuality within the troop structure.

COMPARISON BETWEEN BABOONS
AND LANGURS

The important features of the ontogeny of baboon infants are most clearly seen

TABLE 54-1

**The development of baboon and langur infants in relation to stages
in the mother's reproductive cycle**

Months	0	2	4	6	8	10	12	14	16	18	20	22	24
			LACTATION				ESTRUS				PREGNANCY		
Mother (both species)													
Baboon		Infant-one		Color change		Infant-two				Young juvenile			
						WEANING							
Langur		Infant-one		Color change		Infant-two				Young juvenile			

when contrasted with another monkey species, such as langurs (Jay, 1963). A comparison between the two species reveals great similarity in many fundamentals. Both species live in social groups in which adults are organized in dominance hierarchies and whose membership is stable throughout the year. Both the daily round and the annual cycle of activities are very similar. But there are important differences. In baboons the troop is considerably larger, sexual dimorphism is more pronounced, and there are no individuals living outside the troop. These differences are no doubt closely related to the baboon adaptation to life on the ground, where predator pressure is more constant than it is for the more arboreal langur.

Patterns of physical and social development in the infant are also much the same. In both species the infant is very attractive to the other troop members and begins life in a secure, highly protected environment. Other events in the infant's first year—independent locomotion, change in coat color, orientation to a peer group, weaning, and independence from the mother—also occur in the same order and at approximately the same time (Table 54-1). In both species it is the resumption of the mother's sexual activity which terminates the close mother-infant bond. Because

births are spaced about 2 years apart, and occur during an annual birth peak, the early experience of both baboon and langur infants is conditioned by a peer group rather than by older siblings.

On the other hand, there are striking differences in the details of baboon and langur infant life. Perhaps the greatest contrast concerns the relationship between the adult male and the infant. For the baboon this relationship is very close at birth and steadily increases in importance, until by the middle of the second year the young baboon is more closely associated with the adult males of the troop than with its own mother. The infant langur, however, has no contact with adult males at all until it is 8 months old. At this age the infant-two male tensely approaches adult males for the first time. Although the adult males are tolerant and restrained in these interactions, they are not attentive to the infant langur in any other situation. A female langur has almost no contact with adult males until she is about 3 years old, when she begins to include them among the animals she will groom.

The experience of the newborn infant with the adult females of the troop is also quite different. The newborn baboon does not ordinarily leave its mother's arms during the first month, and the baboon mother will not allow other troop members even to touch her infant for the first week. But the langur newborn is passed from one adult female to another, and may be carried as far as 75 feet from its mother on the day of birth. It is also these adult females who protect the young langur, even chasing adult male langurs who startle the infants. But although it is achieved in different ways, the infant in both species matures in a protected social environment.

Other differences in infant development between baboons and langurs are related to their different locomotor and ecological adaptations. Infant langurs, for example, begin to play in trees at an age when this behavior is still rare in baboons. The abundance of tender, leafy foods available to the infant langur makes it possible for the langur to eat solid food at an earlier age. In these ways morphology, ecological adaptation, and the behavior of the adults combine to mold the maturing infant into a species-specific way of life.

It is also clear, however, that within the spectrum of behavior patterns appropriate for the adult of either species there is wide latitude for individual expression. Unique influences and experiences occur during the life of every infant. Variations in the mother's reproductive physiology, her temperament, and her experience with previous offspring all affect the infant's early life. The dominance status of the mother may strongly influence the development and direction of the infant's social relationships. In baboons, the troop itself may be one in which dominance relations are unstable and there are frequent fights, or one in which fighting is rare. The troop may be small and the infant may never experience the social relations of a large peer group. These different life experiences must have a profound effect on the maturation of the infant, with resulting variations in adult behavior. It is not possible to more than suggest the nature of these social and environmental influences on socialization from observations made during a brief field study. To understand them will require the close coordination of detailed field observations with laboratory experiments.

Summary

This report is based on a 10-month field study of baboons in Kenya during 1959. Although more than 2000 baboons were observed, the description of mother-infant relations is based largely on three troops in which every individual was known. These troops were accustomed to persons in automobiles and observations could be made at close range.

The development of the infant baboon is divided into six periods.

The newborn: Birth to one month. The mother of a newborn infant avoids direct contact with other troop members but stays near the protective adult males of the central hierarchy. The intense relationship between the mother and her newborn includes many behavior patterns, such as grooming and lip-smacking, which are important tranquilizing gestures in adult life. The mother and infant are under the constant protection of the adult males both from danger outside the troop and from aggression within the troop. As a result, the mother is not subject to most dominance interactions and is free to satisfy the needs of her infant. Young infants are an attractive stimulus to other troop members, and their presence in the troop has an integrating effect.

The infant — one: First to the fourth month. An animal birth peak provides most infants with a large peer group. Older infants and young juveniles draw the infant-one into play, but most of the infant's time is spent with other infants its own age. The gathering of mothers in the troop's center provides a context for play among these infant-ones. Interest by other troop members reaches its peak during this period.

The transition period: Fourth to the sixth month. During this period the infant's fur changes from black to brown and it begins to ride its mother's back in a sitting-up posture. The infant may wander as far as 20 feet from its mother and begins to eat some solid food.

The infant—two: Sixth month to one year. This is a period of increasing independence from the mother. Adult females (except the mother) begin to rebuff the infant, but the permissive attitude of the adult males continues. By the end of the tenth month, the infant spends more time in a play group of peers than with its mother. This play group stays near the dominant, central hierarchy males, and special circumstances can produce a very close association between an infant and an adult male.

The weaning period: Eleventh to the fifteenth month. With the cessation of lactation and the resumption of estrous cycles, the mother more vigorously prevents the infant from taking her nipple and from riding her back. Some infants pass through this stage more easily than others; the infants of mothers of low status appear to have the most difficulty. There is evidence that the status of the mother may affect the status of her offspring as adults.

The young juvenile: The second year of life. By the end of this period almost all ties to the mother have been broken, and the mother is caring for a newborn. In a crisis young juveniles are more likely to seek out adult males than their mothers. Constant play with peers is characteristic of this age. Demographic factors influence the experience of the juvenile during this formative age. By about 30 months of age, the juvenile is part of the troop dominance hierarchy and gets little preferential treatment from adult males.

A comparison of the development of baboon and langur infants reveals behavior patterns which are broadly similar but which contrast in detail. The treatment of the neonate by adult females and the relationship between the maturing infant and the adult males differ markedly in the two species. Many of these differences are related to ecological adaptations, reflecting the contrast between a terrestrial and a more arboreal species. In addition, unique experiences during the maturation of infants of both species contribute to the individuality of adult behavior.

REFERENCES

ALTMANN, S. A., 1960   A field study of the sociobiology of rhesus monkeys, *Macaca mulatta.* Unpublished doctoral dissertation, Harvard University.

BOLWIG, N., 1959   A study of the behaviour of the Chacma baboon, *Papio ursinus. Behaviour,* **14**, 136–163.

CARPENTER, C. R., 1934   A field study of the behavior and social relations of howling monkeys. *Comp. Psychol. Monogr.,* **10** No. 2 (whole No. 48).

DEVORE, I., 1962   Baboon ecology, 16 mm sound, color film, University of California at Berkeley.

DEVORE, I., and S. L. WASHBURN, 1960   Baboon behavior, 16 mm sound, color film, University of California at Berkeley.

DEVORE, I., and S. L. WASHBURN, 1963   Baboon ecology and human evolution. In: F. C. HOWELL and FRANCOIS BOURLIERE (Eds.), *African Ecology and Human Evolution,* New York: Wenner-Gren Foundation for Anthropological Research; Viking Fund Publications in Anthropology, 36.

GILBERT, CHRISTINE, and J. GILLMAN, 1951   Pregnancy in the baboon *Papio ursinus. S. Afr. J. Med. Sci.,* **16**, 115–124.

GILLMAN, J., and CHRISTINE GILBERT, 1946   The reproductive cycle of the Chacma baboon *(Papio ursinus)* with special reference to the problems of menstrual irregularities as assessed by the behaviour of the sex skin. *S. Afr. J. Med. Sci.,* **11** (Biol. Suppl.), 1–54.

HALL, K. R. L., 1960   Social vigilance behaviour of the Chacma baboon, *Papio ursinus. Behaviour,* **16**, 261–294.

HALL, K. R. L., 1961   Feeding habits of the Chacma baboon. *Advanc. Sci.,* **17**, 559–567.

HAMBURG, D. A., 1963   Emotions in perspective of human evolution. In: P. KNAPP (Ed.), *Expression of Emotions in Man,* New York: International Universities Press.

HARLOW, H. F., and MARGARET K. HARLOW, 1962   Social deprivation in monkeys. *Sci. Amer.,* **207** (5), 136–146.

IMANISHI, KINJI, 1960   Social organization of subhuman primates in their natural habitat. *Curr. Anthrop.*, **1**, 393–407.

ITANI, J., 1959, printed in 1962   Paternal care in the wild Japanese monkey, *Macaca fuscata fuscata*. *Primates, the Journal of Primatology*, **2** (1) 61–93.

JAY, PHYLLIS, 1963   Mother-infant relations in langurs. In: HARRIET L. RHEINGOLD (Ed.), *Maternal Behavior in Mammals*, New York: John Wiley and Sons.

KOFORD, C. B., 1963   Rank of mothers and sons in bands of rhesus monkeys. *Science*, **141**, 356–357.

KUMMER, H., 1957   Soziales Verhalten einer Mantelpavian-Gruppe. *Schweiz. Z. Psychol.*, **33**, 1–91.

WASHBURN, S. L., and I. DEVORE, 1961a   The social life of baboons. *Sci. Amer.*, **204** (6) 62–71.

WASHBURN, S. L., and I. DEVORE, 1961b   Social behavior of baboons and early man. In: S. L. WASHBURN (Ed.), *Social Life of Early Man*, New York: Wenner-Gren Foundation for Anthropological Research; Viking Fund Publications in Anthropology, **31**.

ZUCKERMAN, S., 1932   *The Social Life of Monkeys and Apes*, London: Kegan Paul, Trench, Trubner and Co.

EVELYN SHAW

55   The Development of Schooling Behavior in Fishes*

The schooling behavior of fishes is a good example of allelomimetic behavior (reading 49). Factors controlling the development of this behavior have been under investigation by Evelyn Shaw of the American Museum of Natural History. The following reading presents some of her observations and experiments on the problem.

Reprinted from *Physiological Zoology*, 1960, 33, 79–86, by permission of the author and the University of Chicago Press. Copyright 1960 by the University of Chicago.

Introduction

Knowledge of the development of behavior is essential to the eventual understanding of the organism in its adaptation to the total environment (Schneirla, 1957). Knowing when and how patterns of behavior emerge, from their very beginnings, helps to define those features of the external and internal "milieu" which are critical to the manifestation of behavior. In undertaking a study of schooling, its development was followed. Observations were made on the first approaches and responses of fry to one another and on the subsequent events which led to schooling orientation. As these patterns were revealed and as they were incorporated in the animal's behavioral repertoire, it was possible to evaluate the extent of their flexibility and rigidity, particularly when the fish were reared under varied environmental conditions or when early experience with different situa-

* This research was supported by grants from the National Science Foundation (G-4986) and the National Institutes of Health (M-2322). The laboratory facilities at the Marine Biological Laboratory were provided by the Marine Biological Laboratory through their contract with the Office of Naval Research.

tions was restricted or enriched. By observing all these aspects of development, a clearer understanding of the specific factors of attraction and orientation which result in continuous schooling was obtained.

Materials and Methods

The development of schooling in the common silversides, *Menidia menidia* (Linnaeus) and *Menidia beryllina* (Cope) was observed during the summers of 1957 and 1958 at Woods Hole, Mass. These species live sympatrically in shoal water. During May, June, and July the adults are in spawning condition, and spawning takes place over wide areas (Bumpus, 1898). The extruded eggs sink to the bottom, adhering to the substratum by adhesive threads. *M. menidia* is reported to spawn in water more saline than water found at the spawning sites of *M. beryllina*.

During the spawning season the adults were stripped of their gametes by applying gentle abdominal pressure. The eggs were fertilized readily and developed normally under laboratory conditions. No differences were detected in the embryonic development of both species; therefore, subsequent discussions do not distinguish between the two.

REARING TECHNIQUE

Approximately 40 eggs were placed into each finger bowl containing sea water, which was changed daily. Hatching at laboratory temperatures, 23-27° C., occurred 8-10 days after fertilization. Newly hatched fry were transferred to either shallow troughs with continuously running fresh sea water or to large finger bowls containing sea water, which was changed every third day. The fry were fed live nauplii of the brine shrimp *Artemia*, two days after hatching (Rubinoff, 1958). Approximately 1,000 fry were reared and observed in the laboratory and approximately 10,000 fry were observed in the field.

OBSERVATIONS

In the laboratory, observations of one half-hour each were made in the morning, afternoon, and evening from the time of hatching until the fry were four weeks old, posthatching. During this period the fry grew from 4.5 mm. to 14-16 mm.; they attained a length of 12 mm. by the third week after hatching. The fry were measured with calipers from the tip of the snout to the posterior edge of the caudal fin. The lengths of the fry from the same broods did not vary more than 0.25 mm.; the fry were kept at the same population density in the rearing tanks and fed standard quantities of food.

The Development of Schooling in the Laboratory

During all the observations from hatching onward the fry were found in aggregations of 15-30 individuals, concentrated in only one or two areas of their holding vessels. The aggregates were found near the walls of the vessels, were a single "fish layer" in depth, and a few millimeters below the surface. No differences were noted in the behavior of fry reared in troughs as compared with those reared in finger bowls, nor were any differences detected in the schooling of *M. menidia* and *M. beryllina*.

DEVELOPMENT OF APPROACH AND ORIENTATION

Fry, 5-7 mm. in length—A fry frequently approached the tail, the head, or the lateral mid-body region of another fry to within 5 mm.; both usually darted away rapidly (Fig. 1).

Fry, 8-9 mm. in length—A fry frequently approached the tail of another fry and subsequently the two fry, when 1-3 cm. apart, generally took a parallel course for 1-2 seconds (Fig. 2). If either fry approached the other, head-first, or approached perpendicular to the mid-body

FIG. 1. Fry 5–7 mm. in length. Parallel orientation is not seen.

region, no orientation occurred, and the fry darted off rapidly in opposite directions, very much like the behavior seen in fry, 5-7 mm. in length.

Fry, 9-9.5 mm. in length—Often four or five fry, 1-3 cm. apart, lined up parallel and swam together for 5-10 seconds.

Fry, 10-10.5 mm. in length—When a fry swam toward the tail of another fry, two responses often occurred; both fry vibrated when they were near each other, and one fry invariably followed the other with the result that, in a crowded area, 4-6 fry oriented and swam parallel for as long as 30-60 seconds. When these schools dispersed, the fry tended to remain aggregated.

Fry, 11-12 mm. in length—As many as 10 fry swam together, in parallel orientation (Fig. 3). Occasionally the school disrupted but reformed within several seconds. The fish-to-fish distances ranged from 1.0 cm. to 3.5 cm., and considerable man-

FIG. 2. Fry 8–9 mm. in length. The first indications of parallel orientation and incipient schooling are seen.

euvering of position occurred within the school.

Fry, 12-13 mm. in length—Separate schools, containing 10-20 fry were formed. The fry were a single "fish layer" in depth, and they ranged freely over the tanks, no longer hovering near the walls.

Fry, over 14 mm. in length—Often all the fry in the tank formed into a single school. The orientation of the fry was more precisely parallel and the fish-to-fish distance was less variable, ranging from 1.0 to 1.5 cm. On rare occasions the fry were as close as 0.5 cm. or as far apart as 2.5 cm.

In summary, schooling is seen to develop as a response, initially, between two fry, with the numbers of participating fry

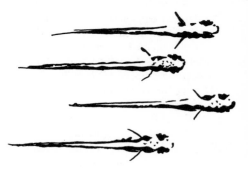

FIG. 3. Fry 11–12 mm. in length. Fry are oriented parallel and schooling is established.

increasing as they grow. Approach and orientation follow characteristic patterns. The first approaches, head on, do not result in orientation; later approaches toward the tail do result in parallel orientation.

THE DEVELOPMENT OF VISUAL ATTRACTION

Vision is evidently the primary sensory stimulus in fish-to-fish attraction, as reported by a number of investigators and summarized by Atz (1953) and Breder (1959). To determine whether or not visual attraction develops parallel to the emergence of schooling, the following experiment was inaugurated (Shaw, 1958). A freely swimming fish was placed in a

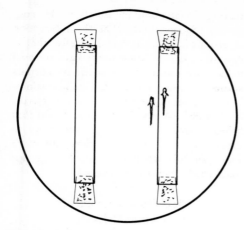

FIG. 4. Technique for experiments on visual attraction.

TABLE 55-1

The development of visual attraction

SIZE OF FISH (MM.)	NO. TESTED	NO. ORIENTING PARALLEL IN CONTROL TUBE FOR 5 SECONDS OR MORE	NO. ORIENTING PARALLEL TO TUBE CONTAINING FISH FOR 5 SECONDS OR MORE
5	20	0a	0
6	20	0a	0
7	16	0a	0
8	18	1	9
9	20	3	13
11	20	2	10
12	20	2	12
13	18	1	3
14	18	0	8
15	22	0	15
16	12	0	10

a Did not orient, or approach.

shallow bowl (9″ diameter) containing two narrow glass tubes (6″ long, ⅜″ diameter) filled with water and plugged at each end with a cork (Fig. 4). A 5-minute record was taken of the number of times the freely swimming fry oriented parallel and closely to the tube for at least 5 seconds. At the end of 5 minutes, one of the tubes was replaced by an identical tube containing a fry the same size as the freely swimming fry, and another 5-minute observation was taken. The fry within the tube was restricted to swimming up and down the length of the tube. Orientation of the freely swimming fry to the control tubes and to the tube containing a fry, is given in Table 55-1.

No fry, 8-14 mm. in length, oriented parallel to either tube before 3½ min. Of these, 70 per cent oriented parallel to the tube containing a fry between 3½ to 4½ min.; 30 per cent between 4½ to 5 min. Among the fry 15-16 mm. in length, one fry 15 mm. in length and two fry 16 mm. in length oriented parallel to the tube containing a fish within 50 sec.; the remaining fry responded within 3 min.

Fifty per cent of the fry 8-12 mm. in length oriented parallel to the inclosed fish for 10 sec.; 50 per cent oriented for 5 sec. Thirty-six per cent of the fry 13-14 mm. in

length oriented for 20 sec.; 45 per cent for 10 sec.; and 19 per cent for 5 sec. Forty per cent of the fry 15-16 mm. in length oriented parallel for 60 sec.; 28 per cent for 30 sec.; and 2 per cent for 20 sec. One fry, which oriented for 60 sec., changed direction seven times.

A conspicuous pattern of behavior was seen among the fry as they approached and began to orient along the tube. The entire body of the fish vibrated for 1-2 seconds. This is quite different from that seen in typical swimming motion. It was not determined whether the fry in the inclosed tube also vibrated. The significance of this vibration is not yet understood, but it may possibly be important to the processes of orientation within the school.

CURRENT ORIENTATION AS A STIMULUS TO SCHOOLING BEHAVIOR IN *Menidia*

Most fish including *Menidia* show a positive rheotaxis when placed in a moderate current flow. Newly hatched *Menidia* immediately orient upstream and maintain a constant swimming speed within the current. It seemed possible that orientation into a current could, for instance, accustom preschooling fish to seeing their species mates in certain visual patterns which would influence the fish in their mutual response in such a way that this familiar visual pattern would be maintained. To evaluate the influence of current flow on the development of schooling, fish were reared to a length of 15 mm. in bowls of still water. Under these conditions schooling developed at the same age and with the same characteristic patterns found among fishes reared in a moderate current flow.

Menidia REARED IN RESTRICTED ENVIRONMENTS ("ISOLATION")

Embryos, in very early phases of development (the optic buds were just appearing), were placed in individual bowls containing sea water. The interiors of the bowls were lined with a thin coat of parafin which prevented the embryos from seeing out of their respective bowls and from seeing their own reflection along the sides of the bowl. The major features of the environment consisted of the embryo, the bowl, and the water contained therein.

Of 400 fish reared in isolation only 4 grew to 15 mm. in length. When each of these 4 fish was presented to a school of fish of the same size, they joined the group immediately. Initially, however, they seemed unable to maintain their position in the school; they often bumped into species mates, and they occasionally swam away from the school. At the end of four hours, however, fish reared in isolation could not be distinguished from those reared in groups.

The high rate of mortality was not clearly understood, as the socially reared controls yielded high survival rates. It was noted that the "isolates" did not begin to feed and apparently died of starvation, implying that the presence of brood mates is a requisite to the initiation of feeding. Breder (1946) found great difficulty in rearing *Brachydanio* in "isolation." He suggested the possibility that the interaction of groups was such, metabolically, that it may have had a rather immediate survival value; for example, aquarium keepers know that a non-feeding fish will be stimulated to feed in the presence of an actively feeding fish. Welty (1934) also found that fishes in groups stimulated each other to greater activity and that they ate more food per fish when they were in groups than when they were isolated.

Field Observations of Schooling Behavior

During late June, July, and August thousands of small fry school in shoal waters in and around the Woods Hole area. Each school generally contains between 30-50 fry, either made up of the earliest schooling fry, 12-16 mm. in length, or of slightly larger fry, 16-20 mm. in length. Schools of fry 16-20 mm. in length swam at uniform speeds, exhibited consistent parallel orientation, and displayed an impressive synchronization. The fish-to-fish distance of 0.8-1.0 cm. varied little. Generally, 4 to 5 fry swam abreast in the school and 6 to 7 fry swam along its length, thereby creating a rectangularly shaped school.

In comparison with the above groups, schools of fry 12-16 mm. in length did not always swim at uniform speeds, nor did they consistently exhibit parallel orientation. The fish-to-fish distance varied between 0.5-2.5 cm., and stragglers were often seen. The school was generally rectangular in shape, but because of the variable fish-to-fish distances, it appeared more loosely structured than the above group.

Separate schools in the above size groups were sighted in relatively small areas; for example, an area 20' × 10' harbored 6 discrete schools. If these schools were disturbed, and forced to swim away from the locality, they would return soon after the disturbance subsided. Apparently schools tend to remain in the same areas, for as the summer progressed and return visits were made to the same spot, larger and larger fry were found. The gradual size increase can be attributed to the normal growth rate of the fry.

Pre-schooling fry were located only on two occasions. Once, 8 fry, 7-10 mm. in length, were observed drifting on the surface of the water, 6 feet in depth. The fry were randomly oriented, swimming activity was minimal, and the fish-to-fish distance varied from 6″ to 2′. On another occasion over 100 fry were found in shallow water along the bank, scattered among Sedge grass, *Spartina alterniflora*, roots. The fry were closely packed and randomly oriented. However, when these preschooling fry were disturbed, they formed into a temporary school for several seconds. Breder (1946) found that startling adult *Brachydanio* caused them to draw together temporarily into a school. In contrast, among the schooling fry a disturbance often caused a brief disruption of the school.

Discussion

The most conspicuous features of schooling fish are their constancy in orientation and their synchronization of speed and direction of movement. Parr (1927) observed that schools are characterized by great stability through the most varied environmental conditions and that this stability and their schooling early in life indicate that schools must be dominated by internal factors. Keenleyside (1955) maintains that schooling is a separate and specific instinct as it has some of the characteristics of an instinctive activity. However, by assuming an "original nature" of primarily internal factors, one may overlook many stimulative influences upon the organism during its lifetime (Schneirla, 1957); and this assumption may ultimately preclude the study of changing influences, during the animal's life, upon any given behavioral phenomenon. A knowledge of

the animal's life history is important, particularly since we know from numerous ontogenetic studies that past experiences and early experiences frequently affect subsequent behavioral responses (Beach, 1954). Although fishes have a relatively stereotyped behavioral repertoire, there is no reason to assume that their responses to social situations cannot be altered by past experiences, just as their responses to physical situations are altered by past experiences (Breder, 1959).

One way in which the effect of early schooling experience on later schooling can be determined is by rearing individuals in situations where they do not have the opportunity to gain any schooling experience. By rearing a fish in physical and visual isolation from species mates, we are able to learn which behavioral patterns will emerge. This type of experiment, however, will not tell us what is "native" to the animal (Schneirla, 1956); it will tell us only of the type of response that will appear from a fish reared in conditions of reduced environmental stimuli, since the organism is still capable of gaining many other types of experience during its so-called "isolation." Of the 400 fish reared in separate chambers, only 4 survived to the age of schooling. When each of the 4 was presented to a group of schooling fish, they joined the school. Recent evidence (Shaw, unpublished manuscript) has shown that acara (*Aequidens latifrons*) fry reared under similar conditions of "isolation" also joined a school, as Breder (1946) found to be the case in *Brachydanio*. However, in sharp contrast to these results, acara fry reared in "isolation" and subsequently placed together did not form a school, although they did aggregate into groups of two's and three's. It seems fairly obvious that the responses of the fry are influenced by the stimulating conditions of the situations into which they are placed.

Initially, when the four isolates mentioned above joined the school, they were unable to orient parallel to other fish or to maintain consistency in their fish-to-fish distances, frequently dropping out of the school or bumping into their species mates. Although these fish had no previous experiences with any species mates, they were able within four hours to adjust to the situation in which they were placed. However, the fact that they showed initial and early disorientation is significant, for it suggests that even though these fish are attracted to the schooling group, they need a certain amount of experience in orientation before they are able to orient. Tending to reinforce this view are the observations of schooling development. For contrary to Morrow's expectations (1948), schooling does not appear immediately after hatching but develops gradually over a period of several weeks. During development the direction of approach changes from primarily a head-on approach to an approach toward the tail. Fry 5-7 mm. in length show the head-on approach; fry over 10 mm. approach toward the tail; the transitional period is seen among fish 8-10 mm. in length. In the head-on approach each fry sees a changing visual pattern, an oval mass, bright black spots (the eyes) coming steadily closer until the intensity is great enough to force a withdrawal of the fry— in this case, a veering off. In contrast, a fish approaching toward the tail of another fish also sees a changing visual pattern of small silvery and black spots and a ribbon-like transparent tail; but this pattern is moving steadily away from him, presenting a stimulus of lesser intensity, which the fish continues to approach. In the earliest stages parallel orientation may simply reflect the forward momentum of the fish swimming in that direction. Later, as the visuomotor co-ordination becomes more highly developed, the fish is able to select this more moderate stimuli and avoid "the more intense stimuli." Schneirla (1959) has postulated that in many organisms mild stimuli attract, strong stimuli repel.

Unfortunately, because of the high mortality rate of the isolates, it was impossible to determine whether there are critical periods of experience in the formation of a school. Judging by the rapidity which with "isolated" fry, 15 mm. in length, joined the school, we anticipate that later experiences, that is, those of fry 10, 11, or 12 mm. in length, may be more influential in schooling formation. Approaches during that time are toward the tail and result in brief parallel orientation, whereas the earlier responses, mainly head-on approaches, result in disorientation.

Paralleling to a large extent the development of schooling is the development of visual attraction. Freely swimming fry, 8 mm. or more in length, responded to fish inclosed in a glass tube, approaching the tube and orienting parallel to the tube. However, although two freely swimming fry, 5-7 mm. in length, approached each other, a freely swimming fry did not approach the fry in the glass tube. The discrepancy in this behavior has several possible explanations. First, fish of this age may have had an insufficient accumulation of experiences with species mates to be attracted to the modified image of a species mate in the tube. Second, at this time of early development they may require certain kinds of responses from species mates which cannot be given by a fish restricted in a glass tube. Third, the approach may be random and not necessarily related to schooling, and fourth, the fish may not be able to swim sufficiently well to orient. At later stages of development these fish are attracted to the visual image of a species mate and will orient parallel for a brief period, the time of orientation gradually increasing in length as the fry grow older. An important aspect of schooling is that it is an interaction between fishes, and interresponses from each fish are required to maintain a school; and, although the visual image gradually becomes a stronger attracting stimulus for the freely swimming fry, it is insufficient for maintaining orientation.

A number of questions are raised regarding the development of schooling under field conditions. At first it appears that the vastness of the sea would enormously reduce the chances of these fish finding one another, forming into aggregates, and, finally, schooling. Yet when we examine plankton tows, we find that the tows frequently contain large numbers of preschooling *Menidia* (Williams, personal communication). These fry, therefore, do have the opportunity to gain orientative experiences with one another as they are carried by the currents. As they grow and develop both physically and in experience, the fry no longer drift with the plankton but form into the many schools of young found along the shores.

Summary

1. The development of schooling behavior in *Menidia* is described. Schooling was observed in the laboratory and found to develop gradually, following characteristic patterns of approach and orientation.

2. Schooling development was also observed under natural conditions. Fry 7-10 mm. in length were not found in schools, whereas many schools of fry over 12 mm. in length were found.

3. Visual attraction develops gradually, paralleling the appearance of schooling.

4. Current is not a necessary stimulus to orientation within a school.

5. Four fry reared in "isolation" joined a school. The significance is discussed.

6. The significance of experience in the approach of fry to each other and in orientation within the school is discussed.

REFERENCES

ATZ, J. W., 1953   Orientation in schooling fishes. *Proc. Conf. Orientation in Animals.* O.N.R., pp. 103–30.

BEACH, F. A., and J. JAYNES, 1954   Effects of early experience upon the behavior of animals. *Psych. Bull.,* **51**: 239–63.

BREDER, C. M., 1959   Studies on social groupings in fishes. *Bull. Amer. Mus. Nat. Hist.,* **117**: 397–481.

BREDER, C. M., and F. HALPERN, 1946   Innate and acquired behavior affecting the aggregation of fishes. *Physiol. Zoöl.,* **19**: 154–90.

BUMPUS, H. C., 1898   The breeding of animals at Woods Hole during the months of June, July and August. *Science* (N.S.), **8**: 850–58.

KEENLEYSIDE, M. H. A., 1955   Some aspects of the schooling behavior of fish. *Behaviour,* **8**: 183–248.

MORROW, J. E., 1948   Schooling behavior in fishes. *Quart. Rev. Biol.,* **23**: 27–38.

PARR, A. E., 1927   A contribution to the theoretical analysis of the schooling behavior of fishes. *Occasional Papers Bingham Oceanog. Coll.,* No. 1.

RUBINOFF, IRA, 1958   Raising the atherinid fish *Menidia Menidia* in the laboratory. *Copeia,* No. 2, pp. 146–47.

SCHNEIRLA, T. C., 1956   Interrelationships of the "Innate" and the "Acquired" in instinctive behavior. In: *L'Instinct dans le Comportement des Animaux et de l'Homme,* ed. Masson & Cie., pp. 387–452.

SCHNEIRLA, T. C., 1957   The concept of development in comparative psychology, pp. 78–108. In: *The Concept of Development,* ed. DALE B. HARRIS, Minneapolis: University of Minnesota Press.

SCHNEIRLA, T. C., 1959   An evolutionary and developmental theory of biphasic processes underlying approach and withdrawal. In: *Nebraska Symposium on Motivation,* Lincoln: University of Nebraska Press.

SHAW, E., 1958   The development of visual attraction among schooling fishes. *Biol. Bull.,* **115**: 365 (abstr.).

WELTY, J. C., 1934   Experiments in group behavior in fishes. *Physiol. Zoöl.,* **7**: 85–128.

A BASIC LIBRARY
IN ANIMAL BEHAVIOR

The following books are recent general reviews of animal behavior. Their coverage is broad; each contains parts relevant to most of the major sections of *Readings in Animal Behavior*. To avoid repetition, they are listed here and are not included in the "Suggestions for Further Reading" sections of the various introductions.

Bliss, E. L., ed., *Roots of Behavior*. New York: Harper & Row, 1962.

Hafez, E. S., ed., *The Behaviour of Domestic Animals*. London: Baillière, 1962.

Thorpe, W. H., *Learning and Instinct in Animals*. (2d ed.) London: Methuen, 1963.

Thorpe, W. H., and O. L. Zangwell, eds., *Current Problems in Animal Behavior*. London: Cambridge, 1961.

Waters, R. H., D. A. Rethlingshafer, and W. E. Caldwell, eds., *Principles of Comparative Psychology*. New York: McGraw-Hill, 1960.

INDEX

INDEX

AUTHOR INDEX

Boldface numbers indicate readings in which the author's work is discussed. Numbers in parentheses indicate that the author is referred to by that reference number, rather than by name, on the page indicated.

Ader, R., **24,** 282 (84)
Adkins, R. J., **40,** 434 (1)
Adlersparre, A., **51,** 531
Agar, W. E., **6,** 88
Allee, M. N., **49,** 500
Allee, W. C., **6,** 81; **16,** 196; **49,** 496, 497, 500, 502
Allen, A. A., **2,** 26; **49,** 497
Almquist, J. O., **29,** 327
Alpert, M., **20,** 232; **24,** 281 (69)
Altmann, S. A., **54,** 546
Anand, B. K., **14,** 173
Anderson, A. L., **14,** 166
Anderson, O. D., **6,** 84
Andersson, B., **12,** 161
Andrew, R. J., **2,** 27; **5,** 59, 64, 66; **47,** 478
Anliker, J., **14,** 173
Antliff, H. R., **15,** 186 (26)
Armstrong, E. A., **49,** 498
Arnold, W. J., **40,** 434 (9)
Aronson, L. R., **3,** 44; **5,** 64; **11,** 143 (4), 145 (4, 11); **15,** 178 (5); **16,** 188–205; **23,** 254 (1); **29,** 314; **45,** 460
Atz, J. W., **16,** 194; **55,** 560
Autrum, H., **32,** 354 (1)

Baerends, G. P., **2,** 17, 23, 25, 28, 30; **3,** 42, 43, 46; **5,** 59, 64; **12,** 149; **45,** 460
Baerends-van Roon, J. M., **3,** 42, 43, 46; **5,** 64; **45,** 460
Bagg, H. J., **6,** 79, 80, 82

Baggerman, B., **16,** 190
Baglioni, S., **16,** 195
Bailey, C. J., **14,** 174
Ball, G. G., **40,** 434 (15)
Ball, J., **15,** 178 (6, 7)
Baltzer, F., **32,** 352 (2)
Banks, E. M., **23,** 254 (3); **24,** 281 (65)
Baron, A., **24,** 282 (80); **40,** 434 (13)
Basset, G. C., **6,** 79
Bastock, M., **6,** 86
Bates, R. W., **17,** 212 (22)
Bauer, F. J., **50,** 508
Baylor, E. R., **32,** 354 (3), 355 (3)
Beach, F. A., **1,** 3–14; **4,** 49–56; **5,** 60, 61; **7,** 100 (12); **11,** 143 (3, 5, 6); **15,** 178 (1, 8, 9), 187 (9, 34, 35); **16,** 189, 190, 195, 198, 200, 201, 202; **22,** 236 (2), 238 (1, 21), 239 (1, 2), 240 (21), 242 (2); **24,** 280 (60); **27,** 303; **29,** 314, 323; **44,** 455; **48,** 484, 485; **49,** 503; **55,** 563
Beber, B. A., **15,** 186 (24)
Beck, L. H., **1,** 12
Beeman, E. A., **49,** 502
Belfer, M. L., **24,** 282 (84)
Bell, R. W., **26,** 291, 294
Bennett, E. L., **6,** 76; **18,** 213–222
Benoit, J., **16,** 195; **51,** 522
Benzer, S., **7,** 98
Berger, P., **32,** 355 (4)
Bernstein, L., **22,** 238 (3); **24,** 240 (3), 279 (52)

571

SUBJECT INDEX

Numbers in boldface refer to entire readings. Numbers in roman type refer to specific pages.